Research on Technology and the Teaching and Learning of Mathematics: Volume 1

Research Syntheses

a volume in
Research on Technology and the Teaching and Learning of
Mathematics: Syntheses, Cases, and Perspectives

Series Editors:
M. Kathleen Heid and Glendon W. Blume
The Pennsylvania State University

Research on Technology and the Teaching and Learning of Mathematics: Syntheses, Cases, and Perspectives

M. Kathleen Heid and Glendon W. Blume, Series Editors

Research on Technology and the Teaching and Learning of Mathematics: Volume 1. Research Syntheses (2008)
edited by M. Kathleen Heid and Glendon W. Blume

Research on Technology and the Teaching and Learning of Mathematics: Volume 2. Cases and Perspectives (2008)
edited by Glendon W. Blume and M. Kathleen Heid

Research on Technology and the Teaching and Learning of Mathematics: Volume 1

Research Syntheses

edited by

M. Kathleen Heid and Glendon W. Blume
The Pennsylvania State University

Information Age Publishing, Inc.
Charlotte, North Carolina
www.infoagepub.com

NATIONAL COUNCIL OF
TEACHERS OF MATHEMATICS

Library of Congress Cataloging-in-Publication Data

Research syntheses / edited by M. Kathleen Heid and Glendon W. Blume.
 p. cm. — (Research on technology and the teaching and learning of mathematics)
 Includes bibliographical references.
 ISBN 1-931576-18-1 (pbk.) — ISBN 1-931576-19-X (hardcover) 1. Mathematics—Study and teaching. 2. Technology—Study and teaching. 3. Mathematics—Research. I. Heid, Mary Kathleen. II. Blume, Glendon W.
 QA11.2.R46 2008
 510.71—dc22

                          2008017761

ISBN 13: 978-1-931576-18-5 (paperback)
ISBN 13: 978-1-931576-19-2 (hardcover)

Printed in the United States of America

CONTENTS

PREFACE

M. Kathleen Heid and Glendon W. Blume

Over 60 years ago, J. Abner Peddiwell (under the tutelage of Harold Benjamin) spun the tale of the *Saber-Tooth Curriculum* (1939), the hypothesized curriculum that defined education in an era once dominated by cave dwellers, wooly mammoths, and saber-toothed tigers. The story recounted the ways in which our hypothetical ancestors taught fish-grabbing (even after fishing nets were available and waters were too muddy to make it possible to see the fish) and tiger-scaring with fire (even after the saber-toothed tiger grew to extinction because they had succumbed to pneumonia due to a glacier). The study of fish-grabbing and of tiger-scaring remained a part of the curriculum long after they had outlived their initial usefulness, not for the purposes of catching fish and protecting the community from tigers, but for retroactively contrived purposes of building character, agility, and bravery.

The tale of the *Saber-Tooth Curriculum* serves to alert curriculum developers and educators to the nonpermanent nature of the content of curricula in schools, the tenacity with which we maintain curricula that are in place no matter whether they are serving their intended purpose, and the difficulty of embracing new curricula with learning goals that have changed based on newly available technology. In the story of the incorporation of technology into mathematics curricula, we hear echoes of the *Saber-Tooth Curriculum*. We have new tools and we need to learn how best to use them in pursuit of educational goals that best reflect the opportunities afforded education in a technology-present environment. The stage has been set for the systematic examination of the impact of technology on the teaching and learning of mathematics that is the purpose of these volumes. Knowledge of that impact will enable the creation and implementation of curricula that capitalize on technology and will help teachers orchestrate the use of technological tools in school mathematics classrooms.

According to the National Council of Teacher of Mathematics's *Principles and Standards for School Mathematics* (2000), "Technology is essential in teaching and learning of mathematics; it influences the mathematics that is taught and enhances students' learning" (p. 24). The first part of this principle is a value statement; the second part is a claim the support for which is open to examination. How does research inform this call for technology in mathematics teaching and learning? In response to the need to craft appropriate roles for technology in school mathematics, new technological approaches have been applied to the teaching and learning of mathematics, and the effects of these technological approaches have been examined by researchers worldwide.

The technologies with which these volumes deal are what have come to be called cognitive technologies (technologies that transcend the limitations of the mind) and mathematics-specific technologies (technologies that are used primarily for mathematics or are particularly amenable to mathematics uses). In individual chapters, authors make other distinctions important to their particular uses of technology. At times authors of research articles do not specify versions of software that were used in their studies. In those cases and when the software is commonly used, we do not include publication information for the software (e.g., Logo, Maple).

Volumes 1 and 2 of *Research on Technology and the Teaching and Learning of Mathematics: Syntheses, Cases, and Perspectives* are the products of a multi-year effort to gather and analyze what the field has learned through research on technology and the teaching and learning of mathematics. Technological approaches to school mathematics have not as yet been widely adopted largely due to a general impression by both practitioners and researchers that technology-intensive mathematics education is untested. These volumes are intended to bring the community of mathematics education researchers to a greater awareness of theory and research on the impact of technology on mathematics learning and teaching. *Volume 1: Syntheses* provides insight into what research suggests about the nature of mathematics learning in technological environments. Included in this volume are syntheses of research on technology in the learning of specific areas of mathematics (rational number, algebra, elementary and secondary geometry, mathematical modeling, and calculus) in addition to research syntheses of the more global issues of equity and the process of incorporating technology into mathematics teaching. The authors provide thoughtful analyses of bodies of research with the goal of understanding the ways in which technology affects what and how students learn. Each of the chapters in this volume is written by a team of experts whose own research has provided important guidance to the field.

Volume 2: Cases and Perspectives has a dual focus. It features descriptive cases that provide accounts of the development of technology-intensive curricula and technological tools. In these cases the writers describe and analyze various roles that research played in their development work and ways in which research, curriculum development, and tool development can inform each other. These thoughtful descriptions and analyses will provide documentation of how this process can and does occur. Each of these chapters is written by individuals who were intimately involved in the development of leading-edge mathematics-specific technology or technology-intensive mathematics curricula and who saw research as an essential part of that development. The remaining chapters in the second volume address overarching research-related issues and perspectives on the use of technology in the teaching and learning of mathematics. Each of these perspectives is written by a leading scholar who accounts for a global issue with the potential for providing overall guidance to research that involves technology and the teaching and learning of mathematics.

ACKNOWLEDGMENTS

Early versions of the chapters in these two volumes were discussed at two conferences held at The Pennsylvania State University. Those conferences were sponsored by the Conferences on Research on Technology and the Teaching and Learning of Mathematics Grant # ESI-0087447 from the National Science Foundation. We thank the participants in those conferences (researchers, teacher educators, teachers, policymakers, software developers, and curriculum developers) for the insights they offered—insights that have undoubtedly made the collection of chapters richer. Of course, any opinions, findings, and conclusions or recommendations that drew on those discussions are those of the authors and editors and do not necessarily reflect the views of the National Science Foundation.

We are grateful to all of those who have made the production of these volumes possible. First, we thank the authors for their generosity in sharing the kinds of expertise that can only come from contributing leading insights for so long in such an important area. The chapters benefited greatly from the contributions of the dozens of reviewers (who shall remain anonymous). We, and the authors, thank them.

We thank our colleague Rose Mary Zbiek who offered her encouragement and patient support when work on these volumes overtook our lives. We thank Vincent Lunetta, whose collaboration with us on the NSF Graduate Research Traineeship program led to the idea of writing a monograph (now two large volumes) and holding a conference that engaged our doctoral students with researchers from around the world. We thank George Bright for his encouragement and support in bringing the conferences into being. We are thankful for the work of Jim Renney, Kristen Hall, Tracy Scala, and Linda Haffly who helped plan and orchestrate the conferences at which chapters were discussed and who coordinated the travel for attendees from 10 countries. We could not have coordinated the production of these volumes without the help of three special individuals. Thanks go to Gulseren Karagoz Akar for her diligent editorial assistance, to Linda Haffly for always being there to support in whatever way was helpful, and to Tracy Scala for the countless ways in which she helped us manage the task of coordinating and communicating about these two volumes of scholarly contributions. We also wish to thank our families, especially Ruth Blume, for their patience during the long process of preparing these volumes.

REFERENCES

National Council of Teachers of Mathematics. (2000). *Principles and standards for school mathematics*. Reston, VA: Author.

Peddiwell, J. A. (1939). *The saber-tooth curriculum*. New York: McGraw-Hill Book.

CHAPTER 1

THE LEARNING OF RATIONAL NUMBER CONCEPTS USING TECHNOLOGY

John Olive and Joanne Lobato

The teaching and learning of fractions is not only very hard, it is, in the broader scheme of things, a dismal failure.

—G. Davis, Hunting, and Pearn (1993)

In looking at the use of technology in the learning of rational number concepts we took the above quote seriously. Fractions are the experiential basis for rational numbers, so without a firm understanding of fractions students are destined to continue to fail to learn rational number concepts. Thus we were interested in finding studies that revealed how the use of technology might help address this "dismal failure" in student learning.

There are two different ways to frame the question of the role of technology in learning: (a) What is the effect of technology? and (b) How does the use of technology change the nature of what is learned? Both approaches are important in addressing the problem of student learning. Treating technology as an independent variable, however, has several lim-

Research on Technology and the Teaching and Learning of Mathematics:
Vol. 1. Research Syntheses, pp. 1–53

itations. An effect study may report positive gains in mathematical performance but is rarely designed also to investigate how the technology led to the improvements. Effect studies seldom make the nature of students' meaning making in the technological environment the subject of investigation. In order to control for other factors, effect studies often embrace a narrow view of mathematics and a traditional pedagogy. Finally, the effect of the particular curricular activities, approach, and sequence used in the technologically intensive project is often conflated with the effect of the technology. Thus, our primary goal in this chapter is to investigate how technology both affords and constrains the nature of what students learn about rational number constructs. Our review and synthesis of the research literature in the domain of teaching and learning rational number concepts with technology provided us with the data to address this question.

We restricted our search of the literature to published articles and reports (including published proceedings of major conferences) of empirical research findings. Eight research projects involving the use of technology in the learning of rational number concepts emerged from this process. Five projects used technology as a medium for investigating children's thinking and will be the focus of this chapter. Three projects investigated the effects of technology and will be summarized more briefly (in the section The Effects of Technology on Learning About Rational Numbers). A ninth study (briefly described in the section Implications for Curriculum Developers, Teachers, Researchers, and Policymakers) introduces the question of an aesthetic dimension in students' learning on which well-designed computer environments can capitalize.

In reviewing the research literature we focused primarily on the development of children's rational number concepts and secondarily on the technology. Since children's mathematical development drove our search for uses of technology that may or may not have enhanced that development, the chapter begins with a discussion of semantic and psychological analyses of the domain of rational numbers. We also provide examples in the first section, Semantic and Psychological Analyses of Rational Number, of how these dual analyses framed our investigation of the role of technology in the learning of rational number constructs. The second section, Projects That Used Technology as a Medium for Investigating Children's Thinking, describes the use of technology and summarizes the major findings from the five research projects that used technology as a medium for investigating children's thinking. The third section, Learning of Rational Number Concepts: Contributions and Limitations of Technology, provides a synthesis of this research in order to address our primary question of how technology enables and constrains the learning of rational number constructs. Since this section is a synthesis of findings from the original research articles, not from the summaries presented in the second section, additional research findings are presented in the third section. The review of the computer effect studies is summarized in the fourth section, The Effects of Technology on Learning About Rational Number.

While the chapter is, in some sense, building up to the synthesis and conclusions in the third and fourth sections, there are two reasons why we include an examination of individual projects prior to the synthesis section. First, in order to draw connections across projects, it is important to understand enough details about how each of the projects used its particular technological environments. Including sufficient detail within the third section would have disrupted the flow of that section. Second, a review of research in a particular area should provide researchers with a comprehensive overview of the work that has been done in the area, including pointers to research articles and summaries of major findings. We conclude the chapter with implications for curriculum developers, teachers, academics, and policymakers.

SEMANTIC AND PSYCHOLOGICAL
ANALYSES OF RATIONAL NUMBER

There has been a great deal of discussion and research during the last quarter of the twentieth century concerning the learning and teaching of rational numbers. Kieren's seminal work established that rational number is not a single construct but rather is better characterized as a set of related but distinct subconstructs (Kieren, 1976, 1980, 1988, 1993). Researchers involved in the influential Rational Number Project (Behr, Harel, Post, & Lesh, 1992; Behr, Wachsmuth, Post, & Lesh, 1984) based much of their work on the four subconstructs suggested by Kieren (1988): (a) quotient, (b) measure, (c) ratio number, and (d) multiplicative operator. The quotient subconstruct focuses on the interpretation of a rational number as the result of a division, (e.g., $\frac{3}{4}$ is the amount of cookie that each person receives when three cookies are divided equally among four people). The measure subconstruct focuses on a rational number as an extensive quantity, (e.g., as a single number that measures a directed distance from zero on a number line in terms of some unit distance). A rational number also can be conceived as a ratio of two integers (e.g., the fraction $\frac{1}{4}$ can describe the ratio of one can of orange concentrate to four cans of water). The multiplicative operator subconstruct can be interpreted in several ways, as a stretcher/shrinker, a duplicator/partition-reducer, or a multiplier/divisor (Behr et al., 1993). We interpret this sub-construct in the sense of rules for "taking a fractional part" of some quantity, with the end result of reducing or enlarging that quantity. For instance, the fraction $\frac{3}{2}$ can represent the input-output rule of a "function machine" that for every two equal parts of an input quantity, three equivalent parts will be output. Behr and colleagues (1984) added a fifth sub-construct—part-whole relationships. The part-whole subconstruct focuses on the comparison of a quantity to a dividable unit, in which the unit may vary and in which the unit can be a region or a discrete set of objects. Kieren (1976) had originally regarded part-whole relations as a separate construct but later (Kieren, 1993) subsumed these relations under his measure and quotient subconstructs. These five subconstructs have been adopted, in some form or another, by most researchers in the field as guideposts for their research. Several researchers have argued that a complete understanding of rational number depends on an understanding of each of the subconstructs and of their interrelationships (Behr, Lesh, Post, & Silver, 1983; Kieren, 1976; Vergnaud, 1983).

The preceding semantic analysis of rational number subconstructs is helpful for understanding the adult views of rational number; however, it is insufficient for describing children's construction of fractional knowledge. From a psychological point of view, the construction of fractional knowledge involves specific actions and mental operations. The following mental operations have been identified by several researchers (Confrey, 1992; Freudenthal, 1983; Olive, 1999; Piaget & Szeminska, 1965; Steffe, 1988, 1992, 1994; Streefland, 1993; von Glasersfeld, 1981, 1995).

1. *Unitizing* is the mental act of forming unit items out of sensory experiences. When the result of sequential unitizing acts can be taken to stand for the activity itself, the result is a *numerical composite* (e.g., six is taken to be the result of counting from one to six).

2. *Uniting* is the compounding or joining together of unit items (and therefore acts on the results of unitizing). When the joined objects can be acted on as a new, single object while still exhibiting its constituent parts, the result is a *composite unit* (e.g., five ones can be taken as one five, and the one five can be decomposed into five ones).

3. *Units-coordination* requires coordinating the elements of one composite unit with a different composite unit. It is the basis for mul-

tiplicative thinking (e.g., when finding the result of taking four bags with three apples in each bag, a child needs to coordinate each element in her composite unit of four with her composite unit of three in order to construct "four threes" and calculate the result).

4. *Fragmenting* is the act of (mentally) breaking something apart (e.g., 15 apples can be regarded as 10 apples and five apples, or a piece of candy can be broken in two without a necessity for equal parts—"I'll take the big half").

5. *Segmenting* is the act of successively marking off equivalent portions of a quantity (e.g., when finding how many bags of apples, with three apples per bag, can be made out of 12 apples, a child may count by threes up to 12, keeping track of how many threes she counted).

6. *Sharing* a quantity can involve distributing equal amounts of the quantity to a specified number of people (or objects) until the quantity is exhausted (e.g., 10 apples shared among five people: Give each person one apple then another apple), or separating the quantity into a specified number of equal parts (i.e., partitioning the quantity).

7. *Partitioning* a quantity involves separating the quantity into a specified number of equal parts while the quantity remains as a whole (e.g., prior to sharing 10 apples among five people the 10 apples are separated into five groups of two apples each). In the case of partitioning a continuous quantity, the child has to mentally project a grid (or template) with the specified number of equal parts onto the quantity.

8. *Splitting* can be thought of as breaking a partitioned unit apart. The fundamental split is to break into two equal parts. The difference between splitting and partitioning is that the parts no longer remain in the whole. Thus, a split of 10 into two results in two individual sets of five rather than the 10 objects separated into two equal groups. A candy bar split into five equal pieces is no longer one whole candy bar but five individual pieces of candy.

9. *Disembedding* a part from a partitioned whole is a mental act of lifting the part from the whole while still leaving the whole intact. Thus, both the part and the whole can be discerned as separate entities (e.g., after partitioning a bar into eight equal parts, a child mentally focuses on just one of those parts and compares that one part to the eight, realizing that the bar is eight times as long as this one part).

10. *Replicating* a quantity means to make copies of the quantity (e.g., making three copies of a unit bar).

11. *Iterating* a quantity involves uniting replicates of the quantity to produce a partitioned whole or composite unit (e.g., iterating $\frac{1}{4}$ of a candy bar four times would produce a partitioned bar equivalent to the original candy bar).

12. *Measuring* involves comparing a given quantity to a specified unit using iterations or partitions of the unit (e.g., my candy bar is $\frac{5}{4}$ of your candy bar because it took five of your $\frac{1}{4}$-pieces to make my candy bar).

Both types of analyses, semantic and psychological, help frame our investigation of the role of technology in the learning of rational number concepts. For instance, one way that technology can enhance the learning of rational number concepts is through the use of computer tools that allow students to enact psychological operations that are difficult to perform with physical materials. In order to establish a relation between a part and a whole in a fractional situation, the child needs to mentally disembed the part from the whole. With physical materials it is not possible to remove a part from the whole without destroying the original whole. With static pictures the part is either embedded in the whole or is drawn separate from the whole. In the former case the child has to mentally unitize one part of the whole while maintaining the unity of the whole and compare these two abstracted units. In the latter case the child has to compare the separate units while imagining that one is embedded in the other. Using a computer tool that provides the child with the ability to dynamically pull a part out of a partitioned whole while leaving the whole intact, the child can enact the disembedding operation that is necessary to make the part-to-whole comparison. This example of one way in which technology can enhance learning draws upon the psychological analysis of rational numbers.

The semantic analysis is also useful in examining the role of technology in learning rational number concepts. Since the subconstruct view of rational number has dominated researchers' views of what it means to understand rational number for so many years, it is not surprising that several of the projects reviewed in this chapter focus on dynamically simulating one or more of the subconstructs via a computer microworld. In the next section, we review one project that focused on developing fractions as operators using an input-output simulator.

PROJECTS THAT USED TECHNOLOGY AS A MEDIUM FOR INVESTIGATING CHILDREN'S THINKING

In the following review of the projects that used technology as a medium for investigating children's thinking, we will articulate the specific ways in which each project used technology.

The University of Georgia (UGA) Fractions Project

This project worked primarily within the psychological framework outlined in the previous section. Indeed, many of the constructs outlined in that analysis emanated from the research in this project. In terms of the semantic analysis of rational numbers outlined in the preceding section, the UGA fractions project focused primarily on the part-whole relationships along with the multiplicative operator and measure subconstructs.

Project Description
Steffe and Olive (1990) designed and conducted a 3-year constructivist teaching experiment with 12 children in order to develop cognitive models of children's construction of fractions. Third-grade students in a public elementary school in Georgia were selected based on the level of abstraction of their whole number schemes (Steffe, 1992). The selected children exhibited a broad range of whole-number schemes, from an Initial Number Sequence (INS) through an Explicitly Nested Number Sequence (ENS) (Steffe & Cobb, 1988) to a Generalized Number Sequence (GNS) (Olive, 1999; Steffe, 1992). A detailed explanation of Steffe's number sequences can be found in Olive (2001a). The important distinctions to be made concerning these number sequences are that children with only an INS are constrained to additive reasoning, whereas the ENS provides children with the necessary operations to engage in multiplicative reasoning and the GNS extends this level of reasoning to *thinking* with multiplicative structures and thus, the construction of exponential structures.

A team of teacher/researchers, led by Steffe and Olive, worked with the 12 children, primarily in pairs, outside of the classroom, once a week for approximately 20 weeks per year for 3 years. All teaching episodes were videotaped. The theoretical framework for the project is that of radical constructivism. The major hypothesis to be tested was that children could (and should) reorganize their whole number knowledge in order to build schemes for working with fractional quantities and numbers in meaningful ways. This hypothesis contrasts with the prevailing assumption that whole number knowledge is a "barrier" or "interferes" with rational number knowledge (Behr et al., 1984).

Computer microworlds called Tools for Interactive Mathematical Activity (TIMA) (Biddlecomb, 1994; Olive, 2000; Olive & Steffe, 1994; Steffe & Olive, 2002) were specifically designed for the teaching experiment and were revised during the teaching experiment, based on the children's interactions within these environments. The TIMA provide children with possibilities for enacting their mathematical operations with whole numbers and fractions. They also provide the teacher/researcher with opportunities to provoke perturbations in children's mathematical schemes and observe children's mathematical thinking in action.

The software consists of on-screen manipulatives analogous to counters or beads (regular geometrical shapes that are called "toys"), sticks (line segments), and fraction bars (rectangular regions), together with possible actions that the children can perform on these objects. These possible actions potentially engage the user in the fundamental operations involved in the development of numerical schemes previously outlined. These operations are unitizing, uniting, fragmenting, segmenting, partitioning, replicating, iterating, disembedding, and measuring. For example, using TIMA Bars, a child can partition a bar into five equal parts, disembed one of the parts by actually pulling it out of the bar (i.e., a copy of the part is lifted from the bar leaving all five parts still in the bar), and then use the REPEAT action to iterate this one part to create a bar that is six times as large as $\frac{1}{5}$ of the original bar (see Figure 1.1).

Figure 1.1.   Making $\frac{6}{5}$ of a unit bar by disembedding $\frac{1}{5}$ and repeating it six times.

Results

The major purpose of this project is that of theory building based on in-depth analyses of several case studies of the children's interactions and cognitive constructions over the 3-year period. The in-depth analyses of the various case studies were completed in 2004 as part of a second grant from the National Science Foundation (Steffe, 1998). More than 25 articles and two doctoral dissertations have been published concerning children's progression from whole number thinking to fractional reasoning, and the role of the TIMA in this progression (Biddlecomb, 1994, 1999; D'Ambrosio & Mewborn, 1994; Kaput, 1994; Kieren, 1994; Olive, 1993, 1994, 1999, 2000, 2001b, 2002a, 2002b, 2003; Olive & Steffe, 1994, 2002; Steffe, 1993, 1994, 1999, 2002, 2003, 2004; Steffe & Olive, 1996, 2002; Steffe & Spangler, 1993; Steffe & Tzur, 1994; Steffe & Wiegel, 1994, 1996; Tzur, 1995, 1999, 2000, 2002, 2003).

In one of the dissertation studies, Biddlecomb (1999) identified the conceptual challenges that a child (Jerry) who had only constructed an INS and not an ENS, must meet in order to make sense of fractional quantities. Jerry was able to use numerical patterns to fragment a stick in TIMA Sticks (a thick line segment created by dragging the computer mouse across the screen). The results of these fragmentations, however, were (initially) prefractional in that Jerry did not maintain the necessity for equal-sized parts when checking his estimates for one-half. Through the activities with TIMA Sticks he was able to use his initial number sequence to construct what Steffe and Wiegel (1994) have called a *connected number*. Connected numbers are initially constructed by a child mentally projecting his or her concept of a whole number (e.g., eight) into an unmarked line segment to establish an "interiorized continuous but segmented unit" as a situation of the child's number sequence (p. 121). Thus, connected numbers carry with them a notion of numerical length. The connected number 3 combined with the connected number 5 would be the same length as the connected number 8. This connected number 8 would contain within it an implicit nesting of the number sequence from 1 to 8. Jerry's case study (and those of other children in the project who had established only an INS and not an ENS) points to the critical role that connected numbers played in making sense of fractions. They provided a way for children to use their discrete adding, subtracting, and multiplying schemes to find unknown lengths using known lengths, and thus establish part-whole relations in the context of continuous quantities.

A major obstacle for children like Jerry in constructing meaning for unit fractions is their lack of an iterable unit. While they are able to take one of n parts of a stick as being $\frac{1}{n}$ of the stick, they do not see the reverse relation: that n iterations of the $\frac{1}{n}$ must recreate the original stick. A number of papers provide examples of how children with at least an ENS are able to take advantage of the copying and repeating actions in TIMA Sticks to establish an iterable unit fraction as an inverse relation to their composite units-coordinating scheme (a multiplying scheme for whole numbers) (Olive, 2000, 2001b, 2002b; Olive & Steffe, 2002; Steffe, 2002, 2003; Steffe & Tzur, 1994; Tzur, 1995, 1999). Olive (2001b) illustrates the construction of this inverse relation in his case study of Joe, a fourth-grade student in the Fractions Project. Joe's interpretation of "one-third" was something that when multiplied by 3 gave the total number. This was an iterative approach to establish meaning for unit fractions. Joe's strategy supports the major hypothesis of the project, that fractions could emerge from such reorganizations of children's whole number schemes (Olive, 1999, 2000, 2001b, 2002b, 2003; Olive & Steffe, 2002; Steffe, 2002, 2003, 2004; Steffe & Olive, 1990).

Another major contribution of the project is the articulation of the schemes involved in the construction of the Rational Numbers of Arithmetic (RNA). For Steffe and Olive, the RNA are more than fractions but less than equivalence classes of fractions that belong to a quotient field. The child is aware of the operations needed, not only to reconstruct the unit whole from any one of its parts, but also to produce any fraction of the unit whole from any other fraction. For example, given a bar that is said to be $\frac{2}{5}$ of another bar, the child would partition the given bar into two equal parts and then iterate one of those parts five times to create the other bar. If given a bar that is $\frac{3}{4}$ of some unknown bar and asked to create $\frac{2}{3}$ of the unknown bar, the child could partition the given bar into three equal parts and then partition one of those three parts into three smaller parts to construct $\frac{1}{12}$ of the unknown bar. The child could think of doing this because of previous experience creating a partition of a bar from which the child could pull both a fourth and a third of the bar. The child could then use that $\frac{1}{12}$-part to construct $\frac{2}{3}$ by iterating the $\frac{1}{12}$-part 8 times.

From an adult mathematical perspective, these operations could be viewed as providing closure on the set of fractional numbers, and thus creating a field in the formal sense. In terms of the psychological framework outlined in the first section, Olive (2002b) suggests that the construction of the RNA entails a modification of the child's Generalized Number Sequence for whole numbers wherein units are constructed *within* a unit that is *within* another unit. The last example (making $\frac{2}{3}$ of a bar from $\frac{3}{4}$ of an unknown bar) illustrates the construction of a $\frac{1}{12}$-unit fractional part within the $\frac{1}{4}$-unit fractional part in order to create $\frac{2}{3}$ using the common unit fraction of $\frac{1}{12}$.

Olive (1999) provides a detailed development of the fractional schemes and accommodations made by Arthur and Nathan, the two most advanced children in the project. Four distinct modifications of the children's fractional schemes were discerned:

1. The construction of *iterable unit fractions*, whereby the children could regard a fractional whole a priori as a multiple of any of its unitary parts. The children could produce fractions greater than the fractional whole through unit iteration and understand that the fraction is greater than the fractional whole (e.g., twice $\frac{6}{11}$ is $\frac{12}{11}$, and $\frac{12}{11}$ is one whole and $\frac{1}{11}$) (Tzur, 1999).

2. A *fraction composition scheme*, whereby the children could form *any fraction of any other fraction* as a fraction of the original whole (e.g., $\frac{3}{4}$ of $\frac{2}{5}$ is $\frac{3}{10}$ of one).

3. A *common partitioning fractional scheme* with which they could find a common partition of a unit bar for any two fractions. This required units-coordinations at three levels that is a coordination of two *iterable composite units*. For example, in order to find a common partition for making both thirds and fifths of a bar, Nathan coordinated his number sequences for fives and for threes until he found a common multiple. The three levels of units were the composite unit of 15 that was the composition of both five threes and three fives, the composite units of fives and of threes, and the singleton units that constituted these composite units (Olive, 2003).

4. The construction of *comeasurement units for fractions* with which they could produce any fraction from any other fraction (e.g., make $\frac{1}{9}$ of

a unit stick starting with $\frac{1}{12}$ of the stick by finding $\frac{1}{36}$ as a comeasurement unit for both $\frac{1}{12}$ and $\frac{1}{9}$).

The investigation suggests that the operations and unit types associated with the children's whole number sequences contributed to the reorganization of their fractional schemes rather than interfering with those schemes. The reorganization involved an integration of their whole number knowledge with their fractional schemes whereby whole number division was regarded as the same as multiplication by the reciprocal fraction (Olive, 1999).

The TIMA technology used with the students in this project provided them with ways of enacting their mental operations and visualizing the quantitative relations that they constructed. As Olive (2002a) points out in his discussion of one student's construction of fractional schemes, the TIMA were critical affordances in his constructions:

> The ability to make a stick in TIMA: Sticks that is "nine times as long as the $\frac{1}{7}$-stick" through repetitions of a $\frac{1}{7}$-stick gave Joe concrete evidence of his iterable unit fraction. He had made a modification in his whole-number multiplication scheme that enabled him to use a unit fraction in the same way that he could use units of 1 with his composite units. The TIMA software gave Joe the tools to build a bridge from whole numbers to fractions. (p. 361)

The Copycat Project, La Trobe University

Project Description

G. Davis, Hunting, and Pearn (1993) conducted a 2-year constructivist teaching experiment involving ten 8- and 9-year-old children. They focused on an operator approach to teaching basic fraction concepts using a computer tool called Copycat designed by Hunting, Davis, and Bigelow (1991), in conjunction with a computer graphics utility Super-Paint (Aldus Corporation, 1994). They conducted teaching sessions, usually with pairs of children outside of their regular classroom, twice each week for 3-week periods. Approximately 30 teaching sessions were held with each pair of children during the 2-year period. Each session was videotaped for later analysis. During the period of the teaching experiment the researchers requested that the children have no other instruction on the topic of fractions. The children attended a state-funded primary school in a predominantly middle class area of Melbourne, Australia. The mathematical ability of the children ranged from below average to well above average (Hunting, Davis, & Pearn, 1996).

The researchers set out to test the hypothesis that children could develop an understanding of fractions as multiplicative operators "provided they act on appropriate environments and can internalize those actions as mental records" (G. Davis et al., 1993, p. 69). They argued that the operator approach to fractions (modeled as "m output for every n input," where m and n are whole numbers) builds on children's whole number knowledge and operations. The notion of *equivalent operators* was tested by comparison of outputs when the operators acted on the same input set. Similarly, order comparisons could be made on the same basis. Two different composition operations on operators were described: (a) The results of each operator acting on the same input are then "taken together" (addition); and (b) the result of the first operation is "followed by" the second operator acting on this result (multiplication). The researchers argued that by defining comparison of and operations on fractions in terms of the resulting output from a given input, the focus would be taken off of the numerator and denominator aspects of a fraction and might, thus, reduce the confusion reported in other research when children compared fractions solely on the basis of the numerator or denominator.

The SuperPaint software was used as a shape duplicator in the early teaching episodes. The children could create the outputs for a specific operator by making appropriate duplicates of the input shapes. For instance, having made 12 copies of a square, the children were asked to make a different square (filled with a different pattern). They were then asked to "make as many of those [pointing to the new square] as would make one-third of all of those [pointing to the 12 original squares]" (G. Davis et al., 1993, p. 70). The Copycat hypercard program was used to automate the output for a given input for specified operators. For instance, a similar situation (finding one-third of 12) would be modeled as in Figure 1.2 using the Copycat program.

On the first click on the **Go** button, three balls disappear from the in-tray and one ball appears on the output tray. The numeral 12 disappears from the **In** window and the numeral 1 appears in the **Out** window. The balls continue to disappear from the in-tray, three at a time and balls appear on the output tray, one at a time, while the numeral in the **Out** window increases by one. When all balls have disappeared from the in-tray, and four balls are on the output tray, the 12 balls reappear on the in-tray along with the numeral 12 in the **In** window (see Figure 1.3) and applause is heard. If an input that is not a multiple of the denominator is entered onto the in-tray (using the up and down arrows shown in Figure

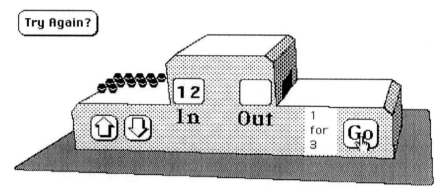

Figure 1.2.   An input of 12 in a "1 for 3" Copycat.

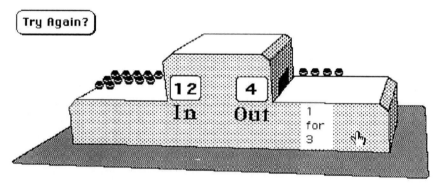

Figure 1.3.   Copycat's state after performing the "1 for 3" operation.

1.2) the machine will not run when the **Go** button is clicked. An audible message is heard complaining, "You can't do this to me!" The numerator and denominator for the fraction operator are chosen from menu items. The numerator can be a number from one to eight; the denominator can be selected from the numbers one to six, eight, and 10.

Results

The input-output operator metaphor, utilized in the Copycat software, appeared to contribute to the generation of some original schemes for comparing fractions. Hunting and colleagues (1996) describe three such schemes in their detailed case study of two boys, Shannon and Elliot, over both years of the project. In the first set of comparison tasks (comparing pairs of unit fractions to determine which was larger) using Copycat, both children used what the researchers called an *equal outputs* scheme, whereby they used different inputs to produce the same output. For example, in comparing one-half and one-third, they set the machine to one-half and used two as the input. They then set the machine to one-third and used three as the input. In both cases, the output was the same. In explaining which was larger, Shannon switched to an *equal inputs* scheme, "So if you put in six you would have two coming out, and if you put in six for the half you would have three coming out" (p. 363). Shannon occasionally argued on the basis of equal outputs, "You don't have to use as much bits (items) to make one come for one-half as for one-third" (p. 363).

Hunting and colleagues contend that the equal outputs scheme

> is a more fundamental scheme because it does not require the coordination of numerical sequences between different fractions whereas the equal inputs scheme requires a sound knowledge of whole number relationships—principally, strategies to find numbers divisible by each fraction's denominator. (p. 366)

For example, Elliot determined that one-half was greater than one-fifth using an input of 10, arguing that one came out for every five in the one-fifth machine but one came out for each two in the one-half machine. When trying to compare one-third and one-fifth in the same episode, Elliot could not come up with an input that worked for both machines so he argued that the two fractions were the same using an equal outputs scheme: "They're the same. If you put in six, two will come out; if you put in ten, two will come out" (p. 364).

Shannon developed an advanced scheme, which the researchers called a *scaling* scheme, to find a fraction between two given fractions. Shannon would scale (usually double or halve) the numerator and denominator of a fraction to find an equivalent fraction. He used this strategy in combination with the equal inputs scheme, based on the behavior of the Copycat. For instance, in finding a fraction between two-fifths and one-third, Shannon proposed one-and-three-fourths fifths. He argued that this would be more than one-third by taking three times one-and-three-fourths to get five-and-one-fourth fifteenths and compared that to $\frac{5}{15}$ for one-third. He then showed that one-and-three-fourths fifths was the same as $\frac{7}{20}$, "Cause you're using up four one-and-three-quarter fifths, which is equaling up to seven, and then four plus twenty, so $\frac{7}{20}$" (Hunting et al., 1996, p. 371). The researchers comment, "The impressive feature of Shannon's scheme was not that he understood that equivalent fractions were related by a scaleable property but that he could make this knowledge work for him in a powerful way" (p. 374).

The researchers reached a conclusion similar to that of the researchers from the UGA fractions project, namely, that whole number knowledge can serve as a positive basis for the development of fraction concepts (rather than being viewed as a source of interference). Furthermore, they provide evidence that the development of rational-number knowledge and the development of whole-number knowledge appear to be interdependent. Shannon's number sense with whole numbers appeared to propel his development of fraction understanding; Elliot's lack of flexibility with particular whole-number concepts seemed to constrain his fraction learning at times. The researchers from the Copycat project attributed the interdependence of whole-number and rational-number knowledge to the operator approach using the Copycat software: "Fraction settings provided by the Copycat program allowed students to investigate problems of order and equivalence meaningfully by drawing on and expanding their prior knowledge of whole-number relationships" (Hunting et al., 1996, p. 376). However, the constraints built into the simulation (namely the "black box" functioning of the machine and the exclusive use of discrete quantities) also limited the set of possible problems and the ways in which the problems could be solved. In terms of the previously outlined framework, this project focused on the multiplicative operator subconstruct of fractions to the exclusion of the other subconstructs.

Children as Designers

Project Description

Harel (1990), and later Kafai and colleagues (Kafai, 1993, 1995, 1996; Kafai & Ching, 1997) conducted a series of studies in which children used Logo to design tutorials or games for others. A typical task was for fourth-grade students to create representations of fraction concepts that could be used to teach third-grade students. In one project, a child used Logo to program a picture of a one-dollar bill with four quarters underneath. Two of the quarters were highlighted and animated to "walk" around the screen until they resided near the words "two-fourths of one dollar." The contexts for children's representations for fractions varied from pizzas and gears to musical rhythms and manipulatives.

The Children as Designers approach is based on the constructionist principle that "learners are particularly likely to make new ideas when they are actively engaged in making some type of external artifact—be it a robot, a poem, a sand castle, or a computer program—which they can reflect upon and share with others" (Harel & Papert, 1991, p. 1). Constructionism is a theoretical perspective (put forward by Papert, 1993 and his group at Massachusetts Institute of Technology) in which learning is viewed as a product of children's construction of artifacts. The construction is viewed as individual activity in a social context, drawing from the social interactionism suggested by Vygotsky's research (Kozulin, 1986; Vygotsky, 1978), as well as by the developmental psychology of Piaget (Piaget & Szeminska, 1965).

The intent of the Children as Designers studies was not to focus on any one rational number subconstruct or any single representation (Harel, 1990). Instead, children worked in a technological environment in which they could explore relations between multiple representations (e.g., pictures, words, and mathematical symbols) and connect different rational number subconstructs (e.g., by designing a screen that combined a part-whole understanding of $\frac{3}{4}$ in a visual area model with a measure interpretation of 0.75 on a number line). In practice, many of the results involve the part-whole subconstruct, with an emphasis on the ideas of fraction meaning, equivalence, and ordering. The technology served the roles of tutee (in the sense that the child programmed or "taught" the computer to perform some desired action, via Logo programming) and tutor-maker (in the sense that the children created tutorials and games for other children). Thus, as a special-purpose tool (i.e., a microworld or a simulation), the role of technology in this project differs from the role of the computer in the UGA Fractions Project or the Copycat Project.

Results

Harel (1990) followed 17 fourth-grade students over a 4-month period while the children planned, designed, and programmed software in LogoWriter (Logo Computer Systems, Inc., 1986) to explain fraction concepts to third-grade students. The experimental learning environment was called Instructional Software Design (ISD). Two control classes were selected: an "isolated Logo" class (in which students programmed once a week using worksheets as exercises) and an "integrated Logo" class (in which students programmed every day and integrated small-scale creative Logo projects into various topics of the curriculum). All three classes followed the regular (and traditional) mathematics curriculum, including a 2-month unit on fractions.

The experimental group outperformed the control groups on measures of mastery of both Logo and fractions. The experimental group acquired greater meta-cognitive skills and made gains on conceptual items in a test of rational-number understanding, comprised mostly of items used in the Rational Number Project (Behr et al., 1983). Most

What is the denominator of the fraction that tells us what part of the picture below is shaded? A) five-thirds; B) five; C) three; D) two; or E) not given

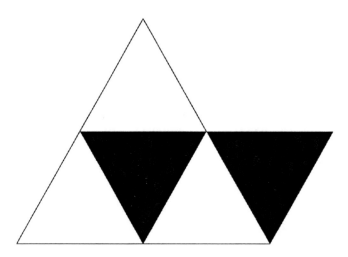

Figure 1.4.   Translation item from the Rational Number Project.

impressive were the gains on translation items. The students' performance on the test item shown in Figure 1.4 provides some insight into how the Children as Designers approach contributed to the gains. The test item involves a translation from pictures into symbols and was particularly difficult for students in the Rational Number Project, in part because the picture included a perceptual distraction (i.e., one part was "outside" the triangular region). However, the scores of children in the experimental group on this item were twice those of children in the control groups and twice those of the seventh-grade students from the Rational Number Project.

Harel hypothesized that several factors contributed to the high scores of the experimental group. First the "perceptual distracter" was not a distracter for children who were trained in their Logo experiences to decompose the picture into geometrical components. Thus, aspects of Logo programming may have contributed to particular fraction understandings. Second, the expertise in translating across representations might be a result of the experimental students' personal goals of representing and explaining fractions to another person, which helped them overcome the difficulties, identified in the pretests, in understanding fractional representations. Although the ISD approach did not include direct teaching of fraction concepts, the movement across representations was an embedded part of the design projects. Harel provides an example of how one student's personal goal of representing thirds with circular regions prompted her to wrestle with the geometry of partitioning circles into equal parts, a much harder task than the "name the shaded portion of geometric shape" tasks, which dominate traditional instruction.

Kafai (1993, 1995, 1996) extended Harel's approach by asking fourth-grade students to design computer video games (rather than tutorials) for teaching fractions to third-grade students. Students integrated fractions in the games in two ways: (a) extrinsically, in which the game template (as in Nintendo or Pacman) could be used with any content, not just mathematics (i.e., players typically advance by answering drill questions correctly); and (b) intrinsically, in which the subject matter is integrated with the game idea. Kafai reported that the second type of integration was rare. Kafai (1993) compared the performance of students in her Game Design Project with the performance of students from Harel's ISD project and reported that "the growth of the game designers' knowledge was not of the same order as the instructional designers' performance" (p. 267). One explanation offered for this difference is that the idea of fractions was more central in the ISD project. The context engaged students in thinking about what was difficult about fractions and how to represent fractions to other children. The Game Design Project, in contrast, gave children more latitude in determining how central fractions would be to the game. Creating an interesting or playful game context was the most dominant feature. While the Game Design treatment "did not promote the same richness and incentive for students to think through and create representations" (p. 301) as did the ISD treatment, students in the Game Design treatment did make significant improvements in their ability to translate flexibly between different modes of fraction representations.

In a follow-up study, Kafai and Ching (1997) explored the integration of fractions into children's game design by examining how four fifth-grade girls designed computer games (using only paper and pencil but not actually programming) to teach fractions to fourth-grade students. Each student initially designed an arcade-style game with extrinsic integration of fractions. Through the researchers' intervention of posing a challenge to the students "to think about a different way to learn about fractions when you are not asking questions," the students developed games with intrinsic and constructivist integration. Intrinsic games included fractions as an integral part of the scene and game objective, for example, a beach in which varying numbers of people are in and out of the water, and the player is to determine what fraction of the people are in or out of the water. Constructivist games allowed users to create their own fractions from what was provided, for example, creating fractions by coloring in parts of a given animal.

In a related study, Franke, Kafai, and Shih (1997) asked 16 prospective elementary teachers to design (but not program) a set of computer games for their students. When left to their own devices, most teachers created arcade-style games (with extrinsic integration) that did not differ much from the initial game designs of younger children (Kafai, 1995; Kafai & Ching, 1997). The initial game designs consisted of drill and practice of fraction equivalence in symbolic form. Only one group of teachers added something at the last minute to show the students a pictorial overlay in an attempt to demonstrate equivalence. When teachers were provided with conceptual design tools such as game screens that facilitated an integration of content and game context, the games as well as the teachers' thinking increased in sophistication.

The British Logo Project

In reference to the framework in the first section, the problems posed in the British Logo Project focused on the ratio subconstruct of rational number with particular emphasis on provoking proportional reasoning strategies that involved the use of iteration and measurement. The researchers were particularly interested in how students reasoned—additively or multiplicatively—when working with the Logo tasks.

Project Description

Hoyles and Noss (1989, 1992) provide reports of children working on ratio and proportion tasks using the Logo programming language. The 1989 article reports a case study of seven 13-year-old children working on a task to scale the letter N. These students were followed for a period of 4 years, but the article reports on their work during one session from the fourth year. The activities occurred in the researchers' computer laboratory. The researchers were interested in the ways in which the computer served as a catalyst in the children's mathematical thinking. Both computer and off-computer activities were used in the instruction. The researchers took a social constructivist view of mathematics learning, stemming from Vygotsky's (1978) notion of the zone of proximal development—the gap between what a learner can do on his or her own and the "potential development as determined through problem solving under adult guidance or in collaboration with more capable peers" (p. 86). The researchers posed the question as to whether or not interaction within a computer environment might help to bridge that gap. They were particularly interested in whether the computer environment could provide scaf-

1. Draw this N on the computer

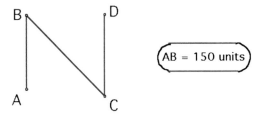

2. The N below is the same shape as the one you have just drawn.

Without using the computer, write down how long you think the length of QR is.

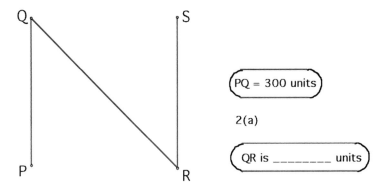

Figure 1.5.   N task from Hoyles and Noss (1989, p. 69).

folding for the development of multiplicative strategies for solving the N task through recognition of symmetries and angle dependencies. Figure 1.5 shows an example task from the study.

The 1992 article reports results from a classroom teaching experiment conducted over a period of 6 weeks. The two researchers taught a class of 28 secondary school 13-year-old students, for 1.5 hours every week in a room with 12 computers. The students worked within the context of a Logo microworld designed to provoke a multiplicative approach to scaling a closed geometric figure (pentagon) created using a Logo procedure referred to as HOUSE (see Figure 1.6). The goal of the study was to identify relationships between pedagogy and student behavior in a computer environment. The study was prompted by the recognition that students can interact with an exploratory computer environment without coming

```
TO HOUSE
  HT
  FD 50
  RT 60
  FD 70
  RT 60
  FD 70
  RT 60
  FD 50
  RT 90
  FD 121
  RT 90
END
```

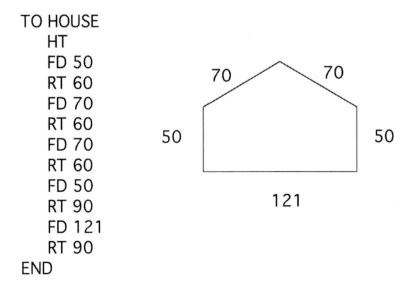

Figure 1.6.   Logo procedure to create a HOUSE, from Hoyles and Noss (1992, p. 34).

to appreciate the mathematical ideas intended by the designers of the computer-aided activities.

Results

Using Logo appeared to positively affect the use of proportional strategies in the letter N task (Hoyles & Noss, 1989). When the students were asked to solve the problem using paper and pencil, they tended to use incorrect additive or pre-proportional strategies. By using Logo, six of the seven children developed proportional strategies, namely, they recognized that the diagonal of the N was longer than the leg by an amount that is proportional to the length of the leg. (The seventh student did not use a coherent strategy for the task.)

Three aspects of the computer environment appeared to affect the development of proportional strategies: (a) the visual feedback (e.g., one student used an incorrect constant-differences strategy to create a larger N and was able to see that the diagonal in the resulting figure was not long enough); (b) the formalization of the proportional relationship required to program the computer; and (c) the exploratory nature of the environment (e.g., one student, who recognized that there was some sort of relationship between the leg and diagonal of the N, was stumped when working on paper but explored a range of possible relationships using the computer). The researchers concluded that the Logo environment provided scaffolding for the children whereby they "could search for the relationships that seemed to be just beyond their grasp" (Noss & Hoyles, 1989, p. 67). The researchers further suggested, "the programming environment provided a vehicle for *thinking about the general within the specific*" (p. 67, italics in the original). They also suggested, "The paper-and-pencil mode activates a fixed answer to a fixed question while the computer activates a dynamic answer" (p. 67).

Hoyles and Noss (1992) introduced the term *strategic apertures* to describe strategies that were supported by the use of technology and that were unavailable with paper and pencil. The researchers designed the Logo microworld and activities with the pedagogical intent of providing such strategic apertures. For example, in an activity that preceded the HOUSE activities, students played a "target game" designed to help challenge the common misconception that "multiplication always makes bigger." Students were given a target number, say 100, and a starting number, say 13. The goal was to locate a factor that could be multiplied by 13 to produce a product of 100. The only rule was that students were not allowed to use division. Some students used an iterative multiplicative strategy. For example, one pair of students began with an initial guess of $13 \times 8 = 104$. They then tried various number types (like -4) until they determined that they could multiply 104 by a decimal less than 1 to obtain a product smaller than 104. They tried a variety of decimal multipliers (like 13×0.25) until they settled on a progressive iterative strategy (e.g., $100.4445 \times 0.99 = 99.440055$; $99.440055 \times 1.0001 = 99.4499990055$; and so on). This iterative strategy was considered a strategic aperture—a strategy available because of the technology. The use of technology also shaped this activity through the immediacy of the feedback generated by the computer and by the display of a very large number of decimal places that allowed students to refine the accuracy of their result. Refining the accuracy in this way appeared to be particularly motivating to the students.

The researchers argued that the opening of these strategic apertures could be exploited pedagogically. For example, when students were using Logo to edit HOUSE to make a new HOUSE that was proportional, where a wall of the first house was 30 and the enlarged side was 50, many students had difficulties. The researchers responded by encouraging students to guess and improve their guesses using the strategic aperture opened in the Target Game. Hoyles and Noss argue that this type of pedagogical intervention exploited features of the technological environment but did not interrupt students' activities.

Generalization of Learning Mathematics in Multimedia Environments

Project Description

A major mathematical goal of the Generalization of Learning project is to support the development of slope understanding so that students can productively generalize their understanding to make sense of a variety of real world situations involving slope. The mathematical focus has been on the ratio subconstruct of rational numbers, specifically the construction of a *ratio-as-measure*. This term was coined by Simon and Blume (1994) to indicate that the ratio is the measure of some attribute like speed, steepness, or sweetness.

The researchers' interest in the construction of ratios-as-measures grew out of their prior work investigating the difficulties high school students experienced in "transferring" their understanding of slope to real-world situations (Lobato, 2003, in press; Lobato & Thanheiser, 1999). For example, in one study, they found that conceiving of slope as a measure of a wheelchair ramp was not a straightforward application for many ninth-grade algebra students because students had difficulty making sense of the relationships among measurable attributes of objects in the situation (Lobato, in press; Lobato & Thanheiser, 1999). For example, the majority of the 17 subjects did not appear to understand the effect of increasing or decreasing the length of the base or the length of the platform on the steepness of a wheelchair ramp.

Lobato and Thanheiser (2000) hypothesized that reconceiving static situations such as the wheelchair ramp as dynamic, with the help of computer software, would enable students to explore the effect of changing various quantities on the attribute measured by slope and to construct a structure in which two quantities covary dynamically in a constant ratio. Existing software were utilized and adapted rather than creating new software. The Geometer's Sketchpad (GSP) (Jackiw, 1995), a general-purpose tool, was used to allow students to create families of ramps with the same steepness and to explore dynamic models of wheelchair ramps (Figure 1.7).

Speed simulations from MathWorlds (Roschelle & Kaput, 1996), software developed for the SimCalc Project, were adapted to allow students to explore how different characters would travel at the same speed and to investigate how changes in distance and time affect speed. Math-Worlds was designed to examine the mathematics of change via links between graphs and technological representations of motion phenomena. For the purposes of the Generalization of Learning project, the graphs were hidden. Speed was developed as a multiplicative relationship between quantities prior to the use of graphical representations with the intention that students would see graphs as representations of

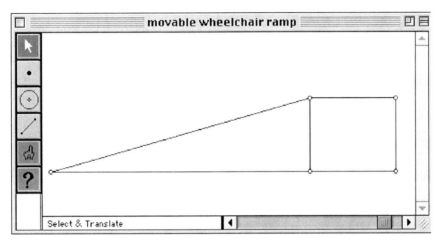

Figure 1.7.   Dynamic sketch of a wheelchair ramp in The Geometer's Sketchpad.

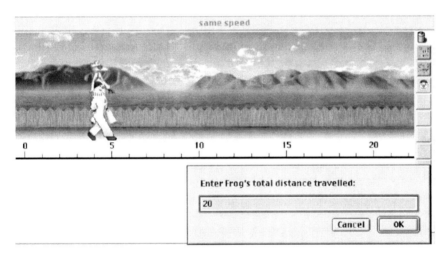

Figure 1.8.   Screen from SimCalc MathWorlds.

something (Lobato & Bowers, 2000). A special microworld was developed for the Generalization of Learning project, in which students could control the starting position, distance, and time describing the travel of characters across the screen[1] (as illustrated in Figure 1.8). MathWorlds was used instead of having students act out the motions, because constant speed is more easily simulated by technology than by people, who tend to accelerate or decelerate.

1. ***"Same Speed" Problem.*** The clown travels 10 cm in 4 s. Use MathWorlds to enter distance and time values for a second character, the frog, so that the frog travels at the same speed as the clown. Find as many distance and time values as you can.
2. ***"Same Steepness" Problem.*** Use Geometer's Sketchpad to make as many ramps as you can with the *same steepness* as a ramp with a height of 2 cm and a length of 3 cm.

Figure 1.9.   "Same attribute" tasks.

Both software environments afforded exploration of problems that the researchers labeled "same attribute" tasks (see Figure 1.9). Generating a family of values such as distance-and-time pairs, each having a given value of an attribute such as speed, helped support the development of ratios connected to the measurement of particular attributes.

Two teaching experiments were conducted. The first teaching experiment (TE1) involved nine eighth-, ninth-, and 10th-grade students for 30 hours of instruction over 2 weeks in a university computer lab during the summer. The second teaching experiment (TE2) involved eight ninth- and 10th-grade algebra students for approximately 30 hour-long, weekly sessions in an after-school program.

Results

A compilation of the results from a variety of papers emanating from the teaching experiments indicates the following cognitive milestones in the development of students' understanding of ratio-as-measure: (a) identifying and isolating the attribute that is being measured, (b) determining which quantities affect the attribute and how, (c) conceiving of two quantities as independent quantities of equal status, (d) understanding the characteristics of a good measure, and (e) creating a ratio as either a multiplicative comparison or a composed unit in such a way that the ratio is a measure of some attribute in the situation (Lobato, in press; Lobato, Clarke, & Ellis, 2005; Lobato & Ellis, 2002; Lobato & Siebert, 2002; Lobato & Thanheiser, 2000, 2002). Each milestone involves *quantitative* aspects of coming to reason with ratios. Quantity is used in the sense of Thompson (1994) to refer to the ways in which people conceive of measurable attributes of objects, events, or situations (e.g., the height of a ramp). It is not used to mean "numeric," as it is used in many other domains such as statistics. Numbers are not quantities but can be values of quantities, for example, 6 feet. The following paragraphs describe and provide an illustrative example for each milestone.

Isolating Attributes

The exploration of speed in both teaching experiments began with a simulation of two characters walking across the screen at constant but unequal rates. Students were asked to determine which character was walking faster and to figure out a way to measure how fast each character was walking. Measuring tools were not provided until students asked for them, and then both computer and noncomputer tools, such as rulers and timing devices, were made available. Although the students had been exposed to the $d = rt$ formula in their regular school mathematics classes, none of the students identified distance and time as the two quantities to measure. Students had difficulty isolating the attribute of speed (how fast one moves through space) from other attributes such as how fast one moves his feet (leg locomotion). For example one pair of girls in TE2 measured the number of steps each character took over time, and concluded incorrectly that the characters were going the same speed since each walked 7 steps in 2.8 s (Lobato & Thanheiser, 2002). These students referred to their everyday experiences of being children trying to keep up with their parents and feeling like they were going faster than their parents. Thus, "fastness" as an attribute was ambiguous and the various types of "fastness" had to be sorted out.

Similarly, students in TE1 struggled to isolate the attribute of steepness in the wheelchair ramp situation from the attribute of the work required to climb the ramp (Lobato, in press; Lobato et al., 2005). This is reasonable since two nonidentical ramps of same steepness will take unequal amounts of work to climb, and students with everyday experiences with hill climbing and skateboarding may focus on work as the more salient attribute. Lobato and colleagues (2005) document the struggle and eventual success of the students in TE1 to isolate steepness as an attribute.

Determining the Effect of Changing Various Quantities

Once students isolate an attribute such as steepness or motion through space, they then need to determine which quantities affect that attribute. In both teaching experiments, students explored how changing time and distance affected the motion of an object by entering distance and time values for various characters in MathWorlds. In one problem, students were asked to enter a time and a distance for the frog so that it would travel slower than a clown traveling 15 cm in 6 s. Students experienced several difficulties (Lobato & Thanheiser, 2002). For example, in TE2, Priyani and Adolfo kept returning to the idea that speed could be measured by time alone—an idea that has roots in the everyday experience of determining the speed of runners. Since the distance in a race is fixed, one can measure how fast a runner travels by simply timing the race. As a result of associating speed with time, Priyani and Adolfo could correctly argue that they could make the frog go slower by increasing the time and faster by decreasing the time. However, when asked to give both characters the same time and change only the distance to make the frog go slower, Priyani thought the problem could not be solved, and Adolfo reasoned incorrectly that having the frog walk a greater distance would make him go slower. Thus they were surprised to run the simulation and see that this was not the case. The software played a critical role in their development by helping create a perturbational experience and by allowing students to explore how changes in distance affect speed.

Constructing Independent Quantities of Equal Stature

In a case study from TE1, Lobato and Siebert (2002) report an important shift in student reasoning that is related to the student's ability to construct a ratio between height and length in the wheelchair ramp situation. In an interview conducted before the teaching experiment, an eighth-grade student (Terry) appeared to view height as more important than length in determining the steepness of a ramp. Furthermore, when asked how decreasing the length of the base would affect the steepness, Terry treated length as dependent upon height. He moved the rightmost part of the ramp to the left (without changing the height of the rightmost part), used his understanding of the effect of changing the height to reason that he had as a consequence made the new ramp taller and steeper, and then reasoned indirectly that the length of the base of the new ramp had been decreased in the process. After instruction, Terry appeared to conceive of height and length as independent quantities of equal stature, as evidenced by the changes in his visual images and his ability to operate on length independently of height. Lobato and Siebert (2002) document how this shift appeared to be linked to his ability to reason proportionally in the ramp situation, something he was unable to do in the pre-interview.

Characteristics of a Good Measure

One characteristic of a measure is that it can legitimately be indirect rather than direct. When asked to create measures of how fast a character walks or of the steepness of a wheelchair ramp, many students in both teaching experiments created direct measures (e.g., measuring speed with time alone or steepness with slant height). The software environments allowed students to create multiple instances of the object or event with the same direct measure and see if the attributes were the same. This process involves a characteristic of a measure that Lobato and Thanheiser (2002) call "reproducibility." If one imagines a ramp with a height of 8 cm and a base of 4 cm, then the ratio of height to length (the slope) is a good measure of the steepness of the physical object partly because someone else can create a different ramp with a slope of 2 and the two ramps will share the same steepness (i.e., the amount of steepness is "reproduced" in the second ramp), even though the ramps are not identical. Lobato and colleagues (2005) document how students in TE1 explored the limitations of their direct measures by testing whether or not the measures were reproducible.

Formation of Ratio-as-Measure

There is an extensive literature base investigating students' ratio and proportional reasoning (see, for example, a review by Fuson & Abrahamson, 2005). One goal of the Generalization of Learning project was to extend this research by exploring the formation of ratio as a measure of attributes typically measured by slope. Researchers observed two types of ratio-as-measure constructions in the teaching experiments: ratio as a composed unit and as a multiplicative comparison. These constructions occurred in the context of the "same attribute" tasks.

Lobato and colleagues (Lobato & Siebert, 2002; Lobato & Thanheiser, 2000, 2002) document the nonstraightforward process by which students in TE1 eventually formed a composed unit of distance and time values so that the unit measured speed. Specifically students progressed from the use of strictly numeric (and often nonproportional) reasoning to the following type of quantitative reasoning. Some students argued that if the frog went 20 cm in 8 s, it would travel at the same speed as the clown (who went 10 cm in 4 s) because one could think of the frog as walking 10 cm in 4 s, and then simply repeat its journey of 10 cm in 4 s for a total of 20 cm in 8 s. Since the two journeys were identical, the same speed was preserved. These students seemed to form a "10 cm: 4 s" composed unit (a rudimentary type of ratio), which then constituted a foundation from which more sophisticated ratio reasoning developed.

In the formation of a second type of ratio—multiplicative comparison—GSP appeared to play an important role (Lobato & Thanheiser, 2002). For example, one student (Brad) had created the family of ramps shown in Figure 1.10. Interestingly, Brad discovered the "slope" function in the "measure" menu of GSP and found that the slope of one of his ramps was 0.25. He remembered that slope was "rise over run" from his regular high school algebra class and linked steepness with slope. Although he correctly identified the "rise" and "run" of his ramp, he was unable to explain what the 0.25 meant in terms of the ramp situation. After creating more ramps in GSP and looking for patterns, Brad formed a multiplicative comparison by noticing that the length of each ramp was four times as large as the height and that each height was $\frac{1}{4}$ (or 0.25) of the corresponding length.

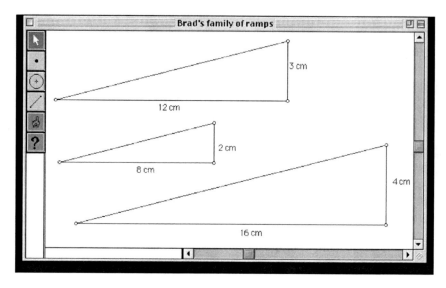

Figure 1.10.   Brad's construction of ramps with the same steepness.

The Generalization of Learning project indicates that technology can play an important role in helping students learn to deal with the quantitative aspects of constructing ratio as measure. Understanding the modeling and proportional reasoning aspects of ratio-as-measure tasks can, in turn, help students develop an understanding of slope that is more robust and generalizable (Lobato, 2003).

LEARNING OF RATIONAL NUMBER CONCEPTS: CONTRIBUTIONS AND LIMITATIONS OF TECHNOLOGY

In the five projects that used technology as a medium for investigating children's learning, the various technological environments provided children with tools and opportunities to express and explore their mathematical ideas. We formed five conclusions about the nature of the relationship between technology and the learning of rational numbers from our synthesis of the projects. These conclusions are preliminary since each project was exploratory and involved a small sample size, usually in more ideal or "best practice" situations.

- *First conclusion:* The nature of what students learn about rational numbers appears to be related to the match between the affordances and constraints of the technology and the mental operations involved in constructing rational numbers; if such links are missing then a greater demand is placed on the teacher and the nontechnology activities.

An affordance is a relation between a resource in the environment and an agent that supports activity (Gibson, 1986). For example, the TIMA Bars microworld from the UGA Fractions project affords the disembedding of a part from a whole without disrupting the whole. A constraint is a regularity that holds in some domain, usually dependent on some conditions, like causal relations (Barwise & Perry, 1983). A constraint built into the Bars microworld is that bars can only be partitioned into a whole number of equal parts. A child cannot directly ask the computer to make a fraction of a bar. This constraint requires the child to make a fraction of a bar by first partitioning that bar and then either breaking the bar apart (or cutting it), or by using the disembedding action as previously described.

The design of the TIMA microworlds in the UGA Fractions project was unique in its intent to closely match the affordances and constraints of the computer environment with the mental operations involved in constructing rational numbers (as specified in the section titled Semantic and Psychological Analyses of Rational Number). For example, the mental operation of iterating is supported by the affordances allowed in the computer environment by the REPEAT function. This match between the affordances of the microworld and the mental operation of iteration appears to be related to children's development of important fraction concepts. For example, Olive (2000, 2002a) and Steffe and Tzur (1994) provide examples of how children take advantage of the repeating actions in TIMA Sticks to establish an iterable unit fraction, (i.e., to understand that $\frac{1}{n}$ of a stick, iterated n times will produce the original stick). Tzur (1999) and Olive (2002a) further demonstrate how children reorganize their fraction knowledge by abstracting the result of iterating unit fractions to produce nonunit fractions (e.g., by iterating $\frac{1}{7}$ to obtain $\frac{5}{7}$ or $\frac{9}{7}$)—an advanced conception referred to as the iterative fractional scheme.

The role of the Copycat technology would appear to be similar to the role of the TIMA, in that the input-output machine in Copycat was used by the teacher/researcher and the children to create problem situations for the children to solve. However, the constraints built into the simulation limited the set of possible problems and the ways in which they could be solved. The Copycat software was constrained to working with whole number inputs that were multiples of a user-specified fraction denominator. In the UGA project, the TIMA software was used to visualize and operate with any part or multiples of parts of any designated unit. On the other hand, the Copycat software afforded the investigation of the multiplicative operator subconstruct of rational numbers, unlike any of the other projects reviewed in this chapter.

The relationship between the affordances of technology and the development of particular aspects of rational number is also suggested by the impressive findings of the Children as Designers studies. In particular, the use of Logo appeared to afford movement across various representations of fractions and provided experience composing and decomposing fractional regions.

Three of the projects illustrate that when particular links between the mental operations and the affordances and constraints of the technology are missing, then pedagogical intervention or the use of additional activities is needed to compensate explicitly for the lack. For example, the MathWorlds software was utilized in the Generalization of Learning project because it provided a venue for exploring the quantitative complexity of constructing a ratio as a measure of speed. It was not designed to afford the construction, iteration, and partitioning of ratios as composed units. Hence, off-screen activities such as classroom discussions, student explanations, and the use of diagrams were more critical in the Generalization of Learning project. Lobato and Thanheiser (2000, 2002) reflect that it is unlikely that students in the teaching experiments would have progressed beyond guess-and-check strategies or numeric patterns without class discussions and the use of diagrams. Thus the MathWorlds environment provided a rich context in which important questions were raised, but not typically resolved, without other resources. In contrast, Geometer's Sketchpad could support iterating by stacking or aligning "unit" ramps to form larger ramps, as well as partitioning, even though the software was not specifically designed to afford these actions.

A second example of how off-screen activities can compensate for on-screen constraints involves the Copycat software. Because a Copycat machine operates as a "black box," the user cannot observe the processes by which the machine works. For example, in a study of four third-grade students (G. Davis et al., 1993), one child, Elliot, was unable to predict correctly the output of the "two for three" machine. The teacher tried to focus Elliot's attention on what the machine did to the input items by putting six items into a "one for three" machine and watching two come out. Elliot seemed puzzled until the teacher reminded Elliot how the machine worked, namely that for every three items that come in, one item comes out. Once the focus turned to the functioning of the machine, Elliot was able to determine that 10 items would come out of the "one for three" machine when 30 items were put in. He was also able to determine that 20 items would come out of the "two for three" machine when 30 items were used as the input, but he did so by modeling the process using manipulatives. Only one of the children related the "two for three" operator as being twice the "one for three" operator, and this relation grew out of her work with arrays of cubes using SuperPaint software. In these episodes, the children appeared to need supplementary activities that helped them understand, via their own activity, the operator process (not simply the outcome of operating).

Finally, in the Children as Designers project, Harel (1990) concluded that the results might be generalizable to other topics in mathematics such as proportional reasoning. Further research is needed to substantiate the claim that children can learn more than introductory concepts, without also substantially improving the nature of the mathematical instruction received by the children and possibly improving the subject matter knowledge of their teachers. In fact, the repeated finding by Kafai and colleagues (Kafai, 1995, 1996; Kafai & Ching, 1997) that children tend to create games with little conceptual content can be explained by the fact that the students do not know much more than facts and procedures. In order to prompt increasingly sophisticated integration of fraction content with games, Kafai and colleagues had to intervene. In sum, when extending the "children as designers" approach to more sophisticated mathematical content, a stronger role for the teacher might be needed.

- *Second conclusion:* Technological tools can allow students to perform actions such as disembedding, which are critical for the development of rational number understanding but difficult, if not impossible, to perform without technology.

Examples from three of the projects illustrate this point. In the section, Semantic and Psychological Analyses of Rational Number, we described in detail how the TIMA computer tools from the UGA fractions project allow children the ability to dynamically pull a part out of a partitioned whole while leaving the whole intact. Thus children can enact the disembedding operation that is necessary to establish a relation between a part and a whole in a fractional situation. A second example is the strategic apertures described by Hoyles and Noss (1992). They explain how the Logo microworld was used to support an iterative multiplicative strategy (in the Target Game), a strategy that was unavailable with paper and pencil. The technology allowed students the opportunity to reflect upon the effects of multiplying by decimals and negative numbers, thus increasing the base of their experiences from which they could make generalizations (and helping reorganize their understanding of notions like "multiplication makes bigger") before they had developed computational fluency with such number types.

A final example involves both software environments used in the Generalization of Learning project. Because constant speed is difficult to attain in everyday experience, MathWorlds was particularly helpful for developing an understanding of a ratio as a measure of speed. Because dynamically manipulating diagrams of ramps or hills is nearly impossible to accomplish with physical materials, GSP played a critical role in the construction of a ratio as a measure of steepness. By allowing students to create and test "same speed" and "same steepness" values, both environments seemed to support an image of "extension," namely, that other pairs of values would produce the same speed or same steepness, which appears to have been important for the construction of ratio. Furthermore, both environments allowed students to systematically test the effect of changing quantities on a given attribute, something that is difficult to achieve without technology. For example, in MathWorlds students could fix the time, vary the distance, run the simulation, and observe how increasing or decreasing the distance affected the character's speed. Similarly, in GSP students could change the length of the base of the ramp or the length of the platform in order to see what effect the changes had on the steepness of a dynamic ramp. These results would appear to support Kaput's (1996) argument for the advantages of cybernetic manipulatives: "Computer-instantiated objects offer the opportunity for overcoming the constraints of physicality when [these constraints] unnecessarily limit the mathematical properties or actions that we might want students to learn" (pp. 170-171).

- *Third conclusion:* The construction of technological artifacts for others leads to richer representations of fractions than typically occurs in school instruction.

The Children as Designers projects extended the role of the computer to that of toolmaker, as children designed instruction and games for younger children. The toolmaker role placed the children in a very different social position than in any of the other projects reviewed in this chapter. Rather than responding to tasks set by the teachers, students played a much greater role in determining the direction of the project. Children were concerned about what might be valuable, fun, and engaging for other children. The design projects (especially in Harel's ISD treatment) provided opportunities for much richer discussions of multiple representations of fractions than what typically occurs in school instruction. The programming challenges involved in creating pictorial representations of fractions did, however, engage the children (as designers) in conceptual problem solving. Figuring out how to get Logo to partition a circle into three equal parts in order to show thirds, for instance, was a genuine mathematical challenge for the children.

- *Fourth conclusion:* Technological environments can unintentionally afford additive strategies rather than the multiplicative strategies that lead to powerful rational number concepts.

Hoyles and Noss (1992) note that exploiting certain features of the computer environment can provide solution paths that allow the student to bypass or avoid the mathematics that the teacher designed the computer-aided activity to address. Hoyles and Noss describe an example in which the student used an incorrect additive strategy to create a larger house (namely by adding a constant difference to each side). This produced a gap at the base of the house (see Figure 1.11). The student was able to create a larger house (which "solved" the problem to the satisfaction of the student) by edging the turtle slowly but surely toward its target by an iterative process. The researchers interpreted this as a perceptual rather than an analytic solution.

Resolving this problem via a pedagogical intervention was not straightforward. The researchers developed an off-computer activity that identified the same type of gap-closing problem that arose the day before in the Logo environment. The researchers were surprised that the students had no problem identifying a multiplicative solution to the problem on paper,

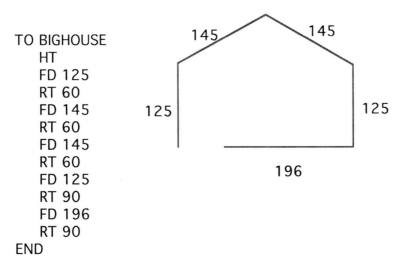

```
TO BIGHOUSE
   HT
   FD 125
   RT 60
   FD 145
   RT 60
   FD 145
   RT 60
   FD 125
   RT 90
   FD 196
   RT 90
END
```

Figure 1.11.   The result of using an additive strategy to enlarge the HOUSE in Figure 1.6 (from Hoyles & Noss, 1992, p. 34).

even though additive strategies had cropped up during the computer activity. The researchers hypothesized the discussion was too far removed from the computer work and the emerging classroom culture inhibited students from admitting to the additive strategies they had used on the computer. Interestingly, none of the students chose the additive response on the worksheet, although many had done so on the computer. The reverse situation also occurred (Hoyles & Noss, 1992). A collaborative activity involving pairs of students trying to find the rule used by another pair to enlarge the HOUSE indicated that while one pair would use a multiplicative scale factor with their Logo procedure to produce a larger HOUSE, they would use an additive strategy to try to find the missing measures on the other students' HOUSE (an off-computer activity).

The use of MathWorlds in the Generalization of Learning Project also afforded several unintended conceptions (Lobato & Ellis, 2002; Lobato & Thanheiser, 2000, 2002). First, students developed a practice of judging same speeds by looking to see whether the characters walked "neck-and-neck" for the duration of the shorter journey of the two characters. This might explain why some students did not initially account for the time and distance of the character that kept walking after the first character stopped and consequently did not represent the proportional relationships in their drawings (for details, see Lobato & Thanheiser, 2002). Second, throughout the discussion, despite the teacher's efforts to focus on explanations and reasoning as ways to settle mathematical disagreements, the students seemed to view the computer simulation as the highest authority. Finally, every student in the teaching experiments recorded at least some incorrect time and distance values as representing a "same speed" value because it was often visually difficult to distinguish which character was going faster if the ratios were close, for example, a character traveling 11 cm in 4.5 s *appears* to be going the same speed as a character traveling 10 cm in 4 s.

Hoyles and Noss (1992) identify a more general and unanticipated result of beginning with a pedagogical approach that encouraged students to "play around" in exploratory microworlds. They call the situation the *play paradox*. By exploiting the diverse ways of exploring and solving a problem offered by an exploratory computer environment, students are as likely to avoid encountering the "mathematical nuggets so carefully planted by their teachers" (p. 46). The researchers' strategy for tackling the play paradox was to encourage the students to *reflect* on the task at hand. They point out that this was often more heavy-handed than they might have advocated in their previous Logo studies.

- *Fifth conclusion:* Studying learning in technological environments has contributed to a significant expansion of the conceptual analysis of rational numbers and to an understanding of the relationship between children's whole number and rational number knowledge.

A great deal of work has been done to identify aspects of rational number understanding (such as the subconstructs and psychological operations identified in the framework discussion). However, several of the projects have contributed to further articulation of the particular rational number concepts that are fundamental for children to understand, from the point of view of children's mathematics rather than from an adult's view. These projects have also led to the development of learning trajectories for children's construction of rational number concepts.

The UGA Fractions project expanded the ideas concerning fractions in significant ways. For example, basic fraction meaning is often developed in schools as a part of a whole, (e.g., $\frac{3}{4}$ is 3 out of 4 equal parts of some given whole). However, students with this understanding of fractions frequently encounter difficulty in making sense of improper fractions like $\frac{7}{4}$, arguing that it is not possible to have more than 4 out of 4 parts. In contrast, the UGA Fractions project has identified a different and more generalizable conception. Its approach emphasizes the construction of fractions as iterable unit items and as operations. The TIMA computer environments provided a medium in which the children could embody these constructs through visualization and action. Using the possible actions of the TIMA microworlds, children constructed iterable unit fractions as building blocks for proper and improper fractions. An iterable unit fraction is the product of an inverse relation between a unit fraction as a part of a whole and the partitioned whole as generated from iteration of that unit fraction. In developing composition of fractions (e.g., $\frac{3}{4}$ of $\frac{2}{3}$ of a whole), the project brought out the necessity to conceptualize fractions as both operators and quantitative relations.

The project also generated a new subconstruct of rational number referred to as the rational numbers of arithmetic. This new subconstruct can be thought of as the bridge that leads from fractions to rational numbers (viewed as an infinite quotient field). The researchers' claim is that children have the potential to construct the rational numbers of arithmetic when they can create any fraction (of a referent whole) from any other fraction (of the same whole) by finding a comeasurement unit for the two fractions. Both the UGA Fractions project and the Copycat project demonstrated that fractional schemes can emerge for children as reorganizations of their whole-number schemes, which is contrary to previous research that suggested that whole-number knowledge interfered with children's development of fractional knowledge.

THE EFFECTS OF TECHNOLOGY ON
LEARNING ABOUT RATIONAL NUMBERS

The following three projects investigated the effects of a particular technology on children's learning: (a) the Math*Logo Project; (b) the Mastering Fractions video-disc project; and (c) The PLATO Fractions Curriculum Project. We briefly describe each project, summarize the results, and offer conclusions based on this summary.

Project Descriptions

The Math*Logo project was designed to improve the proportional reasoning of college freshmen enrolled in remedial mathematics courses at the University of Minnesota, Duluth (Guckin & Morrison, 1991). Twenty-three students in a remedial mathematics program took the Math*Logo-based experimental course; the remaining 41 remedial mathematics students served as a control group and were assigned to a conventional mathematical skills course. Both courses provided approximately 30 hours of instruction. The Math*Logo group worked in a computer lab with three students per computer. A structured problem-solving/discovery approach to learning was employed in the Math*Logo course. Students worked through a sequence of structured activities in Logo that were grouped into three course segments (microworlds). The content included the quotient, multiplicative operator, and ratio subconstructs of rational numbers.

A video-disc fractions curriculum, called Mastering Fractions, was founded on a theory of instructional design developed by Engelmann and Carnine (1982). The direct instructional approach was based on four tenets, (a) incremental review; (b) discrimination practice (i.e., problem types are mixed in practice sets), (c) example selection (i.e., examples are carefully constructed and sequenced so that students will avoid misconceptions), and (d) explicit strategy teaching, (i.e., an approach in which general mathematical principles are explicitly taught). Though the curriculum emphasized performance and mastery of procedures, it would be a mistake to conclude that concepts were not valued or addressed. Kelly, Carnine, Gersten, and Grossen (1986) persuasively argue that the basal textbooks of the time typically presented a pictorial approach to equivalent fractions that reduced rational number concepts to whole number counting (e.g., two pies are shaded in the text to show $\frac{1}{3}$ and $\frac{2}{6}$, and students are asked to determine the value of "?" in "$\frac{1}{3} = \frac{?}{6}$," which they can do by counting two shaded parts in the picture). The conceptual approach followed in the Mastering Fractions curriculum relied on teaching a set of interrelated rules and properties (namely that $\frac{1}{3} = \frac{2}{6}$ because $\frac{1}{3} \times \frac{2}{2} = \frac{2}{6}$; more generally $\frac{b}{b} = 1$ and $a \cdot 1 = a$ for any real numbers a and b, $b = 0$), and it focused on the part-whole subconstruct of rational numbers.

The PLATO fractions curriculum (Dugdale & Kibbey, 1980) was developed through a National Science Foundation grant to the University of Illinois over a period of 4 years, beginning in 1973. It was part of the first attempt to design a graphics-capable, computer-based, curriculum for elementary children. The curriculum covered proper fractions, mixed numbers, and an introduction to decimal notation (Dugdale & Kibbey, 1990). It included approximately 100 computer programs, a teacher's manual, and booklets and worksheets for students. The PLATO computer-management system allowed teachers to personalize the curriculum for individual students by assigning topics and levels. The system also structured activities for students based on individual background information entered by the teacher or stored by the system during students' interaction with the system. Many of the programs were mastery-based, "with the difficulty and complexity of the task automatically adjusted (up or down) based on the student's performance" (p. 207).

While the PLATO project could be regarded as the forerunner for the modern computer-delivered curriculum packages, Dugdale and Kibbey (1990) make it clear that their intent as both designers and researchers of the fractions curriculum package was not to implement a behaviorist model that is now common among these modern packages. The pedagogical approach of the PLATO fractions curriculum was rooted in the ideas of Piaget's (1973) constructivism, Dewey's (1963) emphasis on developing mathematical activity in a mathematical community, Polya's (1957) problem-solving heuristics, and R. B. Davis' (1967) "discovery" approach. Although we have included this project in the "effect studies" category, it really straddles both "effect" and "learning tool" categories. In addition to summative assessments, extensive observations of students using PLATO were conducted over a period of several years, along with student interviews and teacher interviews. Dugdale (2008) provides a more extensive overview of the PLATO curriculum.

An example of one of the fractions programs is Darts (Dugdale & Kibbey, 1990). Darts addresses the measure subconstruct of rational number. Students estimated positions on a vertical number line using rational numbers (fractions, decimals or mixed numbers). The computer screen displayed a vertical number line labeled with the points 0, 1 and 2. Balloons were attached to the left side of the number line at various positions. The student entered a rational number or expression (e.g., $\frac{1}{3} + \frac{1}{6}$) that would indicate where a dart was to be thrown. The dart flew across the screen from the left and stuck in the number line, popping a balloon if it hit one. The dart did not have to hit the exact position at which the balloon was attached to the number line. If the dart passed through any part of the balloon, it would be counted as a hit. The fractional numeral (in the form entered by the user) was displayed on the right side of the number line next to the dart. The intent of the PLATO Darts was to encourage estimation and student-generated strategies rather than to require exact input.

Summary of Results Across the Three Projects

Each of the projects reported positive effects of the technology on student learning. Gukin and Morrison (1991) reported significant gains on a test of proportional reasoning for their students. For example, on the pretest, 15 of the 23 students in the Math*Logo treatment were assessed as non-proportional, compared with 32 of the 41 students in the control group. On the posttest, all 18 of the Math*Logo students completing the course were assessed as reasoning proportionally, compared to 16 of the 28 students who completed the regular course. On the surface this project seems to indicate a possible solution to a widespread problem facing colleges across the nation. The Math*Logo approach to remedial mathematics courses for college freshmen appears to have been very successful in enhancing students' proportional reasoning. However, not enough detail about the content and conduct of the course was provided to allow adequate evaluation of the authors' claims, in particular, how central the use of Logo was to the improvement in proportional reasoning.

Kelly and colleagues (1986) compared the effectiveness of the videodisc curriculum with a traditional basal program and found that students in the experimental group performed significantly better on paper-and-pencil fraction items. Comparisons were also made between the videodisc version and overhead transparency versions of the Mastering Fractions curriculum, but no significant differences were found. This suggests that the positive learning outcomes reported in the Mastering Fractions project were a result of the structured curricular activities rather than a result of the particular technological medium used to deliver the curriculum. In fact, Kelly and colleagues state that the potential of the video-disc technology lies in its ability to "assist the teacher in the consistent implementation of sound instructional procedures" (p. 16). That is, the video-disc medium is not necessary (overhead transparency versions of the curriculum work equally well), but the video-discs help deliver the instruction consistently.

Educational Testing Service (ETS) conducted an external evaluation of the PLATO elementary materials. Data indicated significant (and large) positive achievement and attitudinal effects for the fractions curriculum at all grade levels (fourth, fifth, and sixth grades) (Swinton, 1978). The observations and interviews of students using the PLATO fractions curriculum suggest that students developed strong intuitions about equivalent fractions and relative size of fractions. Dugdale and Kibbey (1990) report a variety of estimation strategies that appeared to be supported in part by the visual representations of the Darts environment and by the limited computer feedback. For example, one strategy they observed was finding an appropriate unit fraction $(\frac{1}{n})$ that could be used to partition the number line so that multiples $(\frac{m}{n})$ could be used to hit several balloons. They report how one student used her fingers to mark off intervals up the number line after each use of $\frac{1}{n}$ (for increasing integer values of n), "searching for balloons that could be hit with fractions of denominator n" (p. 217). Dugdale and Kibbey (1990) contend that "graphic feedback, reflecting the input and leaving the diagnostic thinking to the student, gives a *wide bandwidth* of information from which the student notices only what is relevant" (p. 218). They provide an example of another student who counted twelve and one-half finger widths between integers on the number line: "She thought for a moment, then used 25ths, calling each *half*-finger width equal to $\frac{1}{25}$" (p. 218).

Conclusions From the Effect Studies

Limiting computer feedback can play a role in encouraging problem solving. The role of technology in both the PLATO and video-disc projects was one of tutor or computer-assisted instruction (CAI). The design features of the earlier PLATO curriculum were, however, less directive and less structured than those incorporated into the video-disc materials. The designers of PLATO intentionally avoided the kind of stimulus-response format used by much of the drill-and-practice software used in elementary schools today. The programs appeared to foster student-generated problem-solving strategies by limiting the type and amount of feedback given by the programs. The feedback provided by the PLATO modules was intended to provoke thinking strategies on the part of the user, rather than merely indicating whether a response was correct.

Dugdale and Kibbey (1990) discuss the benefits of the limited (but mathematically accurate) feedback provided by the Darts program (the fraction numerals to the right of the number line, indicating the position of each dart, and the exploded balloon when one was hit). As designers of the software they could have attempted to give feedback based on hypothetical sources of errors and branching (as in computer-assisted-instruction tutors driven by artificial intelligence [AI] engines). The designers contend that because they did not provide such AI-driven feedback, students used the mathematical feedback to generate their own strategies and correct their own misconceptions. For instance, a student might enter a negative number, expecting $-1\frac{1}{4}$ to be *higher up* than -1 on the number line and be encouraged to modify his or her conception upon seeing the feedback. Additionally the user was free to input any rational expression; thus, there was not the structured sequence of simple-to-complex problems that appears to be programmed into the video-disc modules.

Caution should be used when interpreting the effect of computer visual representations. One of the tenets of the video-disc project was that the mathematical properties could be represented unproblematically through demonstrations and visuals used in the video-disc environment. The only examples cited by the researchers of the integration of technology with content rest on representationist assumptions of the transparency of visual displays. For example, Kelly and colleagues write:

> When equivalent fractions are taught, kids see a fraction on a balance beam. The side with the fraction tips down. When an equivalent fraction is placed on the other side the balance becomes level. (Hence) ... the video sequence shows what equality means in a vivid, compelling manner. (Kelly et al., 1986, p. 16)

Although researchers have argued against the position that visual representations or physical materials are transparent carriers of mathematical meaning (Cobb, 1991; Meira, 1998), the position is seductive, as is evidenced by the ubiquitous use of visual demonstrations in commercial software dealing with rational numbers. Thus, it is important to point out that the assumptions made by the video-disc authors were not examined in light of how children might think while using the program. A contrasting perspective on the role of visual representations is that taken by the UGA Fractions project. Here the visual objects of the TIMA microworlds (toys, bars, and sticks) are objects on which students may act and construct mathematical meaning based upon the reflective abstraction of their actions. Since the meaning making is assumed to be interpretive in nature, the researchers make the investigation of the particular (and often unintended) student constructions the primary object of their research.

Guidelines for developing technological learning environments. Dugdale and Spiro (1990) list nine aspects of the PLATO materials that could be interpreted as fitting within a constructivist framework of learning (although they use the label *cognitive flexibility theory*). Most (if not all) of these aspects could be attributed to the five projects reviewed in earlier sections of this chapter. These attributes provide a valuable set of guidelines for developing technological learning environments and are described as follows: (a) foster constructive approaches to solving problems; (b) lay important groundwork for future topics; (c) foster situation-specific adaptive flexibility; (d) foster a nonalgorithmic sense of numbers and a qualitative sense of mathematics; (e) foster multiple perspectives on a problem; (f) provide integration with a larger environmental context; (g) foster the ability to apply learning to new, more complex situations; (h) foster active participation and desirable attitudes about the subject matter; and (i) foster desirable attitudes about the students themselves.

IMPLICATIONS FOR CURRICULUM DEVELOPERS, TEACHERS, RESEARCHERS, AND POLICYMAKERS

Implications for Curriculum Developers

A clear implication for developing curricula for children's learning of rational number concepts is that children's own ways and means of operating with fractional quantities have to be central in the design of the curriculum. The five projects that used technology as a medium for investigating children's learning of rational number concepts can provide curriculum developers with research-based models of children's ways and means of operating. It is also clear from this synthesis that both the design of the technology and the way it was used in the various projects helped to shape children's learning. Curriculum developers should take advantage of the various technologies while remaining aware of their limitations. Providing technological tools that enable children to enact their own mathematical operations can be a very powerful aid to children's learning. Simulation software that provides students with phenomena to explore and carry out experiments (as in the MathWorlds simulations) can also be productive in engendering learning. Incorporating Logo programming activities into the curriculum could also be beneficial. All of these recommendations for incorporating technology into the curriculum, however, are dependent on having informed and well-prepared teachers to implement the technology and the curriculum in ways that enhance students' learning.

Implications for Teachers

All of the research projects reviewed in this synthesis found that interaction with a teacher was necessary for meaningful learning to take place. Neither the technology nor children's own explorations were sufficient for conceptual learning of rational number constructs. While the different technological environments provided both affordances and constraints, the learning of rational number constructs occurred through interaction with others. As Hoyles and Noss (1992) pointed out, the intervention of the teacher was a necessary pedagogical component in their students' learning about ratio and proportion. This point has wide-ranging implications for the use of technology in teaching rational number concepts— the technology cannot stand alone. It has to be interpreted by both teacher and students and embedded within a pedagogy that is necessarily complex. Part of that complexity is the relationship between off-computer and on-computer activities. All of the projects reviewed in this chapter intimated that students were engaged in discussion of and reflection on their computer-based learning activities in activities that took place outside of the technological medium.

Implications for Researchers

The field of rational number research is at the stage of building useful models of children's thinking. Future research should move to the stage of small-scale classroom teaching experiments, aided by technology, that build on our understanding of children's thinking. Such classroom teaching experiments need to take into account both the social interactions and the pedagogical complexities of working with technological tools. While the research reviewed in this chapter supports the teaching of fractions as necessary for understanding rational number, we would like to see well-designed classroom teaching experiments that address the use of decimal calculations with handheld calculators as a viable approach to teaching rational number in the middle grades. Research on the use of handheld calculators in the learning of rational number concepts was markedly absent from the literature through which we searched.

Research should also begin to investigate what types of technological environments children find aesthetically appealing and how the factor of aesthetic appeal influences engagement and learning of rational number concepts. An exploratory study by Sinclair (2001) investigated the use of a novel, Web-based *color calculator* that represented the decimal form of any fraction both as a string of digits and as a sequence of colored squares arranged in a rectangular pattern (each of the digits 0 through 9 was represented by a different color). The 15 students in her study were able to explore patterns in the numerical representation by changing the width of the rectangle of colored squares. For instance, the color representation of the fraction $\frac{1}{7}$, when arranged in a rectangle with a width that was a multiple of six, showed columns of each of the six colors representing the repeating digits in the decimal notation (see Figure 1.12).

Sinclair's goal was to investigate the role of the aesthetic in students' mathematical learning. She argues that the aesthetic dimension plays a central role in determining what mathematics is personally or epistemologically relevant to children. In her conclusions regarding the use of her Colour Calculator (CC) she reported the following:

> This environment certainly prompted the students to make new understandings of fractions and decimals and in particular, to explore characteristics and relationships they are not usually encouraged to explore. The CC environment highlighted some of the incomplete fraction and decimal

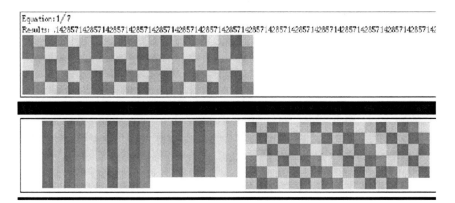

Figure 1.12.   Screen captures from the Colour Calculator showing different tabular representations of $\frac{1}{7}$: widths 18 and 17 (from Sinclair, 2001).

understanding that students have and allowed them to gain a new understanding of what a fraction *is*, as opposed to what you can do to fractions—
add them, generate equivalent ones, etc. Additionally, the CC appears to be
an environment in which students are interested and motivated to discover
certain things about numbers, using fractions and decimals, that are different than what is emphasised in current school curricula. (p. 6)

Sinclair's exploratory study raises an important issue for both designers of mathematics curriculum activities and software environments: Is
the activity aesthetically appealing to students and does the aesthetic
dimension engage students in important mathematics? Her study also
indicated that students' use of decimal notation was disconnected from
their understanding of common fractions. Researchers in mathematics
education need to pay attention to and study this apparent disconnect.

Implications for Policymakers

Policymakers need to look carefully at all of the above implications
when making decisions that affect the design and implementation of curricula, the preparation and continued professional development of teachers, and the funding of research in the area of rational number. They
should also pay close attention to what this synthesis suggests concerning
the use of technology in the teaching and learning of rational number
concepts when making decisions regarding both the acquisition and use
of technology in schools. Because the technology cannot stand alone, policymakers must make sure that the financial resources and release time
are in place for teachers to learn both what the research indicates about
how children learn rational number concepts, and how they can take
advantage of the various technological tools to support that learning.
Decisions to put powerful technologies into schools without the necessary
attention to how the technology is to be used and by whom, could waste
precious resources and provide fuel for the technological Luddites in our
society to block very promising innovations. Our review also suggests that
while carefully designed tutorial systems (like the PLATO fractions curriculum) can provide children and teachers with opportunities for deepen-
ing understanding of certain concepts, the *delivery* of canned curricula
through expensive technological systems (as in the Mastering Fractions
Video-disc curriculum) may not be cost-efficient since the research indicates that the learning gains were just as good when the curriculum was
delivered using less expensive media. This point is particularly important
given the increasing pressure on school systems (from commercial curriculum companies) to purchase computer-managed learning systems that
cost hundreds of thousands of dollars. Such systems are often sold on the

premise that they are "teacher-proof" or that they relieve the teacher of many of the chores of managing the instruction. Our review of the available research literature clearly indicates that the teacher's involvement in the instructional decisions and interactions with students is critical for meaningful learning to occur.

NOTES

1.   This chapter was written as part of the activities of NSF project REC-9814853 Construction and Interaction: Children's Fractional Schemes (L. P. Steffe, director), and NSF project REC-9733942 Generalization of Learning Mathematics Through Multimedia Environments (J. Lobato, director). The opinions are solely those of the authors and do not necessarily reflect the position of the National Science Foundation. Susan McClellan of The Pennsylvania State University provided invaluable assistance in the search of the literature. Her work was supported in part by Grant No. GER 94-54048 from the National Science Foundation.
2.   This MathWorlds script was designed by Jeremy Roschelle and Janet Bowers.

REFERENCES

Aldus Corporation. (1994). SuperPaint [Computer software]. San Diego, CA: Author.

Barwise, J., & Perry, J. (1983). *Situations and attitudes*. Cambridge, MA: MIT Press.

Behr, M., Harel, G., Post, T., & Lesh, R. (1992). Rational number, ratio, and proportion. In D. Grouws (Ed.), *Handbook of research on mathematics teaching and learning* (pp. 296-333). New York: Macmillan.

Behr, M. J., Harel, G., Post, T., & Lesh, R. (1993). Rational numbers: Toward a semantic analysis—Emphasis on the operator construct. In T. P. Carpenter, E. Fennema, & T. A. Romberg (Eds.), *Rational numbers: An integration of research* (pp. 23-48). Hillsdale, NJ: Erlbaum.

Behr, M. J., Lesh, R., Post, T. R., & Silver, E. A. (1983). Rational number concepts. In R. Lesh & M. Landau (Eds.), *Acquisition of mathematics concepts and processes* (pp. 91-126). New York: Academic Press.

Behr, M. J., Wachsmuth, I., Post, T. R., & Lesh, R. (1984). Order and equivalence of rational numbers: A clinical teaching experiment. *Journal for Research in Mathematics Education, 15*, 323-341.

Biddlecomb, B. D. (1994). Theory-based development of computer microworlds. *Journal of Research in Childhood Education, 8*, 87-98.

Biddlecomb, B. D. (1999). *The initial number sequence as a mechanism for the construction of fraction schemes*. Unpublished doctoral dissertation, The University of Georgia, Athens.

Cobb, P. (1991). Reconstructing elementary school mathematics. *Focus on Learning Problems in Mathematics, 13*, 3-32.

Confrey, J. (1992). Splitting, similarity and rate of change: A new approach to multiplication and exponential functions. In G. Harel & J. Confrey (Eds.), *The development of multiplicative reasoning in the learning of mathematics* (pp. 291-330). Albany: State University of New York Press.

D'Ambrosio, B. S., & Mewborn, D. S. (1994). Children's construction of fractions and their implications for classroom instruction. *Journal of Research in Childhood Education, 8*, 150-161.

Davis, G., Hunting, R. P., & Pearn, C. (1993). What might a fraction mean to a child and how would a teacher know? *Journal of Mathematical Behavior, 12*, 63-76.

Davis, R. B. (1967). *Exploration in mathematics.* Palo Alto, CA: Addison-Wesley.

Dewey, J. (1963). *Experience and education.* New York: Collier.

Dugdale, S. (2008). Research in a pioneer constructivist network-based curriculum project for children's learning of fractions. In G. W. Blume & M. K. Heid (Eds.), *Research on technology and the teaching and learning of mathematics: Vol. 2. Cases and perspectives* (pp. 3-30). Charlotte, NC: Information Age.

Dugdale, S., & Kibbey, D. (1980). *The fractions curriculum of the PLATO elementary school mathematics project* (2nd ed.). Urbana: University of Illinois Computer-Based Education Research Laboratory, CERL Publications.

Dugdale, S., & Kibbey, D. (1990). Beyond the evident content goals—Part I: Tapping the depth and flow of the educational undercurrent. *Journal of Mathematical Behavior, 9*, 201-228.

Dugdale, S., & Spiro, R. J. (1990). Beyond the evident content goals—Part II: Toward a theory of educational undercurrent. *Journal of Mathematical Behavior, 9*, 229-232.

Engelman, S., & Carnine, D. (1982). *Theory of instruction: Principles and applications.* New York: Irvington.

Franke, M. L., Kafai, Y. B., & Shih, J. (1997, April). *Pre-service teachers' conceptions of learning through making games.* Paper presented at the meeting of the American Educational Research Association, Chicago, IL.

Freudenthal, H. (1983). *Didactical phenomenology of mathematical structures.* Boston: Kluwer.

Fuson, K. C., & Abrahamson, D. (2005). Understanding ratio and proportion as an example of the Apprehending Zone and Conceptual-Phase Problem-Solving Models. In J. Campbell (Ed.), *Handbook of mathematical cognition* (pp. 213-234). New York: Psychology Press.

Gibson, J. J. (1986). *The ecological approach to visual perception.* Hillsdale, NJ: Erlbaum.

Guckin, A., & Morrison, D. (1991). Math*Logo: A project to develop proportional reasoning in college freshmen. *School Science and Mathematics, 91*, 77-81.

Harel, I. (1990). Children as software designers: A constructionist approach for learning mathematics. *Journal of Mathematical Behavior, 9*, 3-93.

Harel, I., & Papert, S. (1991). *Constructionism.* Norwood, NJ: Ablex.

Hoyles, C., & Noss, R. (1989). The computer as a catalyst in children's proportional strategies. *Journal of Mathematical Behavior, 8*, 53-75.

Hoyles, C., & Noss, R. (1992). A pedagogy for mathematical microworlds. *Educational Studies in Mathematics, 23*, 31-57.

Hunting, R. P., Davis, G., & Bigelow, J. (1991). Higher-order thinking in young children's engagements with a fraction machine. In R. P. Hunting & G. Davis (Eds.), *Early fraction learning: Recent research in psychology* (pp. 73-90). New York: Springer-Verlag.

Hunting, R. P., Davis, G., & Pearn, C. (1996). Engaging whole-number knowledge for rational-number learning using a computer-based tool. *Journal for Research in Mathematics Education, 27*, 354-379.

Jackiw, N. (1995). The Geometer's Sketchpad (Version 3.0) [Computer software]. Berkeley, CA: Key Curriculum Press.

Kafai, Y. B. (1993). *Minds in play: Computer game design as a context for children's learning.* Unpublished doctoral dissertation, Harvard University, Cambridge, MA.

Kafai, Y. B. (1995). *Minds in play: Computer game design as a context for children's learning.* Hillsdale, NJ: Erlbaum.

Kafai, Y. B. (1996). Learning design by making games. In Y. B. Kafai & M. Resnick (Eds.), *Constructionism in practice: Designing, thinking, and learning in a digital world* (pp. 71-96). Hillsdale, NJ: Erlbaum.

Kafai, Y. B., & Ching, C. C. (1997, April). *Making games for learning: The development of integrated fraction understanding.* Paper presented at the meeting of the American Educational Research Association, Chicago, IL.

Kaput, J. (1994). Rational numbers and rationality: What are we learning and what needs to be done? *Journal of Research in Childhood Education, 8*, 142-149.

Kaput, J. (1996). Overcoming physicality and the eternal present: Cybernetic manipulatives. In R. Sutherland & J. Mason (Eds.), *Technology and visualization in mathematics education* (pp. 161-177). London: Springer-Verlag.

Kelly, B., Carnine, D., Gersten, R., & Grossen, B. (1986). The effectiveness of videodisc instruction in teaching fractions to learning-disabled and remedial high school students. *Journal of Special Education Technology, 7*(2), 5-17.

Kieren, T. E. (1976). On the mathematical, cognitive, and instructional foundations of rational numbers. In R. Lesh (Ed.), *Number and measurement: Papers from a research workshop* (pp. 101-144). Columbus, OH: ERIC/SMEAC.

Kieren, T. E. (1980). The rational number construct—Its elements and mechanisms. In T. E. Kieren (Ed.), *Recent research on number learning* (pp. 125-150). Columbus, OH: ERIC/SMEAC.

Kieren, T. E. (1988). Personal knowledge of rational numbers: Its intuitive and formal development. In J. Hiebert & M. Behr (Eds.), *Number concepts and operations in the middle grades* (pp. 53-92). Reston, VA: National Council of Teachers of Mathematics.

Kieren, T. E. (1993). Rational and fractional numbers: From quotient fields to recursive understanding. In T. Carpenter, E. Fennema, & T. Romberg (Eds.), *Rational numbers: An integration of research* (pp. 49-84). Hillsdale, NJ: Erlbaum.

Kieren, T. E. (1994). Orthogonal reflections on computer microworlds, constructivism, play and mathematical understanding. *Journal of Research in Childhood Education, 8*, 132-141.

Kozulin, A. (1986). The concept of activity in soviet psychology. *American Psychologist, 4*, 264-274.

Lobato, J. (2003). How design experiments can inform a rethinking of transfer and vice versa. *Educational Researcher, 32*, 17-20.

Lobato, J. (in press). How rethinking assumptions about the "transfer" of learning can inform research, instructional practices, and assessment. In C. Rasmussen & M. Carlson (Eds.), *Making the connection: Research and teaching in undergraduate mathematics*. Washington, DC: Mathematical Association of America.

Lobato, J., & Bowers, J. (2000, April). An overview of the three research perspectives. In J. Lobato (Chair), *Expanding the representational approach to include quantitative and phenomenological perspectives in research on functions and rates*. Symposium conducted at the annual meeting of the American Educational Research Association, New Orleans, LA. (ERIC Document Reproduction Service No. ED 441866)

Lobato, J., Clarke, D., & Ellis, A. (2005). Initiating and eliciting in teaching: A reformulation of telling. *Journal for Research in Mathematics Education, 36*, 101-136.

Lobato, J., & Ellis, A. B. (2002). The focusing effect of technology: Implications for teacher education. *Journal of Technology and Teacher Education, 10*, 297-314.

Lobato, J., & Siebert, D. (2002). Quantitative reasoning in a reconceived view of transfer. *The Journal of Mathematical Behavior, 21*, 87-116.

Lobato, J., & Thanheiser, E. (1999). Re-thinking slope from quantitative and phenomenological perspectives. In F. Hitt & M. Santos (Eds.), *Proceedings of the twenty-first annual meeting of the North American Chapter of the International Group for the Psychology of Mathematics Education: Vol. 1* (pp. 291-299). Columbus, OH: ERIC Clearinghouse for Science, Mathematics, and Environmental Education.

Lobato, J., & Thanheiser, E. (2000). Using technology to promote and examine students' construction of ratio-as-measure. In M. L. Fernández (Ed.), *Proceedings of the twenty-second annual meeting of the North American Chapter of the International Group for the Psychology of Mathematics Education: Vol. 2* (pp. 371-377). Columbus, OH: ERIC Clearinghouse for Science, Mathematics, and Environmental Education.

Lobato, J., & Thanheiser, E. (2002). Developing understanding of ratio as measure as a foundation for slope. In B. Litwiller (Ed.), *Making sense of fractions, ratios, and proportions: 2002 yearbook* (pp. 162-175). Reston, VA: National Council of Teachers of Mathematics.

Logo Computer Systems, Inc. (1986). LogoWriter [Computer software]. Québec, Canada: Author.

Meira, L. (1998). Making sense of instructional devices: The emergence of transparency in mathematical activity. *Journal for Research in Mathematics Education, 29*, 121-142.

Olive, J. (1993, April). *Children's construction of fractional schemes in computer microworlds, Part II: Constructing multiplicative operations with fractions*. Paper presented at the SIG-RME Research Pre-session of the 71st annual meeting of the National Council of Teachers of Mathematics, Seattle, WA.

Olive, J. (1994). Building a new model of mathematics learning. *Journal of Research in Childhood Education, 8*, 162-173.

Olive, J. (1999). From fractions to rational numbers of arithmetic: A reorganization hypothesis. *Mathematical Thinking and Learning, 1*, 279-314.

Olive, J. (2000). Computer tools for interactive mathematical activity in the elementary school. *International Journal of Computers for Mathematical Learning, 5*, 241-262.

Olive, J. (2001a). Children's number sequences: An explanation of Steffe's constructs and an extrapolation to rational numbers of arithmetic. *The Mathematics Educator, 11*, 4-9.

Olive, J. (2001b). Connecting partitioning and iterating: A path to improper fractions. In M. van den Heuvel-Panhuizen (Ed.), *Proceedings of the 25th annual conference of the International Group for the Psychology of Mathematics Education (PME-25): Vol. 4* (pp. 1-8). Utrecht, The Netherlands: Freudenthal Institute.

Olive, J. (2002a). Bridging the gap: Interactive computer tools to build fractional schemes from children's whole-number knowledge. *Teaching Children Mathematics, 8*, 356-361.

Olive, J. (2002b). The construction of commensurate fractions. In A. D. Cockburn & E. Nardi (Eds.), *Proceedings of the 26th Conference of the International Group for the Psychology of Mathematics Education (PME-26) Vol. 4* (pp. 1-8). Norwich, United Kingdom: University of East Anglia.

Olive, J. (2003). Nathan's strategies for simplifying and adding fractions in third grade. In N. A. Pateman, B. J. Dougherty, & J. T. Zilliox (Eds.), *Proceedings of the 27th Conference of the International Group for the Psychology of Mathematics Education (PME-27): Vol. 3* (pp. 421-428). Honolulu, HI: CRDG, University of Hawaii, College of Education.

Olive, J., & Steffe, L. P. (1994). TIMA: Bars [Computer software]. Acton, MA: William K. Bradford.

Olive, J., & Steffe, L. P. (2002). The construction of an iterative fractional scheme: The case of Joe. *Journal of Mathematical Behavior, 20*, 413-437.

Papert, S. (1993). *The children's machine: Rethinking school in the age of the computer.* New York: Basic Books.

Piaget, J. (1973). *To understand is to invent.* New York: Grossman.

Piaget, J., & Szeminska, A. (1965). *The child's conception of number.* New York: Norton.

Polya, G. (1957). *How to solve it: A new aspect of mathematical method.* New York: Doubleday.

Roschelle, J., & Kaput, J. (1996). SimCalc MathWorlds for the mathematics of change. *Communications of the ACM, 39*, 97-99.

Simon, M. A., & Blume, G. W. (1994). Mathematical modeling as a component of understanding ratio-as-measure: A study of prospective elementary teachers. *Journal of Mathematical Behavior, 13*, 183-197.

Sinclair, N. (2001). The aesthetic is relevant. In M. van den Heuvel-Panhuizen (Ed.), *Proceedings of the 25th annual conference of the International Group for the Psychology of Mathematics Education (PME-25): Vol. 4* (pp. 185-192). Utrecht, The Netherlands: Freudenthal Institute.

Steffe, L. P. (1988). Children's construction of number sequences and multiplying schemes. In J. Hiebert & M. Behr (Eds.), *Number concepts and operations in the middle grades* (pp. 119-140). Reston, VA: Erlbaum & National Council of Teachers of Mathematics.

Steffe, L. P. (1992). Schemes of action and operation involving composite units. *Learning and Individual Differences, 4*, 259-309.

Steffe, L. P. (1993, April). *Interaction and children's mathematics.* Paper presented at the annual meeting of the American Educational Research Association, Atlanta, GA.

Steffe, L. P. (1994). An introduction to this special issue: Mathematical learning in computer microworlds. *Journal of Research in Childhood Education, 8*, 85-86.

Steffe, L. P. (1998). *Construction & interaction: Children's fractional schemes.* Athens, GA: The University of Georgia.

Steffe, L. P. (1999). Individual constructive activity: An experimental analysis. *Cybernetics & Human Knowing, 6*, 17-31.

Steffe, L. P. (2002). A new hypothesis concerning children's fractional knowledge. *Journal of Mathematical Behavior, 102*, 1-41.

Steffe, L. P. (2003). Fractional commensurate, composition, and adding schemes: Learning trajectories of Jason and Laura: Grade 5. *Journal of Mathematical Behavior, 22*, 237-295.

Steffe, L. P. (2004). On the construction of learning trajectories of children: The case of commensurate fractions. *Mathematical Thinking and Learning, 6*, 129-162.

Steffe, L. P., & Cobb, P. (1988). *Construction of arithmetical meanings and strategies.* New York: Springer-Verlag.

Steffe, L. P., & Olive, J. (1990). *Children's construction of the rational numbers of arithmetic.* Athens, GA: The University of Georgia.

Steffe, L. P., & Olive, J. (1996). Symbolizing as a constructive activity in a computer microworld. *Journal of Educational Computing Research, 14*, 103-128.

Steffe, L. P., & Olive, J. (2002). Design and use of computer tools for interactive mathematical activity (TIMA). *Journal of Educational Computing Research, 27*, 55-76.

Steffe, L. P., & Spangler, D. (1993, April). *Learning an iterative fraction scheme.* Paper presented at the SIG-RME Research Pre-session of the 71st annual meeting of the National Council of Teachers of Mathematics, Seattle, WA.

Steffe, L. P., & Tzur, R. (1994). Interaction and children's mathematics. *Journal of Research in Childhood Education, 8*, 99-116.

Steffe, L. P., & Wiegel, H. (1994). Cognitive play and mathematical learning in computer microworlds. *Journal of Research in Childhood Education, 8*, 117-131.

Steffe, L. P., & Wiegel, H. (1996). On the nature of a model of mathematical learning. In L. P. Steffe & P. Nesher (Eds.), *Theories of mathematical learning* (pp. 477-498). Hillsdale, NJ: Erlbaum.

Streefland, L. (1993). The design of a mathematics course: A theoretical reflection. *Educational Studies in Mathematics, 25*, 109-135.

Swinton, S. (1978, March). *Outcomes of the PLATO elementary demonstration.* Paper presented at the annual meeting of the American Educational Research Association, Toronto, Canada.

Thompson, P. W. (1994). The development of the concept of speed and its relationship to concepts of rate. In G. Harel & J. Confrey (Eds.), *The development of multiplicative reasoning in the learning of mathematics* (pp. 181-234). Albany: State University of New York Press.

Tzur, R. (1995). *Interaction and children's fraction learning.* Unpublished doctoral dissertation, The University of Georgia, Athens.

Tzur, R. (1999). An integrated study of children's construction of improper fractions and the teacher's role in promoting the learning. *Journal for Research in Mathematics Education, 30,* 390-416.

Tzur, R. (2000). An integrated research on children's construction of meaningful, symbolic, partitioning-related conceptions, and the teacher's role in fostering that learning. *Journal of Mathematical Behavior, 18,* 123-147.

Tzur, R. (2002). From theory to practice: Explaining successful and unsuccessful teaching activities (case of fractions). In A. D. Cockburn & E. Nardi (Eds.), *Proceedings of the 26th Conference of the International Group for the Psychology of Mathematics Education (PME-26): Vol. 4* (pp. 297-304). Norwich, United Kingdom: University of East Anglia.

Tzur, R. (2003). Teacher and students' joint production of a reversible fraction conception. In N. A. Pateman, B. J. Dougherty, & J. T. Zilliox (Eds.), *Proceedings of the 27th Conference of the International Group for the Psychology of Mathematics Education (PME-27): Vol. 4* (pp. 315-322). Honolulu, HI: CRDG, University of Hawaii, College of Education.

Vergnaud, G. (1983). Multiplicative structures. In R. Lesh & M. Landau (Eds.), *Acquisition of mathematics concepts and processes* (pp. 127-174). New York: Academic Press.

von Glasersfeld, E. (1981). An attentional model for the conceptual construction of units and number. *Journal for Research in Mathematics Education, 12,* 83-94.

von Glasersfeld, E. (1995). Sensory experience, abstraction, and teaching. In L. P. Steffe & J. Gale (Eds.), *Constructivism in education* (pp. 369-383). Hillsdale, NJ: Erlbaum.

Vygotsky, L. S. (1978). *Mind in society: The development of higher psychological processes.* Cambridge, MA: Harvard University Press.

CHAPTER 2

ALGEBRA AND FUNCTION DEVELOPMENT

M. Kathleen Heid and Glendon W. Blume

BACKGROUND

Algebra occupies an undeniable central role in school mathematics programs, no other school mathematics topic has caused as much debate concerning its nature and role in school mathematics curricula, and no other mainstream school mathematics topic is more likely to be profoundly affected by the growing presence of technologies in schools. Functions and computational algorithms have had a central role throughout the history of U.S. mathematics education, and mathematical technologies are particularly suited to affect the nature of student interaction with both functions and algorithms. Although computational routines have always dominated the content of school algebra, the commitment of school curricula to function has wavered. In the next section a review of a few pivotal points in the history of algebra in U.S. schools establishes the importance of function in school algebra, and a subsequent section outlines the potential impact of technology in the development of student understanding of both function and computational algorithms.

Research on Technology and the Teaching and Learning of Mathematics:
Vol. 1. Research Syntheses, pp. 55–108
Copyright © 2008 by Information Age Publishing

Algebra in the History of U.S. Mathematics Education

Algebra entered school curriculum considerations in the United States when in 1820 Harvard University first required algebra for admission. Since that time, the nature of school algebra has periodically come into question. For the next century, debate continually simmered over the content of school algebra. Much of the debate centered on issues of the role of function and the importance and appropriate level of rigor and symbolic manipulation. In 1893, the Committee of Ten established algebra as an essential part of the U. S. school curriculum and defined it in terms of the symbolic manipulation aspects that would characterize work in school algebra. Twenty years later, the Mathematical Association of America (MAA) National Committee on the Reorganization of Mathematics in Secondary Education (1923) recommended reduction of elaborate manipulations in algebra (Jones & Coxford, 1970, pp. 40, 47). The 1923 report (as cited in Bidwell & Clason, 1970, p. 395) noted that

> *Drill in algebraic manipulation should be limited to those processes and to the degree of complexity required for a thorough understanding of principles and for probable applications either in common life or in subsequent courses which a substantial proportion of the pupils will take.* It must be conceived as a means to an end, not as an end in itself. (emphasis in original)

Attention to symbolic manipulation continued to be the heart of school algebra through most of the twentieth century. Throughout the history of U.S. mathematics education, however, there has been a recurring tension between recommendations about the role of function and the realization of that role in school curricula. While an entire chapter of the 1923 MAA report was dedicated to discussion of the importance and unifying nature of the function concept, its recommendation on the centrality of function did not immediately take hold in standard-setting organizations. The College Entrance Examination Board (CEEB), established "to bring uniformity to college entrance requirements and ... to set a uniform standard that might serve to guide the work of the secondary school" (Jones & Coxford, p. 171), adopted for testing all of the recommendations in the 1923 Report except that concerning function. It was not until its 1959 report that CEEB's Commission on Mathematics recommended stressing function as a unifying idea in mathematics. On the other hand, in its 1940 report, Mathematics in General Education, the Progressive Education Association listed function as one of seven concepts that both enter into problem solving and play a unifying role in mathematics.

While policy-setting organizations were proposing function as central content for school algebra, textbooks and tests (arguably the most central determiners of school mathematics) were not ready to embrace function as the central organizing feature of school algebra. Algebra tests in 1898-1920 paid little attention to function; Wentworth's 1898 Elementary Algebra appended a chapter on graphs that began with a brief discussion of function but its exercises neither mentioned function nor used functional notation (Donoghue, 2003). The 1930s saw an increase in focus on function, followed by a turn away from function in the popular 1949 Welchons and Krickenberger's *Algebra, Book One*, which focused on algebra as an extension of arithmetic rather than on function (Donoghue, 2003).

The past 50 years have seen a gradual swing toward inclusion of function in school textbooks. There was little emphasis on function in the 1961 School Mathematics Study Group (SMSG) *First Course in Algebra* (the concept of function was introduced in the final chapter), and the popular Dolciani Algebra (Dolciani, Berman, & Freilich, 1963) that was derived from SMSG emphasized algebraic structure rather than function. An SMSG course (1960) intended for more advanced students did focus on elementary functions, and another of the "New Math" curricula, Secondary School Mathematics Curriculum Improvement Study (1972a, 1972b) took mapping and transformation (a type of function) as central themes. The curriculum reform, begun in the early 1980's with the first edition of the University of Chicago School Mathematics Project (UCSMP) series, opened the door to curricula that paid significant attention to function. UCSMP started cautiously, dedicating the last chapter of its beginning Algebra text (1990a) to function and featuring function in a subsequent text at the advanced algebra level (1992). Curriculum writers during the last two decades of the twentieth century (sparked by the release of NCTM's *Curriculum and Evaluation Standards for School Mathematics* (NCTM, 1989) and support from the National Science Foundation for curricula that implemented the ideas in the Standards) made a conscious effort to develop students' understanding of function as a central feature in their curricula (e.g., *Contemporary Mathematics in Context* (Core-Plus), Fey & Hirsch, 2007). A key reason for this recent shift in emphasis was the advent of classroom-accessible electronic computing.

Technology Shifts the Algebra Curriculum Argument

Fey and colleagues (Fey et al., 1984) reinitiated the debate about the role of function in school mathematics when they called into question the thrust of school algebra programs in the United States in light of new and anticipated technologies. They pointed to the impending likelihood in technological environments of new roles for manipulative skills and mathematical modeling, and they rejoined the perennial call for a central organizing role for function in the school curriculum. With technology that could respond to commands to execute routine skills, a skills-first curriculum was no longer an unquestioned assumption. The increasingly sophisticated multirepresentational capacity of technology allowed easy and linked access to a range of external representations for function and raised the prospect of a more prominent role for function. Now, over two decades later, we reflect on what research has indicated about the ways in which technology can affect the teaching and learning of algebra.

TECHNOLOGY, MATHEMATICAL ACTIVITY, AND THE DEVELOPMENT OF CONCEPTS AND PROCEDURES

Not surprisingly, in concert with the debates about algebra over the past two centuries, there is a considerable amount of research focused on the effects of technology on the development of the concept of function and on the role of technology in enhancing symbolic manipulation skills and understanding. We will include in our analysis a discussion of research on the effects of technology on the development of the function concept and of symbolic manipulation skills and understanding. We will start a bit more globally, however, considering the ways that technology can affect mathematical activity and mathematical content in classrooms, recognizing that those effects are related to the ways in which technology can foster a transformation of mathematics teaching. We will also discuss the nature of the relationship between the teacher and the technology, namely, to what extent the technology has become a facile tool—an instrument—for the teacher. The diagram in Figure 2.1 is intended to suggest that technology can impact mathematical activity through affecting the content and tasks of algebra as well as its teaching. The extent to which technology affects teaching is a function of the extent to which the technology has developed into an instrument for the teacher. Moreover, technology can affect mathematical activity directly by extending or inhibiting student approaches to mathematical tasks. And finally, it is mathematical activity and reflection on that activity that affects the development of procedural and conceptual understanding.

In the following section, we describe some of the ways in which technology can affect mathematical activity in algebra, as illustrated in research literature. The remainder of the chapter synthesizes research findings about the effects of these changed environments on the development of mathematical concepts and procedures.

Ways in Which Technology Can Affect Mathematical Activity in Algebra

Differences in mathematics learning are functions of differences in the mathematical activity in which students engage, and technological envi-

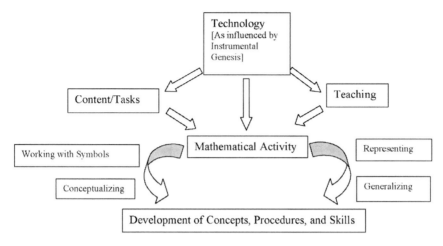

Figure 2.1.   Ways that technology (and the relationship of the user to the technology) affects mathematical activity, content, teaching, and tasks of algebra, and consequently, conceptual and procedural development.

ronments afford opportunities for a broad range of mathematical activity, particularly in algebraic settings. In the spirit of activity theory (Wertsch, 1998), technological tools used in classroom settings mediate the learning that occurs as well as the cognitive activities in which students engage. Technology can change the nature of opportunities for the mathematical activities of conceptualizing, representing, generalizing, symbolic work, and modeling as well as for student roles.

Conceptualizing

Technology both limits and expands opportunities for conceptualizing in algebra. Spreadsheets, for example, bring new algebra objects into being but simultaneously limit the level of students' encounters with algebra. Spreadsheets are viewed by many as an intermediate step between arithmetic and algebra: "Spreadsheets add an algebraic organization to an arithmetic resolution" (Haspekian, 2005). On the other hand, most spreadsheets cannot handle variables and relations directly and so limit access to fundamental algebraic concepts. Chazan (1999), however, posits that features of technology (such as the spreadsheet) that facilitate a variable taking on a series of values assist in the conceptualization of a variable as something that varies.

Tools such as computer algebra systems suggest the treatment of functions as objects, manipulable as mathematical entities. This capacity, coupled with the ability to handle function rules numerically, provides a venue in which students can view function as both a process and a mathematical object. Some have used *procept* to designate a symbol that can be viewed as both process and object (Gray & Tall, 1994). Gerny and Alpers (2004) point out this proceptual ability to shift between viewing function as an action and viewing it as an object is inherent in other technologies such as their microworld in which students design racing courses for miniature cars and develop function rules to describe the speed of the cars on the courses. Finally, a number of researchers have discussed transparency as it relates to students' development of conceptual understanding in the context of technology (Ainley, 2000; Doerr & Zangor, 2000; Meira, 1998). In concert with activity theorists (e.g., Wertsch, 1998), these researchers caution against viewing mathematical meaning as inherent in the technology, but rather as a function of the activity of the user with the technology (Meira, 1998). Lave and Wenger (1991) state: "The transparency of any technology ... cannot be viewed as a feature of an artifact in itself but as something that is achieved through specific forms of participation, in which the technology fulfills a mediating function" (p. 102).

Representing

Technologies afford students opportunities to learn and use a gamut of alternative external representations,[1] and through mathematical activities, these representations can mediate students' perceptions of different mathematical facets of the entity being represented. The dynamic capability of technology, coupled with the capacity for hot-linking, has enticed curriculum developers to generate approaches to the study of function based on newly available representations. Nachmias and Arcavi (1990), for example, describe a computer-generated parallel axis representation (PAR) of function, and Heid, Zbiek, Blume, and Choate (2004), have written computer-intensive high school mathematics curricula that engage students in learning about function through dynamaps (dynamic, interactive PARs in which the user controls the input value on one of the two parallel axes and the corresponding output value is automatically generated on the other axis). Use of dynamic tools in the exploration of different families of functions affords students opportunities to explore rate of change, optimal values, and monotonicity through a dynamic lens.

Availability of multiple representations can enable an entirely new perspective on a concept. Spreadsheets (numerical and symbolic) can make tabular representations of function a viable entry point for students, and tabular representations of function can turn attention to a recursive definition of function and a covariational approach to function (Confrey, 1994; Confrey & Maloney, 2008). This covariational approach, especially one aided by technology, affords students the opportunity to enhance their understandings not only of function but also of the concept of rate. The simultaneous availability of multiple representations of a concept can facilitate the development of meaning for the concept. Schwarz and Hershkowitz (1999) point out specific ways that a multirepresentational environment may affect understanding of function. For example, they see the zooming, scaling, and scrolling capacity of tools and the activity of transforming as influencing students' reasoning about the whole-parts relations among different graphical representations of the same function.

In addition, different representations for function may highlight different features of particular functions[2] for a student (Confrey & Smith, 1992). Students may see minima more clearly in a Cartesian-coordinate graph than through a symbolic representation, they may see differing rates of change more easily through comparison of dynamaps, and they may see a physical manifestation of function more easily through a dynamic geometry model (Hoyos, 1999). Once students identify a feature of a representation that is particularly salient in their thinking, technology can afford opportunity for exploration; Confrey and Smith (1992), for example, point out how the easy access to graphical representations allowed a student to discover multiplicative self-similarity as a characteristic of the graph of $f(x) = 10^x$ (no matter the maximum value of the range, the graphical representations of $f(x) = 10^x$ appear similar).

Representations produced with the aid of technology may have a different relationship to concept development than those same representations produced by hand. Ainley (2000) pointed out that the dynamic and interactive features of computer-generated graphs support the user's control of the appearance of the graph and make the computer-based tools more likely candidates as technical tools or instructional devices than graphs that are generated by hand. Meira (1998), however, posited that transparency is not a property of a physical artifact but rather a function of the environment in which the activity with the artifact takes place. He demonstrated that mathematical activity involving physical artifacts (such as a winch apparatus or a spring apparatus to exemplify a linear relationship) was not necessarily more transparent in meaning to students than mathematical activity involving purely numerical inscriptions (such as tables of values for the same relationships). He found the opposite, accentuating that the nature of the mathematical activity was fundamental to making meaning.

Generalizing/Abstracting

Not only can technological tools support generalization activities, but they also can affect the very nature of those generalization activities (Kieran, Boileau, & Garançon, 1996; Hershkowitz et al., 2002). With their capacity for the rapid and easy generation of large numbers of symbolic, numerical, and graphical examples, technological tools provide convenient windows that can support students in discerning patterns and developing generalizations. Different tools support different generalizing strategies; for example, spreadsheets may be effective in supporting recursive generalizing (Hershkowitz et al., 2002) and provide a venue in which teachers can highlight connections between explicitly defined functions and their recursively defined counterparts. Computer algebra systems coupled with dynamic geometry tools make the search for algebraic invariant properties a natural corollary. Technologies also provide venues in which to consider the effects of changes in parameters on various families of functions, and Hoyos (1999) observed that the capacity for direct manipulation of parameters seemed to foster the recognition of invariant geometric properties.

Generalizations can arise not only from examples expressed in the same representational register (e.g., graphical, symbolic, numerical; see Duval 1995, 1998 for further explanation of representational register), but also from the simultaneous access that representations in different registers provide to multiple approaches to a problem. Not only can technology provide students with access to multiple approaches, but the approaches students choose to pursue with technology can be much less "costly" in terms of time and effort expended than if they were pursued without technology. Also, in the course of using technology students often discover new relationships, and since there is not a great cost to pursue those avenues, students may be more likely to pursue them (Dreyfus & Hillel, 1998).

In some instances technology requires students to treat as objects entities that they would not otherwise be likely to treat as objects; for example, ISETL operates on function as input and generates function as output. This may facilitate the acquisition of an object conceptualization of function (Ayers, Davis, Dubinsky, & Lewin, 1988). Yerushalmy and Schwartz (1993) observe that providing an environment in which functions can be manipulated as singular entities and which relegate evaluating and graphing to the tool should help students encapsulate function as process into function as object. They also note that the power of various representations for developing the function concept generate important instruction-related questions—whether symbolic representation is more powerful in displaying function as process and whether graphic representation is more powerful for function as entity.

Technology also provides an arena for abstraction, through its ability to provide simultaneous access to global and local views of the mathematical objects of interest (Hillel, Lee, Laborde, & Linchevski, 1992). The capacity to write conditional function rules in CASs (computer algebra systems), access to writing CAS programs, and access to tools like ISETL open up the possibility of creating procedures of a range of chunk sizes, thus facilitating flow between macroprocedures and microprocedures (Heid, 2003). For example, a spreadsheet allows one to focus on local changes in cell contents while recalculation of all cells can provide the basis for a more global view of the impact of those changes. An issue related to simultaneous access to global and local views is whether choice of representational register affects the information obtained from either the local or global view.

Working With Symbols

Access to technological tools that allow automatic generation and operation on symbolic expressions highlights the need for a reconceptualization of the role of symbolic work in school mathematics. For decades, researchers have anticipated these and other changes in mathematics in a technological world (Fey et al., 1984; Heid, Choate, Sheets, & Zbiek, 1995; Noss, 2001; Yerushalmy, 2004), including changes in the order in which particular facets of mathematics are learned. Noss (2001) observed that "The changes in representational forms which computational technologies make available challenge us to rethink the kinds of didactical sequences and hierarchies of knowledge that are appropriate in learning environments." Changes in hierarchies of knowledge would most certainly involve changes in the role of algebraic symbols. In recent years, technology has fostered a number of significant changes in representational form, many of which had the potential for changing the content of fundamental importance in mathematics classrooms. For example, technological access to three-dimensional graphs has raised functions of two variables and interpretation of their symbolic representations to a central role in school algebra (Heid et al., 2003; Noss, 2001). Access to linked representations has resulted in new potential in the school curriculum for semiqualitative modeling that does not require first writing a symbolic expression as well as for connections between finite differences and continuous change (Yerushalmy, 2004). Flexible CAS symbolic and graphing capacities have brought new attention to recursively defined functions, affirming the attraction students seem to have for comparison of vertical entries in tables of function values. Among the many suggestions for curricular changes is a response to the reluctance to include CAS in school mathematics:

> Instead of modifying the system so that it does not merely give the answer, we could modify the curriculum so that equation-solving is no longer the focus of the course. In most introductory courses, relatively little time is spent on word problems and practical applications; this new course would reverse the trend. (Nunes-Harwitt, 2004/2005, p. 160)

Certain types of technology afford users access to particular facets of symbolic work. Work with spreadsheets highlights the need for symbolic notation as users seek to identify cells by their positional relationship to other cells. Work with the symbolic manipulation facets of CAS generates a need to deal with equivalence. Offering students the option of working in different representational registers (including the symbolic) reveals students' preferences for one representation over another. Bills, Ainley, and Wilson (2006) demonstrated how spreadsheets were used by some students in their study as semiotic mediation in forming meaning for algebraic symbolism. Using the design principles of purpose and utility, these researchers developed spreadsheet activities designed "to provide opportunities for students to use algebraic notation and ideas in purposeful ways" (p. 37). The context for one game, the Fairground Game, a spreadsheet activity designed to foster in students the need for algebraic symbolism, required students to try to make a particular target number (e.g., in Figure 2.2, the target number is 57) by placing given numbers in five initial cells (in Column A in Figure 2.2).

CAS technology offers students the capacity for automated processing of symbolic expressions. Technology packages that include a complete CAS along with dynamic construction tools afford students the opportunity to offload the symbolic work, to link results obtained in symbolic expressions to graphical and numerical representations, and to view dynamic graphical, pictorial, and numerical representations of symbolic rules with changing parameters. Just as students manipulating symbolic

	A	B	C	D	E
1	1				
2	5	6			
3	3	8	14		
4	4	7	15	29	
5	2	6	13	28	57

	A	B	C	D	E
1	1				
2	5	=A1+A2			
3	3	=A2+A3	=B2+B3		
4	4	=A3+A4	=B3+B4	=C3+C4	
5	2	=A4+A5	=B4+B5	=C4+C5	= D4+D5

Figure 2.2.   The Fairground Game: a spreadsheet activity in which students placed the integers 1 to 5 in column A to produce a target value in E5.

expressions by hand exhibit patterns of misunderstanding, however, there are common obstacles students have difficulty surmounting in working with the technology-generated output from the CAS (Drijvers, 2000). Drijvers and van Herwaarden (2000) observe the increased difficulty students working with a CAS have in distinguishing the different roles of letters (some as variable and some as parameters). With the capacity of the CAS to handle complicated expressions involving both variables and parameters, students using the CAS may be more likely to be confronted with the need to distinguish variables from parameters.

Computer algebra systems, and in particular symbolic manipulation programs, are likely to generate a need to deal with equivalence of symbolic expressions. Artigue (2002) identifies symbolic reasoning as one of two types of contributions that CAS has the potential to make in the development of mathematical knowledge, but she posits that use of CAS is unlikely to develop symbolic reasoning. Ruthven (2002), however, points out that early studies (Heid, 1988) have given evidence that symbolic reasoning of a particular type can develop in the context of CAS. "[I]nstrumenting graphic and symbolic reasoning through using CAS influences the range and form of the tasks and techniques experienced by students, and so the resources available for more explicit codification and theorisation of such reasoning" (p. 275).

Mathematical Modeling

A variety of implementations of technology arise in studies that have addressed aspects of the development of mathematical modeling that relate to algebra (For more in-depth discussion of technology and mathematical modeling, see Doerr & Pratt, 2008). These implementations employ the use of video, microcomputer and calculator-based laboratory devices, arrays of tools such as CAS, spreadsheet, and dynamic geometry tools, and special-purpose modeling tools (e.g., Algebra Sketchbook (Schwartz & Yerushalmy, 1995)). Technology in the service of mathematical modeling brings new players to the conversation about quantitative relationships in physical settings. Graphs derived from videos may make salient certain aspects of the situation (Boyd & Rubin, 1996). Some computer programs have been designed to provide a middle ground between natural language and symbolic representation that helps students enhance their understanding of mathematical modeling (Schwartz & Yerushalmy, 1995). Technology can also provide direct access to derived quantities, and Noble and Nemirovsky (1997) uncover some of the intricacies of students' learning to interpret those quantities when students can physically manipulate features of the situations. In this interaction among technology, physical situation, student, and teacher, the computer can become a conversation piece for teachers and students (Tinker & Thornton, 1992).

The videodisc-based scenarios for word problems in the Jasper series (Bransford et al., 1996) also address aspects of mathematical modeling in the learning of algebra. The Jasper series addresses students' difficulties in generating subproblems by providing a context in which this generation can be required.

> We also found that instruction in the context of Jasper had powerful effects on students' abilities to formulate and solve subsequent complex problems. In contrast, students whose instruction consisted of the one- and two-step word problems that comprised the overall Jasper problem showed very poor abilities to transfer to new complex problems (e.g., CTVG, 1993a; Van Haneghan et al., 1992). (p. 217)

Zbiek (1998) explored the modeling strategies of preservice secondary mathematics teachers to develop and validate functions as mathematical models of real world situations. She identified four general strategies, distinguished by the extent and nature of curve fitter use and the relative dominance of mathematics versus reality affecting the development and evaluation of models:

1. *Fitted function selector*: The student immediately uses the curve fitter to generate each of the fitted functions available on the tool and picks the one that has the best fit. This leaves the choice of the model to the tool; there is no judgment by the user.
2. *Potential function generator*: The student generates all of the possible rules but does not rely only on the percent goodness of fit to decide which rule is best. Instead, validation depends on the extent to which the characteristics of each of the functions match the features of the real-world situations.
3. *Scatterplot graphing tool*: The student uses the tool to create scatterplots but considers functions beyond the ones that the tool fits.
4. *Unneeded or unused tool*: The students rely on their expectations of real world relationships between the quantities accounting for some but not all of the ordered pairs in the data set.

Zbiek's study raises an important issue for the use of technology in mathematical modeling, namely, the extent to which the users allow the tool to make decisions for them. When students use powerful tools to develop models, teachers need to pay careful attention to the extent to which students are making decisions as opposed to opting to have the tool make decisions for them. This issue is highlighted particularly in the context of modeling, but clearly arises in other contexts as well, for example, in the extent to which students make decisions when using a CAS for symbolic manipulation.

RESEARCH ON TECHNOLOGY AND THE
TEACHING AND LEARNING OF ALGEBRA

An examination of research on the impact of technology on the teaching and learning of algebra suggests that several focus areas have dominated the research arena. Much of the research in the area of technology and algebra education examines the ways in which technology extends access to more and different mathematical representations. Other research focuses on the impact of technology on the acquisition of conceptual and procedural knowledge, mostly in the context of curricular approaches designed to capitalize on the availability of technology, and much of it in the context of transformed curriculum content. This section presents highlights of research in these areas.

Technology and Representations

One of the most frequent and compelling arguments for the potential of technology to impact the learning of mathematical concepts centers on the capacity of technologies to expand the range and nature of external representations afforded users of these technologies. As Schwarz and Dreyfus (1995) pointed out, learners can think about properties as features of an external representation or as features of the mathematical object itself. It is important to keep in mind, however, that the external representation is not the object itself, and that it is the mathematical object about which students should learn to reason. Artigue (2002) points out a theoretical perspective on the relationship between the "ostensive" and "non-ostensive" objects of mathematical activity:

> Mathematical objects are not directly accessible to our senses: they are "non-ostensive" objects; we work with them through ostensive representations which can be of very diverse nature: discourse in natural language, schemas, drawings, symbolic representations, gestures, manipulatives. Work with ostensive objects both shapes the development of the associated non-ostensive objects, and is shaped by the state of development of these. (p. 270)

Instrumentation and Representational Fluency
Through technology, external representations (ostensive objects) afford students the opportunity (but not a guarantee) for rapid and dynamic

interactivity with mathematical objects. The availability of these external representations alone is not sufficient to determine their effects without concurrent consideration of the relationship between the user and the technology. Researchers have used the term *instrumentation* (Guin & Trouche, 1999) to describe that relationship and the terms representational fluency and representational versatility (Hong & Thomas, 2002; Sandoval, Bell, Coleman, Enyedy, & Suthers, 2000) to describe characteristics of that relationship. For the purposes of this chapter, we view representational fluency as a reference to a user's representation-related abilities, including the ability to construct various external representations and the ability to interpret the features of one representation in the context of another representation of the same mathematical entity or in the context of the real-world situation being represented. Representational fluency also refers to a user's knowledge of particular representations that can be employed for selected illustrations or explanations, to a user's facility in using the representations to justify claims, and to a user's ability to link multiple representations meaningfully. Finally, representational fluency includes not only the ability to translate across representations, but also the ability to extract meaning about a mathematical entity from the coordination of and generalization of results from a variety of representations.

Alternative Strategies

The availability of multirepresentational tools coupled with students' representational fluency affords opportunities for students to change the ways they operate in the context of algebra problems and exercises. These tools foster the development by students of different approaches to problems—in particular, problems that require them to move between available representations and to capitalize on the power of those available representations. Several studies have documented students' development of some degree of representational fluency in the context of multirepresentational tools in that students successfully acquire facility with the constituent representations and movement between those representations. For example, Eisenberg and Dreyfus (1994) report that students who used Green Globs (a game-like program that challenged students to create function rules for graphs that would hit targeted points) in six lessons over a 5-hour period exhibited a readiness to approach problems by visual means, to process information visually, and to use qualitative arguments. In a CAS environment, university students in a functions course (Hillel et al., 1992) were successful in translating back and forth between representations and coordinating data coming from the different sources. Borba and Confrey (1996) demonstrated that software that provides linked multiple representations of functions can, for example, help students use the graphical representation of the function to reason about its symbolic representation. Huntley and her colleagues (Huntley, Rasmussen, Villarubi, Sangtong, & Fey, 2000) noted that students using the Core-Plus curriculum outperformed students in non-Core-Plus classes on problems requiring movement among the symbolic, numerical, and graphic representations featured in the curriculum. They explained:

> Conventional algebra curricula are beginning to take advantage of the representational features of graphing calculators. But in none of the curricula studied by control students in our study were the developers as deeply committed as in the Core-Plus Mathematics curriculum to making functions and their graphic, numeric, and symbolic representations the heart of school algebra. Our data show that this commitment leads to greater facility in solving problems that require use of graphic, numeric, and verbal information forms as well as ability to translate information from one representation to another. (p. 356)

The greater facility in solving problems noted in some of the aforementioned studies may be related to students developing new representation strategies. Ruthven (1990) examined how access to graphing calculators influenced students' approaches to developing a symbolic representation from a graph; he also studied students' abilities to extract information from verbally contextualized graphs (e.g., interpretation of a speed vs. time graph for a bicycle trip—similar to the Interpreting Graphs software). From students' written explanations of their reasoning on the symbolization task Ruthven identified three fundamentally different approaches that were typical of students' refinement in their identification of function rules for graphs. The students progressed from their initial identification of the graph as indicative of membership in a particular family of functions to a more precise symbolic description of the graph. The three approaches were: an analytic-construction approach (a deductive approach), a graphic-trial approach (a somewhat global approach), and a numeric-trial approach (a more local approach).

In the analytic-construction approach students attempted to use their mathematical knowledge, particularly that which linked graphic and symbolic forms, to construct, from information provided by the graph, a precise symbolic description (e.g., use of knowledge of the effects of transformations of a graph on symbolic form or knowledge of the relationship between zeroes of a polynomial function and its factored form). This method was the most frequently used method for both groups of subjects. However, students with access to the graphing calculator were able to use it to check their symbolic results. Those using the analytic-construction approach, when checking an incorrect symbolization via graphing, were able to obtain information that was helpful in revising that symbolization. The second approach, the graphic-trial approach, relied on repeated modification of a symbolic expression in light of information obtained from comparison of a sequence of graphs to the given graph, for example, use of information generated from observation of the effects of changes in the parameters in the symbolic form on the features of successively generated graphs. In a few instances Ruthven found evidence of a hybrid approach that was attributed to transition between the graphic-trial approach and the analytic-construction approach—either information obtained from graphic trials triggered insights necessary for the analytic-construction approach, or the students reverted to graphic trials when they were unable or reluctant to further pursue the analytic-construction approach. In the numeric-trial approach a symbolic conjecture was formulated, often based on information provided from the coordinates of a small number of points on the graph, and then modified on the basis of comparison of calculated values of the expression with corresponding values given on the graph. The only instance of use of the numeric-trial approach by calculator users was a hybrid numeric-graphic approach in which the subject identified various coordinates from a graph and eventually ascertained a relationship between them.

Ruthven's study suggests that graphing-calculator-using students will not necessarily take advantage of the fullest power of their technologies. The students in his study had easy access to numerical and graphical representations, and many used that capability as their preferred strategy. The students who favored the numeric-trial approach or the graphic-trial approach may not have seen the need to use symbolic representations for the problems at hand, or they may not have felt comfortable reasoning with the more abstract symbolic representations.

This issue becomes more salient with the increasing availability of the CAS (symbolic manipulation capabilities in graphing calculators). Studies of the use of computer algebra systems by mathematically sophisticated college students in the solution of nonroutine mathematics problems gave evidence of students' tendency not to reason from symbolic representations when graphical and numerical representations are available (Heid, Blume, Iseri, Flanagan, & Kerr, 1998). Because reasoning from symbolic representations is not a given when students use technology, strategies need to be developed for helping students take advantage of symbolic representations in multirepresentational environments, in particular in the context of computer algebra systems. This observation generalizes— learning within a multiple linked representation environment does not necessarily lead to linked use of those representations. Moreover, although students in some case studies were observed making connections (e.g., Borba & Confrey, 1996), use of multiple representations does not guarantee that students will connect the representations (Schoenfeld,

Smith, & Arcavi, 1993). Participants in a study by Yerushalmy (1991), for example, used visual (relating to the graph) or computational (relating to the symbolic expression) arguments to solve algebraic problems, and did not use this combination of types of arguments for cross-checking purposes. It is important that opportunities exist for students to connect representations. Yerushalmy observed that intentionally and directly teaching students to combine visual and computational methods for both solving and cross-checking may be necessary to help students obtain maximal benefit from a linked multiple representation environment.

In facilitating use of alternative strategies, multiple representations may allow students to avoid interpretation of unfamiliar results and, instead, resort to a different solution path without confronting a discordant result. One example occurred in a study of middle school students' use of a CAS in their first encounters with symbolic algebra (Heid, Hollebrands, & Iseri, 2002). Kevin, a precocious seventh grader, was puzzled when he encountered a situation in which a CAS produced a positive value for $\left|\sqrt{x+5}\right|$ when the value of x was -10. Apparently conceiving of absolute value as "taking the positive value" and not knowing that the CAS interpreted absolute value as the modulus of a complex number (so that $\left|\sqrt{-10+5}\right| = \left|\sqrt{5}i\right| = \sqrt{(\sqrt{5})^2} = \sqrt{5}$), Kevin was surprised at the result and quickly found an alternative path to solving the problem on which he was working. Kevin's strategy resembles one of Trouche's work methods. Trouche's (2005b) observations of work methods students use when working with CAS includes a resourceful work method, a method characterized by a student's use of multiple approaches. It could be that access to multiple representations increases the likelihood of students' adopting a resourceful work method—or that students who gravitate toward a resourceful work method are likely to take advantage of multiple representations.

Multirepresentational tools commonly provide students with access to numerical and graphical approaches that are not readily available without technology. The availability of numerical and graphical approaches may displace symbolic approaches from of its central role in school mathematics. Moreover, such multirepresentational environments may facilitate students moving from a local approach to a global approach in their mathematical reasoning. Yerushalmy (1991) addressed the strategies students use in multirepresentational environments. She reported that after using a linked multiple representation environment (the Function Analyzer) in whole-class exploration mode, eighth grade subjects who were first learning the topic of algebraic functions were able to use strategies that reflected a focus on the entire graph (e.g., move it, observe it, and relocate it). Only later did students use the special numerical values in the table to analyze the graph. Although numerical approaches are one (local) way to understand functions and their graphs, more global approaches were afforded from the outset by the linked multirepresentational environment. Students in the Yerushalmy study (1991) used graphical representations to reason about the symbolic form of a function. Two naïve, unexpected conjectures about classifying graphs and functions emerged. One type of classification included geometric comparisons between global aspects of graphs—traditional ones based on graph shape, continuity, and so on, and ones based on the physical location of the graph on the coordinate system (e.g., the number of and combinations of quadrants through which the graph passed and location relative to a particular point such as the origin). The other category included symbolic comparisons between global aspects of expressions (strongly connected to their symbolic form, including less relevant aspects such as number of terms, form of the expressions, and order of terms in the expression). After having been exposed to a linked multirepresentational environment, students developed global graphic and symbolic approaches without needing to develop those from some initial, more local approach.

Visual Reasoning

Several studies have concluded that use of tools that enable graphical representations in algebra may contribute to improved visual reasoning skills (Eisenberg & Dreyfus, 1994; Shoaf-Grubbs, 1994; Ruthven, 1990; and there is additional supporting evidence from studies cited in Dunham & Dick, 1994). Improvement in spatial–visual skills may be another result of the use of graphical representations in that a reasonable explanation for this improvement is that exposure to symbolized graphic images may develop competence on spatial–visual tasks (Ruthven, 1990). Ruthven reports a positive effect of calculator use for female subjects in that female students outperformed males in the project group, but underperformed males in the comparison group. It may be that, because of prior deficits in these areas, females benefited differentially from exposure to symbolized graphic images and that tool use contributed to a reduction in their uncertainty along with a corresponding increase in confidence.

New Content

The availability of multiple representations has accelerated and changed the introduction of particular aspects of algebra and functions into the school curriculum. Technology-intensive functions-based algebra curricula have exemplified viable alternatives to the standard symbolic-manipulation-based approach (e.g., Fey et al., 1995/1999; Yerushalmy, 1991). Chazan (1999) described how his shaping of a technology-intensive approach to algebra allowed him to treat the unifying concept of function (rather than procedures) as the primary object on which to focus the study of algebra. Both changing the nature of the concept and accelerating its introduction, Kaput (1994) developed ways to use a computer simulation (which later evolved into SimCalc) to introduce interactive representations of rate of change to young learners. As Stroup (2002) pointed out, one reason that enables the early introduction of these calculus concepts is that technology affords the opportunity for a qualitative approach to calculus and, as such, calls on different cognitive structures than those required for standard calculus.

Caveats

Availability of multiple representations, however, is not sufficient for learning to occur if those representations are sequential and not simultaneously present. Yerushalmy and Schwartz (1993) note that "sequential learning of the symbolic and graphical representations does not promote a tendency on the part of the learner to move between them. Each of the representations presents a separate symbol system for the learner with no mutual and constructive interaction" (p. 44). As discussed previously in this chapter, the availability of multiple representations does not ensure enhanced learning—what matters is the action taken on those representations as well as the reflection on that action. Simon and colleagues (2004) explain the essential role that reflection plays in conceptual learning in their theory of reflection on activity–effect relationships. They posit that reflection on the relationship between activity and effect has the potential for addressing the "learning paradox" (Pascual-Leone, 1976), how learners develop new concepts when they have not developed the mental structure to support those concepts. The importance of reflection on action is also noted by Stylianou and colleagues (Stylianou, Smith, & Kaput, 2005), who conducted an exploratory study of undergraduate preservice teachers' understanding of graphical representations of motion functions. Twenty-eight preservice elementary teachers participated in a two-week study using CBRs to represent motions. These students improved in a range of ways in their use of graphs in problem solving. However, the researchers observed that:

> While it was tempting to attribute the learning that the study participants experienced to the actual CBR devices, we stepped back and looked at the context in which these gains in mathematical knowledge and changes in attitude towards teaching practices took place. Each time we recorded an individual pre-service teacher experiencing a new mathematical insight, the experience was the outcome of a discussion with her/his peers about graphs. (p. 319)

Experience with multiple representations, even a broad range of linked representations that include hands-on physical experiences, may not be sufficient to generate learning without reflection on activity–effect relationships.

In addition to reflection having an effect on multi-representational activities, user interface also makes a difference in students' understanding of function. As Kaput (1989) pointed out, the particular configuration of multiple linked representations available to the student influences the opportunities for developing mathematical meaning:

> Appropriate experience in a multiple, linked representation environment may provide webs of referential meaning missing from much of school mathematics and may also generate the cognitive control structures required to traverse those webs and tap the real power of mathematics as a personal intellectual resource. However, one must choose such representations carefully and, even more importantly, ensure that the learning environment supports rich sets of actions that will expose underlying invariances and thus enable the student to weave a flexible and enduring web of mathematical meaning. (p. 180)

Creating representations that supported actions that would reveal invariances was at the heart of one investigation. In order to investigate students' inability to abstract mathematically correct features from machine-produced graphs, Olsen (1994/1995) developed a computer program, the Function Explorer, which represents functions using parallel number lines, perpendicular number lines, and a table. The representations allow for dynamic input (of the independent variable value), and instantaneous update of the linked representations. A randomized controlled experiment was performed, to test the instructional effectiveness of the number lines representations. Seventy-four eighth grade students were randomly assigned, within each of four classes, to two treatment groups. The first group used the program with all of its representations, while the second group had the parallel number lines representation hidden. Results indicated that the group using the number lines representations were better able to interpret pointwise and global features of graphs. This treatment, however, did not enhance student understanding of the definition of function, use of letters in function notation, and the relationship between the formula and graph. The author credits the effectiveness of the dynamic number lines to the transparency of input and output values, and to the fact that the representations are controlled by the learner. The environment provided to students in this study seemed to support student action that could reveal underlying invariances, as recommended by Kaput.

Relationship of Technology to the Acquisition of Routine Skills and Concepts in Algebra

Central to the debate on the use of technology in the teaching and learning of algebra is concern about how technology might affect the acquisition of routine mathematical procedures and the development of mathematical concepts. Consequently, much of the research on the impact of technology in algebra instruction has focused on that facet of the debate. There has been little research, however, on the effects of mathematical technological tools on the acquisition of symbolic manipulation skills in algebra. Instead, researchers have theorized about the nature of skill development. This section of the chapter will discuss the nature of symbolic skills and understanding and the development of conceptual understanding, focusing on the development of understanding of function.

Acquisition of Symbolic Skills and Understanding

Theory-based discussion of the effects of technology on symbolic skills and understandings has included a broadening of perspective on what constitutes symbolic skills and understanding. School algebra instruction has typically centered on developing and refining students' abilities to re-express algebraic expressions and equations as equivalent expressions and equations. Mathematical technologies have challenged the central role of symbolic manipulation because graphical and numerical capabilities of technology have provided alternative solution techniques for solving problems that were commonly approached symbolically and because technology-based symbolic manipulation technologies are readily available to schools. As a consequence, the prospect of technology-driven mathematics classrooms has evoked fear that students' ability to execute routine symbolic manipulation skills would atrophy or never develop. The acquisition of facility with executing symbolic manipulation, however, is only part of the picture regarding students' understanding of symbolic algebra. Lagrange (1999, 2000/2001) and Artigue (2002) have pointed out the importance of a more expanded view of symbolic manipulation in the context of what they have called "technique." They describe technique as "a complex assembly of reasoning and routine work" (Artigue, 2002, p. 248), embodying not only the ability to execute a routine procedure but also the complex of understandings surrounding the rationale for and use of the procedure "to help students to develop instrumental and paper/pencil schemes, rich in mathematical meanings and to give sense to symbolic calculations as well as graphical and numerical approaches"

(Lagrange, 1999, p. 51). Lagrange points out that techniques related to the use of technology for symbolic work and the conceptual aspects of the symbolic work are related, particularly when the technology is a CAS: "Using symbolic computation in the teaching of mathematics requires teachers and researchers to think in depth about the relationship between the conceptual and the technical part of the mathematical activity rather than opposing them" (Lagrange, 1999, p. 55). While acknowledging that techniques are often evaluated in terms of their pragmatic value (their efficiency, validity, and so on), Artigue (2002) contends that "they also have an epistemic value, as they contribute to the (theoretical) understanding of the objects they involve" (p. 248). One can imagine the epistemic value of students using a CAS to generate positive-integral powers of a binomial expression and observing patterns of the coefficients. When calculation is completed by hand, students may notice the source of the coefficient values and the knowledge generated is likely to be quite different. Artigue points to division as an example of a technique whose epistemic value changes when one moves from executing the long division algorithm to pushing a button on a calculator:

> At a more elementary level, through the iteration of the division process, pupils can understand very early why the decimal expansion of a rational number is necessarily periodic. The use of a calculator, which gives the beginning of the decimal expansion of any rational number instantaneously, and in most simple cases allows the student to conjecture about both the periodicity and the actual period, no longer has the epistemic value of the paper & pencil gesture. (p. 260)

There has been little empirical research on the development of technique in the context of technology-intensive algebra, although the previously mentioned study by Trouche described characteristic ways in which students work in CAS environments. Trouche (2004; Trouche, 2002 as described by Artigue, 2002) identified five work methods[3] that influence the ways that the grade 12 scientific students in his study related to their graphical and symbolic calculators. The five profiles ("theorist," "rationalist," "scholastic," "tinkerer," and "experimentalist") are characterized by an ordered triple that describes the type of resources the student favors, the meta-knowledge the student activates, and the ways of validation the student favors. The "tinkerer," for example, prefers to use the calculator to conduct investigations and to determine validity by accumulating consistent machine results, whereas the "rationalist" prefers paper and pencil in demonstrations of validity through inference. Given the significantly different capacities suggested by these choices of artifacts and strategies, students' approaches to learning algebra are likely to differ as their work methods differ. It is not clear whether the work method influences how students learn algebra or whether their approach to algebra determines their work method.

Acquisition of Concepts

Mathematics education researchers have described conceptual understanding using a variety of analogies, including developed networks of connections (Hiebert & Carpenter, 1992) and acquisition of mathematical entities as objects (Asiala, Brown, DeVries, Dubinsky, Mathews, & Thomas, 1996; Sfard, 1991). Computing technology is thought to offer an intermediary between the student and the abstract mathematical object, affording students the opportunity to operate on or manipulate something that is tangible in order to reason about abstract mathematical objects (Yerushalmy, 1997). Those who have looked at understanding of mathematical entities in the context of technology suggest that differences in conceptual understandings may be reflected in differences in where the mathematical entities exist for the person—in the computer or by direct access. Lagrange (2005) describes this difference by contrasting technology-assisted instructional actions by students and by mathematicians: "To students, instrumented gestures and techniques evoke objects existing mainly in the 'enactive' interaction with the computer whereas mathematicians directly make sense of computer processing in terms of mathematical notions" (p. 167).

Technology affords mathematics curriculum developers the opportunity to develop curricula that focus on the mathematical objects instead of primarily on the operations to be performed on those objects. That is, the context of technology affords curriculum developers the opportunity to focus the curriculum on function instead of on solving equations and producing equivalent forms of expressions. Chazan (1999) elaborated on his creation of a technology-intensive functions-based Algebra course, and characterized the advantages of this use of technology as allowing him and his students to treat function as the core object of study:

> Identification of the central objects of study was central in helping students see algebra in the world around them. This understanding also helped make algebra less mysterious by helping students understand mathematical tasks in terms of the characteristics of desired solutions. This sort of understanding is precisely what I felt I was not able to provide to students when the teaching of algebra felt like slogging through a list of disconnected techniques. Thus, when using the functions-based approach, I was able to help students understand the goals of problems for which they did not have solution algorithms and to work productively on such problems. (p. 143)

As pointed out by Lagrange, however, the fact that a curriculum focuses on a mathematical entity such as function does not guarantee that the student sees that entity as the mathematically ideal object.

Understanding of mathematical entities as objects is an evolutionary process, and the works of Sfard (1991), Dubinsky (Asiala et al., 1996), and others provide frameworks for investigating the development of conceptual understanding of mathematical entities. Dubinsky and his colleagues detail the progress of individuals' understanding of a mathematical entity from an action-level understanding (being able to carry out the steps of a procedure, in a fixed sequence), through a process-level understanding (being able to envision the process being carried out without actually going through the steps of the process), and finally to an object-level understanding (being able to act on the process without carrying it out in actuality or mentally). Sfard describes the development from process to object as interiorization (implying an ability to envision a process without carrying it out), condensation (suggesting an ability to think about the process as a whole), and reification (a quantum leap that unifies various representations in an abstract mathematical object). Arriving at an object understanding of a mathematical entity is the result of "encapsulating" or "reifying" the entity. It seems plausible that providing an environment in which functions can be manipulated as entities and in which the actions of evaluating and graphing are automated would help students encapsulate function as a process into function as an object (Breidenbach, Dubinsky, Hawks, & Nichols, 1992; Yerushalmy & Schwartz, 1993). Using technology in its many different roles (e.g., as tools for generalizing, symbolizing, and representing) in combination would seem to be able to contribute to the development of conceptual understanding. Technology affords the user the opportunity to generate a range of examples, and experience with a rational[4] set of examples is an instructional strategy for concept acquisition.[5] Experience with an appropriate range of examples, however, may not facilitate learning unless such experience is accompanied by reflection. This experience/reflection cycle plays an important role in the shift from a process understanding to an object understanding of mathematical entities.

The development of conceptual understanding through the reflective consideration of examples was central to a series of studies built on the APOS theory and using programming (e.g., ISETL[6]). In the process of applying their theory of instruction researchers had students use programming to generate examples in the service of constructing mathematical concepts and engage in activities designed to facilitate reflection on those examples. The researchers observed that students seemed to develop more sophisticated conceptual understanding, characterized by the ability to reify targeted mathematical entities (Asiala et al., 1996; Brown, DeVries, Dubinsky, & Thomas, 1998). While these studies involved college students using a special programming language (ISETL), the role of the computer in facilitating student acquisition of an object understanding of a mathematical entity is confined neither to students at the college level nor to use of the ISETL language. Yerushalmy (1991) observed that, in a study of the use of the Function Analyzer by secondary school students, students may have been operating from a function-as-object perspective. For example, they tended to classify functions holistically on the basis of the location of the graphs with respect to the axes, only later analyzing functions by using particular numerical values. As "tools for representing," a variety of computer tools, including the Function Analyzer, afford students the opportunity to manipulate inscriptions intended to represent mathematical objects, setting the stage for their progress toward an understanding of these entities as objects. It is important, however, to keep in mind that using what seems, from an outside perspective, to be a representation of a mathematical object is not, per se, evidence of an understanding of the entity as an object. The development of an object understanding is a complex process, as noted by Yerushalmy (2000):

> From the findings of this study and of the long-term observation taken by Chazan, (2000), we argue that the complexity of helping students to value algebraic symbols may require more than bridging between representations. It may require [one] to design a systematic sequence that would help students process with familiar objects (recursive patterns) and arrive through encapsulation at constructing forms of explicit algebraic expressions. (p. 145).

Understanding of Function

Myriad researchers have studied students' understanding of function in the context of technological activities, experiences, and curricula. Particularly important results from these studies concern the role of technology in students' development of strategies for using functions as prototypes and in students' reification of the notion of function. In this section, we will limit our discussion to these two areas along with studies that have shed light on the general roles of technology in advancing and inhibiting understanding of the concept of function.

Use of prototypes. Students' work with functions is commonly guided by their use of prototypical functions and either enriched or inhibited depending on the ways in which prototypes come into their thinking. Prototypes have both critical attributes (characteristics that are common to all instances of the entity being represented) and self attributes (characteristics of the prototype that are not common to all instances of the entity being represented) (Schwarz & Hershkowitz, 1999). For example, students frequently use linear functions as prototypes of function; linear functions share with all functions the property of univalence (a critical attribute) but also have the trait of constant rate of change (a self attribute) not characteristic of all functions. Students sometimes treat self attributes as if they were critical attributes, overly restricting their identification of the entity being represented by the prototype.

The technology-assisted generation and use of external representations of function, when coupled with a curriculum that focuses on open-ended investigative activities, can contribute to the development of more robust use of function prototypes. Schwarz and Hershkowitz (1999) report a study in which students in one class using the third revision of an algebra curriculum (call it the G_3 or Tech class), used graphing calculators or multirepresentational software to generate and use a range of representations of function while a comparable class of students using the second version of the curriculum (call it the G_2 or Non-Tech class) studied from a curriculum based on the same syllabus but using different instructional strategies. The Tech class used graphing calculators and/or multirepresentational software tools usually on a weekly basis and worked on contextually-embedded problem situations. They were given control over what representations to use and what tools to use in working with those representations. Their work was usually completed in collaborative small groups and they regularly communicated in writing about their processes. The teacher facilitated work, modeled solution processes, and coordinated whole-class synthesis sessions.

The researchers concluded that students in the Tech class used prototypical functions as levers for concept learning. They used prototypical functions to exemplify a function with designated attributes (e.g., a function that passes through three given points) and as reference points (e.g., using $f(x) = x^3$ to reason about $f(x) = -2x^3$). The researchers contrasted this behavior related to prototypes with that of students in the Non-Tech classes. Students in the Non-Tech classes were more likely to overgeneralize from prototypes (e.g., using linear interpolation to find intermediate values for a function that was clearly nonlinear) and to extend self-attributes of prototypes to all examples (e.g., a function exhibiting curvilinearity was automatically designated as a parabola). Rather than using prototypes to assist them in understanding function, these students were more likely to use prototypes in ways that inhibited their understanding of function. For the Non-Tech using group, prototypes were more likely to function as brakes rather than as levers. This difference in use of prototypes seems inextricably linked to the nature of students' use of technology and the activities in which students were engaged.

The researchers noted that students in the Tech group invoked more examples and linked them to transformations more often than students in the comparison group do. The researchers attributed this difference to the nature of the experience the technology group had with function examples and transformations of functions:

> In other words, we believe that G_3-students, because they had numerous experiences with function examples and transformations in their daily practice, invoked more examples and linked them to transformations more often than the G_2-students. Manipulations on representatives (within or between representations) helped students recognize them as different "windows" representing the same entity. The invariants under transformations on representatives were precisely the attributes of functions, and the manipulations led more G_3-students to internalize these actions by imagining transformations and inferring the function attributes. (p. 386)

The researchers pointed out that the effects of the treatment on the G_3 students was not solely a result of their manipulation of representatives within and between representations, and they attributed those effects also to the learning environment (students working in small groups on investigative activities in open-ended situations followed by a teacher-led synthesis in a whole group setting). The researchers pointed out the development of classroom norms centered on reporting, critiquing, and reflecting on solution processes, and they noted that these norms were more in evidence when students used technology for symbolic manipulation and function graphing. The offloading of these routine tasks presumably freed students to think more reflectively about the problems at hand. In this context, tools for representing became tools for justifying as students' justifications became increasingly linked to their manipulation of representations. These intricate relationships among use of technology, offloading of routine tasks, and increased time to reflect emerge in other research discussed later in this chapter.

Reification. Differential use of prototypes may be a reflection of differences in the levels of understanding students have of function. Researchers and theorists have attempted to characterize the evolution of a process view of function into an object view or structural view and some have reasoned that technology would enable that evolution. Schwarz and Dreyfus (1995) provide a theoretical perspective on the development of concepts such as function. They posit that concept acquisition requires actions accompanied by seeing properties of an entity as invariant under those actions. They claim that the lack of such actions in certain settings (graphical, numerical, etc.) may imply that, for the learner, the properties are features of the setting (e.g., graph) rather than of the mathematical entity itself (function). It seems that a student's reified understanding of function would be exhibited in the extent to which the student sees properties of function as invariant under transformations between settings.

Slavit (1994) expressed the role of function properties in an object or structural view of function and described stages in the development of that view. The first two of the three stages were: (a) equivalence of procedures across representations (e.g., recognizing that solution of $2x + 3 = 0$ and identification of the x-value of the point at which the graph of $f(x) = 2x + 3$ crosses the x-axis are different manifestations of the same property), and (b) equivalence of procedures across function classes (e.g., recognition that the input value that satisfies the relationship $f(x) = g(x)$ is the x-value of the intersection of the graphs of functions f and g for any functions f and g). It seems that those who use prototypes as levers have reached the stage of "equivalence across function classes" evidenced in their ability to use prototypes to reason about related examples and to enhance their understanding of function. Slavit (1994) hypothesized that because classroom use of graphing calculators would enable the instructor to quickly change symbolic function parameters, and hence to focus discussion on global properties of function classes, that graphing calculators would facilitate movement from procedural to structural understanding.

Technology does not always help students develop a structural or object view of function as hypothesized by Slavit (1994) nor does it always help students develop facility with using prototypes as did students in the Schwarz and Hershkowitz (1999) study. Slavit (1994), for example, noted that, after regular use of graphing calculators in their work with elementary families of functions (linear and quadratic), students in his study did not appear to reify function beyond quadratics in terms of functional properties and did not develop a general notion of function as object possessing a variety of properties, although he observed that this was beginning to happen at end of the year as students studied exponential functions. Neither were students in Slavit's study using linear or quadratic function prototypes to extend their knowledge of function nor were they viewing procedures as equivalent across function classes. O'Callaghan's study (1998) of college students using the Computer-Intensive Algebra (CIA) curriculum (Fey et al., 1995/1999) yielded parallel results. O'Callaghan proposed a model of understanding function that included modeling, interpreting, translating, and reifying. Students in O'Callaghan's study used a technology-intensive, functions-based curriculum and exhibited a better overall understanding of functions. Although they performed significantly better than a non-CIA group on tasks involving modeling, interpreting, and translating, there was no significant difference between the groups on the component of reifying. O'Callaghan's results corroborated earlier results of Sheets (1993) in which the researcher compared the understanding of function exhibited by ninth grade CIA students with that of students who had at least two years additional experience in traditional non-technological mathematics courses.

Sheets observed that the CIA students working in multirepresentational technological environments demonstrated greater flexibility in reasoning about functions. The aforementioned studies suggest that incorporation of technology in the context of particular curricula can make differences in aspects of students' understanding of function, although none of the studies guarantee acquisition of a reified understanding of function.

Providing a learning environment. In addition to their potential for contributing to the development of an object understanding of mathematical concepts, technological tools also can facilitate concept development by providing students with a context in which they can develop initial conceptions that provide a basis for later development of more sophisticated conceptions. Graham and Thomas (2000) argued that students need to understand letters as being capable of representing numbers before they can use letters to generalize patterns of numbers. In their study, students used graphing calculators that had the capability of assigning numerical values to locations identified by letters and predicted and tested the results of performing operations (e.g., A+B and A/B) on the values stored in those locations. Students who used the graphing calculator exhibited significantly better performance than students in the comparison group did on a test that measured understanding of the use of letters as specific unknown, generalized number, and variable. The researchers noted that "This environment provides consistent feedback in which students may predict and test, enabling them to construct an understanding of letters in algebra as stores with labels and changeable contents, a firm basis on which to build later subtleties of the concept" (p. 270), namely, the calculator provides an opportunity to operate on variable as placeholder in a way that facilitates a later, more sophisticated, understanding of variable. Similarly, Boers van Oosterum (1990) provided evidence of a more robust development of the concept of variable for students who experienced a technology-intensive, functions-oriented approach to introductory algebra (CIA).

Inhibiting robust conceptual understanding. Tools can enhance or inhibit students developing robust understandings of mathematical concepts. Graham and Thomas provide an example of how students' use of technological tools can develop initial understandings that are necessary for subsequent conceptual development, whereas Friedlander and Tabach (2001) illustrate how students' use of technological tools (specifically spreadsheets) can develop understandings that may inhibit the development of robust understanding of mathematical concepts. Friedlander and Tabach identified three mathematical issues that arise when students work in a spreadsheet environment. One of these was the greater frequency with which students used recursive formulas rather than explicit formulas when describing numbers in a sequence. The authors note that recursive approaches naturally arise from considering differences between successive values, but require a lower level of generalization. Although Friedlander and Tabach may have considered development of this recursive tendency to be problematic, it may just illustrate a different viable perspective that may be nourished in a technological environment. Another issue identified by Friedlander and Tabach is students' "abuse" of the spreadsheet's power by constructing very large tables to identify solutions rather than using a symbolic expression or equation to identify a solution. A third issue was the difference between spreadsheet formulas and algebraic equations (a distinction that complements the distinction Ainley (1994, 1995) makes between computer-based-spreadsheet graphs and paper-and-pencil graphs). Friedlander and Tabach describe students' attempts to represent multiples of eight and their "translation" of a correct recursive spreadsheet formula such as "$= B3 + 8$" into the expression $n + 8$, rather than $8n$, to describe multiples of eight. The issues Friedlander and Tabach raise point out how students might come to understand mathematical concepts differently in a spreadsheet environment from how they might understand them when doing symbolic algebra by hand or with a CAS. Such difficulties, and others that researchers can identify when studying students' uses of technological tools, can provide opportunities to reflect on deeper understandings of the mathematical ideas underlying use of the tool. Friedlander and Tabach point out the need for explicit curricular tasks that address these difficulties.

The Importance of Curricular Context to the Effects of Technology on the Teaching and Learning of Algebra

Although a range of research has documented the potential of technology to affect important aspects of mathematics learning (acquisition of symbolic skills, development of conceptual understanding, and understanding of function), some studies serve as reminders that technology alone cannot enhance the learning of algebra. Since the technology is always embedded in a context, research on its use must address more than just the technology used. The aforementioned study by Schwarz and Hershkowitz (1999) illustrates this claim in that the effects of technology on use of prototypes may have been as much a function of change in instructional approach as it was a result of the incorporation of technology (graphing calculators and multirepresentational software). In a study using the computer algebra system, Derive, Coulombe and Matthews (1995) carefully controlled a variety of aspects of the teaching and learning setting in a functions and graphs course (e.g., laboratory experiences, writing assignments, and collaborative learning) and examined conceptual understanding for subjects from groups for which the only difference was use of a CAS (in this instance, Derive). They found no differences in levels of conceptual understanding between the Derive-using and non-Derive-using subjects. Although the incorporation of technology as the only change does not necessarily make a difference in conceptual understanding, it may be that improvement in conceptual understanding results from changes in strategies and mathematical content afforded by the technology.

A typical example of the importance of a combination of features was seen in a study by Hopkins and Kinard (1998) that combined four features: building on students' intuitive understanding of mathematical principles, use of algebraic manipulatives to help students acquire an understanding of the underlying concepts, developing traditional algebraic techniques out of this understanding, and employing the Texas Instruments TI-92 calculator (CAS-capable calculator) to facilitate computations. This combination resulted in significantly higher performance on the final exam, greater success in the next course, and improved attitudes for the treatment group when compared to a traditional developmental algebra group. Although one is unable to attribute the positive effects in this study exclusively to the use of technology, the study serves as a reminder that for research studies to be maximally informative, they need to examine and carefully document the broader context in which technology is used.

Input-Output Studies on the Acquisition of Routine Skills and Concepts in the Context of Technology-Present Curricula

Much of the research related to students' development of routine algebraic skills has not focused on how students are approaching the learning of algebra but focus instead on an "input-output" model, specifying the context as the implementation of a curriculum and observing students' performance after they have experienced that curriculum. We will discuss in the following paragraphs research related to students' acquisition of routine algebraic skills in the context of curricula that assumes the existence of technology. This body of research yields somewhat mixed results perhaps because studies of the use of technology in the teaching and learning of algebra are almost invariably conducted in the classroom contexts in which students are using an innovative curriculum that requires the use of technology. It is the particular configuration of technology and curriculum that is being investigated in these studies rather than the effects of technology alone. There is very little research on the use of technology for the sole purpose of improving students' acquisition of routine algebraic skills. Instead, researchers have investigated how technology could refocus the curriculum on more conceptual, applications-oriented algebraic ideas. Factors other than technology may affect differences between the technology-using experimental group and the non-technology-using comparison group.

Introductory algebra. In the context of these reformulated curricula, researchers have examined the effects of technology-present and technology-intensive curricula on students' understanding of algebraic concepts, on students' ability to use algebra to solve problems, and on students' acquisition of routine algebraic skills. Heid and colleagues (Heid, 1987, 1996; Heid, Sheets, Matras, & Menasian, 1988) examined the conceptual understanding and routine algebraic skills of ninth grade students who had studied a conceptually based introductory algebra curriculum (CIA) in an environment that included the equivalent of a computer algebra system (symbolic manipulation, graphing utilities, tabular facility). These students were identified by their school as more academically able than the students who completed ninth grade algebra and less academically able than students who completed algebra in eighth grade. From midway through eighth grade until two months before the end of their ninth grade year, students studied the concepts of algebra, using technology to solve equations, to evaluate functions at given values, to graph functions, and to produce tables of function values. During the last two months of the school year students studied standard symbolic procedures. Throughout the course, students in the experimental groups were interviewed and tested—as were students in the comparison groups from both the eighth grade algebra class and the ninth grade algebra class—regarding their conceptual understanding. As measured by a series of task-based interviews, the conceptual understanding of the CIA students was consistently superior to that of the ninth grade students and as good or better than that of the eighth grade algebra students. At the end of ninth grade, the students completed the school's standard final exam—a test that was almost entirely symbolic manipulation. On every test item of this skills-oriented final, the percent of CIA students completing the item correctly was between the percent correct by the eighth grade algebra students and the percent correct by the ninth grade algebra students. In other words, the CIA students performed better than would have been predicted on measures of conceptual understandings and, on every symbolic manipulation item, they scored as they would have been predicted to score based on their perceived ability level.

A range of studies on other implementations of the CIA curriculum examined additional aspects of student learning. Researchers have compared CIA students with comparison groups on problem-solving performance (Matras, 1988/1989), on understandings related to modeling and solving realistic algebra problems (Heid, Sheets, Matras, & Menasian, 1988; Heid & Zbiek 1993), and on understanding of the concepts of variable and function (Boers-van Oosterum, 1990; Sheets, 1993). The problem-solving study (Matras, 1988/1989) was conducted at two demographically different sites; and with the California Achievement total reading, mathematical concepts, and mathematical computation scores as covariates, the CIA group at both sites performed significantly better on the Problem Solving Test (a test of typical algebra contextual problems). On the Triads Test in which students were asked to identify similar structure in word problems, CIA students at one site outperformed the comparison group and there was no significant difference in performance between the two groups at the other site. The results of the study suggested that CIA had a positive effect on algebra word problem solving and, in one but not both of the settings, on the ability of students to perceive similar structure in word problems. One investigation of the effects of CIA on students' understanding of function (Sheets, 1993) compared the understanding of function of ninth grade CIA students to the understanding of function of students who were enrolled in a course that studied function and for which Algebra I and geometry were prerequisites. The CIA students in this study demonstrated greater flexibility in reasoning with multiple representations of function than did comparison students who had at least two years of additional experience in traditional school mathematics programs. Several studies were conducted on CIA students' understandings related to modeling and solving realistic algebra problems. In one study (Heid et al., 1988) based on task-based interviews, CIA students outperformed students from traditional algebra classes in every area of mathematical modeling addressed in the interviews: constructing representations, solving equations or evaluating functions, interpreting results, linking representations, explaining the modeling process, and outlining a solution procedure. A second study (Heid & Zbiek, 1993) analyzed use of mathematical modeling concepts by CIA students; these students varied in the nature of their competence in making sense of the model and answering questions about it, in seeking consistencies among representations, and in adjudicating contradictory observations.

Advanced algebra. While the CIA studies examined students' conceptual understandings and procedural skills in the context of introductory algebra, other studies have investigated the effects of technology on the conceptual understandings and procedural skills of students in more advanced algebra courses. Second-year algebra students in the UCSMP Advanced Algebra course were expected to have continual access to graphing technology (Thompson & Senk, 2001). At three of the four evaluation sites reported in this study, both the UCSMP group and the comparison group used graphing calculators on a regular basis. At the remaining site, the UCSMP group used calculators on a regular basis while the comparison group had no in-school access to graphing calculators. At this site, students in the UCSMP group scored significantly better than the comparison group on a test designed to measure students' performance on multi-step problems. Also at this site, the scores of the UCSMP group were significantly better than those of the comparison group on a multiple choice algebra symbolic manipulation posttest. One cannot attribute the success of the UCSMP group to graphing calculator use, especially since patterns of superior UCSMP performance characterized differences between the matched group even when both groups reported using graphing calculators on a regular basis. On the other hand, this study provides evidence that use of the graphing calculator in and of itself does not automatically lead to diminished procedural skills.

Results contrary to those of the CIA and UCSMP studies arose in the study of the algebraic understandings of students enrolled in the third year of the Core-Plus (CPMP) curriculum. This study investigated students' understanding, skill, and problem-solving abilities in algebra and functions. In a trial (Huntley et al., 2000) of the CPMP curriculum, students in the CPMP group scored significantly better than students in the control group on a test of students' ability to solve algebraic problems when those problems were in context and allowed use of graphing calculators, and students in the control group outperformed students in the CPMP group on every tested category of symbolic manipulation in the absence of context: evaluating expressions, testing equivalence of expressions, solving equations, and solving inequalities. The researchers observed: "We were not surprised that CPMP students, whose program does not focus on symbolic manipulation by paper and pencil, attained lower scores than traditional students whose program consisted of symbolic manipulation almost exclusively" (p. 348).

One might wonder how to account for apparent differences in the results of the studies of these three curricula with respect to symbolic manipulation skills. In the CIA and UCSMP studies, use of technology was not associated with lower performance on tests of algebraic skills. In the CPMP study, the control group performed significantly better than the treatment group on all measures of symbolic manipulation. None of these studies isolated use of technology as the only variable that changed, and each of the studies compared the levels of performance of students who participated in two entirely different curricula. Because the objects of study were the curricula, not the characteristics of the curricula, any observations that can reasonably be made are about the curricula, not about the technology. As suggested by Huntley and colleagues, it is not surprising that students in a curriculum that does not emphasize the acquisition of symbolic manipulation skills will not perform as well on these skills as students in a curriculum that does emphasize them. Nevertheless, the studies do raise questions. Even if the technology was not the cause of particular performance on procedural skills, it may have contributed to enabling a curriculum that focused more on concepts and applications than on routine skills. The question then comes down to whether the goals of the enabled curriculum are more desirable than the goals of the curriculum it replaces. The results of studies of these three curricula also raise a question about whether technology-intensive curricula work differently with students of different abilities. The students in the CIA study were placed by their school in an above average track, the students in the UCSMP study were classified as above average in ability, and the students in the CPMP study were classified as generally below average in ability. Students in all three studies outperformed the comparison groups on the measures of conceptual thinking or problem solving, but only the CIA students and the UCSMP students who used graphing calculators did at least as well as the comparison groups on measures of symbolic manipulation. Seemingly contradictory results such as these necessitate further research to provide possible explanations for such differences. One tentative hypothesis is that while these technological approaches are successful in enhancing the conceptual thinking of all students, their adequacy in helping students acquire symbolic manipulation skills depends on the ability level of the students.

Effects of Symbolic Manipulation Technology

When technology is used as an aid to the routine processing of symbols—arithmetic computation or algebraic symbolic manipulation—concern turns to whether there is a loss in the skills that students would normally acquire. The prototypical curricular use of CAS technology can be characterized in several ways. First, CAS use might be characterized by the relationship of the technique to the traditional approach to symbolic manipulation: CAS can be used as a supplement to regular instruction, CAS can be used as a catalyst for new approaches and as a replacement for some traditional mathematics, or CAS can be used as a replacement for traditional mathematics (Heid & Edwards, 2001). Alternatively, CAS use may be characterized using Buchberger's (1989) "white box/black box" analogy. In short, the CAS can be a black box, in which case the student uses the calculator to produce the results of symbolic manipulations without knowing an algorithm to produce those results by hand. On the other hand, the CAS can be used as a white box, in which case the student uses the calculator to produce the results of symbolic manipulations only after he or she knows how to perform by hand routines that produce these results. There has been considerable debate about whether a white box followed by a black box or a black box followed by a white box sequence or some gray-box combination is most appropriate.

Research has been conducted using curricular approaches following each of these paradigms, usually with the goals of examining the effects of CAS-oriented instruction on the development of symbolic manipulation skills and conceptual understandings. Typically, a study employs the CAS in one of the previously described fashions, and then compares the conceptual and/or procedural understandings or skills of students in the experimental curriculum with those of students in a more traditional curriculum. The experimental curricula were typically designed to produce deeper conceptual or procedural understanding or to help students develop facility in creating and using mathematical models for realistic situations. Typically the early experiments lasted a minimum of one semester and used introductory college calculus students as the subjects. Most of the calculus studies found that CAS-curriculum students developed superior understanding of concepts with no significant deficit in computational skill (Crocker, 1991; Heid, 1984/1985, 1988; Palmiter, 1991; Park, 1993; Shrock, 1989; Vlachos & Kehagias, 2000; for additional details see Tall, Smith, & Piez, 2008). Studying the effects of access to a computer-intensive algebra curriculum both at the collegiate level and at the high school level produced similar results, with improved conceptual understanding without substantial loss of skills (Heid et al., 1988; O'Callaghan, 1998; Hollar and Norwood, 1999; Mayes, 1995). In the aforementioned study by Heid and her colleagues (1988), students studied the concepts and applications of algebra for all but the last month of the school year, and finished the year with a month of exposure to by-hand symbolic manipulation. Computer-Intensive Algebra (CIA) students outperformed non-CIA students on all measures of mathematical modeling; mean final exam scores (primarily assessing symbolic manipulation skills) were lower for the CIA students after studying symbolic skills for one month rather than for an entire school year. These differences did not appear to be educationally different, however, since the differences in scores on a final examination of traditional symbolic manipulation skills were small (the mean score for the control group was 68% and for the experimental groups was 59%, 57%, and 54%). In a different study, one group of 14-16 year olds was taught algebra topics using enhanced muMath (a symbolic manipulation program that was a predecessor to Derive) and the other was taught with the same exercises but without the computer. There was not a significant difference in the two groups on equation solving and factoring, although the computer group did better on the factoring exercises (Thomas & Rickhuss, 1992).

A growing number of researchers have moved from relying solely on the experimental/comparison group design and have attempted to study the nature of student learning and understanding in the context of a variety of CAS-oriented curricular approaches. Most of these studies were conducted in the context of calculus classes, but a few focused on learning in the context of high school algebra courses. Tynan and Asp (1998), for example, observed the effects of making CAS-capable TI-92 calculators available to year 9 students on a range of symbol manipulation tasks and found that the TI-92 students were more inclined than their peers who used non-CAS graphing calculators to persist with algebraic methods for equation-solving tasks. In addition, they found that there was no significant difference between the two classes in their abilities to perform by-hand symbolic manipulation. Yerushalmy and Gilead (1997) investigated the question of how eighth graders approach the solution of equations, when their first few months of algebra consisted of describing and analyzing processes as functions in various representations and who had used Function Supposer in their studies but had not yet studied any methods for solving equations. Most of the students' suggested strategies blended numerical and graphical analysis with algebraic symbols and sometimes even included reasoning about procedures. Students used iconic graphs (not point-plotted graphs) from which they reasoned. Comparisons of functions provided them with a dynamic image for solving equations. The researchers noted that students' work completely contradicted the assumption that inspecting a solution while skipping the analytic process may leave "solving" a meaningless action. The study showed that students may begin their learning of equation solving through the numerical and graphical without first doing by-hand symbolic manipulation.

In a previously described study (Heid, 1996), beginning algebra students in the eighth and ninth grades spent over a year studying from *Concepts in Algebra: A Technological Approach* (CIA), a computer-intensive functions approach to algebra. As previously mentioned, the students had been grouped by ability and were determined by their school to be of higher ability than a ninth grade algebra comparison group and of lower ability than an eighth grade algebra group. The content of the class focused on families of functions and their use in describing and understanding relationships among quantities in real world situations. During this time, students used a toolkit of programs with CAS capability and neither learned nor were taught any symbolic manipulation routines. They then spent the last two months on traditional by-hand symbolic manipulation skills. As reported previously in this chapter, on every item on a final exam of traditional skills, the CIA group performed better than a ninth grade algebra comparison group and slightly worse than an eighth grade algebra group. Task-based interviews with students from all three groups of students showed the CIA students to outperform the students on several problem-solving measures.

One might wonder whether students develop by-hand symbolic manipulation skills merely through the experience of extended work with computer algebra systems. Some indication of a response to this arises from studies of students' learning of calculus. Heid (1984), in a study of a technology-intensive introductory calculus course in which students had access to muMath along with graphing and table-generation tools, found that students did not develop skills in by-hand symbolic procedures as a result of 12 weeks of work with those procedures using muMath, although they made considerable progress in learning the procedures in the subsequent three-week period of the course that focused on the procedures. Not only do students not automatically learn symbolic manipulation skills if they are not taught them, but they also do not automatically learn to outline processes for solving problems (Heid, 1984). Introductory algebra students can, however, learn to use and interpret the results of symbolic manipulation in their reasoning and problem solving without having learned to perform those symbolic manipulation procedures by hand. Yerushalmy (1991) reported parallel results in her study of eighth graders using multirepresentational software to study functions. Students in her study spent more time observing the multiple representations of functions and less time learning techniques of graphing, yet they did not lack the graphing techniques and knowledge required to solve traditional problems.

Technology to Advance Procedural Goals

In each of the aforementioned studies, the technology enabled the goals of the curriculum to shift from ones that were primarily procedural to ones that were more conceptual in nature. There are, nevertheless, significant efforts to use technology to foster traditional procedural goals in algebra. One such body of work is research conducted on cognitive tutors. Cognitive tutors in algebra are intelligent tutoring programs aimed at developing students' algebraic skills. The Cognitive Tutors developed by the Carnegie Mellon group, under the direction of John Anderson, include Algebra Cognitive Tutors. [See Ritter, Haverty, Koedinger, Hadley, & Corbett (2008) for a description of the development of the intelligent tutor software.] The researchers, in conjunction with teachers from the Pittsburgh Public Schools developed the PUMP (Pittsburgh Urban Mathematics Project) Algebra Tutor (PAT) to use in an algebra curriculum whose content mirrors many of the NCTM-Standards-consistent curricula developed during the late 1980's and the early 1990's. The researchers reported significant success in using PAT in ninth grade algebra in the Pittsburgh Public Schools. They report that, on average, the students in the experimental classes outperformed students in the comparison classes by 15% on standardized tests and by 100% on tests they viewed as targeted on Standards-consistent curricula (Koedinger, Anderson, Hadley, & Mark, 1997). The researchers attributed some of the success of their tutors to their use of "model tracing" and "knowledge tracing." "Model tracing" monitors a student's progress through a problem solution, and "knowledge tracing" monitors students' learning from problem to problem. The researchers use this assessment information to individualize problem selection and to adjust the pace of the material for students. The comparison, however, is confounded by the fact that the comparison groups used "traditional" curricula, leaving the reader to wonder whether the positive effects were a result of the tutor, the curriculum, or the combination. It is not clear whether the same differences would have accrued were the comparison groups to have used a *Standards*-consistent non-tutor curriculum.

CONCLUSIONS

Technology can influence the content and teaching of algebra as well as the mathematical activity that takes place in the algebra classroom. Decisions about the use of technology in algebra are a function of the extent to which the technology has become a tool for the teacher, and student learning is a function of the nature of the mathematical activity in which students engage. Technology affects algebra content, algebra tasks, and opportunities in algebra classrooms for mathematical activity. It provides an environment that catalyzes changes in what students do in mathematics classrooms as well as how they do it. These changes occur both through the introduction of new content and through teaching and learning goals that target different understandings of traditional content.

Effects on Mathematical Activity

This chapter has focused on the effects of linked configurations of technology and its curricular environment on mathematical activity (conceptualizing, generalizing, representing, and working with symbols) and, hence, on the learning of algebra.

Conceptualizing

Technology both limits and expands opportunities for developing robust algebraic concepts. A major way in which it expands opportunities to develop the algebra concept of function, for example, is through its capacity to accentuate function as both a process and an object. Effective use of some technologies requires that users treat as objects entities that they would not otherwise be likely to treat as objects. Technology may promote development of object-level understanding of concepts, but this development is not guaranteed.

Whether technology expands or limits opportunities for enhancing understanding of algebraic concepts depends on the transparency of the technology—the extent to which the mathematics in the technology is visible to the learner. The transparency of the technology is a function of the relationship between the user and the technology, and this relationship develops through a reciprocal process of the user transforming the artifact of the technology into an instrument and the technology transforming the approach of the user (Trouche, 2005b; Verillon & Rabardel, 1995).

The impact of technology on development of conceptual understanding has been studied most in the context of understanding the mathematical concept of function. Skills and understandings that support learning about function include the ability to draw on knowledge of families of functions (or prototypical functions) and the ability to view function as a manipulable whole. In the context of appropriate technology-intensive curricular approaches, technology can help students develop a more flexible ability to work with prototypes and a more robust (object) understanding of function. The nature of understanding developed in technological contexts can be affected by the type of technology being used. Understanding of function depends on understanding of variable, and researchers have documented the potential of technological approaches for enhancing understanding of variable.

Generalizing

Mathematical technologies are cognitive technologies (Pea, 1985, 1987)—technologies that "transcend the limitations of the mind" (Pea, 1987, p. 91). One way in which mathematical technologies function is to enable the user to generate large numbers of instances from which to produce generalizations. Different tools support different types of generalizing in algebra. Symbolic capacity of CAS supports search for algebraic invariants. Graphing technology supports recognition of properties of families of functions. The logical structure of spreadsheets support generalizations stated recursively. Technology can provide simultaneous access to the local and global, facilitating smooth movement between macro and micro views of mathematical phenomena. Even with the affordances provided by technological tools in algebra, however, students may not engage in generalizing activities. They may not see the range of instances produced as examples of mathematical phenomena and they may not see the mathematical connections between linked representations. That is, they may not see the general in the specific.

Representing

Technology-enhanced curricular approaches to algebra can change the nature of mathematical activity in the algebra classroom. Technological environments provide opportunities for access to a gamut of mathematical representations, each of which has the capacity to highlight a different set of features for individuals prepared to attend to those features. In algebra, as in other areas of mathematics, the capability of technology to link representations dynamically and to change them rapidly suggests that technologically produced representations may have different relationships to the user than those produced by hand. However, the technology itself is not the determinant of the learning; rather it is the mathematical activity in which the learner engages, and it is the act of representing rather than the physical representation that counts.

Research on technology in the teaching and learning of algebra is conducted in different contextual settings. In different technology-enhanced contexts, students use different sets of representations, they call upon different mathematical abilities and strengths with particular representation types, and they study algebraic content using different representations. Research studies (including year-long studies of the effects of technology-based curricula and of cognitive tutors) point to the importance of curricular setting in the degree of success of technology in the teaching and learning of algebra. Representational fluency, to some extent a product of the nature of instrumental genesis, also plays a prominent role in students' success in technological environments. To best take advantage of technology, it is not the availability of multiple representations but the actions taken on those representations that count (potential actions are more varied in a technological settings). There is a need for reflection on the actions and the results of those actions.

Working With Symbols

The automated symbolic processing made available through computer algebra systems raises a collection of different issues. Symbolic processors expand opportunities for students to build meaning around symbolic representations since their attention can be on the meaning of the symbols instead of on the rules of transformation. While symbolic processors provide the opportunity to build a more robust understanding of mathematical phenomena, when coupled with other representations they also provide ways for students to circumvent work with symbols. Different symbolic technologies require different mathematical understandings: for example, CAS requires greater attention to equivalence, and spreadsheets require paying attention to the mathematical relationships between quantities.

Using technology for work with algebraic symbols requires more than automated symbolic manipulation. This expanded view of work with symbols has been called "technique" (Artigue, 2002; Lagrange, 1999; Lagrange, 2000/2001); it includes the ability to execute a routine procedure, the knowledge of when the use of the procedure is appropriate, the ability to know when results of symbolic manipulation are reasonable, and the understanding necessary to give meaning to the symbolic work. Whereas some theorists have developed the notion of "technique" referring to the "complex assembly of reasoning and routine work" (Artigue, 2002, p. 248), others (e.g., Trouche, 2005b) have described "work methods," characterizations of how a student coordinates the ability to execute the symbolic manipulation, the knowledge of when to apply it, and strategies for determining its accuracy.

Modeling

Technology can provide a link between the real world and the mathematical world. The use of tools for modeling is not unproblematic, however, since students can fail to take advantage of modeling tools when they lose sight of the phenomena they are modeling.

Effects of Curricular Context

The question that can be addressed through examination of research literature is not one of the effects of technology alone on the teaching and learning of algebra. Technology alone does not make the difference in algebra learning. What matters is the nature of the technology use, the content being taught, the extent to which the technology has become an instrument for the teacher and students, and the extent to which students reflect on the mathematical activities in which they are engaged. Studies have supported the notion that technology can be used to productively engage students in developing robust algebraic concepts. Curricular approaches that focus on the development of algebraic concepts and that involve technology are less definitive regarding effects on acquisition of algebraic routines, with some approaches not affecting symbolic manipulation ability negatively and some leaving the technology-present classes with less fluency in symbolic manipulation than their non-tech counterparts.

One technology that has generated considerable interest and some trepidation is the computer algebra system. As is true of other technologies, the effect of the CAS is largely dependent on how it is used. Its uses in research studies have ranged from supplementing a traditional algebra curriculum to serving as a core instrument for a transformed algebra curriculum. CAS can be viewed as a tool for circumventing the need for by-hand symbolic manipulation in order to address other goals or a tool that affords students opportunities to investigate symbolic results and procedures more deeply. In calculus experiments aimed at CAS transforming the curriculum to focus on concepts with minimal attention to the development of manipulative skills, typically students develop deeper conceptual understanding without detrimental effect on by-hand symbolic manipulation skills. Fewer such studies have been completed using algebra students, although there is some indication of similar results in the context of algebra instruction.

General Observations

Research on technology in the teaching and learning of algebra has suggested an array of observations related to the content and processes of school algebra, the processes of mathematical activity in which algebra students engage, and the development of conceptual and procedural understandings. Among those observations are the following:

1. Technology in conjunction with technology-based curricular approaches can effectively change the content and processes of school algebra.

   - Use of technology can influence the progress from a process understanding to an object understanding through work with representations.
   - Work with representations does not guarantee attainment of an object understanding of a concept; to increase the probability of such attainment, curriculum materials need to focus intentionally on developing object understanding.

2. Technology in conjunction with technology-based curricular approaches can affect the processes of mathematical activity in an algebraic setting. Many of these effects are related to the representational capacity of technology.

   - Students can learn to use multiple representations.
   - Students will not necessarily take full advantage of the power of multiple representations when they use them.
   - Students do not necessarily reason from some representations when others are available.
   - Students do not necessarily connect representations when operating in a multiple representation environment; curricula and

teachers need to be intentional about promoting such connections.

- Multiple representations may promote more global approaches.
- Sustained use of graphic representations may lead to improved visual reasoning (spatial-visual) skills.
- Students engaged in mathematical modeling need to learn that they, not the tool, must make decisions.
- We need additional research that helps teachers, curriculum developers, and researchers to understand how students move between, connect, and reason from multiple representations.

3. Technology in conjunction with technology-based curricular approaches can affect the acquisition of algebraic concepts and procedures.

- Use of technology can positively influence the development of algebraic concepts.
- Changes in strategy and mathematical content, not just the incorporation of technology, seem to promote improved conceptual understanding.
- Technology enables the goals and content of algebra curricula to shift from a procedural focus to a more conceptual focus.
- CAS use (often in conjunction with a more conceptually oriented curriculum) generally leads to superior conceptual understanding and no substantial deficit in by-hand skills.
- Students can learn symbolic algebra through experiences with graphical and numeric representations without first doing by-hand symbolic manipulation.
- Use of technology can promote the development of initial concepts (e.g., of variable) that lead to more sophisticated concepts.
- Use of technology can promote the development of different understandings about fundamental algebraic concepts.

Perhaps more so than any other area of school mathematics, technology has the potential for substantially influencing the learning of algebra. This potential is compounded by the growing range of perspectives on the nature of school algebra (Bednarz, Kieran, & Lee, 1996), each with its own collection of objects of study, with newly important concepts, and with changes in views of the importance of particular procedures. At the same time that the nature of school algebra is being called into question, the field of inquiry centered on mathematics education is developing new understandings of what it means to understand different mathematical concepts, procedures, strategies, and objects. Research on the learning of algebra, however defined, continually raises new questions. What is the impact of technology on the acquisition of traditional by-hand symbolic manipulation skills? What is the potential for technology to assist in the development of symbolic reasoning? What are the nontechnological factors that, when combined with the availability of technological tools like the CAS, influence the development of object understandings of mathematical concepts? Current research related to these questions only scratches the surface. Serious and persistent pursuit of answers will significantly advance our understanding of the effects of technology on the teaching and learning of algebra.

NOTES

1. In this chapter, when we refer to "representation," we mean "external representation."
2. We say this recognizing that the mathematical feature does not reside in the representation but rather in the interaction of the student with the representation.
3. An alternative but related conception of work method was offered by Weigand and Weller (2001) in their description of working style as related to choice of tool, representation, and mathematical object.
4. Cooney, Davis, and Henderson (1983) define a rational set of examples as a collection of examples in which irrelevant attributes are systematically varied.
5. We say this with the caveat that learning concepts through examples is not the exclusive route to developing conceptual understanding. Developing conceptual understanding founded on definition is an important feature of mathematics learning, especially at the collegiate level (Edwards, 1997/1998).
6. ISETL is a programming language that can take functions as input and produce functions as output.

REFERENCES

Ainley, J. (1994). Building on children's intuitions about line graphs. In J. P. da Ponte & J. F. Matos (Eds.), *Proceedings of the eighteenth annual conference of the International Group for the Psychology of Mathematics Education* (Vol. II, pp. 1-8). Lisbon, Portugal: University of Lisbon.

Ainley, J. (1995). Re-viewing graphing: Traditional and intuitive approaches. *For the Learning of Mathematics, 15*(2), 10-16.

Ainley, J. (2000). Problem-solving strategies and mathematical resources: A longitudinal view on problem solving in a function based approach to algebra. *Journal of Mathematical Behavior, 19*, 365-384.

Artigue, M. (2002). Learning mathematics in a CAS environment: The genesis of a reflection about instrumentation and the dialectics between technical and conceptual work. *International Journal of Computers for Mathematical Learning, 7,* 245-274.

Asiala, M., Brown, A., DeVries, D., Dubinsky, E., Mathews, D., & Thomas, K. (1996). A framework for research and curriculum development in undergraduate mathematics education. In J. Kaput, A. H. Schoenfeld, & E. Dubinsky (Eds.), *Research in collegiate mathematics education, II* (pp. 1-32). Providence, RI: The American Mathematical Society.

Ayers, T., Davis, G., Dubinsky, E., & Lewin, P. (1988). Computer experiences in learning composition of functions. *Journal for Research in Mathematics Education, 19,* 246-259.

Bednarz, N., Kieran, C., & Lee, L. (Eds.). (1996). *Approaches to algebra: Perspectives on research and teaching.* Dordrecht, Holland: Kluwer Academic.

Bidwell, J. K., & Clason, R. G. (Eds.). (1970). *Readings in the history of mathematics education.* Washington, DC: National Council of Teachers of Mathematics.

Bills, L., Ainley, J., & Wilson, K. (2006). Modes of algebraic communication: moving from spreadsheets to standard notation. *For the Learning of Mathematics, 26*(1), 36-41.

Boers-van Oosterum, M. A. M. (1990). Understanding of variables and their uses acquired by students in traditional and computer-intensive algebra. (Doctoral dissertation, University of Maryland, 1990). *Dissertation Abstracts International, 51*(05), 1538.

Borba, M. C., & Confrey, J. (1996). A student's construction of transformations of functions in a multiple representational environment. *Educational Studies in Mathematics, 31,* 319-337.

Boyd, A., & Rubin, A. (1996). Interactive video: A bridge between motion and math. *International Journal of Computers for Mathematical Learning, 1,* 57-93.

Bransford, J. D., Zech, L., Schwartz, D., Barron, B., Vye, N., & The Cognition and Technology Group at Vanderbilt. (1996). Fostering mathematical thinking in middle school students: Lessons from research. In R. J. Sternberg & T. Ben-Zeev (Eds.), *The nature of mathematical thinking* (pp. 203-250). Mahwah, NJ: Erlbaum.

Breidenbach, D., Dubinsky, E., Hawks, J., & Nichols, D. (1992). Development of the process conception of function. *Educational Studies in Mathematics, 23,* 247-285.

Brown, A., DeVries, D., Dubinsky, E., & Thomas, K. (1998). Learning binary operations, groups, and subgroups. *Journal of Mathematical Behavior, 16,* 187-239.

Buchberger, B. (1989). Should students learn integration rules? *SIGSAM Bulletin, 24*(1), 10-17.

Chazan, D. (1999). On teachers' mathematical knowledge and student exploration: A personal story about teaching a technologically supported approach to school algebra. *International Journal of Computers for Mathematical Learning, 4,* 121-149.

Confrey, J. (1994). Exponential functions, rates of change, and the multiplicative unit. *Educational Studies in Mathematics, 26,* 135-164.

Confrey, J., & Maloney, A. (2008). Research-design interactions in building Function Probe software. In G. W. Blume & M. K. Heid (Eds.). *Research on technology and the teaching and learning of mathematics: Vol. 2. Cases and perspectives* (pp. 183-210). Charlotte, NC: Information Age.

Confrey, J., & Smith, E. (1992). Revised accounts of the function concept using multi-representational software, contextual problems and student paths. In W. Geeslin & K. Graham (Eds.), *Proceedings of the sixteenth annual conference of the International Group for the Psychology of Mathematics Education* (Vol. I, pp. 153-160). Durham, NH: Program Committee of the Sixteenth PME Conference.

Cooney, T. J., Davis, E. J., & Henderson, K. B. (1983). *Dynamics of teaching secondary school mathematics*. Boston: Houghton Mifflin.

Coulombe, W. N., & Mathews, D. N. (1995). A comparative study of mathematics courses with computer and noncomputer laboratories. In L. Lum (Ed.), *Proceedings of the sixth annual International Conference on Technology in Collegiate Mathematics* (pp. 467-473). Reading, MA: Addison Wesley.

Crocker, D. (1991). A qualitative study of interactions, concept development and problem solving in a calculus class immersed in the computer algebra system Mathematica. (Doctoral dissertation, The Ohio State University, 1991). *Dissertation Abstracts International, 52*(08), 2850.

Doerr, H. M., & Zangor, R. (2000). Creating meaning for and with the graphing calculator. *Educational Studies in Mathematics, 41*, 143-163.

Doerr, H., & Pratt, D. (2008). The learning of mathematics and mathematical modeling. In M. K. Heid & G. W. Blume (Eds.). *Research on technology and the teaching and learning of mathematics: Vol. 1. Research syntheses* (pp. 259-286). Charlotte, NC: Information Age.

Dolciani, M. P., Berman, S. L., & Freilich, J. (1965). *Modern algebra: Structure and method, Book one*. New York: Houghton Mifflin.

Donoghue, E. F. (2003). Algebra and geometry textbooks in twentieth-century America. In G. M. A. Stanic & J. Kilpatrick (Eds.), *A history of school mathematics* (Vol. 1, pp. 329-398). Reston, VA: National Council of Teachers of Mathematics.

Dreyfus, T., & Hillel, J. (1998). Reconstruction of meanings for function approximation. *International Journal of Computers for Mathematical Learning, 3*, 93-112.

Drijvers, P. (2000). Students encountering obstacles using a CAS. *International Journal of Computers for Mathematical Learning, 5*, 189-209.

Drijvers, P., & van Herwaarden, O. (2000). Instrumentation of ICT-tools: The case of algebra in a computer algebra environment. *International Journal of Computer Algebra in Mathematics Education, 7*, 255-275.

Dunham, P. H., & Dick, T. P. (1994). Research on graphing calculators. *Mathematics Teacher, 87*, 440-445.

Duval, R. (1995). Geometrical pictures: Kinds of representation and specific processings. In R. Sutherland & J. Mason (Eds.), *Exploiting mental imagery with computers in mathematics education* (pp.142-157). Berlin, Germany: Springer.

Duval, R. (1998). Geometry from a cognitive point of view. In C. Mammana & V. Villani (Eds.), *Perspectives on the teaching of geometry for the 21st century* (New ICMI Study Series n.5, pp. 37-52). Dordrecht, Holland: Kluwer.

Edwards, B. E. S. (1997/1998). Undergraduate mathematics majors' understanding and use of formal definitions in real analysis. (Doctoral dissertation, The Pennsylvania State University, 1997). *Dissertation Abstracts International, 58*(12), 4590.

Eisenberg, T., & Dreyfus, T. (1994). On understanding how students learn to visualize function transformations. In E. Dubinsky, A. H. Schoenfeld, & J. Kaput (Eds.), *Research in collegiate mathematics education. I, CBMS Issues in Mathematics Education Vol. 4*, (pp. 45-68). Providence, RI: The American Mathematical Society.

Fey, J. T., Atchison, W. F., Good, R. A., Heid, M. K., Johnson, J., Kantowski, M. G., et al. (1984). *Computing and mathematics: The impact on secondary school curricula*. Reston, VA: National Council of Teachers of Mathematics.

Fey, J. T., & Heid, M. K. (with Good, R. A., Sheets, C., Blume, G., & Zbiek, R. M.). (1995, 1999). *Concepts in algebra: A technological approach*, Dedham, MA: Janson. (republished in 1999 version, Chicago: Everyday Learning Corporation).

Fey, J. T., & Hirsch, C. R. (2007). The case of Core-Plus mathematics. In C. R. Hirsch (Ed.), *Perspectives on the design and development of school mathematics curricula* (pp. 129-142). Reston, VA: National Council of Teachers of Mathematics.

Friedlander, A., & Tabach, M. (2001). Developing a curriculum of beginning algebra in a spreadsheet environment. In H. Chick, K. Stacey, J. Vincent, & J. Vincent (Eds.), *Proceedings of the 12th ICMI Study Conference: The future of the teaching and learning of algebra* (Vol. 1, pp. 252-257). Melbourne, Australia: The University of Melbourne Department of Science and Mathematics Education.

Gerny, M., & Alpers, B. (2004). Formula 1—A mathematical microworld with CAS: Analysis of learning opportunities and experiences with students. *International Journal of Computers for Mathematical Learning, 9*, 25-57.

Graham, A. T., & Thomas, M. O. J. (2000). Building a versatile understanding of algebraic variables with a graphic calculator. *Educational Studies in Mathematics, 41*, 265-282.

Gray, E. M., & Tall, D. O. (1994). Duality, ambiguity, and flexibility: A "proceptual" view of simple arithmetic. *Journal for Research in Mathematics Education, 15*, 116-140.

Guin, D., & Trouche, L. (1999). The complex process of converting tools into mathematical instruments: The case of calculators. *International Journal of Computers for Mathematical Learning, 3*, 195-227.

Hart, W. W. (1935). *Progressive high school algebra*. Boston: D. C. Heath.

Haspekian, M. (2005). An "instrumental approach" to study the integration of a computer tool into mathematics teaching: The case of spreadsheets. *International Journal of Computers for Mathematical Learning, 10*, 109-141.

Heid, M. K. (1985). An exploratory study to examine the effects of resequencing skills and concepts in an applied calculus curriculum through the use of the microcomputer. (Doctoral dissertation, University of Maryland College Park, 1984). *Dissertation Abstracts International, 46*(06), 1548.

Heid, M. K. (1987). *"Algebra with computers": A description and evaluation of student performance and attitudes*. Research report to a school board. University Park, PA.

Heid, M. K. (1988). Re-sequencing skills and concepts in applied calculus using the computer as a tool. *Journal for Research in Mathematics Education, 19*, 3-25.

Heid, M. K. (1996). A technology-intensive functional approach to the emergence of algebraic thinking. In C. Kieran, N. Bednarz, & L. Lee (Eds.), *Approaches to algebra: Perspectives for research and teaching* (pp. 239-255). Dordrecht, Holland: Kluwer.

Heid, M. K. (2003). Theories that inform the use of CAS in the teaching and learning of mathematics. In J. T. Fey, A. Cuoco, C. Kieran, L. McMullin, & R. M. Zbiek (Eds.), *CAS in mathematics education* (pp. 33-52). Reston, VA: National Council of Teachers of Mathematics.

Heid, M. K., Blume, G., Flanagan, K., Iseri, L., & Kerr, K. (1998). The impact of CAS on non-routine problem solving by college mathematics students. *International Journal for Computer Algebra in Mathematics Education, 5*, 216-249.

Heid, M. K., Blume, G., Flanagan, K., Iseri, L., Kerr, K., & Marshall, J. (1997, March). *The interplay among multiple representations and student understanding in the context of availability of a computer algebra calculator.* Paper presented at the annual meeting of the American Educational Research Association, Chicago.

Heid, M. K., Blume, G. W., Zembat, I. O., MacCullough, D. L., MacDonald, B. & Seaman, W. (2003). Understanding of multivariate function: The case of prospective secondary mathematics teachers. In D. S. Mewborn, P. Sztajn, D. Y. White, H. G. Wiegel, R. L. Bryant, & K. Nooney (Eds.), *Proceedings of the 24th annual meeting of the North American Chapter of the International Group for the Psychology of Mathematics Education* (Vol. 1, pp. 283-293). Columbus, OH: ERIC Clearinghouse for Science, Mathematics, and Environmental Education.

Heid, M. K., Choate, J., Sheets, C., & Zbiek, R. M. (1995). *Algebra in a technological world*, Addenda Series, Grades 9-12. Reston, VA: National Council of Teachers of Mathematics.

Heid, M. K., & Edwards, M. T. (2001). Computer algebra systems: A revolution or a retrofit for today's classroom? *Theory into Practice, 40*(2), 128-136.

Heid, M. K., Hollebrands, K., & Iseri, L. (2002). Reasoning, justification, and proof, with examples from technological environments. *Mathematics Teacher, 95*, 210-216.

Heid, M. K., Sheets, C., Matras, M., & Menasian, J. (1988, April). *Classroom and computer lab interaction in a computer-intensive algebra curriculum.* Paper presented at the annual meeting of the American Educational Research Association, New Orleans, LA.

Heid, M. K., & Zbiek, R. M. (1993). The nature of understanding of mathematical modelling by beginning algebra students engaged in a technology-intensive conceptually based algebra course. In J. R. Becker & B. J. Pence (Eds.), *Proceedings of the fifteenth annual meeting of the North American Chapter of the International Group for the Psychology of Mathematics Education* (Vol. 1, pp. 28-34). Pacific Grove, CA: San Jose State University.

Heid, M. K., Zbiek, R. M., Blume, G. W., & Choate, J. (2004). Technology-intensive mathematics [CD]. Unpublished materials.

Hershkowitz, R., Dreyfus, T., Ben-Zvi, D., Friedlander, A., Hadas, N., Resnick, T., et al. (2002). Mathematics curriculum development for computerized environments: A designer-researcher-teacher-learner activity. In L. D. English

(Ed.), *Handbook of international research in mathematics education* (pp. 657-694). Mahwah, NJ: Erlbaum.

Hiebert, J., & Carpenter, T. (1992). Learning and teaching with understanding. In D. A. Grouws (Ed.), *Handbook of research on mathematics teaching and learning* (pp. 65-97). New York: Macmillan.

Hillel, J., Lee, L., Laborde, C., & Linchevski, L. (1992). Basic functions through the lens of computer algebra systems. *Journal of Mathematical Behavior, 11*, 119-158.

Hollar, J. C., & Norwood, K. (1999). The effects of a graphing-approach intermediate algebra curriculum on students' understanding of function. *Journal for Research in Mathematics Education, 30*, 220-226.

Hong, Y. Y., & Thomas, M. O. J. (2002). Representational versatility and linear algebraic equations. *Proceedings of the International Conference on Computers in Education* (Vol. 2, pp. 1002-1006), Auckland, New Zealand: ICCE.

Hopkins, L., & Kinard, A. (1998). The use of the TI-92 in developmental algebra for college students. In C. Leinbach (Ed.), *Proceedings from the 3rd International DERIVE and TI-92 Conference* [CD]. Urbana, IL: MathWare.

Hoyos, V. (1999). Connections between different mathematical domains using technological tools: The analytical character of the algebraic task-resolution. In F. Hitt & M. Santos (Eds.), *Proceedings of the twenty-first annual meeting of the North American Chapter of the International Group for the Psychology of Mathematics Education* (Vol. 2, pp. 370-377). Columbus, OH: ERIC Clearinghouse for Science, Mathematics, and Environmental Education.

Huntley, M. A., Rasmussen, C. L., Villarubi, R. S., Sangtong, J., & Fey, J. T. (2000). Effects of Standards-based mathematics education: A study of the Core-Plus mathematics project algebra and functions strand. *Journal for Research in Mathematics Education, 31*, 328-361.

Jones, P. S., & Coxford, A. F. (1970). *A history of mathematics education in the United States and Canada*. Washington, DC: National Council of Teachers of Mathematics.

Kaput, J. J. (1989). Linking representations in the symbol systems of algebra. In S. Wagner & C. Kieran (Eds.), *Research issues in the learning and teaching of algebra* (pp. 167-194). Reston, VA: National Council of Teachers of Mathematics.

Kaput, J. (1994). Democratizing access to calculus: New routes to old roots. In A. Schoenfeld (Ed.), *Mathematical thinking and problem solving* (pp. 77-156). Hillsdale, NJ: Erlbaum.

Kieran, C., Boileau, A., & Garançon, M. (1996). Introducing algebra by means of a technology-supported, functional approach. In C. Kieran, N. Bednarz, & L. Lee (Eds.), *Approaches to algebra: Perspectives for research and teaching* (pp. 257-293). Dordrech, Hollandt: Kluwer.

Koedinger, K. R., Anderson, J. R., Hadley, W. H., & Mark, M. A. (1997). Intelligent tutoring goes to school in the big city. *International Journal of Artificial Intelligence in Education, 8*, 30-43.

Lagrange, J. -B. (1999). Complex calculators in the classroom: Theoretical and practical reflections on teaching pre-calculus. *International Journal of Computers for Mathematical Learning, 4*, 51-81.

Lagrange, J. -B. (2000/2001). Integration des instruments informatiques dans l'enseignement: Une approche par les techniques [Integration of computer instruments in instruction: A technique approach]. *Educational Studies in Mathematics, 43*, 1-30.

Lagrange, J. -B. (2005). Curriculum, classroom practices, and tool design in the learning of functions through technology-aided experimental approaches. *International Journal of Computers for Mathematical Learning, 10*, 143-189.

Lave, J., & Wenger, E. (1991). *Situated learning: Legitimate peripheral participation.* Cambridge, MA: Cambridge University Press.

Mathematical Association of America. (1923/1970). The reorganization of mathematics in secondary education. In J. K. Bidwell & R. G. Clason (Eds.), *Readings in the history of mathematics education.* Washington, DC: National Council of Teachers of Mathematics.

Matras, M. A. (1989). The effects of curricula on students' ability to analyze and solve problems in algebra. (Doctoral dissertation, University of Maryland College Park, 1988). *Dissertation Abstracts International, 49*(07), 1726.

Mayes, R. L. (1995). The application of a computer algebra system as a tool in college algebra. *School Science and Mathematics, 95*, 61-68.

Meira, L. (1998). Making sense of instructional devices: The emergence of transparency in mathematical activity. *Journal for Research in Mathematics Education, 29*, 121-143.

Nachmias, R., & Arcavi, A. (1990). A parallel representation of linear functions using a microcomputer-based environment. *Journal of Computers in Mathematics and Science Teaching, 9*(4), 79-88.

National Council of Teachers of Mathematics. (1989). *Curriculum and evaluation standards for school mathematics.* Reston, VA: Author.

Noble, T., & Nemirovsky, R. (1997). On mathematical visualization and the place where we live. *Educational Studies in Mathematics, 33*, 99-131.

Noss, R. (2001). For a learnable mathematics in the digital culture. *Educational Studies in Mathematics, 48*, 21-46.

Nunes-Harwitt, A. (2004/2005). Opportunities and limitations of computer algebra in education. *Journal of Educational Technology Systems, 33*, 157-163.

O'Callaghan, B. R. (1998). Computer-intensive algebra and students' conceptual knowledge of functions. *Journal for Research in Mathematics Education, 29*, 21-40.

Olsen, J. R. (1995). The effect of the use of number lines representations on student understanding of basic function concepts. Doctoral dissertation, University of Northern Colorado, 1994). *Dissertation Abstracts International-A, 55*(09), 2753.

Palmiter, J. (1991). Effects of computer algebra systems on concept and skill acquisition in calculus. *Journal for Research in Mathematics Education, 22*, 151-156.

Park, K. (1993). A comparative study of the traditional calculus course versus the Calculus & Mathematica course (Doctoral dissertation, University of Illinois at Urbana-Champaign, 1993). *Dissertation Abstracts International-A, 54*(01), 119.

Pascual-Leone, J. (1976). A view of cognition from a formalist's perspective. In K. F. Riegel & J. A. Meacham (Eds.), *The developing individual in a changing world: Vol. 1. Historical and cultural issues* (pp. 89-110). The Hague, The Netherlands: Mouton.

Pea, R. D. (1985). Beyond amplification: Using the computer to reorganize mental functioning. *Educational Psychologist, 20*, 167-182.

Pea, R. D. (1987). Cognitive technologies for mathematics education. In A. H. Schoenfeld (Ed.), *Cognitive science and mathematics education* (pp. 89-122). Hillsdale, NJ: Erlbaum.

Ritter, S., Haverty L., Koedinger, K. R., Hadley, W., & Corbett, A. T. (2008). Integrating intelligent software tutors with the mathematics classroom. In G. W. Blume & M. K. Heid (Eds.), *Research on technology and the teaching and learning of mathematics: Vol. 2. Cases and perspectives* (pp. 157-182). Charlotte, NC: Information Age.

Ruthven, K. (1990). The influence of graphic calculator use on translation from graphic to symbolic forms. *Educational Studies in Mathematics, 21*, 431-450.

Ruthven, K. (2002). Instrumenting mathematical activity: Reflections on key studies of the educational use of computer algebra systems. *International Journal of Computers for Mathematical Learning, 7*, 275-291.

Sandoval, W. A., Bell, P., Coleman, E., Enyedy, N., & Suthers, D. (2000, April). *Designing knowledge representations for epistemic practices in science learning*. Paper presented at the annual meeting of the American Educational Research Association, New Orleans, LA.

Schoenfeld, A. H., Smith, J. P., & Arcavi, A. (1993). Learning: The microgenetic analysis of one student's evolving understanding of a complex subject matter domain. In R. Glaser (Ed.), *Advances in instructional psychology* (Vol. 4, pp. 55-175). Hillsdale, NJ: Erlbaum.

School Mathematics Curriculum Improvement Study. (1972a). *Unified modern mathematics, Course 1, Part 2*. New York: Teachers College, Columbia University.

School Mathematics Curriculum Improvement Study. (1972b). *Unified modern mathematics, Course 5*. New York: Teachers College, Columbia University.

School Mathematics Study Group. (1960). *Elementary functions*. New Haven, CT: Yale University Press.

School Mathematics Study Group. (1961). *First course in algebra*. New Haven, CT: Yale University Press.

Schrock, C. S. (1989). Calculus and computing: An exploratory study to examine the effectiveness of using a computer algebra system to develop increased conceptual understanding in a first semester calculus course (Doctoral dissertation, Kansas State University, 1989). *Dissertation Abstracts International, 50*(07), 1926.

Schwartz, J. L., & Yerushalmy, M. (1995). On the need for a bridging language for mathematical modeling. *For the Learning of Mathematics, 15*(2), 29-35.

Schwarz, B., & Hershkowitz, R. (1999). Prototypes: Brakes or levers in learning the function concept? The role of computer tools. *Journal for Research in Mathematics Education, 30*, 362-389.

Schwarz, B., & Dreyfus, T. (1995). New actions upon old objects: A new ontological perspective on functions. *Educational Studies in Mathematics, 29,* 259-291.

Sfard, A. (1991). On the dual nature of mathematical conceptions: Reflections on processes and objects as different sides of the same coin. *Educational Studies in Mathematics, 22,* 1-36.

Sheets, C. (1993). Effects of computer learning and problem-solving tools on the development of secondary students' understanding of mathematical functions. (Doctoral dissertation, University of Maryland College Park, 1993). *Dissertation Abstracts International, 54*(05), 1714.

Shoaf-Grubbs, M. M. (1994). The effect of the graphing calculator on female students' spatial visualization skills and level-of-understanding in elementary graphing and algebra concepts. In E. Dubinsky, A. H. Schoenfeld, & J. Kaput (Eds.), *Research in collegiate mathematics education I, CBMS issues in mathematics education* (Vol. 4, pp. 169-194). Providence, RI: American Mathematical Society.

Simon, M. A., Tzur, R., Heinz, K., & Kinzel, M. (2004). Explicating a mechanism for conceptual learning: Elaborating the construct of reflective abstraction. *Journal for Research in Mathematics Education, 35,* 305-329.

Slavit, D. (1994, April). *The effect of graphing calculators on students' conceptions of function.* Paper presented at the annual meeting of the American Educational Research Association, New Orleans, LA.

Stroup, W. M. (2002). Understanding qualitative calculus: A structural synthesis of learning research. *International Journal of Computers for Mathematical Learning, 7,* 167-215.

Stylianou, D. A., Smith, B., & Kaput, J. J. (2005). Math in motion: Using CBRs to enact functions. *Journal of Computers in Mathematics and Science Teaching, 24,* 299-324.

Tall, D., Smith, D., & Piez, C. (2008). Technology and calculus. In M. K. Heid & G. W. Blume (Eds.), *Research on technology and the teaching and learning of mathematics: Syntheses, cases, and perspectives: Vol. 1. Research syntheses* (pp. 207-258). Charlotte, NC: Information Age.

Thomas, P. G., & Rickhuss, M. G. (1992). An experiment in the use of computer algebra in the classroom. *Education and Computing, 8,* 255-263.

Thompson, D. R., & Senk, S. L. (2001). The effects of curriculum on achievement in second year algebra: The example of the University of Chicago School Mathematics Project. *Journal for Research in Mathematics Education, 32,* 58-84.

Tinker, R. F., & Thornton, R. K. (1992). Constructing student knowledge in science, In E. Scanlon & T. O'Shea (Eds.), *New directions in educational technology* (pp. 153-170). Berlin, Germany: Springer-Verlag.

Trouche, L. (2004). Managing the complexity of human/machine interactions in computerized learning environments: Guiding students' command process through instrumental orchestrations. *International Journal of Computers for Mathematical Learning, 9,* 281-307.

Trouche, L. (2005a). An instrumental approach to mathematics learning in symbolic calculator environments. In D. Guin, K. Ruthven, & L. Trouche (Eds.), *The didactical challenge of symbolic calculators: Turning a computational device into a mathematical instrument* (pp. 137-162). New York: Springer.

Trouche, L. (2005b). Instrumental genesis, individual and social aspects. In D. Guin, K. Ruthven, & L. Trouche (Eds.), *The didactical challenge of symbolic calculators: Turning a computational device into a mathematical instrument* (pp. 197-230). New York: Springer.

Tynan, D., & Asp, G. (1998). Exploring the impact of CAS in early algebra. In C. Kanes, M. Goos, & E. Warren (Eds.), *Teaching mathematics in new times, Proceedings of the 21st annual conference of the Mathematics Education Research Group of Australasia* (Vol. 2, pp. 621-628). Brisbane, Australia: MERGA.

University of Chicago School Mathematics Project. (1990). *Algebra.* Glenview, IL: Scott, Foresman.

University of Chicago School Mathematics Project. (1992). *Functions, statistics, and trigonometry.* Glenview, IL: Scott, Foresman.

Verillon, P., & Rabardel, P. (1995). Cognition and artifacts: A contribution to the study of though[t] in relation to instrumented activity. *European Journal of Psychology in Education, 9,* 77-101.

Vlachos, P., & Kehagias, A. (2000). A computer algebra system and a new approach for teaching business calculus. *International Journal of Computer Algebra in Mathematics Education, 7,* 87-104.

Weigand, H. G., & Weller, H. (2001). Changes of working styles in a computer algebra environment—The case of functions. *International Journal of Computers for Mathematical Learning, 6,* 87-111.

Wertsch, J. V. (1998). *Mind as action.* Oxford: Oxford University Press.

Yerushalmy, M. (1991). Student perceptions of aspects of algebraic function using multiple representation software. *Journal of Computer Assisted Learning, 7*(1), 42-57.

Yerushalmy, M. (1997). Reaching the unreachable: Technology and the semantics of asymptotes. *International Journal of Computers for Mathematical Learning, 2,* 1-25.

Yerushalmy, M. (2000). Problem-solving strategies and mathematical resources: A longitudinal view on problem solving in a function based approach to algebra. *Educational Studies in Mathematics, 43,* 125-147.

Yerushalmy, M. (2004, July). *Does technology transform the content of algebra curricula? An analysis of critical transitions for learning and teaching.* Paper presented at the International Congress on Mathematical Education, Copenhagen, Denmark.

Yerushalmy, M., & Gilead, S. (1997). Solving equations in a technological environment. *Mathematics Teacher, 90,* 156-162.

Yerushalmy, M., & Schwartz, J. L. (1993). Seizing the opportunity to make algebra mathematically and pedagogically interesting. In T.A. Romberg, E. Fennema, & T. P. Carpenter (Eds.), *Integrating research on the graphical representation of functions* (pp. 41-68). Hillsdale, NJ: Erlbaum.

Zbiek, R. M. (1998). Prospective secondary school mathematics teachers' strategies for developing and validating functions as mathematical models in the presence of computing tools. *Journal for Research in Mathematics Education, 29,* 184-201.

CHAPTER 3

LEARNING AND TEACHING GEOMETRY WITH COMPUTERS IN THE ELEMENTARY AND MIDDLE SCHOOL

**Douglas H. Clements, Julie Sarama,
Nicola J. Yelland, and Brad Glass**

With their graphical as well as mathematical capabilities, computers seem well-poised to facilitate elementary and middle school students' learning of geometry and their development of spatial sense. Students can see and construct multiple examples of geometric objects, apply transformations to these objects, and connect various representations of geometric concepts while using computers. In this chapter, we review research addressing such technological potentialities for several categories of computer environments: turtle geometry, dynamical geometry software, computer manipulatives, and other software approaches, such as computer-assisted instruction and games. For each environment, we review research on learning and teaching specific geometric topics, including shape, measurement, and transformations. We considered all studies located through extensive computer and library searches. We address themes that cut across these categories and conclude with implications for instruction and

Research on Technology and the Teaching and Learning of Mathematics:
Vol. 1. Research Syntheses, pp. 109–154

curriculum development. We begin with a brief description of each of the environments.

COMPUTER ENVIRONMENTS

Historically, one of the first geometric computer environments available was turtle graphics, usually as a component of the Logo programming language. With Logo, students direct the movements of an on-screen turtle to draw geometric paths and shapes. For example, students could create a rectangle by entering the command "repeat 2 [fd 20 rt 90 fd 50 rt 90]," which means run the list of commands twice, starting with forward 20 steps, turn right 90°, and so forth. Certain turtle geometry environments (e.g., Clements & Meredith, 1994; Clements & Sarama, 1996) include enhanced capabilities, such as performing geometric motions and other transformations on shapes, such as slide 30 10 (which performs a slide, or translation, of a figure, increasing its x-coordinates by 30 and its y-coordinates by 10).

Dynamical geometry software (DGS) environments allow students to alter the original objects by moving components, such as vertices and edges, to different locations on the screen. As the original objects are modified, the results of all constructions and transformations applied to those objects are updated immediately on the screen. The students also can measure lengths, angles, and areas of objects on the screen and then can observe how the measures are affected as the object is altered dynamically. The Geometer's Sketchpad (Jackiw, 1991, 2002) and Cabri Geometry II (IMAG-CNRS Université Joseph Fourier, 1998) are two common examples of DGS environments.

Static construction environments, such as Geometric Supposer (Schwartz & Yerushalmy, 1986/2000), were available prior to the existence of DGS environments. These environments typically allow students to construct geometric objects on the computer, to apply common Euclidean constructions, and to make measurements based on the constructions. However, static environments do not allow students to manipulate directly the original objects and to observe immediately the effects of the manipulations. Instead, the environment can apply the students' previously recorded constructions to a similar object.

Similar to the DGS environments, another type of computer environment involves computer manipulatives and tools or procedures that act on and transform these manipulatives. For example, students might manipulate software versions of pattern blocks, acting on them with tools that might include geometric motions and dilations. Frequently, such computer manipulatives are developed for younger students, and attempt to closely mirror physical objects and actions.

Computer-assisted instruction (CAI) includes examples of software designed to assist individuals' learning of specific concepts via tutorial or drill-and-practice strategies. Another strategy for learning specific concepts is the computer game.

TURTLE GEOMETRY

The earliest and most extensively researched computer environment for learning geometry is turtle geometry, an approach to exploring geometry by directing a turtle, or on-screen pointer, via various versions of the Logo programming language or related programs. Given the constant state of change in the field of computers in education, one might question the perceived relevance of turtle graphics. There are at least three reasons that this research is significant. First, various versions of Logo are still being sold (and shareware versions downloaded) and used in classrooms; also, numerous alternate forms of turtle geometry exist (e.g., "Maps and Movement," Education Development Center, 1993). Second, students' work in Logo environments has much to teach us about learning in other similar, yet distinct, computer and non-computer environments that are not necessarily computational. Further, the research has implications for the development of theories about the learning and teaching of mathematics.

Why Turtle Geometry?

Action—physical and mental—is deemed important to the learning of geometry by most major theoretical perspectives. Piaget and Inhelder (1967) claimed that a child's representation of space is not a perceptual "reading off" of the child's spatial environment, but is the result of prior active manipulation of that environment.

Action is also important to both learning and teaching according to the theory of Pierre and Dina van Hiele. This theory posits that students progress through levels of thought in geometry (van Hiele, 1986). At Level 0, students do not reliably distinguish circles, triangles, and squares from nonexemplars of those classes and appear to be unable to form reliable mental images of these shapes (this level has been added to the original formulation and has received empirical support, see Clements, Swaminathan, Hannibal, & Sarama, 1999). Level 1 is the visual level, in which students can only recognize shapes as wholes and cannot form mental images of them. A given figure is a rectangle, for example, because "it looks like a door." At Level 2, the descriptive/analytic level, students recognize and characterize shapes by their properties. For instance, a student might think of a square as a figure that has four equal sides and four right angles. At Level 3, the abstract/relational level, students can form abstract definitions, distinguish between necessary and sufficient sets of conditions for a concept, and understand and sometimes even provide logical arguments in the geometric domain. They can classify figures hierarchically (by ordering their properties) and give informal arguments to justify their classifications (e.g., a square is identified as a rhombus because it can be thought of as a "rhombus with some extra properties"). At Level 4, students can establish theorems within an axiomatic system.

In this theory, progress is dependent upon instruction more than age. Teachers can "reduce" subject matter to a lower level, leading to rote memorization, but students cannot bypass levels and achieve understanding. The latter requires working through certain "phases" of instruction. The van Hiele theory also includes a model of teaching that progresses through five phases in moving students from one level of thinking to the next. In Phase 1, Information, the teacher places ideas at the student's disposal. In Phase 2, Guided Orientation, students are actively engaged in exploring objects (e.g., folding, measuring) so as to encounter the principal connections of the network of conceptual relations that is to be formed. In Phase 3, Explicitation, students are guided to become explicitly aware of their geometric conceptualizations, describe these conceptualizations in their own language, and learn traditional mathematical language. In Phase 4, Free Orientation, students solve problems whose solution requires the synthesis and utilization of those concepts and relations. In Phase 5, Integration, teachers encourage students to reflect on and consolidate their geometric knowledge, with an increased emphasis on the use of mathematical structures as a framework for consolidation and, eventually, place these consolidated ideas in the structural organization of formal mathematics. At the completion of Phase 5, a new level of thought is attained for the topic. Only in the Explicitation and Integration phases is the learner's intention sharply directed.

Instruction Phase 2 centers around students' manipulation of objects. Research indicates that computer environments, including most of the types discussed in this chapter, can facilitate that type of manipulation. As a Logo example, consider how turtle geometry activities might be used to encourage students to progress to Levels 2 (descriptive/analytic) and 3 (abstract/relational) in the van Hiele hierarchy. For instance, with the concept of rectangle, students initially are able only to identify visually presented examples, a Level 1 (visual)[1] activity. Using Logo, however, students can be asked to construct a sequence of commands (a procedure) to draw a rectangle (see the rectangle procedure at the upper right of Figure 3.1). This "allows, or obliges, the child to externalize intuitive expectations. When the intuition is translated into a program it becomes more obtrusive and more accessible to reflection" (Papert, 1980a, p. 145). That is, in constructing a rectangle procedure as part of instructional Phase 2, the students must analyze the visual aspects of the rectangle and reflect on how its component parts are put together, an activity that encourages Level 2 thinking. Furthermore, if asked during a Phase 4 activity to design a rectangle procedure that takes the length and width as inputs, students must write a type of definition for a rectangle, one that the computer understands. Students thus begin to build intuitive knowledge about the concept of defining a rectangle, knowledge that later can be synthesized in instructional Phase 5 and eventually integrated and formalized into an abstract definition—a Level 3 activity. Asking students whether a square or a parallelogram can be drawn by their rectangle procedure (if given the proper inputs) encourages students to think about the ways in which they begin to consider the structure and properties of the shape in coherent and logical ways, another Level 3 activity.

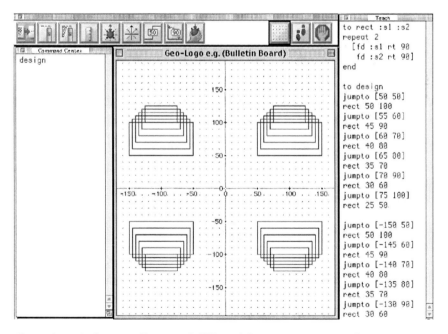

Figure 3.1.   Using coordinate and differential geometry commands to create a design of congruent rectangles in Geo-Logo.

Early empirical findings on Logo were ambiguous (Clements, 1985). Reviews concluded that there were conflicting results about the effects of Logo on overall mathematics achievement. Experiments by Logo's developers generated positive reports (Papert, Watt, diSessa, & Weir, 1979). In the United Kingdom, low-achieving 11-year-old boys with 2 years of directed Logo programming experience improved to perform at the same level as a control group on one general mathematics test but fell behind the control group on another test (Howe, O'Shea, & Plane, 1980). Other studies showed little positive effect on mathematics achievement (Akdag, 1985; Pea, 1983), although there were promising results for geometric concepts (Lehrer & Smith, 1986; Noss, 1987).

More recent reviews generally have been positive (Clements & Sarama, 1997; Yelland, 1995), as illustrated by the following quotation from McCoy (1996):

> Logo programming, particularly turtle graphics at the elementary level, is clearly an effective medium for providing mathematics experiences ... when students are able to experiment with mathematics in varied representations, active involvement becomes the basis for their understanding. This is particularly true in geometry. (p. 443)

The Logo Geometry project conducted a major evaluation of the Logo Geometry (LG) curriculum, including 1,624 kindergarten to Grade 7 U.S. students and their teachers (Clements, Battista, & Sarama, 2001). The curriculum is described in detail elsewhere (Battista & Clements, 1991; Clements et al., 2001) so only a brief summary is provided here.

The curriculum is divided into three strands: Paths, Shapes, and Motions. The concept of path is explicitly taught and used as an organizing idea for beginning geometric concepts. Students walk paths and discuss their movements, then construct similar paths in Logo. This includes lessons about grids and basic turtle geometry commands, Logo procedures, turn measure, and debugging. In the fifth and final lesson, students apply some of their previously learned skills in a problem-solving environment, and learn about the process of "undoing" (i.e., finding the inverse for) a sequence of actions. They are asked to write procedures that move the turtle from one point on a scene (depicted on the computer screen) to another (one of three restaurants) and then return the turtle to the starting point along the same path. The students must find a pattern for returning to the starting point (undoing the original commands) so that they can bring the turtle home even if the destination is off the screen (which requires replacing the last command with its inverse; e.g., LT 90 for RT 90).

Once students firmly grasp the concept of path, the curriculum asks them to think about special paths such as squares and triangles. The goal of this second strand of the curriculum is to have students view these shapes as paths and thus begin analyzing the shapes in terms of their constitutent components and properties. The sequence of lesson topics is squares, rectangles, equilateral triangles, regular polygons, classifying angles, interior angles of a polygon, parallel lines and parallelograms, and classification of quadrilaterals.

The goal of the third and final strand is for students to develop concepts in motion (transformational) geometry. Fundamental to this strand are the ideas that there are an infinite number of figures congruent to a given figure and that these figures may be related by a combination of geometric motions (i.e., isometries of the plane). Lesson topics include introduction to symmetry, mirror images and symmetric figures, introduction to geometric motions, planar motions with Logo tools, spatial visualization and prediction of the effects of these motions, congruence and motions, symmetry and motions, and motions as flips. Most teachers separated the strands by one or more months across a school year.

The evaluation included a wide assortment of research techniques: pre- and posttesting with paper and pencil, interviews, classroom observations, and case studies (Clements et al., 2001). Across grades K-6, LG students scored significantly higher than control students on a general geometry achievement test, making about double the gains of the control groups. These are especially significant because the assessment was a paper-and-pencil test that did not allow the experimental group access to the computer environments in which they had learned and because the curriculum is a relatively short intervention, lasting only 6 weeks.

Research across the various projects and studies has focused on the following concepts: plane figures, especially students' levels of geometric thinking about those figures; measurement; and motion geometry, congruence, and symmetry. We discuss each of these in turn.

Shape

Logo experience appears to encourage students to view and describe geometric objects in terms of the actions or procedures used to construct them (Clements & Battista, 1989; Clements et al., 2001). When asked to describe geometric shapes, students with Logo experience proffer not only more statements overall, but also more statements that explicitly mention components and geometric properties of shapes, an indication of Level 2 (descriptive/analytic) thinking (Assaf, 1986; Clements & Battista, 1989, 1990; Lehrer & Smith, 1986). Guided Logo experience appears to enhance significantly students' concepts of plane figures (Butler & Close, 1989; Clements, 1987). In one study, students with guided

Logo experience were able to apply their knowledge of geometry better than did a comparison group, but there was no difference between the groups in their knowledge of basic geometric facts. The researchers concluded that the use of Logo influenced the way in which students mentally represented their knowledge of geometric concepts (Lehrer, Randle, & Sancilio, 1989).

Results of the Logo Geometry project provide support for the hypothesis that LG is effective in developing schemes for basic geometric figures that improve performance on van Hiele-based assessments. A close analysis of specific responses showed that LG students developed rule-based, conceptual knowledge of shapes—for example, using verbally mediated properties and ideas, rather than only visual images, to classify shapes. Further, they performed substantially better than control students on hierarchical classification, and on a related competence of attributing statements of geometric properties, especially in the intermediate grades. Most students were just beginning to progress to Level 3 in the van Hiele hierarchy for the two-dimensional shapes that were assessed. Many students held multiple conceptions, some of which were evoked and applied only in certain situations. One episode the researchers analyzed illustrates the role turtle geometry played (Clements et al., 2001). Fifth-grader Jonathan had just successfully made and analyzed several rectangle procedures. He then used his "general" rectangle procedure in conjunction with a "turn" command to draw a tilted rectangle (labeled 4 in Figure 3.2), and is now attempting to make a nonrectangular parallelogram (labeled 7).

Teacher: Could you use different inputs, or is it just impossible?

Jonathan: Maybe, if you used different inputs. [Jonathan types in a new initial turn. He stares at the picture of the parallelogram on the activity sheet. He examines his Logo code for a while.] No, you can't. Because the lines are slanted, instead of a rectangle going like that. [He traces a rectangle over the parallelogram.]

Teacher: Yes, but this one's slanted [indicates the tilted rectangle, labeled 4, that Jonathan had successfully drawn with the Logo procedure].

Jonathan: Yeah, but the lines are slanted. This one's still in the size [shape] of a rectangle. This one [parallelogram]—the thing's slanted. This thing [rectangle] ain't slanted. It looks slanted, but if you put it back [shows a turn by gesturing, meaning to turn it so that the sides are vertical and horizontal] it wouldn't be slanted. Any way you move this [the parallelogram], it wouldn't be a rectangle. The lines are slanty to each other. So, there's no way.

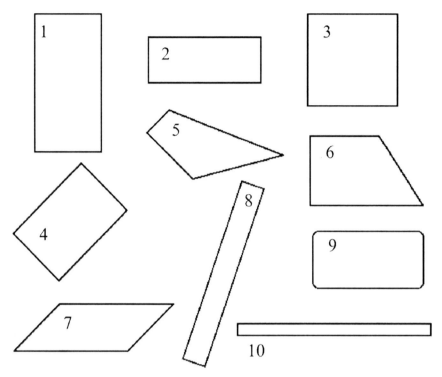

Figure 3.2.   Shapes that students are to attempt to reproduce with a "rectangle" procedure.

When Jonathan examined his code rather than rerunning it again, we believe he "ran through the procedure definition in his head," which contributed to his emerging sense of the properties of shapes and of his certainty that a given shape was not a member of the class of rectangles.

It has been noted that social and affective variables were important in distinguishing differences in performance that were gender based in Logo contexts (Hoyles & Sutherland, 1989; Yelland, 1994a, 1994b). Yet it is important to note that such studies did not qualitatively distinguish between the differences, but rather described the various ways in which boys and girls approached and deployed strategies in computer-based spatially oriented tasks. What is evident is that we need to be aware that such differences may exist and be sure that we value both approaches. At the current time it often seems as if traditional views concerning expertise with computers have elevated characteristics that are more compatible with masculine performance and interactions, and in doing so have often considered the performance of females as being deficient. There is now a range of empirical evidence to reveal that gender differences are artifacts of task and measures of performance (Ching, Kafai, & Marshall, 2002; Edwards, 1991; Yelland, 2002).

Thus, appropriate use of Logo can help elementary and middle school students to analyze these figures and how their components are put together. Logo environments and tasks provide students with opportunities to analyze and reflect on the properties of two-dimensional shapes, at least within the Logo setting. Also, the need to build Logo procedures allows students to develop understandable, implicit definitions of these shapes. These experiences facilitate a transition from Levels 0 and 1 (pre-recognition and visual) to Level 2 or 3 (descriptive/analytic or abstract/relational) of geometric thought, at least in the specific domains of two-dimensional shapes and geometric motions (Assaf, 1986; Clements & Battista, 1989; Clements, Sarama, & Battista, 1998; Hughes & Macleod, 1986; Kynigos, 1993; Lehrer & Smith, 1986). This is likely due to Logo's incorporation, implicitly, of the types of properties that will be developed by Level 1 thinkers explicitly, something that textbooks often fail to do (Battista & Clements, 1988a; Fuys, Geddes, & Tischler, 1988).

Measurement

Angles, Angle Measure, and Turns

Considering the critical role that turtle rotations play in forming geometric figures (e.g., Jonathan's formation of rectangle 4 in Figure 3.2), it might be expected that Logo experiences facilitate the development of the geometric concepts of angle and angle measure. Several research studies have reported that, while the Logo experience does not eliminate "errors," it appears to have a significant, positive effect on students' ideas about angle. For example, responses of control students in one study were more likely to reflect little knowledge of angle and to use common language such as "a corner" and "a line tilted." In contrast, the responses of the Logo students indicated more generalized and mathematically oriented conceptualizations,[2] such as "Two segments that come together at a point. It's sort of a place where two lines come together" (Clements & Battista, 1989, p. 456).

Several researchers have reported a positive effect of Logo on students' angle concepts (Browning, 1991; Clements & Battista, 1989; du Boulay, 1986; Frazier, 1987; Kieran, 1986a; Kieran & Hillel, 1990; Olive, Lankenau, & Scally, 1986). For example, students who worked with the LG curriculum did not identify angles from a set of figures better than control students did, but did significantly outperform control students in drawing an angle (Clements et al., 2001). Their angle concept appeared richer in that they were much more likely to draw nonprototypical examples of angles. LG students' descriptions of angles emphasized the concept of rotation, and, to a lesser extent, bending, more than did those of control students, and they were more able to draw "larger" angles. There was no difference between LG and control groups on angle measure estimation, but LG students substantially outperformed the control group on applying knowledge of angle measure in analytical and problem-solving situations.

One micro-genetic study confirmed that students transform physical and mental action into concepts of turn and angle (Clements & Burns, 2000). Students synthesized and integrated two schemes, "turn as body movement" and "turn as number," as originally identified in an earlier study (Clements, Battista, Sarama, & Swaminathan, 1996). They used a process of psychological curtailment in which students gradually replace full rotations of their bodies with smaller rotations of an arm, hand, or finger, and eventually internalized these actions as mental imagery in which, perhaps, an internalized, schematized, projection of a body part rotated.

Logo experiences may foster some misconceptions of angle measure, including considering the amount of rotation along the path (e.g., the exterior angle in a polygon) or the degree of rotation from the vertical (Clements & Battista, 1989). In addition, such experiences do not replace previous misconceptions of angle measure. For example, students' misconceptions about angle measure in computer environments and difficulties coordinating the relationships between the turtle's rotation and the constructed angle have persisted for years, especially if not properly guided by their teachers (Clements, 1987; Cope & Simmons, 1991; Hoyles & Sutherland, 1986; Kieran, 1986a; Kieran, Hillel, & Erlwanger, 1986). In general, however, Logo experience appears to facilitate understanding of angle measure. Logo students' conceptualizations of angle size are more likely to reflect mathematically correct, coherent, and abstract ideas (Clements & Battista, 1989; Findlayson, 1984; Kieran, 1986b; Noss, 1987) and show a progression from van Hiele Level 0 (prerecognition) to Level 2 (descriptive/analytic) in the span of the treatment (Clements & Battista, 1989). If Logo experiences emphasize the difference between the angle of rotation and the angle formed as the turtle traced a path, misconceptions regarding the measure of rotation and the measure of the angle may be avoided (Clements & Battista, 1989; Clements et al., 2001; Kieran, 1986b). For example, the implementation of LG effectively facilitated students' development of concepts of internal and external angles (Clements et al., 2001). Not all concepts are significantly affected; however, most experiences were of short duration. This is important, as benefits often do not emerge until more than a year of Logo experience (Kelly, Kelly, & Miller, 1986-87).

An important note is that tools based on research and fine-tuned through field testing can encourage students' mathematization. For example, Turtle Math (Clements & Meredith, 1994) was designed based on six general principles culled from the research, for instance, "encourage the growth of the abstract from the visual" (Clements & Sarama, 1995). However, the specific tools were changed to fit students' needs based on early pilot work. For example, we found that we needed turn tools that measured turns precisely and also simple tools that quickly and clearly illustrated the turtle's heading and gave general benchmarks (rays at 30-degree intervals). Finally, we needed commands (LTF for "left face," equivalent to lt 90) that avoided quantifying turns at all in the first group of lessons. This process resulted in a version of Logo more likely to support students' learning. In one study, Geo-Logo's (Geo-Logo is the same environment as Turtle Math, but with different activities) slow turns supported by the use of lines as representations of rays to emphasize the measure of the turn helped students build dynamic imagery for rotations (Sarama, 1995). The measurement and labeling tools encouraged them to eschew guessing, when they were required to use such mathematical processes as measurement and analysis. Unlike regular Logo, the graphics in the drawing window always precisely reflect the commands in the command center. In this way, the set of commands serve as a proleptic procedure, that is, its structure encouraged students to view and use it as a procedure before they formally defined it as such. This feature helped students encode contrasts between different commands.

Length

There is evidence that Logo experiences affect measurement competencies beyond the measure of rotation and angle, because Logo permits the student to manipulate units and to explore transformations of unit size and number of units without the distracting dexterity demands associated with measuring instruments and physical quantity. For example, young Logo students were more accurate than control students in measure tasks (Campbell, 1987). The control students were more likely to underestimate distances, particularly the longest distances, to have difficulty compensating for the halved unit size, and to underestimate the inverse relationship between unit size and unit numeracy. In a study of third-grade students, the Geo-Logo environment was critical in providing meaningful tasks that helped promote students' growth through three levels of strategies for solving length problems (Clements, Battista, Sarama, Swaminathan, & McMillen, 1997b; Sarama, 1995). Students' integration of number and geometry was especially potent and synergistic in the

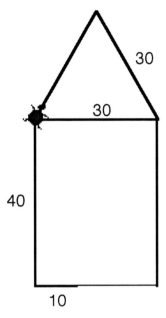

Figure 3.3.   A missing measures problem with directions, "Write a Logo procedure to draw this figure."

Logo environment. For example, students learned both geometric concepts and arithmetic in solving "missing measure" problems, such as that
pictured in Figure 3.3 (Clements & Meredith, 1994; Clements & Sarama,
1996).

Other studies (Yelland, 2002) have revealed that the Geo-Logo environment, when embedded in an investigative curriculum context, is a
powerful medium for learning in which students are able to experiment
actively with measures of length and angle in dynamic ways that were not
possible without the technology. In such contexts students developed
understandings about units of measurement that were built up over time
and that reflected an ability to recognize the need for consistency in units
of measurement as well as an ability to estimate and modify quantities of
measure to match varying situations. As an example, in one curriculum
unit there was the opportunity to compare the differences in measure of a
given distance with varying "step sizes." That is, two turtles had to move
the same distance, but one turtle's step size was a multiple of the other's.
Students could complete the activities without making the requisite connections between number and distance, but when scaffolded by the
teacher they were able to articulate sophisticated levels of reasoning about

the context that illustrated that they were cognizant of the relationship between unit size and measure. In the last in a series of four tasks, Jesse (aged 7 years) was able to predict the measure for a given distance on the basis of his previous experience in the environment. He was trying to determine the distance between two points by comparing steps that were three times bigger than those of his turtle, which had traversed the distance with 8 of its steps. His realization that the numbers could be connected by a factor of 3 was sudden and dramatic:

Jesse: Because see every step is 3 times bigger and it equals 3 ... so and ours is 3 of little ones, that's how, that's how I was working it out.
Teacher: So for every step ...
Jesse: 8 times 3
Teacher: So for every step, there's 3 little ones in it
Jesse: So I reckon it's 28
Teacher: So how could you do it on the calculator?
Jesse: 3 times 8
Teacher: Ok, do you want to try that Jesse?
Girl: 3 times 8 [pause] ... 24 ... he said 28!

The geometric setting provided both motivations and models for thinking about number and arithmetic operations. The motivations included game settings and the desire to create geometric forms. The models included length and rotation as settings for building a strong sense of both numbers and operations on numbers, with measuring and labeling tools supporting such construction. Conversely, the numerical aspects of the measures provided a context in which students had to attend to certain properties of geometric forms. The measures made such properties (e.g., opposite sides equal in length) more concrete and meaningful to the students. For example, students had to keep opposite lengths equal in certain missing length problems. They could use the length label tool to inspect each length. The dynamic links between the two domains of symbolic text and graphics structured in the Geo-Logo environment (e.g., a change in code automatically reflected in a corresponding change in the geometric figure) facilitated students' construction of connections between their own number and spatial schemes. Finally, Geo-Logo provided feedback that students used to reflect on their own thinking (Yelland, 2002).

For example, in a maze activity that built on previous experiences in a computer maze task with only right angle turns, one third-grade girl was able to use her experience to estimate that a turn was 120 degrees and further extended her intuitive thinking by then recognizing that an upcoming turn was approximately half of this size and therefore had to be 60 degrees. In a paper-and-pencil task the same girl had not successfully calculated half of 120 in a pretest context. Students also created contexts in which they used mathematical ideas and concepts that they would not have encountered in the traditional mathematics curriculum for their level. For example, in one task they were required to create a robot with component parts of a given perimeter (e.g., eyes of 100 steps). Making a square was relatively easy, because 100 divided by 4 yielded 25 steps for a side. However, one pair wanted their eyes to be equilateral triangles and thus used a calculator to divide 100 by 3 and the resultant number of 33.33 (reoccurring) caused great excitement for them as it was not only a whole line of threes but it had a "dot" which they had not encountered prior to this time. These third-grade students would not normally encounter decimals until year 5 of the mathematics curriculum, but were so fascinated by the dot that they wished to use it for all the parts of their robot and sought to use decimal numbers in each case.

Students exploring geometric concepts in Logo environments are also able to learn more sophisticated ideas about measurement, as well as about directions and coordinates. For example, one microworld allowed the turtle to measure distances and turns relative to previously con-structed points on the plane, thus emphasizing non-intrinsic geometry as well as the turtle's intrinsic geometry (Kynigos, 1992). The turtle facili-tated learning this set of ideas as well. For example, students adopted and used the notion of the turtle "putting its nose to look" at some direction rather than "turning this much" (Kynigos, 1992, p. 106). Several studies, then, indicate that enriching the primitives and tools available to students can facilitate their construction of geometric notions and can increase analytical, rather than (only)[3] visual, approaches (Clements & Battista, 1992a; Kynigos, 1992).

Measurement, Arithmetic, and Problem Solving

Work with LG significantly improved primary grade students' recogni-tion of the relevance of arithmetic processes in the solution of geometric measurement problems, and it improved their ability to apply these pro-cesses accurately (Clements et al., 2001). This has been confirmed in sev-eral additional studies with the Geo-Logo environment (Clements et al., 1996; Clements et al., 1997b; Masters, 1997; Yelland, Clements, Masters, & Sarama, 1996; Yelland & Masters, 1997).

Students sometimes use the support of the meaningful tasks and com-puter environment to "extend their reach" intellectually. One third-grade girl, for example, could predict accurately that the "turn will be 60°

because it was half of that last one" (120°) even though she could not calculate half of 120 on an interview or on a test (Masters, 1997). Students in
the Masters study also invented new concepts for themselves that were not
part of the curriculum, such as decimal numbers.

Geometric Motions, Symmetry, and Congruence

Research indicates that Logo experiences can also aid the learning of
motion geometry and related ideas such as congruence and symmetry. In
one study, students working with a Logo unit on motion geometry made
only slow progress beyond van Hiele Level 0 (prerecognition) (A. T.
Olson, Kieren, & Ludwig, 1987). There was, however, definite evidence of
a beginning awareness of the properties of transformations. In another
study, middle school students achieved a working understanding of transformations and used visual feedback to correct overgeneralizations when
working in a Logo microworld, with some evidence that this was superior
to students' learning without the use of Logo (Edwards, 1991).

Another study specifically investigated the effects of computer and non-
computer environments on learning of geometric motions (Johnson-Gentile, Clements, & Battista, 1994). Two treatment groups of fifth-grade students, one of which used specially designed Logo computer environments
and one of which used manipulatives and paper and pencil, received eight
lessons on geometric motions, identical except for the Logo/non-Logo
aspects. Both treatment groups, especially the Logo group, performed at a
higher level of geometric thinking than did a non-treatment control
group. The Logo group outperformed the non-Logo group on the delayed
posttest—the same assessment administered a month after the posttest.
Therefore, there was support for the effectiveness of the use of a Logo-
based curriculum and for the notion that the Logo-based version
enhanced the construction of higher-level conceptualizations of motion
geometry. This conclusion was based on examination of the differences
between the groups on specific items. The greatest differences were on
those items that required students to resist applying intuitive visual thinking and apply analytical thinking in a comprehensive manner.

The need in Logo environments for more complete, precise, and
abstract explication may account for students' creation of conceptually
richer concepts for motions. That is, in Logo, students have to specify
steps to a non-interpretive agent, with thorough specification and detail.
The results of these commands can be observed, reflected on, and corrected; the computer serves as an explicative agent. In non-computer
manipulative environments, one can make intuitive movements and cor-
rections without explicit awareness of geometric motions. For example,

even young students can move puzzle pieces into place without conscious awareness of the geometric motions that can describe these physical movements. In contrast, with Logo, the use of a computer language makes the motions "more obtrusive and more accessible to reflection," in Papert's words, previously quoted.

Perhaps for similar reasons, Logo can aid students' development of symmetry concepts. Students as young as first grade have been observed using such mathematical notions as symmetry in their Logo work (Kull, 1986). In addition, students through middle school who are involved in Logo (Edwards, 1991; Gallou-Dumiel, 1989; J. K. Olson, 1985) learn symmetry concepts. One student used a specially-designed Logo symmetry microworld to learn such concepts and effectively transferred her mathematical understandings to a paper-and-pencil problem (Hoyles & Healy, 1997). Similarly, LG microworlds helped students score significantly higher than control students on posttest measures of symmetry, both on tasks asking them to draw all the symmetry lines for given figures and those that asked them to draw the "other half" of a figure to create a symmetric figure. For the latter, there was a tendency for these effects to be particularly strong for young (kindergarten) LG students (Clements et al., 2001). Compared to students using paper and pencil, students using Logo work with more precision and exactness (Gallou-Dumiel, 1989; Johnson-Gentile et al., 1994). For example, writing LG commands for the creation of symmetric figures, testing symmetry by flipping figures via LG commands, and discussing these actions apparently encouraged students to build richer and more general images of symmetric relations and to reflect on the construction of symmetric figures and abstract the properties of symmetry. Students had to abstract and externally represent their actions in a more explicit and precise fashion for the LG activities than they did in other activities such as free-hand drawing of symmetric figures. This is supported by findings that differences between Logo and manipulatives groups existed on those items that required students to resist applying intuitive visual (only) thinking and to apply analytical thinking in a comprehensive manner (Johnson-Gentile et al., 1994). LG students also performed better than control students on congruence items, not so much by identifying whether pairs of figures were congruent as by justifying their answers (Clements et al., 2001). This suggests a movement away from van Hiele Level 1 (visual) thinking toward Level 2 (descriptive/analytic) thinking. Interestingly, the largest difference was for those questions with congruent pairs of figures. This difference suggests that LG helped students more on questions in which describing a difference (e.g., "this one is bigger") could not be used as a springboard to justification, as describing congruency forced students to focus on precise similarities or processes used to establish them. In summary, there is evidence in support of the hypothesis that Logo experiences can help elementary to middle school students become cognizant of their mathematical intuitions and facilitate growth from (only) visual thinking to descriptive/ analytic geometric thinking in the domains of shapes, symmetry, congruence, and motions (Clements & Battista, 1989, 1990, 1992b; Edwards, 1991; Gallou-Dumiel, 1989; Lehrer & Smith, 1986; Olive et al., 1986; A. T. Olson et al., 1987).

Summary and Conclusions

Exploring and programming in Logo environments can help students construct elaborate knowledge networks (rather than mechanical chains of rules and terms) for geometric topics. Empirical research identifies several unique characteristics of Logo that can facilitate students' learning (the following list is taken from Clements et al., 2001).

- The commands and structure of the Logo language can be consistent with geometric symbols and structures in ways that are pedagogically useful. For example, turtle geometry commands such as FD and RT focus students' attention on critical aspects of figures.
- Drawing with Logo's turtle graphics and creating run-able code are meaningful and interesting settings for students; these settings then motivate the use and learning of geometric and other mathematical ideas (Ainley, 1997).
- The turtle world involves measures that are visible, quantifiable, and formalizable, helping to connect spatial and numeric thinking (Clements et al., 2001; Clements et al., 1996; Clements et al., 1997b; Noss & Hoyles, 1992a).
- Logo can encourage the manipulation of screen objects in ways that facilitate students' thinking of them as mathematical objects and thus as representatives of a class. In this way, Logo can evoke more abstract geometric thinking (Clements et al., 2001).
- Logo can provide scaffolding for mathematical analysis; that is, a symbolic representation on the computer can allow the student to erect scaffolding around the solution of a problem, and subsequently attend to only those elements of the solution for which details need to be filled in (Noss & Hoyles, 1992a).
- Logo can help structure students' play to encourage symbolic and mathematical characteristics of exploratory mathematical activity (Hoyles, 1993). Or, as Papert (1993) states, "The computer simply, but very significantly, enlarges the range of opportunities to engage as a *bricoleur* or *bricoleuse* in activities with scientific and mathematical content" (p. 145).

DYNAMICAL GEOMETRY SOFTWARE ENVIRONMENTS

Why Dynamical Geometry Software (DGS)?

Research results suggest that elementary and middle school students can improve their understandings of geometry concepts while using DGS such as Cabri Geometry (IMAG-CNRS Universite Joseph Fourier, 1998) and The Geometer's Sketchpad (Jackiw, 1991, 2002). The use of dynamic environments also may help students improve their visualization skills (Dixon, 1997) and their ability to focus on interrelationships of the parts of a geometric shape (Battista & Borrow, 1997). However, it appears that students benefit most from using the environments when they interact with figures that are constructed to retain certain properties. The figures might be developed by students themselves or could be contained in pre-pared files that are available to students.

Initially, students tend to use the programs as basic drawing packages (Foletta, 1995; Pratt & Ainley, 1997; Vincent, 1998; Vincent & McCrae, 1999). In this case, assembling components, such as points, segments, lines, and circles, produces figures that look like the desired outcome, but the figures usually do not retain the desired characteristics when the components are "dragged" on the screen. Figure 3.4 illustrates the effects of dragging a vertex of a right triangle that was produced using The Geometer's Sketchpad as a drawing program. In addition to drawing, dynamic environments can be used to construct figures that will retain certain properties when various components are dragged on the screen. Figure 3.5 illustrates an example of dragging a vertex of a right triangle that was constructed to remain a right triangle.

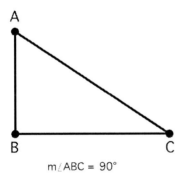

m∠ABC = 90°

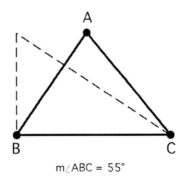

m∠ABC = 55°

Figure 3.4.   A right triangle that was drawn. The right side of the figure shows the result when point A is dragged to the right.

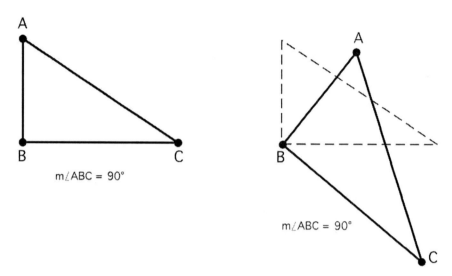

Figure 3.5.   A right triangle that was constructed. The right side of the figure shows the result when point A is dragged to the right (and somewhat downward).

Shape

Vincent and McCrae (1999) relate the process of drawing, rather than constructing, to van Hiele Level 1 because students at that level are focusing mainly on the visual appearance of shapes. One technique that helps some students move away from drawing and towards constructing in dynamic environments is asking them to produce figures that could not be "messed up" by dragging (Vincent & McCrae, 1999). For example, students could be asked to produce a rectangle that always would be a rectangle regardless of how its components were dragged. While working on these types of tasks, students began to focus on geometric properties of the figures and on relationships between properties of the figures and then used the capabilities of the programs to construct figures so that the properties and relationships would always hold. When working on the rectangle example, students focused on the necessity of having right angles and on having two pairs of opposite sides of equal lengths. Their focus on the necessity of right angles is similar to Jonathan's focus on the angles of a rectangle while working within the Logo Geometry curriculum (see the excerpt with dialogue between Jonathan and the teacher that was presented earlier in this chapter). Vincent and McCrae (1999) associate focusing on properties of the figures with the second van Hiele level (descriptive/analytic) and focusing on relationships within the figures with the third van Hiele level (abstract/relational).

Having students develop conjectures about geometric figures they have drawn is another possible approach to engaging students in thinking at the abstract/relational van Hiele level within a dynamic geometry environment (Hoyles, 2001; Hoyles & Healy, 1999). For example, Hoyles and Healy asked middle-school-aged students "to construct with Cabri [Geometry I] a quadrilateral in which the angle bisectors of two adjacent angles cross at right angles" (p. 107) and to identify and prove properties of the quadrilateral. The students made measurements within Cabri and looked for measurements that remained constant while dragging components of the quadrilateral. From these observations, some of the students deduced properties of the shape and focused on relationships among parts of the shape, similar to the students in the Vincent and McCrae (1999) study. However, the students did have difficulties developing proofs for their conjectures about the properties and relationships.

There also is evidence that students can progress through the van Hiele levels by focusing on the parts of shapes and on relationships among the parts while using *prepared figures* within a DGS program. Battista and Borrow (1997) noted that fifth-grade students viewed researcher-constructed geometric shapes (referred to as "shape makers"[4]) as representations of classes of shapes, such as squares, rectangles, parallelograms, and trapezoids. Manipulating the shape makers in the dynamic environment and then reflecting on their manipulations helped the students to move from thinking about the shapes holistically (indicative of the visual level) to focusing on the relationships among parts of the shapes, including class hierarchies (indicative of descriptive/analytic and abstract/relational levels). In a sense, their manipulations of the shape makers were "physical" actions within a computer environment, as described previously in this chapter. Students also have improved their understanding of properties of shapes and relationships among parts of shapes while using geometry environments such as the Geometric Supposer (Schwartz & Yerushalmy, 1986/2000). For example, eighth-grade students enrolled in a course that integrated the use of Geometric Supposer were less apt to have the common misconception that a triangle's altitude is always a segment in the interior of the triangle (Yerushalmy, 1991). The students enrolled in the course also developed the ability to use and check many examples while exploring patterns and to form accurate definitions for various geometry concepts.

Geometric Transformations

Students also have been able to develop and deepen their understandings about transformation geometry concepts in the presence of DGS environments. Dixon (1997) used The Geometer's Sketchpad in teaching four classes of eighth-grade students for approximately 3 weeks. The students used the dynamic environment's capabilities to apply reflections and rotations to points of the plane and then conjectured about the properties of those types of transformations. Five classes of eighth-grade students formed the control group. They studied reflections and rotations using manipulatives rather than the computer. Students who had access to the dynamic environment outperformed students in the control group on measures involving concepts of reflection and rotation. This suggests that the use of DGS is helpful in improving middle school students' understandings of reflection and rotation.

A study by Glass (2001) provides additional insights into middle school students' conceptualizations of translations, reflections, rotations, and compositions of same-type transformations. Each of the eighth-grade students in the study spent approximately five hours working through a series of tasks in an individual interview setting. In contrast to using the software's menu options, as in Dixon (1997), the students interacted with pre-constructed dynamic representations of the three transformation types in The Geometer's Sketchpad. For example, the specific translation being represented was determined by the direction and magnitude of a vector on the screen. The students could change the specific translation by changing the direction and/or magnitude of the vector via dragging. Similarly, the students could interact with the reflection representation by dragging the visible line of reflection to change its location in the plane or its inclination. Similarly, they changed the specific rotation being represented by moving the center of rotation or by altering a dial-like controller that determined the angle of rotation. The most common strategy students used was centered on the perceived movement from the location of the pre-image to the location of the image. For example, students identified examples of reflections based on their perception of the image beginning on top of the pre-image and then flipping to its displayed location. The focus on a movement of the pre-image suggests that the student may be utilizing a visual level of understanding of transformation.

One concern about the use of dynamic environments in studying transformation geometry concepts is that students will focus on the dynamic movement rather than on the resulting relationships between pre-image and image pairs. However, middle school students also can focus on end results of a motion, rather than on the motion, in identifying transformation types (Glass, 2001). For example, they focused on the direction the image faced in relation to the pre-image. If the image faced the opposite direction as the pre-image, then the students tentatively identified the represented transformation as a reflection rather than a translation. Further, a few students utilized properties of transformations in their discussion, for example, observing that corresponding vertices of the pre-image and image were equidistant from the apparent line of reflection. Glass (2001) suggested that students who consistently provided reasons from the motion-based category had conceptualized transformations as processes and may not have had an object view of transformation. In comparison, students who utilized reasons from the end-result and property-based categories were able to think of transformations as objects, as well as processes. It appears that the capability to dynamically link alternative representations of the same transformation type provides an environment in which students may begin to develop an object understanding of transformation.

Summary and Conclusions

Similar to the case with Logo-based environments, research results suggest the use of DGS can be beneficial to students in their development of understandings of geometric shapes and figures. In some situations, middle school students can progress from the first van Hiele level (visual) to the second and third van Hiele levels (descriptive/analytic and abstract/relational) while using the environments to construct figures that retain certain properties (Pratt & Ainley, 1997; Vincent, 1998; Vincent & McCrae, 1999). Students also can deepen their understandings of geometric shapes and figures while working with preconstructed figures (Battista & Borrow, 1997; Olive, 1991).

DGS environments also appear to facilitate middle school students' learning of transformation geometry concepts (Dixon, 1997). Whether the students are taught how to use the environment's built-in transformation commands or are provided with preconstructed representations of transformations, students can deepen their understandings of translations, reflections, and rotations (Dixon, 1997; Glass, 2001). Further, there is some evidence (Glass, 2001) that the dynamic nature of the environment can influence the development of the students' understandings.

COMPUTER MANIPULATIVES

Computer manipulatives, similar to DGS environments, provide geometric objects and tools that can be used to act on those objects. The objects are usually geometric regions that correspond to physical shape manipulatives, such as tangram pieces. Research indicates that the use of physical manipulatives facilitates the learning of sound representations of geometric concepts (Clements & Battista, 1992b). Use of manipulatives seemed to allow students to try out their ideas, examine and reflect on them, and modify them. This approach seemed to maintain student interest, assist students in creating definitions and new conjectures, and facilitate students' insight into new relationships. Unfortunately, in the past, nearly half of the teachers reported that their students used manipulatives less than once a week, or not at all (Driscoll, 1983). There are signs that in kindergarten classrooms use of manipulatives has been higher in recent years (Hausken & Rathbun, 2004); however, the early percentages may not have changed for higher grades over the years, with only 54% and 40% of fifth- and eighth-grade teachers reporting weekly use of manipulatives (Stecher, Barron, Kaganoff, & Goodwin, 1998). Surveys substantiate that use of manipulatives remains low in traditional classrooms (Ross, McDougall, Hogaboam-Gray, & LeSage, 2003). This may be important, because manipulative use for a school year or longer results in significant positive effects, but use of shorter duration often does not (Sowell, 1989). Further, even though most teachers claim they are using reform-oriented methods when they use manipulatives, teachers with a more didactic, compared to cognitive, orientation to teaching taught their students to use the manipulates to represent standard algorithms (Niederhauser & Stoddart, 2001).

Why Computer Manipulatives?

Most practitioners and researchers argue that manipulatives are effective because they are "concrete." By "concrete," they probably mean objects that students can grasp with their hands—what we called physical manipulatives. This sensory nature ostensibly makes manipulatives "real," connected with one's intuitively meaningful personal self. However, we cannot assume that concepts can be "read off" manipulatives because objects may be manipulated meaningfully without the concepts being illuminated (Clements, 1999). A manipulative's physicality does not carry the meaning of the mathematical idea. Further, when we speak of concrete understanding, we are not always referring to physical objects. Teachers of later grades expect students to have a concrete understanding that goes beyond manipulatives: Shapes (or other geometric objects) should be "concrete" objects that middle-grade students can manipulate mentally. There are different ways, then, to think about "concrete." Students have *Sensory-Concrete* (Clements, 1999) knowledge when they need to use physical material to make sense of an idea. For example, very young students do best with physical cutouts of shapes. *Integrated-Concrete* knowledge is knowledge that is connected in special ways. Memories of physical experiences, mental images, and ideas are concrete. The root of the word concrete means "to grow together." Sidewalk concrete is strong due to the combination of separate particles in an interconnected mass. Integrated-Concrete thinking is strong due to the combination of many separate ideas in an interconnected structure of knowledge (Clements, 1999).

If Integrated-Concrete knowledge is our goal, computers might provide useful representations. They may be just as personally meaningful, and even more manageable, flexible, and extensible than their physical counterparts. For example, one group of young students learned number concepts with a computer felt board environment. They constructed "bean-stick pictures" by selecting and arranging beans, sticks, and number symbols. Compared to a physical bean-stick environment, this computer environment offered equal, and sometimes greater control and flexibility (Char, 1989). In a similar vein, students who used physical and software manipulatives demonstrated a much greater sophistication in classification and logical thinking than did a control group that used physical manipulatives only (J. K. Olson, 1988).

Advantages of Computer Manipulatives for Learning and Teaching Geometry

Sarama and Clements identified two categories of advantages: (a) practical and pedagogical benefits and (b) mathematical and psychological benefits. Illustrations of each follow, taken from the participant observation research with kindergarten-age students (Sarama, Clements, & Vukelic, 1996) using Shapes, a software version of pattern blocks, that extends what students can do with these shapes (see Figure 3.6).

Practical /Pedagogical Benefits

This first group includes advantages that help students in a practical manner or provide pedagogical opportunities for the teacher.

1. *Providing another medium, one that can store and retrieve configurations.* Computers can provide another medium for building, one in which progressive development can take place day after day (i.e., physical blocks have to be put away most of the time—on the computer, they can be saved and worked on again and again, and there is an infinite supply for all students). This was observed when a group of students were working on a pattern with physical manipulatives (Sarama et al., 1996). They wanted to move it slightly on the rug. Two girls (four hands) tried to keep the design together, but they were unsuccessful. Marisssa told Leah to fix the design. Leah

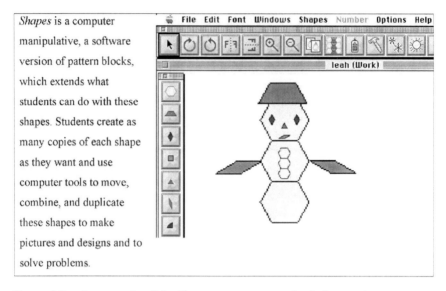

Shapes is a computer manipulative, a software version of pattern blocks, which extends what students can do with these shapes. Students create as many copies of each shape as they want and use computer tools to move, combine, and duplicate these shapes to make pictures and designs and to solve problems.

Figure 3.6.   An example of the Shapes computer manipulatives environment.

tried, but in re-creating the design, she inserted two extra shapes and the pattern was no longer the same. The girls experienced considerable frustration at their inability to get their "old" design back. Had the students been able to save their design, or had they been able to move their design and keep the pieces together, their group project would have continued.

2. *Providing a manageable, flexible manipulative.* Computer manipulatives can be more manageable for students than their physical counterparts. For example, computer-generated shapes may be designed to snap into position on command, connecting accurately with other shapes or other objects, such as a puzzle. Unlike physical manipulatives, computer manipulatives stay where they are put. While working on the *Shapes* software, students quickly learned to glue the shapes together and move them as a group when they needed more space to continue their designs.

3. *Providing an extensible manipulative.* Certain constructions are easier to make with the software than with physical manipulatives. Students were observed making non-equilateral triangles in such an environment by partially occluding shapes with other shapes. For example, they created a 30°-60°-90° triangle by occluding half of an equilateral triangle.

Mathematical/Psychological Benefits

Perhaps the most powerful advantages are that the actions possible with software can embody the processes educators want students to develop and internalize as mental processes. As previously noted, this is not a simple process. It is the student's actions, in interaction with the software and other people that are eventually internalized.

1. *Bringing mathematical ideas and processes to conscious awareness*. A software program's turn and flip tools can help students explicate these motions. For example, when kindergartner Mitchell (Sarama et al., 1996) worked off-computer, he quickly manipulated the pattern block pieces, resisting answering any questions that were asked as to his intent or his reasons. When working on-computer, he was aware of his actions, in that when asked how many times he turned a particular piece, he said, "Three," without hesitation. Thus, he was becoming explicitly aware of the motions and beginning to quantify them.

2. *Changing the very nature of the manipulative*. Software's flexibility allows students to explore geometric figures in ways not available with physical shape sets. For example, students can change the size of the computer shapes, altering all shapes or only some.

3. *Allowing composition and decomposition processes*. Use of software can encourage composition and decomposition of shapes. For example, students can readily "glue" shapes together to make composite units.

Summary

Definitions of what constitutes a "manipulative" may need to be expanded to include computer manipulatives, which, at certain phases of learning, may be more efficacious than their physical counterparts. With both physical and computer manipulatives, educators need to provide meaningful representations in which the objects and actions available to students parallel the mathematical objects (ideas) and actions (processes or algorithms) we wish the students to learn. We then need to guide students to make connections among these representations (Lesh, 1990). We do not yet know what modes of presentation are crucial and what sequence of representations we should use before symbols are introduced (Baroody, 1989; Clements, 1989; Metz, 1995). We should be careful about adhering to the concrete → pictorial → abstract sequence, especially when there is more than one way of thinking about "concrete" (Parmar &

Cawley, 1997). However, we need additional research to show what portion and what sequences of experiences with various media are optimal.
Few studies address such issues. Our goal should be to have students connect manipulative models to their intuitive, informal understanding of
concepts and to abstract symbols, learn to translate between representations, and reflect on the constraints of the manipulatives that embody the
principles of a mathematical system (Thompson & Thompson, 1990). We
need more research on the use of only computer manipulatives.

OTHER SOFTWARE APPROACHES

Computer-Assisted Instruction (CAI)

Although there would seem to be a large array of CAI titles on the mar-
ket there are relatively few that pertain to developing geometric concepts
in the elementary school. In a similar way there have been relatively few
research findings, especially in the recent past, which sought to elucidate
the nature and extent of learning geometric concepts in CAI contexts.
Most of the studies have always considered the virtues of CAI versus traditional teaching methods in treatment studies.

Students instructed in geometry with CAI often score significantly
higher than those having just classroom instruction, from the elementary
years (Austin, 1984; Morris, 1983) to high school (Hannafin & Sullivan,
1996). Consistent with other research, learners may not accurately gauge
the amount of instruction that is optimal for them; researchers recommend using a full computer-assisted instruction program rather than letting students choose how much time to spend working with the program
(Hannafin & Sullivan, 1996).

Early research included the Stanford Drill and Practice Program and
Project Solo based at the University of Pittsburgh (Knight-Burns & Bozeman, 1981). Although each project reported significant gains in mathematics test scores in general, there seemed to be conflicting, and even
confusing claims regarding the relative merits of CAI versus traditional
forms of instruction in mathematics. Research in the area of CAI effectiveness broadly concerns its effectiveness with respect to five variables: (a)
student achievement, (b) student attitude to CAI and subject matter, (c)
time savings relative to unit completions/ mastery learning, (d) learning
retention, and (e) cost factors. However, it was difficult to attribute success
or lack thereof to one specific variable. It also became evident that variables interacted in different ways, sometimes creating effective outcomes.
What became apparent was that the use of CAI in teaching contexts supported by an effective teacher who accommodated the technology into

existing teaching practices was the most effective for student learning (Knight-Burns & Bozeman, 1981). This implication is consistent across all of the types of software reviewed here.

McClurg (1992) investigated the spatial skills of students in Years 3 and 4 (9 and 10 years of age). Specifically she was interested in elucidating whether CAI software could influence understandings and performance in tests of spatial ability. She found a significant treatment effect in favor of students using the CAI software involving the rotation of objects and that this effect was evident irrespective of the gender of the student. The results of the study suggested that the rotation element of problem-solving software might have been the primary influence on the observed gains on Figural Classification tasks. McClurg identified three factors that she claimed positively influenced problem solving: visual perception and discrimination, differentiation of opposite oblique segments, and recognition of reflected images in a context characterized by opportunities for experimentation, discussion, and repetition in the CAI contexts.

Lowrie (1998) considered the relationship between two-dimensional and three-dimensional representations in CAI contexts. He investigated the ways in which two students (7 and 8 years of age) engaged in a computer-based problem-solving activity that required a degree of visual spatial reasoning. Lowrie noted that the CAI activity that required the students to build a room onscreen helped the students to construct spatial understandings associated with perspective and representations, but only when the teacher provided scaffolding to the students. Lowrie argued that students could complete computer-based problems that appeared to focus on visual and spatial understandings without their being able to engage in effective mathematical thinking unless a teacher who could foster the mathematical understandings necessary to complete the tasks provided scaffolding.

Other studies have examined the ways in which problem-solving CAI influenced performance as demonstrated in Basic Skills tests which included geometric or spatial understandings (e.g., The Canadian Test of Basic Skills). For example, one study (reported in Fletcher, Hawley, & Piele, 1990) found that a CAI group performed significantly better on a standard test of mathematics achievement than control groups. In another study, when the use of CAI was supplemented with traditional mathematical instruction, gains were significantly higher (Fletcher et al., 1990).

Games

Computer games have been found to be marginally effective at promoting learning of angle estimation skills (Bright, 1985) and effective in facilitating achievement in coordinate geometry (Morris, 1983). Game design can significantly increase the effectiveness of a program. More effective than manipulating geometric objects is manipulating screen representations of the specific concepts students are to learn (Sedighian & Sedighian, 1996). For example, rather than dragging a shape to turn it, a "direct concept manipulation" interface might have students manipulate a tool for turns, including turn center and amount of rotation. That is, given that the goal is to learn the concept of motion, the direct concept manipulation interface includes tools for the motions themselves. Students manipulate these tools rather than performing the motions directly on the shapes. The dynamic tools used by Glass (2001), which were described in the dynamic geometry section of this chapter, are other examples of direct concept manipulations for translation, reflection, and rotation. Manipulating an on-screen mathematical representation of the transformation being applied to the shape in this way leads to higher achievement than manipulating the shape directly, especially when paired with appropriate use of scaffolding, such as gradually removing visual feedback aids and requiring the use of specific transformations to achieve some configurations (Sedighian & Sedighian, 1996). Thus, the effectiveness of computer games depends on software design such as interface styles and scaffolding, as well as on teacher and student expectations, on the level of integration with other learning activities, and on the pattern of use.

Several studies have investigated the effects of computer games on students' spatial thinking. Video games may have a positive effect on spatial abilities, although short-term experiences may not yield results (Pepin & Dorval, 1986). In a study of fifth-grade students, spatial performance was significantly better in boys than in girls during pretest assessment (Subrahmanyam & Greenfield, 1994). Video game practice significantly improved spatial performance on the posttest assessment for both genders; there was no significant interaction of gender with experimental treatment. However, video game practice was more effective for students who started out with relatively poor spatial skills. This suggests that video games may be useful in equalizing individual differences in spatial skill performance, including those associated with gender. In another study, students already relatively skilled in spatial visualization tended to benefit more from the low active control (passively watching) than the high active control condition. Students who were less skilled benefited from the high active control condition; they apparently learned the strategy of holistic mental rotation, in which an entire object is visualized as turning (Smith, 1993).

Other studies have investigated the effects of Tetris or similar games on spatial abilities, with generally positive results (Bright, Usnick, & Williams, 1992). One study, part of a large-scale curriculum development project funded by the National Science Foundation, investigated the application and development of spatial thinking in an instructional unit on area and motions. The computer application was Tumbling Tetrominoes (Clements, Russell, Tierney, Battista, & Meredith, 1995). Results revealed strong positive effects on spatial abilities and the establishment of spatial-numeric connections; students doubled their scores on a test of spatial thinking after only 2 weeks of instruction (Clements, Battista, Sarama, & Swaminathan, 1997a).

Implications for Pedagogy

Research provides several guidelines for learning and teaching geometry. Because of the larger number of studies in, and longer history of, research involving turtle geometry, investigations of Logo tend to dominate this area, but we attempt to draw implications for all computer environments. Studies have shown that when students' learning is scaffolded by teachers, students work more effectively than when it is not (Yelland, 2003). In this way, the role of the teacher as facilitator proved to be fundamental and critical to computer-based learning environments. Teachers were able to assist students in focusing on the salient aspects of tasks and to create contexts in which students were able to develop skills in metacognition, which ultimately enhanced students' concepts of length (Yelland, 2003). Research has also shown (Yelland & Masters, 1997) that when students are scaffolded effectively in the exploration of spatial concepts they can explore powerful ideas at much younger ages. Yelland and Masters (1997) provided data indicating that Australian students as young as 8 years of age created rectangles using variable side lengths and placed congruent rectangles at specified locations in quadrants. Such mathematical concepts are traditionally not introduced until Year 9 in Australia in most mathematics curricula. The students in this research explored these concepts in Year 3 and were able to articulate the ways in which the concepts of variables, points of location, and quadrants facilitated the programming process in the computer microworld.

However, not all research has yielded positive results regarding technology as a medium for learning. First, few studies report that students "master," or retain and use, the mathematical concepts that are the teachers' goals for instruction. Second, some studies show no significant differences between Logo and control groups (P. A. Johnson, 1986). Without teacher guidance, mere "exposure" to Logo often yields little learning (Clements & Meredith, 1993). Third, some studies have shown limited transfer. For example, the scores of students from two ninth-grade Logo classes did not differ significantly from those of control students on subsequent high school geometry grades and tests (Olive, 1991; Olive et al., 1986). One reason is that students do not always think mathematically, even if the Logo environment invites such thinking (Noss & Hoyles, 1992a). For example, some students rely excessively on visual or spatial cues and avoid analytical work (Hillel & Kieran, 1988). This visual approach is not related to an ability to create visual images but to the role of the visual "data" (i.e., the students' perceptions) of a geometric figure in determining students' Logo constructions. Although helpful initially, this approach inhibits students from arriving at mathematical generalizations if overused. Further, there is little reason for students to abandon visual approaches unless teachers present tasks that can only be resolved using an analytical, generalized, mathematical approach. For example, simple "missing lengths" tasks, as described previously, can be solved by visual estimation, but students find that analysis is more efficient, and necessary for more complicated tasks. Finally, dialogue between teacher and students is essential for encouraging predicting, reflecting, and higher-level reasoning (e.g., Clements et al., 2001; Hoyles & Noss, 1987a).

In sum, studies showing the most positive effects involve carefully planned sequences of activities and teacher scaffolding that supports the development of specific mathematical concepts and understandings. Appropriate teacher mediation of students' work with those activities is necessary for students to construct geometric concepts successfully and to articulate the ways in which these concepts are connected to other conceptual areas of mathematics. This mediation must help students forge links between experiences within computer environments and other experiences and between computer-based procedural knowledge and more traditional conceptual knowledge (Clements & Battista, 1989; Lehrer & Smith, 1986). Care must be taken that such links are not learned by rote (Hoyles & Noss, 1992). Teachers must be involved in planning and overseeing the computer experiences to ensure that students reflect on and understand the mathematical concepts (McCoy, 1996). They need to (a) focus students' attention on particular aspects of their experience, (b) educe informal language and provide formal mathematical language for the mathematical concepts, (c) suggest paths to pursue, (d) facilitate disequilibrium using computer feedback as a catalyst, and (e) continually connect the ideas developed to those embedded in other contexts. Teachers must provide structure for computer-based tasks and explorations to facilitate desired learning. To accomplish all this, teachers need specifically designed computer activities and environments. It is unclear whether it is necessary to have students plan away from the computer. It has been used successfully in some studies (Clements, 1990). Other authors, however, conclude that asking pupils to plan away from the computer can be unnecessarily and unnaturally restrictive (Hoyles & Sutherland, 1989).

CURRICULA AND SOFTWARE

One finding that is consistent across studies is the critical role played by both the teacher and by the curriculum in which the computer software is embedded. The following list summarizes implications for using computer environments in geometry curricula (adapted from Clements & Battista, 1994; Clements et al., 2001).

- Curricula must find the right level of representation for students. For example, it may not be an efficient use of time to have students write procedures to perform geometric motions, but they can efficiently use tools available in enhanced environments (such as Logo or DGS) to perform geometric motions (Battista & Clements, 1988b; Clements & Sarama, 1996; du Boulay, 1986).
- Carefully planned and researched sequences of computer activities lead to greater likelihood of learning (Borer, 1993; Clements et al., 2001).
- Versions of computer environments with tools specifically designed to enhance mathematical activity that are highlighted in the curriculum lead to greater likelihood of mathematical learning than versions without such tools (Clements & Sarama, 1995; Kynigos, 1993; Sarama, 1995).
- The most effective use of computer environments may involve full integration into the mathematics curriculum. For example, too much school mathematics involves exercises devoid of meaning. Computers can provide environments in which students use mathematics meaningfully to achieve their own purposes. They can provide formal symbolizations that students can invoke, manipulate, and understand (Hoyles & Noss, 1987b). Using computer environments in this way can help fulfill the early vision of "teaching students to be mathematicians vs. teaching about mathematics" (Papert, 1980b, p. 177).

TECHNOLOGY AND GEOMETRY

There is evidence that computer environments can support learning and teaching in geometry in new and dynamic ways, as well as complementing and enriching traditional strategies. Unfortunately, the results of empirical studies such as those cited here have had little impact on mathematics curricula around the world. Mathematics in schools occurs mainly on paper, even in settings based on "standards" or reform. It has been demonstrated in this chapter that Logo environments can help students construct elaborate knowledge networks for geometric topics via several unique characteristics that can facilitate students' learning. These characteristics include the following: (a) multiple meaningful representations of geometric objects and processes and tools to link these representations; (b) measures that are visible, quantifiable, and able to be formalized, helping to connect spatial and numeric thinking; and (c) creation of "runable" code (or scripts) that encourages a procedural view of geometric constructs, as well as the habit of exploring, posing, and solving problems. Similarly, DGS environments can allow for similar representations and encourage students to develop viable geometric concepts, as well as to explore geometric properties, situations, and conjectures. Computer manipulatives similarly have both practical /pedagogical benefits such as being more flexible and extensible, and mathematical/psychological benefits such as bringing mathematical ideas and processes to conscious awareness, changing the very nature of the manipulative, and allowing and encouraging a greater variety of geometric actions, such as composition and decomposition processes. Finally, some computer CAI and games have also been shown to improve spatial and geometric understandings of young students.

Such research then affords the opportunities for educators to consider the unique characteristics of computer environments that are able to provide contexts for new types of learning in mathematics in the information age. These characteristics include the following (adapted from Clements & Battista, 1994; Clements et al., 2001).

- Computers can promote the connection of symbolic with visual representations, thereby supporting the construction of mathematical strategies and ideas from initial intuitions and visual approaches (Clements & Burns, 2000; Clements & Sarama, 1995; Noss & Hoyles, 1992a). Thus, computers can serve as transitional devices from physical movements to more abstract mathematical conceptualizations. Computers also can make mathematics more concrete, while simultaneously supporting students' formalization of actions algebraically as a computer program (Hoyles, 1993).

- Representations students create within software programs can help document their actions, leading to meaningful mathematical symbolization. Students can build a symbolic mathematical language based on this documentation.

- Students' thoughts are captured in these symbolic representations and can be reenacted and revised. Their actions, and the graphic geometric actions to which they connect, can become objects of mathematization and reflection (Clements & Sarama, 1997; Kieren, 1992; Noss & Hoyles, 1992a). Students can also return to test ideas and thus return to action-oriented ways of thinking as they extend higher-order ideas (Kieren, 1992).

- Software programs can provide feedback. The feedback of some programs, such as Logo, DGS, manipulative, and other construction programs, is distinct from "right or wrong" feedback associated with CAI materials. Instead, the feedback is an instantiation of students' expression of geometric ideas.

- Software environments can require and so facilitate precision and exactness in mathematical thinking (Gallou-Dumiel, 1989; Johnson-Gentile et al., 1994).

- Software programs can provide a window to students' mathematical thinking (Noss & Hoyles, 1992b; Weir, 1987). Such environments provide a fruitful setting in which teachers can work with and listen to students.

- Because students may test ideas for themselves on the computer, software environments can aid students in moving from naive to empirical to logical thinking (Clements et al., 2001). These environments also encourage students to make and test conjectures. Thus, such environments can facilitate students' development of autonomy in learning (as opposed to seeking authoritative opinion) and of positive beliefs about the creation of mathematical ideas.

- Even if used for less exploratory purposes, software environments allow students to search for relationships that seem beyond their grasp at that moment; they can try a range of possibilities on the computer (Battista & Clements, 1986; Hoyles & Noss, 1989), whereas on paper they often have little recourse but to ask for help or quit.

Unfortunately, research also identifies a reality that is far different from this vision. Few teachers from early childhood through middle school use computers for anything other than drill and practice (Clements & Nastasi, 1992; Manoucherhri, 1999). This leads to three critical, related caveats. First, most of the software that is produced and used for learning mathematics in the elementary and middle grades is not research-based in any sense—it was not developed with formative research nor is there adequate summative research substantiating its effectiveness. This situation should be changed (Clements, 2002). Second, most of the advantages identified for geometric computer environments that have been studied have been observed in small, usually well-supported educational contexts. We need to know more about the scaling up of those environments and their effectiveness in more varied contexts. Third, broad-based improvement in elementary and middle school geometry education attributable to the use of computers probably cannot be expected without dramatic change in the type of software and instructional strategies used in most classrooms.

Several additional findings across studies using different computer environments are notable. First, extended experience with such software environments may be important to realizing their educational potential (Clements et al., 2001). Second, embedding computer activities within the geometry curriculum may also be important to realizing their full benefits. Third, in a similar vein, curriculum and pedagogy need to be consistent with the software used; in the case of innovative geometry environments, investigative and inquiry approaches need to be substantially integrated. Fourth, researchers and teachers consistently report that in such contexts students cannot "hide" what they do not understand. That is, difficulties and misconceptions that are easily masked by traditional approaches emerge and must be dealt with, leading to some frustration on the part of both teachers and students, but also to greater development of mathematics abilities (Clements & Battista, 1989). This leads to the next point. Fifth, evaluation of learning in such environments must be reconsidered (see Galindo, 1998), as traditional approaches did not assess the full spectrum of what was learned; in some cases, these approaches made little sense.

Finally, it is evident that we need to ascertain whether we are focusing on appropriate questions in a context that seems to be under the rule of an economic rationalist philosophy. Policymakers seem to be primarily concerned with value for their dollar. This is a feature that is mirrored in treatment-control studies, often for short periods of time, which attempt to find cause-and-effect features to support their arguments for or against the use of computers. With such marginal use of computers for learning it is of little surprise they have minimal effects in CAI contexts, since their use is not integrated into the whole program. It would seem that governments and policymakers need to justify that for each dollar spent on computers there should be a demonstration of commensurate increases in test scores. On the other hand, curriculum developers (in general) seem to continue their work as though computers serve only a marginal purpose in subject areas and need to mimic popular culture. Their design and approaches reflect content and suggest pedagogies more suited to traditional curricula. In this way the power of potentially revolutionary technologies is often ignored and we miss opportunities to create new sequenced topics that incorporate the embedded use of new information technologies. At present, most schools are continuing the practice of fitting new technologies into old curricula or within the context of traditional didactic teaching methods. What we need to see are ways in which curricula can be reconceptualized to illustrate the ways in which they can be modified to reap the benefits of new technological environments for learning and teaching geometry.

ACKNOWLEDGMENTS

This chapter was supported in part by the National Science Foundation under Grants No. ESI-9730804, "Building Blocks—Foundations for Mathematical Thinking, Pre-Kindergarten to Grade 2: Research-based Materials Development," REC-9903409, "Technology-Enhanced Learning of Geometry in Elementary Schools," and ESI-98-17540: "Conference on Standards for Preschool and Kindergarten Mathematics Education." Work on the research was also supported in part by the Interagency Educational Research Initiative (NSF, DOE, and NICHHD) Grant No. REC-0228440 to Clements, D. H., Sarama, J., Klein, A., & Starkey, P., "Scaling Up the Implementation of a Pre-Kindergarten Mathematics Curricula: Teaching for Understanding with Trajectories and Technologies." Any opinions, findings, and conclusions or recommendations expressed in this material are those of the authors and do not necessarily reflect the views of the National Science Foundation.

NOTES

1. Note that our own interpretation of theories of geometric thinking is that visual/spatial knowledge remains essential at all levels of thinking (see Clements, Battista, & Sarama, 2001). That is, geometric knowledge continues to include nonverbal, imagistic components; every mental geometric object includes one or more image schemes, that is, a recurrent, dynamic pattern of kinesthetic and visual actions (M. Johnson, 1987). Thus, imagistic knowledge is not left untransformed and merely "pushed into the background" by higher levels of thinking. Imagery has a number of psychological layers, from more primitive to more sophisticated (each of which connect to a different level of geometric thinking) that play different (but always critical) roles in thinking, depending on which layer is activated. Thus, even at the highest levels, geometric relationships are intertwined with images, though these may be abstract images.
2. Here, we use "conceptualizations" to refer to mental schemes—mental networks of relationships connecting concepts and processes in specific patterns.

3. Visual here refers to the use of only visual data and the neglect of analysis.
4. For further information about the Shape Makers program, see Battista (2008).

REFERENCES

Ainley, J. (1997). Constructing purpose in mathematical activity. In E. Pehkonen (Ed.), *Proceedings of the 21st conference of the International Group for the Psychology of Mathematics Education* (Vol. 2, pp. 90-98). Lahti, Finland: University of Helsinki.

Akdag, F. S. (1985). *The effects of computer programming on young children's learning.* Unpublished doctoral dissertation, Ohio State University, Columbus.

Assaf, S. A. (1986). The effects of using Logo turtle graphics in teaching geometry on eighth grade students' level of thought, attitudes toward geometry and knowledge of geometry (Doctoral dissertation, The University of Wisconsin-Madison, 1985). *Dissertation Abstracts International, 51,* 2952A.

Austin, R. A. (1984). Teaching concepts and properties of parallelograms by a computer assisted instruction program and a traditional classroom setting (Doctoral dissertation, University of Florida, Tallahassee, 1983). *Dissertation Abstracts International, 44,* 2075A.

Baroody, A. J. (1989). Manipulatives don't come with guarantees. *Arithmetic Teacher, 37*(2), 4-5.

Battista, M. T. (2008). Development of the Shape Makers microworld. In G. W. Blume & M. K. Heid (Eds.), *Research on technology and the teaching and learning of mathematics: Vol. 2. Cases and perspectives* (pp. 131-156). Charlotte, NC: Information Age.

Battista, M. T., & Borrow, C. V. (1997, October). *Shape Makers: A computer microworld for promoting dynamic imagery in support of geometric reasoning.* Paper presented at the nineteenth annual meeting of the North American Chapter of the International Group for the Psychology of Mathematics Education, Columbus, OH.

Battista, M. T., & Clements, D. H. (1986). The effects of Logo and CAI problem-solving environments on problem-solving abilities and mathematics achievement. *Computers in Human Behavior, 2,* 183-193.

Battista, M. T., & Clements, D. H. (1988a). A case for a Logo-based elementary school geometry curriculum. *Arithmetic Teacher, 36*(3), 11-17.

Battista, M. T., & Clements, D. H. (1988b). Using Logo pseudoprimitives for geometric investigations. *Mathematics Teacher, 81,* 166-174.

Battista, M. T., & Clements, D. H. (1991). *Logo geometry.* Morristown, NJ: Silver Burdett & Ginn.

Borer, M. (1993). *Integrating mandated Logo computer instruction into the second grade curriculum.* Unpublished manuscript, Nova University.

Bright, G. (1985). What research says: Teaching probability and estimation of length and angle measurements through microcomputer instructional games. *School Science and Mathematics, 85,* 513-522.

Bright, G., Usnick, V. E., & Williams, S. (1992). *Orientation of shapes in a video game*. Hilton Head, SC: Eastern Educational Research Association.

Browning, C. A. (1991). Reflections on using Lego®TC Logo in an elementary classroom. In E. Calabrese (Ed.), *Proceedings of the third European Logo Conference* (pp. 173-185). Parma, Italy: Associazione Scuola e Informatica.

Butler, D., & Close, S. (1989). Assessing the benefits of a Logo problem-solving course. *Irish Educational Studies, 8*, 168-190.

Campbell, P. F. (1987). *Measuring distance: Children's use of number and unit* (Grant No. MSMA 1 R03 MH423435-01). University of Maryland, College Park.

Char, C. A. (1989). *Computer graphic feltboards: New software approaches for young children's mathematical exploration*. San Francisco: American Educational Research Association.

Ching, C., Kafai, Y. B., & Marshall, S. (2002). "I always get stuck with the books": Creating space for girls to access technology in a software design project. In N. J. Yelland & A. Rubin (Eds.), *Ghosts in the machine: Women's voices in research with technology* (pp. 167-189). New York: Peter Lang.

Clements, D. H. (1985). Research on Logo in education: Is the turtle slow but steady, or not even in the race? *Computers in the Schools, 2*, 55-71.

Clements, D. H. (1987). Longitudinal study of the effects of Logo programming on cognitive abilities and achievement. *Journal of Educational Computing Research, 3*, 73-94.

Clements, D. H. (1989). *Computers in elementary mathematics education*. Englewood Cliffs, NJ: Prentice-Hall.

Clements, D. H. (1990). Metacomponential development in a Logo programming environment. *Journal of Educational Psychology, 82*, 141-149.

Clements, D. H. (1999). 'Concrete' manipulatives, concrete ideas. *Contemporary Issues in Early Childhood, 1*, 45-60.

Clements, D. H. (2002). Linking research and curriculum development. In L. D. English (Ed.), *Handbook of international research in mathematics education* (pp. 599-630). Mahwah, NJ: Erlbaum.

Clements, D. H., & Battista, M. T. (1989). Learning of geometric concepts in a Logo environment. *Journal for Research in Mathematics Education, 20*, 450-467.

Clements, D. H., & Battista, M. T. (1990). The effects of Logo on children's conceptualizations of angle and polygons. *Journal for Research in Mathematics Education, 21*, 356-371.

Clements, D. H., & Battista, M. T. (1992a). *The development of a Logo-based elementary school geometry curriculum* (NSF Grant No. MDR-8651668). Buffalo, NY/Kent, OH: State University of New York at Buffalo/Kent State University.

Clements, D. H., & Battista, M. T. (1992b). Geometry and spatial reasoning. In D. A. Grouws (Ed.), *Handbook of research on mathematics teaching and learning* (pp. 420-464). New York: Macmillan.

Clements, D. H., & Battista, M. T. (1994). Computer environments for learning geometry. *Journal of Educational Computing Research, 10*, 173-197.

Clements, D. H., Battista, M. T., & Sarama, J. (2001). *Logo and geometry* (JRME Monograph Number 10). Reston, VA: National Council of Teachers of Mathematics.

Clements, D. H., Battista, M. T., Sarama, J., & Swaminathan, S. (1996). Development of turn and turn measurement concepts in a computer-based instructional unit. *Educational Studies in Mathematics, 30*, 313-337.

Clements, D. H., Battista, M. T., Sarama, J., & Swaminathan, S. (1997a). Development of students' spatial thinking in a unit on geometric motions and area. *The Elementary School Journal, 98*, 171-186.

Clements, D. H., Battista, M. T., Sarama, J., Swaminathan, S., & McMillen, S. (1997b). Students' development of length measurement concepts in a Logo-based unit on geometric paths. *Journal for Research in Mathematics Education, 28*, 70-95.

Clements, D. H., & Burns, B. A. (2000). Students' development of strategies for turn and angle measure. *Educational Studies in Mathematics, 41*, 31-45.

Clements, D. H., & Meredith, J. S. (1993). Research on Logo: Effects and efficacy. *Journal of Computing in Childhood Education, 4*, 263-290.

Clements, D. H., & Meredith, J. S. (1994). Turtle Math [Computer software]. Montreal, Quebec: Logo Computer Systems, Inc.

Clements, D. H., & Nastasi, B. K. (1992). Computers and early childhood education. In M. Gettinger, S. N. Elliott, & T. R. Kratochwill (Eds.), *Advances in school psychology: Preschool and early childhood treatment directions* (pp. 187-246). Mahwah, NJ: Erlbaum.

Clements, D. H., Russell, S. J., Tierney, C., Battista, M. T., & Meredith, J. S. (1995). *Flips, turns, and area*. Cambridge, MA: Dale Seymour.

Clements, D. H., & Sarama, J. (1995). Design of a Logo environment for elementary geometry. *Journal of Mathematical Behavior, 14*, 381-398.

Clements, D. H., & Sarama, J. (1996, April). Turtle math: Redesigning Logo for elementary mathematics. *Learning and Leading with Technology, 23*, 10-15.

Clements, D. H., & Sarama, J. (1997). Research on Logo: A decade of progress. *Computers in the Schools, 14*(1-2), 9-46.

Clements, D. H., Sarama, J., & Battista, M. T. (1998). Development of concepts of geometric figures in a specially-designed Logo computer environment. *Focus on Learning Problems in Mathematics, 20*, 47-64.

Clements, D. H., Swaminathan, S., Hannibal, M. A. Z., & Sarama, J. (1999). Young children's concepts of shape. *Journal for Research in Mathematics Education, 30*, 192-212.

Cope, P., & Simmons, M. (1991). Children's exploration of rotation and angle in limited Logo microworlds. *Computers in Education, 16*, 133-141.

Dixon, J. K. (1997). Computer use and visualization in students' construction of reflection and rotation concepts. *School Science and Mathematics, 97*, 352-358.

Driscoll, M. J. (1983). *Research within reach: Elementary school mathematics and reading*. St. Louis, MO: CEMREL.

du Boulay, B. (1986). Part II: Logo confessions. In R. Lawler, B. du Boulay, M. Hughes, & H. Macleod (Eds.), *Cognition and computers: Studies in learning* (pp. 81-178). Chichester, England: Ellis Horwood.

Education Development Center. (1993). *Math and more*. Atlanta, GA: IBM.

Edwards, L. D. (1991). Children's learning in a computer microworld for transformation geometry. *Journal for Research in Mathematics Education, 22*, 122-137.

Findlayson, H. M. (1984). What do children learn through using Logo? (D.A.I. Research paper No. 237). Loughborough, United Kingdom: British Logo Users Group Conference.

Fletcher, J. D., Hawley, D. E., & Piele, P. K. (1990). Costs, effects, and utility of microcomputer assisted instruction in the classroom. *American Educational Research Journal, 27*, 783-806.

Foletta, G. M. (1995). Technology and guided inquiry: Understanding of students' thinking while using a cognitive computer tool, the Geometer's Sketchpad, in a geometry class (Doctoral dissertation, The University of Iowa, 1995). *Dissertations Abstracts International, 55/08*, 2311.

Frazier, M. K. (1987). *The effects of Logo on angle estimation skills of 7th graders.* Unpublished master's thesis, Wichita State University, Wichita, KS.

Fuys, D., Geddes, D., & Tischler, R. (1988). *The van Hiele model of thinking in geometry among adolescents* (JRME Monograph Number 3). Reston, VA: National Council of Teachers of Mathematics.

Galindo, E. (1998). Assessing justification and proof in geometry classes taught using dynamic software. *The Mathematics Teacher, 91*, 76-82.

Gallou-Dumiel, E. (1989). Reflections, point symmetry and Logo. In C. A. Maher, G. A. Goldin, & R. B. Davis (Eds.), *Proceedings of the eleventh annual meeting of the North American chapter of the International Group for the Psychology of Mathematics Education* (pp. 149-157). New Brunswick, NJ: Rutgers University.

Glass, B. (2001). *Students' reification of geometric transformations in the presence of multiple dynamically linked representations.* Unpublished doctoral dissertation, University of Iowa, Iowa City.

Hannafin, R. D., & Sullivan, H. J. (1996). Preferences and learner control over amount of instruction. *Journal of Educational Psychology, 88*, 162-173.

Hausken, E. G., & Rathbun, A. (2004). Mathematics instruction in kindergarten: Classroom practices and outcomes. San Diego, CA: American Educational Research Association.

Hillel, J., & Kieran, C. (1988). Schemas used by 12-year-olds in solving selected turtle geometry tasks. *Recherches en Didactique des Mathématiques, 8*(12), 61-103.

Howe, J. A. M., O'Shea, T., & Plane, F. (1980). Teaching mathematics through Logo programming: An evaluation study. In R. Lewis & E. D. Tagg (Eds.), *Computer assisted learning: Scope, progress and limits* (pp. 85-102). Amsterdam, NY: North-Holland.

Hoyles, C. (1993). Microworlds/schoolworlds: The transformation of an innovation. In C. Keitel & K. Ruthven (Eds.), *Learning from computers: Mathematics education and technology* (pp. 1-17). Berlin, Germany: Springer-Verlag.

Hoyles, C. (2001). Steering between skills and creativity: A role for the computer? *For the Learning of Mathematics, 21*, 33-39.

Hoyles, C., & Healy, L. (1997). Unfolding meanings for reflective symmetry. *International Journal of Computers for Mathematical Learning, 2*, 27-59.

Hoyles, C., & Healy, L. (1999). Linking informal argumentation with formal proof through computer-integrated teaching experiments. In O. Zaslavsky (Ed.), *Proceedings of the twenty-third annual conference of the International Group for the*

Psychology of Mathematics Education (Vol. 3, pp. 105-112). Haifa, Israel: Program Committee, 23rd PME Conference.

Hoyles, C., & Noss, R. (1987a). Children working in a structured Logo environment: From doing to understanding. *Recherches en Didactique des Mathématiques, 8*(12), 131-174.

Hoyles, C., & Noss, R. (1987b). Synthesizing mathematical conceptions and their formalization through the construction of a Logo-based school mathematics curriculum. *International Journal of Mathematical Education in Science and Technology, 18*, 581-595.

Hoyles, C., & Noss, R. (1989). The computer as a catalyst in children's proportion strategies. *Journal of Mathematical Behavior, 8*, 53-75.

Hoyles, C., & Noss, R. (1992). A pedagogy for mathematical microworlds. *Educational Studies in Mathematics, 23*, 31-57.

Hoyles, C., & Sutherland, R. (1986). *When 45 equals 60.* London: University of London Institute of Education, Microworlds Project.

Hoyles, C., & Sutherland, R. (1989). *Logo mathematics in the classroom.* London: Routledge.

Hughes, M., & Macleod, H. (1986). Part II: Using Logo with very young children. In R. Lawler, B. du Boulay, M. Hughes, & H. Macleod (Eds.), *Cognition and computers: Studies in learning* (pp. 179-219). Chichester, England: Ellis Horwood.

IMAG-CNRS Universitè Joseph Fourier. (1998). Cabri geometry II [Computer software]. Dallas, TX: Texas Instruments.

Jackiw, N. (1991, 2002). The Geometer's Sketchpad [Computer software]. Emeryville, CA: Key Curriculum Press.

Johnson, M. (1987). *The body in the mind.* Chicago: The University of Chicago Press.

Johnson, P. A. (1986). *Effects of computer-assisted instruction compared to teacher-directed instruction on comprehension of abstract concepts by the deaf.* Unpublished doctoral dissertation, Northern Illinois University, DeKalb.

Johnson-Gentile, K., Clements, D. H., & Battista, M. T. (1994). The effects of computer and noncomputer environments on students' conceptualizations of geometric motions. *Journal of Educational Computing Research, 11*, 121-140.

Kelly, G. N., Kelly, J. T., & Miller, R. B. (1986-1987). Working with Logo: Do 5th and 6th graders develop a basic understanding of angles and distances? *Journal of Computers in Mathematics and Science Teaching, 6*, 23-27.

Kieran, C. (1986a). Logo and the notion of angle among fourth and sixth grade children. In C. Hoyles & L. Burton (Eds.), *Proceedings of the tenth annual meeting of the International Group for the Psychology of Mathematics Education* (pp. 99-104). London: City University.

Kieran, C. (1986b). Turns and angles: What develops in Logo? In G. Lappan & R. Even (Eds.), *Proceedings of the eighth annual meeting of the North American Chapter of the International Group for the Psychology of Mathematics Education* (pp. 169-177). East Lansing, MI: Michigan State University.

Kieran, C., & Hillel, J. (1990). "It's tough when you have to make the triangles angles": Insights from a computer-based geometry environment. *Journal of Mathematical Behavior, 9*, 99-127.

Kieran, C., Hillel, J., & Erlwanger, S. (1986). Perceptual and analytical schemas in solving structured turtle-geometry tasks. In C. Hoyles, R. Noss, & R. Sutherland (Eds.), *Proceedings of the second Logo and Mathematics Educators Conference* (pp. 154-161). London, England: University of London.

Kieren, T. E. (1992). Mathematics in a Logo environment: A recursive look at a complex phenomenon. In C. Hoyles & R. Noss (Eds.), *Learning mathematics and Logo* (pp. 223-245). Cambridge, MA: The MIT Press.

Knight-Burns, P., & Bozeman, W. C. (1981). Computer-assisted instruction and mathematics achievement: Is there a relationship? *Educational Technology, 21*, 32-39.

Kull, J. A. (1986). Learning and Logo. In P. F. Campbell & G. G. Fein (Eds.), *Young children and microcomputers* (pp. 103-130). Englewood Cliffs, NJ: Prentice-Hall.

Kynigos, C. (1992). The turtle metaphor as a tool for children's geometry. In C. Hoyles & R. Noss (Eds.), *Learning mathematics and Logo* (pp. 97-126). Cambridge, MA: The MIT Press.

Kynigos, C. (1993). Children's inductive thinking during intrinsic and Euclidean geometrical activities in a computer programming environment. *Educational Studies in Mathematics, 24*, 177-197.

Lehrer, R., Randle, L., & Sancilio, L. (1989). Learning pre-proof geometry with Logo. *Cognition and Instruction, 6*, 159-184.

Lehrer, R., & Smith, P. C. (1986). *Logo learning: Are two heads better than one?* San Francisco: American Educational Research Association.

Lesh, R. A. (1990). Computer-based assessment of higher order understandings and processes in elementary mathematics. In G. Kulm (Ed.), *Assessing higher order thinking in mathematics* (pp. 81-110). Washington, DC: American Association for the Advancement of Science.

Lowrie, T. (1998). *Using technology to enhance children's spatial sense.* Paper presented at the 21st annual conference of the Mathematics Education Research Group of Australasia (Teaching mathematics in new times), Gold Coast, Australia.

Manoucherhri, A. (1999). Computers and school mathematics reform: Implications for mathematics teacher education. *Journal of Computers in Mathematics and Science Teaching, 18*(1), 31-48.

Masters, J. E. (1997). *Investigations in geometric thinking: Young children learning with technology.* Unpublished master's thesis, Queensland University of Technology, Kelvin Grove, Queensland, Australia.

McClurg, P. A. (1992). Investigating the development of spatial cognition in problem-solving microworlds. *Journal of Computing in Childhood Education, 3*, 111-126.

McCoy, L. P. (1996). Computer-based mathematics learning. *Journal of Research on Computing in Education, 28*, 438-460.

Metz, K. E. (1995). Reassessment of developmental constraints on children's science instruction. *Review of Educational Research, 65*, 93-127.

Morris, J. P. (1983). Microcomputers in a sixth-grade classroom. *Arithmetic Teacher, 31*(2), 22-24.

Niederhauser, D. S., & Stoddart, T. (2001). Teachers' instructional perspectives and use of educational software. *Teaching and Teacher Education, 17*, 15-31.

Noss, R. (1987). Children's learning of geometrical concepts through Logo. *Journal for Research in Mathematics Education, 18*, 343-362.

Noss, R., & Hoyles, C. (1992a). Afterword: Looking back and looking forward. In C. Hoyles & R. Noss (Eds.), *Learning mathematics and Logo* (pp. 427-468). Cambridge, MA: MIT Press.

Noss, R., & Hoyles, C. (1992b). *Windows on mathematical meanings: Learning cultures and computers*. Dordrecht, The Netherlands: Kluwer.

Olive, J. (1991). Logo programming and geometric understanding: An in-depth study. *Journal for Research in Mathematics Education, 22*, 90-111.

Olive, J., Lankenau, C. A., & Scally, S. P. (1986). *Teaching and understanding geometric relationships through Logo: Phase II (Interim report: The Atlanta-Emory Logo Project)*. Atlanta, GA: Emory University.

Olson, A. T., Kieren, T. E., & Ludwig, S. (1987). Linking Logo, levels, and language in mathematics. *Educational Studies in Mathematics, 18*, 359-370.

Olson, J. K. (1985). Using Logo to supplement the teaching of geometric concepts in the elementary school classroom (Doctoral dissertation, Oklahoma State University, 1985). *Dissertation Abstracts International, 47*, 819A.

Olson, J. K. (1988, August). *Microcomputers make manipulatives meaningful*. Paper presented at the Sixth International Congress on Mathematical Education, Budapest, Hungary.

Papert, S. (1980a). *Mindstorms: Children, computers, and powerful ideas*. New York: Basic Books.

Papert, S. (1980b). Teaching children thinking. In R. Taylor (Ed.), *The computer in the school: Tutor, tool, tutee* (pp. 161-176). New York: Teachers College Press.

Papert, S. (1993). *The children's machine. Rethinking school in the age of the computer*. New York: Basic Books.

Papert, S., Watt, D., diSessa, A., & Weir, S. (1979). *Final report of the Brookline Logo project. Part II: Project summary and data analysis (Logo Memo No. 53)*: Cambridge, MA: Massachusetts Institute of Technology, Artificial Intelligence Laboratory.

Parmar, R. S., & Cawley, J. F. (1997). Preparing teachers to teach mathematics to students with learning disabilities. *Journal of Learning Disabilities, 30*, 188-197.

Pea, R. D. (1983). Logo programming and problem solving. In *Chameleon in the classroom: Developing roles for computers (Tech. Rep. No. 22)* (pp. 25-33). New York: Bank Street College of Education, Center for Children and Technology.

Pepin, M., & Dorval, M. (1986, October). Effect of playing a video game on adults' and adolescents' spatial visualization. *Educational Technology, 26*, 48-52.

Piaget, J., & Inhelder, B. (1967). *The child's conception of space* (F. J. Langdon & J. L. Lunzer, Trans.). New York: W. W. Norton.

Pratt, D., & Ainley, J. (1997). The construction of meanings for geometric construction: Two contrasting cases. *International Journal of Computers for Mathematical Learning, 1*, 293-322.

Ross, J. A., McDougall, D., Hogaboam-Gray, A., & LeSage, A. (2003). A survey measuring elementary teachers' implementation of standards-based mathematics teaching. *Journal for Research in Mathematics Education, 34*, 344-363.

Sarama, J. (1995). *Redesigning Logo: The turtle metaphor in mathematics education*. Unpublished doctoral dissertation, State University of New York at Buffalo.

Sarama, J., Clements, D. H., & Vukelic, E. B. (1996). The role of a computer manipulative in fostering specific psychological/mathematical processes. In E. Jakubowski, D. Watkins, & H. Biske (Eds.), *Proceedings of the eighteenth annual meeting of the North American chapter of the International Group for the Psychology of Mathematics Education* (Vol. 2, pp. 567-572). Columbus, OH: ERIC Clearinghouse for Science, Mathematics, and Environmental Education.

Schwartz, J. L., & Yerushalmy, M. (1986/2000). The Geometric Supposer series [Computer software]. Tel Aviv, Israel: Centre for Educational Technology.

Sedighian, K., & Sedighian, A. (1996). Can educational computer games help educators learn about the psychology of learning mathematics in children? In E. Jakubowski, D. Watkins, & H. Biske (Eds.), *Proceedings of the eighteenth annual meeting of the North American Chapter of the International Group for the Psychology of Mathematics Education* (Vol. 2, pp. 573-578). Columbus, OH: ERIC Clearinghouse for Science, Mathematics, and Environmental Education.

Smith, G. G. (1993). Computers, computer games, active control and spatial visualization strategy (Doctoral dissertation, Arizona State University, Tempe, 1993). *Dissertations Abstracts International, 59*, 2330.

Sowell, E. J. (1989). Effects of manipulative materials in mathematics instruction. *Journal for Research in Mathematics Education, 20*, 498-505.

Stecher, B. M., Barron, S., Kaganoff, T., & Goodwin, J. (1998). *The effects of standards-based assessment on classroom practices: Results of the 1996-97 Rand survey of Kentucky teachers of mathematics and writing (CSE Technical Report No. 482).* Los Angeles: University of California, Center for Research on Evaluation, Standards, and Student Testing.

Subrahmanyam, K., & Greenfield, P. M. (1994). Effect of video game practice on spatial skills in girls and boys. *Journal of Applied Developmental Psychology, 15*, 13-32.

Thompson, P. W., & Thompson, A. G. (1990). Salient aspects of experience with concrete manipulatives. In F. Hitt (Ed.), *Proceedings of the 14th annual meeting of the International Group for the Psychology of Mathematics Education* (Vol. 3, pp. 337-343). Mexico City, Mexico: International Group for the Psychology of Mathematics Education.

van Hiele, P. M. (1986). *Structure and insight: A theory of mathematics education.* Orlando, FL: Academic Press.

Vincent, J. (1998, July). *Progressing through the van Hiele levels with Cabri-geometre.* Paper presented at the 21st annual conference of the Mathematics Education Research Group of Australasia (Teaching mathematics in new times), Gold Coast, Australia.

Vincent, J., & McCrae, B. (1999, July). *Cabri geometry: A catalyst for growth in geometric understanding.* Paper presented at the 22nd annual conference of the Mathematics Education Research Group of Australasia (Making a difference), Adelaide, Australia.

Weir, S. (1987). *Cultivating minds: A Logo casebook.* New York: Harper & Row.

Yelland, N. J. (1994a). A case study of six children learning with Logo. *Gender and Education, 6*, 19-33.

Yelland, N. J. (1994b). The strategies and interactions of young children in Logo tasks. *Journal of Computer Assisted Learning, 10*, 33-49.

Yelland, N. J. (1995). Mindstorms or a storm in a teacup? A review of research with Logo. *International Journal of Mathematical Education in Science and Technology, 26*, 853-869.

Yelland, N. J. (2002). Creating microworlds for exploring mathematical understandings in the early years of school. *Journal of Educational Computing Research, 27*, 77-92.

Yelland, N. J. (2003). Making connections with powerful ideas in the measurement of length. In D. H. Clements (Ed.), *Learning and teaching measurement* (pp. 31-45). Reston, VA: National Council of Teachers of Mathematics.

Yelland, N. J., Clements, D. H., Masters, J., & Sarama, J. (1996). Children, computers, and mathematical ideas: Evaluating a research-based version of Logo. In J. Oakley (Ed.), *Designing learning environments for developing understanding of geometry and space* (pp. 309-328). Richmond, Victoria, Australia: Computing Education Group of Victoria.

Yelland, N. J., & Masters, J. E. (1997). Learning mathematics with technology: Young children's understanding of paths and measurement. *Mathematics Education Research Journal, 9*, 83-99.

Yerushalmy, M. (1991). Enhancing acquisition of basic geometrical concepts with the use of the Geometric Supposer. *Journal of Educational Computing Research, 7*, 407-420.

CHAPTER 4

TECHNOLOGY AND THE LEARNING OF GEOMETRY AT THE SECONDARY LEVEL

Karen Hollebrands, Colette Laborde, and Rudolf Sträßer

GLOBAL PERSPECTIVE

Our synthesis of the literature starts from a global perspective that is illustrated in Diagram 4.1.[1] The diagram depicts the learner in "opposition" to the mathematics subject matter, in particular, geometry. Learning of the subject matter is "mediated" by external representations and tools that form the link between the learner and geometry. We begin with a description of the components of this diagram and mention some important theoretical concepts linked to our approach.

We start from the assumption that geometry is a twofold enterprise, namely (a) the study of concepts and logical relations historically coming from an extensive analysis of space, but (at the latest by the end of the 19th century) turned into a globally used dictionary residing within scientific mathematics (geometry as part of scientific mathematics) and (b) the planning and controlling of production and distribution of goods within society by means of spatial concepts, relations, and procedures. (Societal uses of geometry include using geometry for purposes such as controlling

Research on Technology and the Teaching and Learning of Mathematics:
Vol. 1. Research Syntheses, pp. 155–205

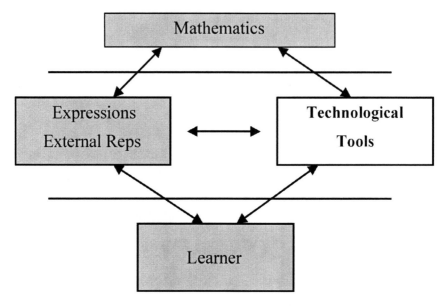

Diagram 4.1.   A perspective for characterizing the learning of geometry with technology.

tolerances of machine tools or designing packages for goods to store them without wasting space).

If we examine mathematics, in particular, geometry, with respect to learning, the *didactical transposition* comes into play. Learning, especially institutionalized learning in schools and classrooms, implies a change in the subject matter from the context of developing, exploring, and proving to a context that is appropriate for its learning and teaching. "To make teaching easier, it isolates certain notions and properties, taking them away from the network of activities … which provide their origin, meaning, motivation, and use" (Brousseau, 1997, p. 21). Chevallard describes this change as compartmentalization, depersonalization, decontextualization, and sequentialization (see Chevallard, 1991, chapter 5). By means of these processes, didactical transposition substantially changes the knowledge from the way it was created to a form in which it can be taught.

For the secondary level, this didactical transposition led to a school geometry that, at least for some countries and this review, can be described as the analysis of points, lines, and circles, and the use of these objects to create a variety of shapes such as angles, triangles, and quadrilaterals. Geometrical relations such as parallelism and perpendicularity link these primitive objects. The objects can be transformed by reflections, translations, rotations, and other transformations. The geometry does not necessarily need to be planar "2D" but can also be about strictly "3D" spatial relations. In some countries geometry is the first course in which students are introduced to and expected to practice deductive reasoning, which sometimes includes proof. An additional topic that has received greater attention is coordinate geometry, which allows for the exploration of geometrical problems using numerical values and algebraic equations. An approach to geometry resulting from such a didactical transposition, by its very nature, is amenable to computer use.

In an international review, "secondary level students" is not a well-defined term because of the variety of ways in which school systems are organized. In Germany, secondary schooling usually starts at age 10 (with minor exceptions), while France has a somewhat longer primary schooling. For the United States, secondary schooling can be thought of as starting at age 14 but often refers to the union of junior high school and senior high school—Grades 7 through 12—so the lower boundary of our age group is a bit unclear. The same is true for the upper boundary if we do not restrict ourselves to the *lower* secondary level. In most countries, there is a clear organizational cut around the age of 16. In order to have a clear guideline, we will focus on learners aged 13 to 18, but we will not hesitate to include younger students (i.e., 11 to 12 years old) or students older than 18 if appropriate from the point of view of the research to be reviewed.

Two additional assumptions are made within our review:

1. We do not take the learner as an isolated individual facing the world, but take the learner as deeply embedded in his or her environment, which is highly structured and defines the ways the individual is learning. For this review, it is especially important to consider the influence of the institution "responsible" for learning, which in our case would be the school embedded within the larger school system.

2. Nevertheless, institutional constraints and the structure of the knowledge to be learned are not the only factors to consider. It is not sufficient to consider the learning of geometry as a mere adaptation of the learner to institutional and knowledge constraints and necessities. The degree of freedom for the individual learner seems to be large enough to start from an essentially constructivist perspective to understand the learning of geometry. To state this another way: Learning is not taken as a simple process of the incorporation of prescribed and given knowledge but rather as the individual's (re)construction of geometry.

As a consequence, we start from the assumption that learners build up an internal representation of geometry, which they may construct from external representations of it. School geometry and the learner are linked by essentially static textual expressions and iconic external representations (such as a textual description of a construction and/or proofs and diagrams—the traditional "drawings") as well as tools created to do geometry—tools like the traditional ruler and compass for paper-and-pencil geometry or Dynamical Geometry Software (DGS) like Cabrigéomètre (Laborde & Sträßer, 1990) or Geometer's Sketchpad (Jackiw, 2001) to do geometry in technologically more advanced environments. The only facts available for analysis and inspection by a researcher are these external representations made on paper or inside technologically advanced tools. These latter representations are of a very different nature and therefore may lead to important changes in teaching and learning geometry. From this perspective, our chapter can be seen as an overview of the consequences of the introduction of specialized modern tools, especially computer software for use in the teaching and learning of geometry at the secondary level.

Choice of Articles to Be Reviewed

Reports of empirical studies that addressed the learning of geometry by students at the secondary level were identified from journal articles, conference proceedings, and book chapters. Studies that were included involved systematic data collection and analysis in the investigation of a research question. Theoretical articles that were related to and contributed to the development of the theoretical framework described in this chapter were also included. Publications that reported only anecdotal data or descriptions of classroom implementations of technological tools for the learning of geometry and included no empirical research results were excluded (see the list of reviewed publications in the Appendix). A total of about 200 studies were included.

A range of technological tools was identified from the research studies. They included: Logo; Boxer (diSessa & Abelson, 1986); The Geometric Supposer (Chazan, 1993a); DGS software and applications for calculators, like Cabri, Geometry Inventor (Arcavi & Hadas, 2000), and Geometer's Sketchpad; and some specific software designed for the purpose of research. From these sources, the following themes emerged:

- the role of representations in the construction of geometrical knowledge by students and in the construction of DG diagrams, in particular, with respect to drawing/figure, connections between symbolic and geometric intuition, and connections among spatial, graphical, and geometric representations;

- the design of tasks and the organization of the milieu oriented by learning aims and its effect on the learning outcome;
- students' constructions within a computer environment, namely, situated abstractions; and
- the instrumental genesis and its relationship to construction of knowledge.

These themes were compared with the initial theoretical framework created by the authors of this chapter, and when the framework was not robust enough to account for results in the research studies, it was revised so that it reflected the themes in the corpus of literature. It was through this cyclical process that the current framework was developed.

INTERACTIONS BETWEEN MATHEMATICS AND REPRESENTATIONS AND INTERACTIONS BETWEEN MATHEMATICS AND TOOLS

Registers

Various kinds of representations or systems of signifiers are used in mathematics. As Duval (1995) emphasized, especially in the domain of geometry, a mathematical activity involves various processes on these systems of signifiers. Duval proposed to use the designation "semiotic register" or simply "register" to refer to a system of signifiers that gives rise to the following processes:

1. *representing* an object in this register: An isosceles triangle may so be represented by a drawing or by various expressions in natural language;
2. *transforming* the representation into another one in the same register (called "treatment" by Duval): For example, "an isosceles triangle" may be transformed into "a triangle with two congruent sides" and $(a + b)^2$ may be transformed into $a^2 + 2ab + b^2$; and
3. *moving from one register to another one* (called "conversion" by Duval).

It is obvious that mathematics has recourse to various registers, not only for communicating knowledge but also and mainly for processing it (Duval, 2000). As it has been stated many times, mathematical objects are only indirectly accessible through representations, and this contributes to the paradoxical character of mathematical knowledge: "The only way of

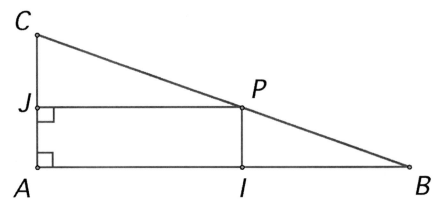

Diagram 4.2.   Drawing for a minimization problem.

gaining access to them is using signs, words or symbols, expressions or drawings. But at the same time, mathematical objects must not be confused with the used semiotic representations" (Duval, 2000, p. 60). The activity of solving problems, which is the essence of mathematics, is based on both the interplay between various registers and treatments within each register. Each register has its own treatment possibilities and favors specific aspects of the mathematical activity. To illustrate this, we will use the following problem as an example (see Diagram 4.2). Let *ABC* be a right-angled triangle with right angle *A*. Let *P* be a point of segment *BC* and *I* and *J* its orthogonal projections onto segments *AB* and *AC*, respectively. Where must *P* be to minimize the length of segment *IJ*?

It would be impossible to solve this problem without representing it in what is usually called a figure but what we will call a drawing (see the following discussion). The immediate perceptual apprehension (i.e., the visual identification of shape or "gestalt") (Duval, 1998, p. 40) of the whole configuration allows one to consider globally all elements and relations of the problem. But the role of the register of the drawing is not reduced to this in the process of solving the problem. One has to find a relation between the length of *IJ* and the position of *P*. It can be achieved by selecting an appropriate subconfiguration in the drawing, namely rectangle *PIAJ*, and by operating on the drawing by extracting visually the shape *PIAJ* and recognizing it as a rectangle. The remaining part of the solution process is displayed in Diagrams 4.3A and 4.3B, in which the path followed by the individual solving the problem goes back and forth between the diagram and natural language as indicated by the arrows. Two cases are illustrated in Diagrams 4.3A and 4.3B: solving in a paper-and-pencil environment and solving in a dynamical geometry environment.

Treatment (a) Diagram in paper and pencil	Assertions in natural language
Focusing on the sub-configuration *PIAJ* (operative apprehension) Recognition of the shape rectangle 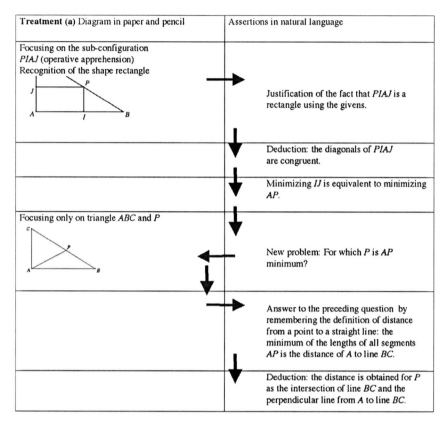	Justification of the fact that *PIAJ* is a rectangle using the givens.
	Deduction: the diagonals of *PIAJ* are congruent.
	Minimizing *IJ* is equivalent to minimizing *AP*.
Focusing only on triangle *ABC* and *P*	
	New problem: For which *P* is *AP* minimum?
	Answer to the preceding question by remembering the definition of distance from a point to a straight line: the minimum of the lengths of all segments *AP* is the distance of *A* to line *BC*.
	Deduction: the distance is obtained for *P* as the intersection of line *BC* and the perpendicular line from *A* to line *BC*.

Diagram 4.3A.   The interplay between diagrams and natural language within one solution path in paper-and-pencil environment.

The number of moves between diagram and natural language as well as the internal treatments in each register may depend on the person solving the problem and the kind of environment or tools used by the problem solver, as shown in Diagrams 3A and 3B.

A novice may have recourse to measuring the diagonals of *PIAJ* and observing their variation when *P* is dragged to get insight on the equality of the lengths of the diagonals, as we have observed with eighth graders. Or a novice may not start with the focus on the relevant sub-configuration. When experimenting with this problem in a dynamical geometry environment at different school levels, some ninth-grade students extracted the configuration of the parallel lines *PJ* and *AB* and tried to use proportionality between lengths.

When experimenting in a paper-and-pencil environment, almost all students, even university students, tried immediately to prove that *IJ* was

Treatment (b) Dynamic diagram	Assertions in natural language
Focusing on the variable sub-configuration *PIAJ* (operative apprehension) Recognition of the invariant rectangular shape	Justification of the fact that *PIAJ* is a rectangle.
	Deduction: the diagonals of *PIAJ* are congruent.
	Minimizing *IJ* is equivalent to minimizing *AP*.
Experimentation on the diagram by dragging *P* and observing the variations of the displayed measure of segment *AP* (for novices)	New problem: For which *P* is *AP* minimum?
Finding out that distance *AP* seems to be minimum when *P* moves on a small interval of segment *BC* for which line *AP* seems to be almost perpendicular to line *BC*.	Answer to the preceding question by remembering the definition of distance from a point to a straight line: the minimum of the lengths of all segments *AP* is the distance from *A* to line *BC*.
	Deduction: The distance is obtained for *P* as the intersection of line *BC* and the perpendicular line from *A* to line *BC*.

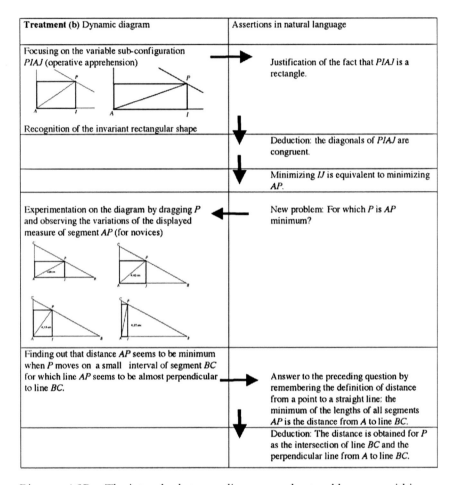

Diagram 4.3B.   The interplay between diagrams and natural language within one solution path in dynamic geometry.

minimized for *P* at the midpoint of segment *BC*; students did not try to create several diagrams with different positions of *P*. In a dynamical geometry environment, possibilities of experimenting on the diagram are broader: It is possible to measure lengths and angles to determine the feasibility of two measures being equal by dragging point *P*. So it is possible to start the problem in a completely different way, just by finding experimentally the spatial position of *P* minimizing *IJ*. In light of this example, we would claim that the solving processes depend on available registers and tools by facilitating some operations while making others more difficult or impossible. For example it is unlikely that students would draw several rectangles *AIPJ* on the same triangle *ABC* when they could easily change rectangle *AIPJ* by moving point *P* on segment *BC*.

In whatever environment in which one may be working, solving geometry problems is very often based on moves between the diagram and discursive statements. Beyond the case of geometry, the importance of moving from one representation to another one in problem solving has been advocated (Douady, 1985; Goldenberg, Cuoco, & Mark, 1998; Kaput, 1992; 1995; Robert, 1998); this movement from one representation to another is important in shifting perspective and in establishing connections among representations.

Multiple Representations and Interplay Among Settings

Based on the idea of cognitive disequilibrium from Piagetian psychology, the interplay among various settings is viewed by Douady (1985) as a vehicular element in solving a mathematical problem: The change of setting may offer a way of moving forward in the construction of the solution. A *setting* is a domain of mathematics made of objects and attached signified and signifiers[2] that gives rise to a common set of linked mathematical methods and processes.[3] Douady distinguishes, for instance, between algebraic and arithmetical settings. A mathematician starts solving a problem in the setting in which it is expressed (geometric, algebraic, functional—i.e., in terms of functions), but as soon as the concepts and methods of this setting no longer provide a path to a solution, the mathematician attempts to overcome the difficulty by moving to another setting which provides new tools. The solving process is made up of moves between settings and treatments within a setting. A computer environment offers a set of objects and tools, and the notion of interplay between settings can be extended to computer environments. It may be of interest to the solver to move between a graphical environment and a symbolic environment to find the roots of an equation (see for example Hershkowitz & Schwarz, 1999). Solvers who are experts are able to decide for themselves about such moves. For students, the role of the teacher is critical to foster these moves. However, the fact that several kinds of environments or tools are available on the same platform facilitates these moves.

The move can also take place between several representations of the same object. In geometry, a DGS such as GEOLOG (Holland, 2001) offers solvers opportunities to move between drawing (graphical representation) and text (representation with words) by providing links between the two representations. While most DGS allow users to view a textual description of a drawing they created with the computer, GEOLOG also allows users to define a drawing by means of a moderately standardized text (for a description see Holland, 2001). To give an example, we show a screen

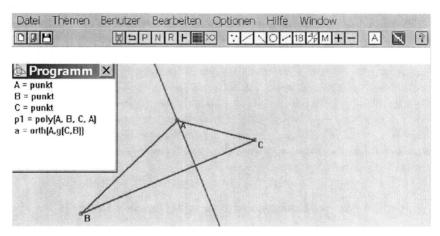

Diagram 4.4.   Textual and graphical representations in GEOLOG.

capture (see Diagram 4.4) from one version of GEOLOG with the textual representation on the left and the graphical representation on the right. The feature specific to GEOLOG is that one can start with the textual representation (on the left) following a given syntax, then ask the software to execute the program to create the drawing (on the right).

The various approaches such as moves between registers, uses of multiple representations, and interplay between and among settings share the common perspective of the importance in the mathematical activity of flexibility among representations, points of views, and methods. One can expect that computer environments afford this flexibility (Kaput, 1992, 1995) by offering various representations that can be linked in the same environment. For example, Santos, Aguero, Borbon, and Paez (2003) investigated how a routine problem is explored differently by high school students when they are working in a paper-and-pencil environment from when they are using dynamic software. In the DGS environment, students resorted to several linked representations, the geometric diagram, and the graphical representation. In particular, students dragged basic parameters and generalized their results. Kynigos and Psycharis (2003) found that working with software that combines symbolic notation and dynamic manipulation helped 13-year-olds to construct meanings related to the notion of curvature.

Representing Geometry With Computing Technology

Any representation of a mathematical object emphasizes some aspects while hiding others or giving a lesser role to them and thus allowing or favoring a certain kind of mathematical treatment while hindering some other. As is visible in the preceding example of the right-angled triangle, diagrams seem to favor a global apprehension of the geometrical object whereas discursive representations are more likely to involve an analytic and sequential approach. A similar process takes place when an artifact mediates knowledge, as is the case for computer environments. Through processes of representation internal to the computer and at the interface, the computer environment may bring new meanings and open new domains of mathematical activity (Noss & Hoyles, 1996). Noss and Hoyles (1996) note that "it can shape and remould the mathematical knowledge" (p. 5).

A well-researched example of this type of change brought about by the implementation process concerns the representation of a point on a line in a DGS. In most DGS settings, there are three different kinds of points: a free point, which can be directly dragged anywhere in the plane (two degrees of freedom); a point on an object such as a circle, line, or segment, which can be dragged only on this object (one degree of freedom); and a constructed point, which cannot be grasped and dragged (zero degrees of freedom) but moves only if an element on which it is dependent is dragged. The kind of behavior of a point on an object under the drag mode is something specific to DGS. Designers of DGS must make decisions about the behavior of such points.[4] When a segment is changed using the drag mode of a DGS, a "point on the segment" still has to be on this segment. Nevertheless, the construction "point on object" does not fix the position of the point on the segment. Most DGS solves this unavoidable problem by keeping the ratio of the respective sub-segments constant. In other software, for example the aforementioned GEOLOG or Cinderella (Kortenkamp & Richter-Gebert, 2001), the distance of a point from an endpoint of a segment is progressively decreasing until the point reaches one of the vertices of the segment. Following Chevallard (1985), who introduced the process of didactic transposition to describe the changes needed in mathematical content in order for it to be taught, Balacheff (1993; Balacheff & Kaput, 1996) introduced the notion of "computational transposition" to denote how knowledge is changed as a result of the incorporation of electronic technology in teaching. As stressed by Balacheff, this raises areas of concern about the epistemological validity of a mathematical computer environment:

- the mathematical relevance of the types of problems allowed by the environment;
- the functional and semiotic characteristics of the interface; and
- the mathematical internal coherence of the system.

Objects as they behave on the screen of the computer may have specific behaviors, just because, as in DGS, the introduction of a fourth dimension (the dynamic aspect of diagrams) introduces new possibilities and properties. In a DGS, a dynamic diagram is constructed through a sequence of operations. Thus, elements of the diagram are linked by dependency relations. A DGS emphasizes the functional aspect of geometrical figures (Laborde, 1993; Mariotti, Laborde, & Falcade, 2003). This led Goldenberg (1995) to consider a geometrical theorem as a property of a function.

Changes introduced by either the new kind of geometry (Laborde, 1999) or by the tool itself may have an impact on meanings and understandings of students. This will be addressed in the following sections.

MATHEMATICAL REPRESENTATIONS AND THE LEARNER

The complementary aspects of diagrams and discourse illustrated in the previous section play an important role in geometry. The strength of an expert lies in his or her abilities to move from diagram to discourse and from recognizing spatial shapes and configurations to reasoning deductively based on theoretical knowledge. Such expertise is not spontaneous for learners. In geometry, graphical representations mark an additional entry into learning. The actual drawing—on paper or on screen when computers are used—normally (re)presents a multitude of geometrical relations. In 1988 Parzysz formulated the difference between drawing and figure. For Parzysz, a *drawing* is the representation of a geometrical object (the referent) while the *figure* is the text defining this theoretical object. With these two representations of the same referent, the drawing and the figure, geometry offers two complementary objects, which can be distinguished and manipulated. A diagram displays *spatial-graphical* shapes and relations (Laborde & Capponi, 1994) as expressed by spatial terminology in expressions like "the round shapes are touching" and "they are overlapping or cutting each other." It is well known that some spatial-graphical relations are more visible at first glance than others. It is easy to see at first glance that two circular shapes are touching each other or that a point is inside a region. But it may be more difficult to recognize perpendicularity when the corresponding lines are neither horizontal nor vertical. This is why primary students may call the same square shape a square or rhombus depending upon its position on a sheet of paper: A square for them must satisfy the additional condition to have its sides horizontal and vertical while a rhombus has its sides oblique. It is only in a second step that more subtle relations may be perceived in a diagram and this process of recognition is achieved thanks to geometrical knowledge and/or by taking into account the discursive description of the problem given in the

problem statement. Here "we" enter into the realm of theoretical relations that may be indicated by conventional signs in a drawing. Duval
(1998) calls this process of associating gestalts and statements (i.e.,
anchoring what is seen in the verbal expression of geometric properties of
the problem statement) a *discursive apprehension*. In the previous example
illustrated in Diagrams 4.2 and 4.3, the focus on the rectangle *PIAJ* may
result from a discursive apprehension since the three right angles are
explicit givens in the problem statement. It is important to note that discursive apprehension is rarely found in secondary students' solution processes.

An expert is able to link a diagram (a "drawing") and the discursive
representation of the same geometrical referent (the "figure" in the sense
of Parzysz), and he or she is able to imagine all possible diagrams ("drawings") associated with a discursive representation or conversely to give
various formulations for describing a diagram. The set of relations associating diagrams and discursive representations referring to the same geometrical referent is called "figure" by Laborde and Capponi (1994). In
this perspective the notion of figure refers to the signified constructed by
the individual, a signified linking spatial-graphical and discursive aspects.
This designation is close to the notion of *figural concept* as developed by
Fishbein (1993). According to Fishbein, a geometrical concept involves
two intrinsically linked components as both sides of a coin, a figural component and a conceptual one. One of the main difficulties for beginners
in geometry is due to the absence of links between spatial-graphical and
discursive aspects, and one important aim of teaching geometry is certainly the construction of those links. The existence of geometry software
providing dynamic diagrams, which are of a different nature than paper
diagrams, changes very much the relations between spatial-graphical and
theoretical aspects.

In DGS like Cabri-geometry,[5] The Geometer's Sketchpad,[6] Geometry
Inventor,[7] and The Geometric Supposer,[8] diagrams result from sequences
of primitives expressed in geometrical terms chosen by the user. When an
element of such a diagram is dragged with the mouse, the diagram is
modified while all the geometric relations used in its construction are preserved. These artificial realities can be compared to entities of the real
world. It is as if diagrams react to the manipulations of the user by following the laws of geometry, just like material objects react by following the
laws of physics. A crucial feature of these realities is their quasi-indepen-
dence from the user once they have been created. When the user drags
one element of the diagram, it is modified according to the geometry of
its constructions rather than according to the wishes of the user. This is
not the case in paper-and-pencil diagrams that can be slightly distorted
by students in order to meet their expectations. In addition to the drag

mode, dynamical geometry environments offer specific features—macro-constructions, trace, locus, and so on—differing from paper-and-pencil tools (Sträßer, 2002).

Computer diagrams are also external objects whose behavior and feedback requires interpretation by the students. Geometry is one means, among others, of interpreting this behavior. In the design of DGS, spatial invariants in the moving diagrams represent geometrical invariants and these geometry microworlds may offer as such a strong link between spatial-graphical and geometric aspects. Inspired by the theory of variation in the tradition of the phenomenographic research approach, Leung (2003) suggests that the idea of simultaneity seems to be a promising agent to help to bridge the gap between experimental mathematics and theoretical mathematics, or the transition between the processes of conjecturing and formalizing. Simultaneity is intrinsically related to discernment in the theory of variation: "In DGE, it is possible to define a way of seeing (discernment) in terms of actually seeing invariant critical features (a visual demarcation or focusing) under a continuous variation of certain components of a configuration" (p. 198).

But is this link between spatial and theoretical perceived by students? Approximately one fifth of the studies of the reviewed corpus address the question of drawing versus figure, or they address the question of spatial or visual versus theoretical. They report research conducted in various countries (France, Germany, Israel, Italy, United Kingdom, and United States).

Beginners have difficulty constructing diagrams in a DGS environment that is resistant to the drag mode (i.e., preserves relationships upon dragging) and resort to construction strategies by eye. Noss, Hoyles, Healy, and Hölzl (1994) reported that when 12-year-old students were presented with the task of doubling segment AB they just constructed a point C on a circle with center B and radius BA, and adjusted it approximately so that A, B and C appeared to be collinear.

Bellemain and Capponi (1992) claim that a new contract[9] must be negotiated in the classroom and that it takes time for students to enter into this contract. They mention that all but one pair of students called the teacher to check that their diagram was correct. They did not spontaneously use the drag mode. Sträßer (1992) claims that dragging offers a mediation between drawing and figure and can only be used as such at the cost of an explicit introduction and analysis organized by the teacher. It has also been observed that when students use the drag mode, they do not drag over a large region but restrict their dragging to a small region, as if they were afraid to destroy their construction (Rolet, 1996). Sinclair (2003) observed that twelfth-grade students, although initially intrigued by the ability to drag points, usually stopped dragging after a short time and concentrated on interpreting a static figure. Some of them inadvertently created a special case through their dragging, then generalized from this static, but unsuitable, mode.

An indicator of the difficulty students experience in relating the spatial to the theoretical is also given by their difficulties in interpreting the behaviors of a diagram or of elements of a diagram under the drag mode. Soury-Lavergne (1998 as cited in Sutherland & Balacheff, 1999) shows how the immobility of a point in Cabri-geometry was not related to its geometrical independence from the dragged points. For the student there were two separate worlds, the mechanical world of the computer diagram (in our terms, the spatial) and the theoretical (or geometrical).

The distinction that we made between spatial-graphical and geometrical is expressed in various terms in several papers. Noss and colleagues (1994) show very well how difficult it was for students to construct with Cabri a point Q on a given line so that the length OP was always equal to the length OQ when P is moved (see Diagram 4.5). They explain the difficulty by saying that the students knew where point Q should be (spatial position in our terms) but were unable to find a geometrical construction of this location. They call this distinction empirical/theoretical.

The notion of dependency is the interpretation in a DGS of the notion of geometrical relationship. Geometrical objects that are linked by geometrical relationships can be viewed as dependent. The drag mode is a good way to externalize this theoretical dependency on the diagram. But if students have not constructed a relation between the spatial-graphical level and the theoretical level, they may not recognize or understand the dependency relationship in a DGS. As a consequence, it is not surprising

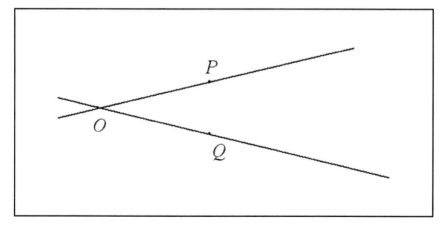

Diagram 4.5.   Lines OP and OQ, such that $OP = OQ$ whenever P is moved.

that several papers (mainly from the United Kingdom) focus on the construction of this notion of dependency by students interacting with a DGS (Hoyles, 1998; Jones, 1996; Pratt & Ainley, 1996). Several functionalities in a DGS such as Cabri (Jones, 1996) are good tools for externalizing the notion of dependency. Among these functionalities are the following: the drag mode, in which a dependent point cannot be dragged directly; the delete function—when an object is deleted all dependent objects are also deleted and a warning message is displayed; and the redefinition of an object—redefining an object in Cabri is changing its dependency relations with other objects. All papers mention that this notion is difficult for students and not understood by them initially. But by interacting with a DGS and by interacting with the teacher they may construct this notion of dependency, as expressed by two pairs of pupils in Pratt and Ainley (1996): "They are all real shapes because you can move them without deforming the shape" (p. 315), and "The initial objects are the ones that everything else depends on" (p. 314). It is also clear from these papers that this notion of dependency is situated in the context of the DGS. It contains some generality, although that generality is in terms of the context or of the tool (this is related to what Hoyles and Noss call situated abstractions—see the subsequent section titled, "Situated Abstractions"). "So because it depends on it, it moves" (a student in Jones, 1996, p. 150).

TOOLS AND THE LEARNER

According to widespread opinion, a mathematician is a person working alone (in an ivory tower!) with only the help of his/her brain and maybe paper and pencil. But a convergence is emerging over the last decades among several theoretical frameworks in mathematics education and psychology. Those perspectives focus attention on the environment in which the mathematical activity is carried out and on the tools that are part of this environment. These tools can no longer be regarded as neutral in the process of doing mathematics and making meaning of mathematics. This shift of attention may be attributed to several causes: the development of mathematics for professional purposes, the rapidly increasing use of calculators and computers in mathematics, and the resulting wave of innovations in mathematics education. This convergence of theories considers mathematical activity to be shaped by the environment in which it takes place and by the available tools. We next mention four theoretical perspectives, two about the learning of mathematics and two based in psychology that are relevant for analyzing the interactions between tools and the learner.

The Notion of Milieu

In the theory of didactical situations in mathematics developed by Brousseau (1997), learning emerges when the learner is faced with a problematic situation requiring adaptation of prior knowledge or construction of new knowledge to come to some solution. Brousseau claims that the evolution of the solving processes can be described (or even explained) as interactions between two systems, the learner and another system "opposing the taught system" (the learner) that Brousseau (p. 57) calls *milieu*. The milieu facilitates some actions from the learner and hinders other ones. Conversely, the learner receives feedback of various types and under various forms from the milieu.

The notion of milieu is very broad and may refer to the material milieu with which the learner is interacting as well as to the larger notion of cultural milieu (the class and its system of implicit rules for example or even the school context). In this paper we will restrict our discussion to a narrower notion of milieu because we are dealing with tools and technologies. From our perspective, tools and technologies are parts of a milieu interacting with the learner and that, corresponding to their specific features, tools and technologies will favor different kinds of interactions.

The description of geometry software in the preceding paragraph can be interpreted in terms of interaction between the learner and a milieu. To use a DGS to construct a diagram of a specific geometrical figure the learner should both select the appropriate primitives or commands and show or designate the appropriate objects on the screen. For example, consider the construction of a line passing through a given point A parallel to a given straight line (D). In a paper-and-pencil environment, the student places a ruler through A and rotates it until it has an estimated slope identical to the slope of (D). This strategy is essentially controlled by perception. Beginners follow a similar spatial-graphical strategy when using DGS. They select the command straight line, show A, and rotate the line until they obtain a good position by eye. But as soon as they drag A or (D), the constructed line does not move and the students understand immediately that their construction is not drag-mode proof and must be changed. In this example, the software provided feedback to the students that may have influenced them to discard their construction. Students did not need the teacher's evaluation of their construction. To construct an object that is not "messable" under the drag mode, the construction of a parallel line should be done by employing the command "Parallel line" and the designation of both point A and line (D). In such an environment, actions of the students are constrained by the software and, as often is the case, actions are assisted by tools. In this case, the constraints of the communication with the software may draw the learner's attention to the notion of parallel line as a function that depends on two arguments (point and line). For beginners, a parallel line refers more to the nature of the line than to a relation.

A didactical assumption in light of the theory of didactical situations claims that the choice of a relevant combination of problem situation and tool(s) may constitute a milieu fostering the emergence of new knowledge (see for example Kordaki & Potari, 2002 about the use of a microworld for area measurement offering several tools and feedback).

As reflected in many studies, the design of tasks is a critical feature for ensuring an evolution of students' mathematical understandings when interacting with technological environments. In other studies, researchers use the computer environment to present students with problems that they must resolve. These problems have certain characteristics: (a) they arise from the environment, and/or (b) they require a solution process different from the usual one in a paper-and-pencil environment and thus call for mathematical knowledge not usually involved in problem solving.

The simple task of constructing a dynamic diagram that meets specific conditions under the drag mode in a DGS is a new type of task originating from the computer environment and, as noted previously, is very difficult for students because it requires a link between the spatial or visual approach and the theoretical one. Tasks of reproducing all of the attributes of a dynamic diagram (called black boxes in Laborde & Capponi, 1994) make sense only in a DGS, in which it is possible to analyze the geometrical invariants of a figure by dragging.

The kind of task requiring solving processes differing from those in a paper-and-pencil environment may focus on aspects of mathematical knowledge that are not usually used as tools for solving problems. An illustrative example can be found in Jahn (2000, 2002). In a paper-and-pencil environment the fact that a geometric object is a set of points is not useful when working with geometric transformations because it is very inefficient to construct the transformed figure by constructing it point by point. Theorems of invariance appear to be very useful in such an environment because they avoid the tedious and quasi-impossible construction point by point. So students are never faced in a paper-and-pencil environment with a situation that requires use of the claim that an object is a set of points. When moving from middle school to high school in France, students must no longer consider a geometrical transformation as operating on figures but as operating on points. This causes a real conceptual break for most students, many of whom do not overcome it. Jahn asked 10th-grade students to draw the image of a circle in an oblique symmetry (affine transformation) with Cabri. Because of the "exotic" character of the transformation for which Jahn was asking, students could no longer productively use invariants of the transformation, and the only way

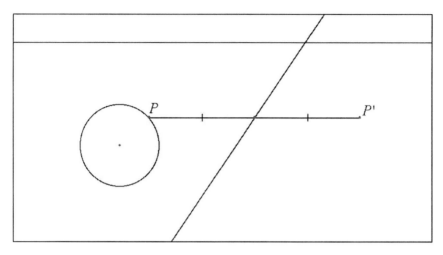

Diagram 4.6.   *P'* is the image of *P* through an affine transformation.

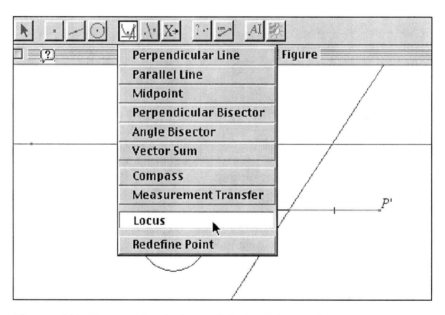

Diagram 4.7.   Constructing the locus of *P'* when *P* is moved.

to produce the image of the circle was to construct it as a locus of the images of a variable point of the circle (see Diagrams 4.6, 4.7, and 4.8). The notion of figure as a set of points is critical in this task. Of course the solution was not immediately found and the teacher had to use feedback

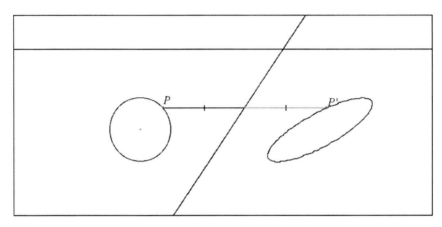

Diagram 4.8.   The resulting drawing.

from the software to disqualify answers such as the circle with its center at the image of the original center and with the same radius as the given circle. Hölzl (1999) uses the same idea with inversion, which is also an "exotic" transformation commonly not taught in schools.

Several researchers have suggested that the role of feedback is critical in students' evolving solutions to mathematical tasks. Leron and Hazzan (1998) describe a strategy of successive refinements due in response to feedback generated by software. Similar results were reported by Hillel, Kieran, and Gurtner (1989) with middle-school students working in a Logo computer environment. Within a Logo programming environment, students enter commands and they can then visually observe and interpret the results of the code and make modifications to their commands (Clements & Battista, 1994). Edwards (1992) found that students who were working with a computer microworld for geometric transformations refined their understandings of transformations based on the visual feedback they received from the computer as they engaged in a matching game. The capability of the software to incorporate knowledge and to react in a way consistent with theory impacts the student trajectory in the solving process. One can recognize here the philosophy underpinning the notion of microworld that is discussed in the following section.

Some researchers also stress that the choice of the tasks in relation to the affordances of the dynamical geometry environment may be critical for the development of understandings of the students. Pratt and Davison (2003) conclude from an investigation on the use of Interactive White Board (IWB) with a dynamical geometry software that the visual and kinesthetic affordances of the IWB are insufficient to encourage the fusion of conceptual and visual aspects of children's figural concepts when these affordances are embodied in tasks that simply focus on the visual transformation of geometric figures. They also conclude that the kinesthetic affordances of the IWB need to be embodied in tasks based on the utilities of contrasting definitions that draw attention to the conceptual aspect. The same type of conclusion about the use of preconstructed dynamic diagrams is drawn by Sinclair (2003): The design of the accompanying material has the potential to support or impede the development of exploration strategies and geometric thinking skills.

Situated Abstractions

Although the idea of microworld as a "model of knowledge domain to be investigated with the software" (Noss & Hoyles, 1996, p. 65) was conceived independently of the theory of didactic situations, it also incorporates the idea of how the learner's knowledge evolves through exploration in an artificial reality reifying a domain of knowledge, but without the noise of the genuine reality (Minsky & Papert, 1971; Thompson, 1987). When interacting with the microworld the learner is supposed to reconstruct the knowledge underlying the microworld by modeling the phenomena observed on the screen of the computer. In this interaction with the computer, learners may construct what Noss and Hoyles (1996) call *situated abstractions*. Situated abstractions are invariants that are shaped by the specific situation in which the learner forges them. Although those invariants are situated, they simultaneously contain the seed of the general that could be valid in other contexts:

> Within a computational environment, some at least of these objects and relationships become real for the learner (we are using "real" here to mean something other than simply ontologically existent—perhaps meaningful or broadly connected are better descriptions): Learners web their own knowledge and understandings by action within the microworld, and simultaneously articulate fragments of that knowledge encapsulated in computational objects and relationships—abstracting *within*, not *away from*, the situation. In computational environments, there can be an explicit appreciation of the form of generalized relations within them (the relational invariants) while the functionality and semantics of these invariants—their meanings—is preserved and extended by the learner. (p. 125)

Computational environments seem to constitute an appropriate place for observing the construction of situated abstractions. Our review of research provided examples of such constructions. The notion of invariant points in Turtle Mirror (Hoyles & Healy, 1997) or hyperbolic triangles

(Stevenson & Noss, 1998) in a specific environment is constructed by the learner within the environment—but those ideas contain more generality, which can be extended to other contexts. Some reports of studies not referring to the notion of situated abstraction may present examples that could be interpreted in these terms.

Tool Mediation

Tools or artifacts are material entities designed or used by human beings to accomplish some specific actions more easily or rapidly. They are a medium, or they mediate, the relationship between the human and nature. As said above, mathematics, despite widespread opinion to the contrary, has recourse to tools. According to the Greek tradition, geometry is an excellent place for ruler and compass, which are tools for producing straight lines and circles. These tools are explicitly called for in the demands that appear at the beginning of Euclid's Elements. They fulfill a double function: They produce near-perfect spatial-graphical representations of theoretical objects of geometry (straight line and circle), and they also incorporate theoretical knowledge resulting from a process of modeling shapes in the real world. They are based on a dialectic relationship between practice and theory (Mariotti, 2001). Vygotsky (1978) introduced this idea of dual function by distinguishing between technical tools and psychological tools (or signs, or tools of semiotic mediation). Tool function is externally oriented while sign function is internally oriented—it is a means of internal activity. According to Vygotsky, the process of internalization transforms technical tools into psychological tools that shape new meanings. The tool plays the role of a semiotic mediator. For example, such a process may occur in the move from real actions on the abacus to the evoked actions through a system of drawings and notations representing the abacus (Mariotti, 2001). As this system is used by the child in a way that is progressively more detached from the use of the real abacus it becomes possible to perform the same operations on the system of signifiers without referring to the abacus.

The link with new technologies in mathematics is obvious. They are technological tools embodying mathematical knowledge. For the learner, the underlying mathematics is not visible but by using technology, especially as a tool for solving relevant problems, a process of internalization may occur and the technology may become a sign in the Vygotskian sense, contributing to the construction of meanings that become independent of the technology.

The functional meaning of a parallel line (see example in the section titled, "The Notion of Mileu") may be constructed through the use of a software program; the dependence of a parallel line on two elements will be shaped by the software. It will then be internalized and conceived by the learner, even outside the context of the software program. This internalization process does not necessarily take place. Some conditions about the prior knowledge of students, the design of the tasks, and the interventions of the teacher play an important role. Hollebrands (2003) investigated under what conditions a geometric transformation in a DGE could be viewed as a function. The analysis suggests that, "students' understandings of key concepts including domain, variables and parameters, and relationships and properties of transformations were critical for supporting the development of deeper understandings of transformations as functions" (Hollebrands, 2003, p. 55).

Some specific features of DGS such as the drag mode, macro constructions, modules (Kadunz, 2002), locus and trace (Falcade, Mariotti, & Laborde, 2004; Jahn, 2002) may thus become signs contributing to mathematics learning.

As students interact with the technology, they must consider whether what they are seeing is attributable to mathematics or whether what they are observing is a bias introduced by the tool. Goldenberg and Cuoco (1998) have pointed to some differences between Euclidean Geometry and DGS Geometry. For example, as previously presented (see the section titled, "Representing Geometry With Computing Technology") the behavior of a point on a segment is a direct result of a design decision and is taken as a postulate upon which other DGS theorems are based. Such a postulate does not exist in Euclidean Geometry. A question that arises is: Do students make distinctions between behavior that results as a consequence of the tool design and behavior that is a direct result of mathematics? Scher (2001) found that students did not in fact make those types of distinctions; they considered the behaviors of each type to be of equal importance. Of course, this dilemma is not without answers. One of them is the careful design of the problem situation and of the milieu that is not restricted to technology. Another deals with the critical role of the teacher. The teacher, by his or her interventions, may help in distinguishing between what is contingent on the environment and what is related to theoretical knowledge, and in establishing a correspondence between what is observed and performed in the computer environment and its theoretical counterpart: "Meanings are rooted in the phenomenological experience but their evolution is achieved by means of social construction in the classroom under the guidance of the teacher" (Mariotti, 2001, p. 708). It is also through the questions, the scaffolding, and the interventions of the teacher that students learn. The teacher may act on the milieu and change the milieu, and this constitutes an important element of the learning processes. Fuglestad (2004), reporting a long term experiment with information and communication technology (ICT), mentions some aspects of the role of the teacher: "During the work, at some important steps, the teacher might intervene, ask questions and point to certain examples to try. Students may not discover important cases to try and in such cases an extra question or suggestion could be the clue to further discoveries" (p. 445). Several papers include the social dimension based on a sociocognitive construction of knowledge (Cobb, Wood, Yackel, & McNeal, 1992) showing how the interventions of the teacher may contribute to regulate the construction of the instrument. Taking from Confrey (1995) the distinction between voice (student's conception) and perspective (teacher perspective), Jones (1996) uses the notion of ventriloquating that denotes "the process whereby a voice speaks *through* another voice. As a student begins employing a term such as 'dependency' it is initially only half theirs" (p. 147). When first introduced, it is more the term of the teacher, but it becomes the students' term when the students interpret it with their understandings and experiences. In the same way the role of collective discussion under the guidance of the teacher is crucial as claimed by Hoyos (2002) who experimented with scenarios based on a related use of DGS and historical contexts and artifacts. Certainly the role of the social dimension and of the teacher when technology is used in the classroom, becomes one of the critical points that research should address, or as Hoyles, Noss, and Kent (2004) claim: "As a next step, the research community could usefully identify and present scenarios in use … with the inclusion of the trajectories of students' evolving situated abstractions and how they are shaped and become taken-as-shared as a result of didactical strategies followed by the teacher" (p. 323).

Instrumental Genesis

Twenty years ago the notion of microworld could have been interpreted as implying spontaneous learning just by interacting with the microworld, an idea that Noss and Hoyles (1996, p. 67) consider as false. Much research has shown that what is constructed by the learner is not necessarily what was intended by the designer of the environment or the teacher (see, for example, the notion of angle in Hillel & Kieran, 1987; Hoyles & Sutherland, 1990).

In the last decade, some psychologists (Vérillon & Rabardel, 1995) have shown through empirical research, how the tool or the artifact itself gives rise to a mental construction by the learner using the tool to solve problems. The *instrument,* according to the terms of Vérillon and Rabardel, denotes this psychological construct of the user: "No instrument exists in itself, … it becomes so when the subject has been able to appropriate it for himself ... and ...has integrated it with his activity" (pp. 84-85). The subject develops procedures and rules of actions when using the artifact and so constructs *instrumentation schemes* and simultaneously a representation of the properties of the tool (according to what Vérillon and Rabardel call *instrumentalisation schemes*). But the knowledge acquired by the subject about the tool and the ways to use it may differ from what the tool was intended to do and the ways it was intended to be used. We are faced with a dilemma. On the one hand, tools, and in our case technologies, offer opportunities for learning in that the subject is faced with constraints imposed by the artifact and new possibilities of actions, to identify, to understand and with which to cope. On the other hand, what is constructed and learned is not necessarily identical to what was expected.

This is an important issue for the study of learning processes in computer environments. Our review of literature focused also on whether research has taken into account these instrumentation processes, and the possible differences between the learning outcomes arising from interaction with a computer environment and the learning aims intended by the teacher or the researcher.

Not surprisingly, the drag mode gave rise to several studies of instrumentation processes addressing how schemes of use of the drag mode are related to the critical relationship between drawing and figure, between spatial and theoretical. The way in which students drag as they solve problems was investigated by Arzarello, Micheletti, Olivero, Robutti, Paola, and Gallino (1998), Arzarello, Olivero, Paola, & Robutti (2002), Olivero (2002), Olivero and Robutti (2002), and Smith (2002). They identified three different types of dragging modalities: "wandering dragging," "*lieu muet*" dragging, and dragging to test hypotheses. Wandering dragging refers to a random type of dragging in which the student searches for regularities or interesting behaviors. *Lieu muet* dragging refers to dragging in such a way that some regularity in the drawing is preserved. Dragging to test hypotheses obviously presupposes that regularities have already been detected which are now systematically tested.

These types of dragging may reflect different levels of experimentation. While wandering dragging allows students an opportunity to explore the problem space, *lieu muet* dragging more closely resembles an experiment. It is likely that students would engage in wandering dragging in an attempt to formulate conjectures and *lieu muet* dragging when trying to convince themselves of a conjecture. Dragging to test hypotheses then serves to collect evidence in an attempt to determine whether a given conjecture is true or false. *Lieu muet* dragging and dragging for testing hypotheses are more focused types of dragging that students may not spontaneously consider. Goldenberg (1995) notes that often students do not know how to conduct experiments and are unsure about what to vary

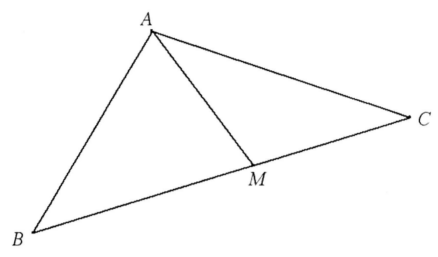

Diagram 4.9. A diagram illustrating the problem posed to Igor in Hölzl's study (1995).

and what to keep fixed. Thus a student's purposeful move from wandering dragging to *lieu muet* dragging represents a cognitive shift from a probably insecure guess to a definite and precise hypothesis on the behavior of the figure. Hölzl (1996) identified the "drag and link approach" in students' construction processes of Cabri diagrams. We now give an example of this approach described in Hölzl (1995, pp. 87-89). Igor tried to solve a problem (see Diagram 4.9) in which two triangles were given, each of which was divided into two isosceles triangles by only one straight line. The question was: "Can any triangle be divided in such a way, or is it valid only for particular triangles?"

Igor created the perpendicular bisector *m* of side *AC* and the angle bisector *w* of angle *B*, then the perpendicular line *l* to *w* passing through *A*. The common point *P* of *m* and *l* provided two triangles *PAB* and *PAC* (see Diagram 4.10). *PAC* is isosceles and *PAB* is isosceles if *P* is on side *BC*.

Igor understood that *P* should be situated on *BC*, in order to produce a suitable response. He could manage it however only on the drawing, by changing the shape of the triangle *ABC* in the drag mode, so that *P* is on side *BC*. He wanted *P* on *BC* by redefining *P* as a point on *BC* but did not succeed (for logical reasons).

In this drag-and-link approach, students relax one (or several) conditions to do the construction and then drag to satisfy the last condition(s). They obtain a diagram that is visually correct and want to secure the diagram by using the redefinition facility of Cabri. But doing so does not

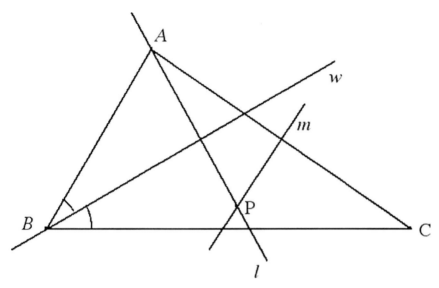

Diagram 4.10.   Igor's construction.

often work because of hidden dependencies. Although Hölzl did not refer to instrumentation, this approach would be called a utilization scheme in terms of Vérillon and Rabardel.

The instrumentation of the drag mode—although not in terms of instrumentation—was also recently investigated by Talmon and Yerushalmy (2004) in prediction tasks. After they had executed a geometric construction using a DGS (The Geometer's Sketchpad 3 and The Geometric Supposer for Windows) according to a given procedure, ninth-grade students and Mathematics Education graduate students were asked to predict the dynamic behavior of points that were part of the construction and to explain their predictions. The study revealed that users often grasp a reverse hierarchy in which dragging an object affects its parent. The authors suggest that this reverse hierarchy may be caused by terms and knowledge built into paper-and-pencil geometry. The instrumentation processes developed by users are influenced by former tools.

PROOF WITH NEW TECHNOLOGY

A somewhat more "general" topic that was not accommodated within the foregoing structure is the ongoing debate on proof in technology-based geometry. Even the development of some DGS was linked with this discussion (see early papers on the Geometric Supposer, e.g., Schwartz &

Yerushalmy, 1987) and with the growing geometrical power and stability of DGS, the role of new technology in finding and writing proofs has led to a continuing discussion (see for instance Furinghetti & Paola, 2003; Harada, Gallou-Dumiel, & Nohda, 2000; Holland, 2001; Keskessa, 1994; Robutti & Domingo, 1998; Saraiva, 1992; the section titled, "Tutoring Programs for Geometry Learning" of this chapter; and the 2000 volume, *44*(1-3), of *Educational Studies in Mathematics* devoted to proof in dynamical geometry environments). To date, it is still an open question whether the "authority" of the computer leads to a greater resistance to proving on the part of the learner, or whether adequately chosen and presented proof problems within a computer "milieu" further the need for proofs by the learner (not only) of geometry. Among arguments in favor of the use of DGS, the need in DGS to carry out explicit construction methods based on theoretical properties could lead to considering them as good environments for introducing formal proof. Among arguments given about students' not seeing the need to construct proofs due to the authority of the computer, the facility of computer programs to provide measurements is often mentioned. Some researchers investigated the role of measurement in proving activity with a DGS (Kakihana, Shimizu, & Nohda, 1996; Vadcard, 1999). It appears that measuring does not simply lead to empirical solutions (or naive pragmatism in terms of Balacheff, 1987) but may play a role in the development of proof. Vadcard identified two functions of measuring in this kind of environment: measuring for exploring that can lead to empirical solutions, and measuring for checking a theoretical result. The result being checked could come from a proof developed by the peer or, conversely, could be aimed at convincing the peer about the validity of a proof. This last activity is not public and remains private. Students do not mention this measuring in their written proof. Vadcard mentions that this latter kind of measuring (for checking a theoretical result) is used by students who are able to develop intellectual proofs of higher level. Measuring consists of what Balacheff (1987) calls a crucial experiment. Flanagan (2001; see also Hollebrands, 2002) also found that U.S. high school students in her study used the measurement capabilities of a DGS for exploring relations among geometrical objects or for checking constructions they designed by drawing on their knowledge of geometrical properties and theorems. In this study, measurements that were used for exploring either resulted in empirical solutions or deductive arguments.

High school students' understandings of the differences between empirical evidence and deductive proof were investigated by Chazan (1993a). The students in this study were using an early version of the Geometric Supposer that did not have dynamic capabilities. Justifications that students in Chazan's study offered to support their conjectures suggested that they believed that empirical evidence is sufficient proof or that proof is simply evidence to support a particular case. Based on his findings, Chazan recommends that students should understand proof as a social activity, that proofs should be valued for their explanatory power, and that they should not be considered an end in and of themselves. He also suggests that teachers should provide activities that will require students to confront their beliefs about empirical evidence and proof (Chazan, 1993b).[10] This view of proof as an explanation of empirical evidence as opposed to proof as solving uncertainty was introduced and developed by de Villiers (1991). His claim is based on a careful analysis of mathematicians' work and of writings about the nature of mathematical activity in general and proof in particular, giving evidence that mathematicians often do not begin the process of proving a statement until they have some inner conviction of the truth of the statement. A paper by Hanna (1998) discusses the influence of computers on the nature of proof, and the title of her article, "Proof as Explanation in Geometry," gives an idea of the main and characteristic argument of the general debate. No longer is the debate solely about how to develop the ability to write formal proofs but rather about the purpose of proof.

Prior to writing a formal mathematical proof, students engage in activities that include noticing patterns and invariants, describing the patterns informally and formally, conjecturing, checking examples or cases, and creating a deductive argument. Edwards (1998) refers to this collection of activities as part of the "territory before proof." Students in Edwards' study were asked to investigate geometric transformations using a microworld by participating in all of the aforementioned activities except deductive reasoning. Edwards found that as students worked with the microworld they were able to notice in specific examples patterns that they believed were generalizable. However, students seemed satisfied to test their conjecture with a single example and so they did little inductive and even less deductive reasoning. Students also were less willing to reformulate a conjecture or to look for disconfirming evidence. Similar to the findings of Chazan, Edwards suggests that teachers must engage students in thinking about how certainty is established when technological tools are present.

Discussion of the role of proof is embedded in a more global debate on the impact of technology on the increasing presence of a more exploratory mathematics (see, for example, one of four topics of the French summer school in Didactics of Mathematics in 1999 titled Proofs, Demonstrations and Writing in Mathematics [*Preuves, démonstrations et écritures mathématiques*] in Bailleul, Comiti, Dorier, Lagrange, Parzysz, & Salin, 1999). Leung and Lopez-Real (2002) provided another interesting example: In a case study, they observed a "Cabri proof by contradiction" of a theorem on cyclic quadrilaterals given by a pair of 16-year-old students in Hong Kong. The construction of a biased quadrilateral (in this case, one with the assumption that opposite angles on all quadrilaterals are supplementary) by the students and the exploration of the locus on which this biased quadrilateral vanishes, led them to elaborate a formal proof by contradiction. The authors propose that it is possible to bridge the gap between the experimental and the theoretical in DGS by introducing the idea of a dynamic template as a kind of visualizer of abstract objects and relationships. The biased quadrilateral vanishing in some specific conditions played the role of dynamic template.

The recent greater integration of DGS into teaching allows for opportunities to design instructional activities, even sometimes over a long-term period aimed at introducing or fostering deductive reasoning and proof (Sanchez & Sacristan, 2003). Four studies show the diversity and novelty of ways offered by DGS to promote understanding of the need for and the roles of proof. Jones (2000) reports on a teaching unit consisting of three phases of instruction about the classification of quadrilaterals in which students had to reproduce a drawing which could not be "messed up" and in some cases satisfying additional conditions. After constructing the drawing the students had to explain why the constructed drawing was the expected one. Explanation in these tasks prefigures proof in the sense that explaining consists of giving the conditions implying that the constructed drawing is the expected type of quadrilateral. This task deals with the idea of implication between properties (or relations), which is necessary in order to understand how proof works. The context that gives meaning to proof (or rather explanation) is the robustness of a drawing under the drag mode. The explanations provided by the students give mathematical reasons for the fact that a drawing remains a specified quadrilateral in the drag mode.

Based on the Vygotskian perspective of the social construction of knowledge and semiotic mediation, Mariotti (2000) reports on a long-term teaching experiment in which the system of axioms and theorems is constructed by students themselves and in which the set of commands introduced in the software at the beginning of the teaching sequence is empty.[11] Proof is the means for justifying that the new command will provide the expected outcome. This is achieved by using what is known about previously implemented commands. The construction of the commands of the system is similar to the construction of theorems. Proof here is a means of being sure that the constructed DGS works as intended. But according to the norms established in the classroom, every student who is confident of the validity of his/her construction should defend it in front of his/her classmates. Proof thus fulfils a twofold role: establishing the validity of a construction for each individual and convincing the other students to accept the construction process.

Marrades and Gutiérrez (2000) report on a teaching experiment designed to enable students to produce deductive justifications of the correctness of their constructions. An analytic framework, which integrates and expands previous frameworks, is used to analyze student answers, to show that the way in which they use the DGS determines their solutions and justifications, and to document how the quality of students' justifications improves over time. The teacher guides the discussion because proof is not the most immediate socially accepted way of conviction among students. The teacher is the warrant of the respect for the justification rules established in the class. The students have a notebook of "accepted" results, which is updated at any time a new theorem has been proven. This notebook plays the role of the extendable system of commands of the DGS in Mariotti's classroom organization. In both papers there is a specific social organization in the classroom for assigning a social role to proof and increasing the need of having recourse to it.

In Hadas, Hershkowitz, and Schwarz (2000), the need for proof is mainly due to cognitive reasons and disequilibria. These authors very carefully designed two sequences of tasks in which the order of the tasks led students to develop expectations which turned out to be obviously wrong when they checked them in the dynamic geometry environment. This created a cognitive conflict and generated in students an intellectual curiosity about why this unexpected result was true. Hadas, Hershkowitz, and Schwarz created a climate of uncertainty in which students felt the need to understand better rather than simply to verify that they were wrong. Although it seems at first glance that the same sequence could be written for environments without DGS, this experiment would be impossible without DGS since the false conjectures came only in the context of other valid conjectures developed within the DGS environment. In other cases the DGS environment gave a counterexample for an expected result. This interplay of conjectures and checks, of certainty and uncertainty was made possible by the exploration power and checking facilities offered by the DGS environment.

These four studies (Hadas et al., 2000; Jones, 2000; Mariotti, 2000; Marrades & Gutiérrez, 2000) illustrate the usefulness of DGS in breaking down the traditional separation between action (as manipulation associated with observation and description) and deduction (as intellectual activity detached from specific objects). DGS contains within it the seeds for a geometry of relations as opposed to the paper-and-pencil geometry of unrelated facts. The break would be already entailed in the use of the DGS (Laborde, 2000). This could explain why students do not enter immediately the new contract of construction of figures in a DGS; they must learn it. Instead of being faced with this break at the level of formulations, in a DGS students are faced with it at the level of actions. Each of the four studies concluded with a positive evolution in the proofs elaborated by students. But it must be stressed that it results from the conjunction of the use of a DGS, of a careful design of the teaching/learning situations and of the tasks, of the social organization, and of the role of the teacher.

VAN HIELE LEVELS AND TECHNOLOGY USE IN GEOMETRY

If we compare geometry with other mathematical topics, we are faced with a unique situation in terms of learning theory. A developmental model, the "van Hiele" model, created by P. M. van Hiele and D. van Hiele-Geldof (1958) and widely propagated by the mathematician and didactician Hans Freudenthal (1973), specifically addresses the learning of geometry. A description of this model is presented in Clements, Sarama, Yelland, and Glass (2008). The van Hiele model has been used frequently in the analysis of the learning of geometry in general and plays a role when the learning context included new technology (e.g., Bell, 1998; Bobango, 1987; Choi, 1996; Frerking, 1994; Smyser, 1994). In these papers, the van Hiele model is used without question in order to "ground" the research on technology use in geometry. As a consequence, the study of computer use in geometry did not advance the van Hiele model of geometry learning, and the van Hiele model did not offer specific suggestions for research on the use of modern technology. Both topics remain rather separated and did not influence each other fundamentally. Other researchers (Olive, 1991; Pegg & Davey, 1998) have tried to create a more integrated model by making connections between the van Hiele model and other models of learning such as the SOLO taxonomy (Biggs & Collis, 1982) and Skemp's (1976) model of mathematical understanding.

DESCRIPTIVE STUDIES

Our search of the literature revealed studies that we classified as descriptive. Without identifying a psychological or epistemological perspective and without a discussion of research methods, there are interesting studies that describe the use of new technology in learning and teaching geometry. They often comment on the role of proof (Hadas & Hershkowitz, 1998, 1999; Healy, 2000; Pesci, 2000) and offer detailed information on how the new technology is used and perceived by the learner. Two German studies address the question, Is it worthwhile using the new technology? They compare instruction (especially assessment activities) in "settings" for computer-using learners/classes with instruction for students who do not use new technology (Gawlick, 2000, 2002a, 2002b; Schumann, 1994). Both studies come to a somewhat mixed conclusion. They both look into classes with students between the ages of 13 and 16 using Cabri-géomètre as DGS. Neither study strengthens the simple hope of taking new technology as a new and first royal road to geometry.

"STOFFDIDAKTIK"

A detailed analysis of German research in Mathematics Education (conducted through a content analysis of the proceedings of the yearly conferences of German-speaking didacticians called "Bundestagung für Didaktik der Mathematik") brings to light a type of research that should be mentioned: "Stoffdidaktik" provides suggestions to teach certain geometric topics in a specific way. Stoffdidaktik normally uses concepts and methods from mathematics to detail a possible way to teach geometry using DGS, for instance, inclusion of a topic (Bock & Werge, 1995); Napoleon's theorem for quadrangles (Schuster, 1993); the length of curves, especially circles, using new technology (Weth, 1995); or computer-aided teaching of three-dimensional problems in analytic geometry (Schumann 2003). Papers of this type are not interested in an analysis of the learning/ teaching process as it happens or has happened, but clearly focus on the description of a *possible* method to teach a mathematical, geometric topic. Consequently, characteristics of the learner and/or teacher are taken into consideration only in a speculative way—if ever. Empirical studies of factual learning processes are not normally part of Stoffdidaktik research. Even with the absence of a theoretical reflection on this type of research, Stoffdidaktik has a long-standing tradition in Germany and about one third of papers on new technology in secondary geometry teaching in the Bundestagung proceedings can be judged as Stoffdidaktik. A few instances of this type of research can also be found in France (see Kuntz, 1999 on inversion) and the United States (see Goldenberg, 2001).

TUTORING PROGRAMS FOR GEOMETRY LEARNING

Intelligent tutoring software programs are developed to assist students in solving problems in a variety of complex knowledge domains. We address here some research in this domain specifically devoted to geometry.

Two intelligent tutoring software programs created for geometry are based on a theory of learning and problem solving named ACT (Anderson, Corbett, Koedinger, & Pelletier, 1995): the Geometry Proof Tutor and ANGLE (A New Geometry Learning Environment) (Anderson, Boyle, & Yost, 1986; Koedinger & Anderson, 1993a, 1993b). The Geometry Proof Tutor was designed to help students construct proofs of given statements in geometry. It is based on a set of rules to represent the correct ways of solving a proof problem (ideal rules) as well as the incorrect ways ("buggy" rules). It also offers immediate feedback when the student is doing an incorrect step in the solving process and immediately proposes the correct step to the student. Researchers in mathematics education (e.g., Guin, 1996) criticized the representation of a students' proving process by a set of production rules and the immediacy of feedback.

The Geometry Proof Tutor was used in several geometry classes in urban schools located in Pennsylvania. All classes—classes for students preparing to go to college and classes for students identified as advanced in mathematics—showed statistically significant improvements on a test given at the beginning and end of the school year on geometric proofs when they used the Geometry Tutor during instruction. However, there were no statistically significant differences between students who used the Geometry Tutor and those who did not. The findings also demonstrate the tutor is much more effective when students are working one-on-one rather than when the computer is used with a pair or larger group of students (Anderson, Boyle, Corbett, & Lewis, 1990; Anderson et al., 1995).

The authors found that the cognitive model underlying the Geometry Proof Tutor did not match how human experts approached geometry proofs. Observations of expert geometry proof writers revealed that prior to executing the proof, the solver would engage in some implicit planning. During the planning phase, the solver skipped some details of the proof (e.g., relationship between congruence and equality) and focused only on the critical information. After the formulation of the solution strategy the solver filled in the details. This type of implicit planning was used to guide the construction of the diagram configuration model that led to a second geometry tutor: ANGLE (Koedinger & Anderson, 1990).

The researchers investigated the effects of ANGLE on students' abilities to write proofs in geometry in four classes in an urban U.S. school with comparison to four control classes for which there were no significant differences from the experimental classes on a pretest. Students who used ANGLE during 20 to 25 classes increased their scores from pretest to posttest by 60% (Koedinger, 1998). However, there were no significant differences on the proof posttest between the control and experimental classes. Only students in the experimental classes taught by the teacher who was involved with the project had scores on the proof test that were significantly higher than those of the control classes (Koedinger & Anderson, 1993a). This finding highlights the important role of the teacher when integrating technology into instruction (see Zbiek & Hollebrands, 2008).

In contrast to this research, a German project was interested not in "intelligence" in the computer, but rather in intelligence "spreading out across the entire pedagogical setting, with the learner at its center. Not the computer, but the learner assisted by the computer should establish diagnosis, set goals and make plans" (Holland, 1994, p. 215). A tutorial software running on personal computers offers tutorials and was developed for a specific class of geometric proof and construction problems, namely "interpolation problems" (a more recent report on this project can be seen in Holland, 2001; the public domain software is available online in German at http://www.uni-giessen.de/~gcp3/geolog.htm[12]). Interpolation problems set the task of transforming a "start situation" into a "goal situation" by stepwise applications of operators from a given set of operators known by the user. Beckmann (1996) gives a report on a teaching experiment using this tutorial system. Beckmann (2001) locates the teaching experiment in a more global view on proof development by students and concludes:

> the software stimulated a precise analyzing of the prerequisites of the proof problem and the discussion of each and every proof step and its support. Interaction was of fundamental importance. It nevertheless remained open to further investigation if an interaction or feedback from the system (in the sense of ITS or a virtual teacher) is desirable or if and how less constrained, more open feedback is more helpful. (p. 29; translated by Rudolf Sträßer)

While intelligent tutors for geometry provide us with different models that may simulate the thinking processes that students employ as they solve proofs in geometry, the research related to their effectiveness with students does not seem overwhelmingly supportive. For the most part, it appears that when regular classroom teachers use tutors, students do not do any better or worse than what they would if they did not use the tutors.

DISCUSSION

From this synthesis emerge some salient common issues among the research papers that were included in our review:

- The computer provides a window on students' understandings;

- In a DGS, construction tasks induce the need to use geometrical knowledge; and

- DGS offers a new perspective in addressing the issue of the teaching and learning of proof.

It appears that in many papers the computer acts as a window on students' understandings and construction of meaning (explicit in Noss & Hoyles, 1996; Jones 1996, 1999; but also implied even if not explicit in many papers). One may consider two reasons why technology offers a window on students' solving processes and understandings. The first is the break with the paper-and-pencil environment. Because of the novelty of the situation, students cannot follow routines they usually apply and are faced with a new situation compelling reflection, exploration, or trial and error. The successive trials or refinements offer some insight to the researcher about student' cognitive processes. The second reason is that often the use of technology requires some expression or designation of commands or primitives to be used. In the communication with the device, the mental processes of the learner are externalized.

In the window offered by DGS on students' strategies, the importance of spatial or empirical strategies in construction tasks is striking. The first reaction of students is very often to draw by eye some elements of the construction to be done. It is only in subsequent steps that students seem to overcome this empirical attitude. The question is, To what extent is this behavior due to the lack of knowledge of how to use the software or to the lack of distinction between a drawing task and a geometric construction task? However, it has been observed that after several trials and successive refinements, students very often move from an empirical strategy to a more geometric strategy. One can consider this evolution as coming from the fact that the task was situated in a DGS environment allowing the joint growth of instrumental and geometric knowledge.

Although the focus on technology as a tool shaping students' strategies is shared by several studies (from the United Kingdom and France, for example), the focus on the construction of the instrument (in the sense of Vérillon & Rabardel, 1995) by the learner seems to be restricted to a few studies. It must be noted that this framework also could be applied to some reports that do not explicitly refer to it (for example Hölzl, 1996, 2001; Jones, 1999).

The importance of studies addressing the question of proof in a computer-based environment is striking. This is, after all, not surprising since proof is especially attached to the tradition of proof in Euclidean geometry. The use of DGS sheds new light on the function of proof, as previously mentioned. Instead of checking the validity of an assertion as it does in the paper-and-pencil environment, proof in a DGS is more explanation-oriented. DGS thus allows epistemological reflection on the nature of proof to develop. It seems that the diversity of ways of designing tasks and organizing interactions in the classroom by integrating DGS is growing. It is as if it took time for the researchers themselves to construct an instrumental genesis of DGS! Some carefully designed teaching sequences based on various theoretical frameworks that were implemented, observed, and analyzed show how DGS renews the contexts for the learning of proof and offers a diversity of access to proof. This phenomenon is undoubtedly linked to the rich and open-ended nature of DGS differing from computer environments in which it is only possible to perform a restricted number of actions.

Some questions still remain open and some issues need to be more closely investigated:

- There is not yet a critical amount of research devoted to long-term teaching with regular use of DGS. Moreover, there is currently a lack of computer-supported geometry teaching. The situation may be changing, however, since researchers are beginning to conduct long-term experimental teaching based on the regular use of DGS.

- There is a need for research on the impact of such a long-term use of a DGS on the nature of students' geometric conceptions.

- Some promising features of DGS have not yet been deeply investigated. These features include macro-constructions, analytical geometry and its link with synthetic geometry, or, in the specific case of Cabri-geometry, the redefinition facility that requires a deep understanding of a construction in terms of functional dependencies.

- There is a need for research on how DGS (or other computer-supported teaching and learning) may affect the learning of 3D geometry.

The first two issues require time to be addressed. DGS must be substantially integrated into the teaching of geometry for an extended period of time in order to obtain some insights into its impact on students' conceptions. However, even if it will soon be possible to find samples of students who learned geometry with DGS on a systematic basis, the methodological question of finding effective ways to access their conceptions remains entirely open. The criticisms of large-scale comparative studies of students' performance are well known and such an investigation would certainly require carefully designed tasks.

The study of students' use of some of the features of DGS mentioned among the issues in the third bullet requires that students have an

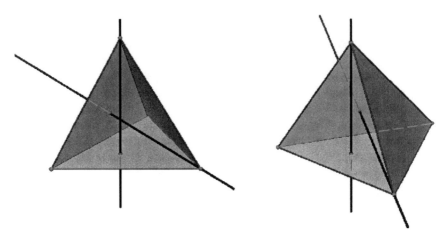

Diagram 4.11.   Two points of view on heights of a tetrahedron in Cabri 3D.

advanced conception of the DGS and hence can be done only in the context of integrated use of a DGS.

The fourth issue is probably not addressed just because 3D geometry is neglected in teaching and therefore also in research. Computer-supported technology, example, Cabri 3D (www.cabri.com,[13] illustrated in Diagram 4.11), could offer a good opportunity to revitalize the teaching of 3D geometry and investigations of the conceptual difficulties associated with some intersection and cross-section problems. The distinction between drawing and figure is reinforced in the case of 3D geometry with the two-dimensional representations of 3D objects, and again technology could offer a window on students' conceptions.

A final comment is that research investigating the learning of geometry with technology has contributed to questioning the learning processes themselves and to developing theoretical reflections or even frameworks that go beyond learning only with technology. The notions of situated abstraction and webbing were developed by researchers who have been working many years on Logo and then on other computer environments. The new potentialities of computer environments when compared to paper-and-pencil environments gave evidence of the dialectical relationship between context and generality in the construction of meaning by students for some notions such as invariant points in a transformation. Similarly, the notion of proof has been revisited and has received new interest since the time of the creation of The Geometric Supposer (Yerushalmy & Chazan, 1990) and of DGS (de Villiers, 1991). Some theoretical constructs or approaches arose in a new context. The distinction between drawing and figure was revisited with the use of DGS, and the notions of operational and discursive apprehensions developed by Duval for the paper-and-pencil environment apply to a new field in which they function differently.

Some researchers also use DGS in resonance with the Vygotskian notion of semiotic mediation and thus give a critical role to the teacher in the process of using tools for the purpose of fostering an internalization process. This role was central neither at the beginning of research on learning with microworlds nor in the genesis of the notion of microworld that was more inspired by a Piagetian approach. DGS was originally designed with a microworld philosophy, and research on its use tends to lead to further challenging theoretical perspectives. It is probably a sign of the richness of the field of research that the use of ICT for learning and teaching is offering most intriguing challenges.

APPENDIX: LIST OF REVIEWED PUBLICATIONS

An ERIC search using the keywords geometry and technology, dynamic geometry, Cabri, Geometric Supposer, Sketchpad, computers and geometry, computers and education, was conducted to locate journal articles published after 1989. The year was selected for the purpose of supplementing previous research syntheses on the learning of geometry with technology. Journals such as *Journal for Research in Mathematics Education*, *The International Journal of Computers for Mathematical Learning*, *Educational Studies in Mathematics*, *Journal of Mathematical Behavior*, *Zentralblatt für Didaktik der Mathematik*, as well as PME Conference Proceedings, and PME-NA Conference Proceedings were searched by hand. In total, about 200 studies were reviewed.

ACKNOWLEDGMENT

This chapter was supported in part by a grant from the National Science Foundation under Grant No. GER 94-54048. Any opinions, findings, and conclusions or recommendations expressed in this chapter are those of the authors and do not necessarily reflect the views of the foundation.

NOTES

1. The authors of this chapter have chosen to use "diagram" to refer to the illustrations that accompany the text—what other chapters refer to as "fig-

ures." They have chosen to do this because one of the main conceptual notions in the chapter is the distinction between diagram and figure. For consistency, they refer to the diagrams inserted in the text using the word diagram and not figure.

2. Signified refers to the meanings constructed by the individual or a community of the content at stake whereas signifier refers to its external representations.

3. A setting differs from a register in that a setting is a domain of mathematics while a register is a type of external representation or a system of signifiers satisfying the three conditions mentioned earlier.

4. For a description and discussion of the respective design decisions in various DGS see Sträßer (2001, pp. 165-187); a more global approach to this problem is presented in Laborde, 2001. Various design decisions additionally imply different mathematical consequences (Hölzl, 1994, p. 80; Sträßer, 2001, p. 186).

5. Cabri-geometry, Copyright 1988-2005, Texas Instruments: http://education.ti.com, Cabrilog: http://www.cabri.com (retrieved January 3, 2006)

6. The Geometer's Sketchpad 4, Key Curriculum Press: http://www.keypress.com (retrieved January 3, 2006)

7. Geometry Inventor, 1994, Logal Math: http://www.riverdeep.net/math/tangible_math/tm_overviews/catn.ovw_GEO.jhtml (retrieved January 3, 2006)

8. The Geometric Supposer 3, Center for Educational Technology: http://www.cet.ac.il/math-international/software5.htm (retrieved January 3, 2006)

9. The word "contract" refers here to "didactic contract" (Brousseau, 1997), the set of implicit and explicit rules governing the rights and duties of the teacher and the students with respect to the use of mathematical knowledge in the classroom.

10. For an earlier study on proof see the report in de Villiers (1991).

11. Cabri allows the user to configure the available tools and menus by adding any new construction or suppressing any tool.

12. Retrieved January 4, 2006.

13. Retrieved January 2, 2006.

REFERENCES

Anderson, J. R., Boyle, C. F., Corbett, A., & Lewis, M. (1990). Cognitive modeling and intelligent tutoring. *Artificial Intelligence, 42,* 7-49.

Anderson, J. R., Boyle, C. F., & Yost, G. (1986). The geometry tutor. *The Journal of Mathematical Behavior, 5,* 5-19.

Anderson, J. R., Corbett, A. T., Koedinger, K., & Pelletier, R. (1995). Cognitive tutors: Lessons learned. *The Journal of the Learning Sciences, 4,* 167-207.

Arcavi, A., & Hadas, N. (2000). Computer mediated learning: An example of an approach. *International Journal of Computers for Mathematical Learning, 5,* 25-45.

Arzarello, F., Micheletti, C., Olivero, F., Robutti, O., & Domingo, P. (1998). A model for analysing the transition to formal proofs in geometry. In A. Olivier & K. Newstead (Eds.), *Proceedings of the 22nd annual conference of the International Group for the Psychology of Mathematics Education* (Vol. 2, pp. 24-31). South Africa: University of Stellenbosch.

Arzarello, F., Micheletti, C., Olivero, F., Robutti, O., Paola, D., & Gallino, G. (1998). Dragging in Cabri and modalities of transition from conjectures to proofs in geometry. In A. Olivier & K. Newstead (Eds.), *Proceedings of the 22nd Conference of the International Group for the Psychology of Mathematics Education:* (Vol. 2, pp. 32-39). South Africa: University of Stellenbosch.

Arzarello, F., Olivero, F., Paola, D., & Robutti, O. (2002). A cognitive analysis of dragging practises in Cabri environments. *Zentralblatt für Didaktik der Mathematik, 34,* 66-72.

Bailleul, M., Comiti, C., Dorier, J.-L., Lagrange, J. B., Parzysz, B., & Salin, M. -H. (Eds.). (1999). *Actes de la IX° École d'Été de Didactique des Mathématiques* [Notes of the IX° Summer School in Didactics of Mathematics]. Caen, France: Rectorat de l'Académie de Caen.

Balacheff, N. (1987). Processus de preuve et situations de validation. *Educational Studies in Mathematics, 18,* 147-176.

Balacheff, N. (1993). Artificial intelligence and real teaching. In C. Keitel & K. Ruthven (Eds.), *Learning through computers: Mathematics education and technology* (pp. 131-158). Berlin, Germany: Springer-Verlag.

Balacheff, N., & Kaput, J. (1996). Computer based learning environments in mathematics. In A. Bishop, K. Clements, C. Keitel, J. Kilpatrick, & C. Laborde (Eds.), *International handbook of mathematics education* (pp. 469-501). Dordrecht, The Netherlands: Kluwer Academic.

Beckmann, A. (1996). Kongruenzgeometrisches Beweisen am Computer [Geometric congruence proofs on the computer]. *Praxis der Mathematik, 38,* 270-275.

Beckmann, A. (2001). Probleme beim Beweisenlernen, DGS als Lösung? [Problems in learning proof: Is DGS the answer?]. In H. -J. Elschenbroich, T. Gawlick, & H. -W. Henn (Eds.), *Zeichnung—Figur—Zugfigur* (pp. 21-30). Hildesheim, Berlin: Franzbecker.

Bell, D. (1998). Impact of an inductive conjecturing approach in a dynamic geometry-enhanced environment. (Doctoral dissertation, Georgia State University, 1998). *Dissertation Abstracts International, 59-05A,* 1498.

Bellemain, F., & Capponi, B. (1992). Spécificité de l'organisation d'une séquence d'enseignement lors de l'utilisation de l'ordinateur [Specificity of organizing a teaching sequence when using a computer]. *Educational Studies in Mathematics, 23,* 59-97.

Biggs, J., & Collis, K. (1982). *Evaluating the quality of learning: The SOLO taxonomy (Structure of Observed Learning Outcome).* New York: Academic Press.

Bobango, J. (1987). Van Hiele levels of geometric thought and student achievement in standard content and proof writing: The effect of phase-based instruction. (Doctoral dissertation, The Pennsylvania State University, 1987). *Dissertation Abstracts International, 48-10A,* 2566.

Bock, H., & Werge, C. (1995). Lösen von Stereometrieaufgaben mit Hilfe interaktiver 2-D-Software—Erfahrungen mit Schülern [Solutions of stereometric problems with the help of interactive 2-D software: Experiences with students]. In K. P. Müller (Ed.), *Beiträge zum Mathematikunterricht 1995. Vorträge auf der 29. Bundestagung für Didaktik der Mathematik vom 6. bis 10.3.1995 in Kassel* (pp. 102-105). Bad Salzdetfurth: Franzbecker.

Brousseau, G. (1997). *Theory of didactical situations in mathematics: Didactique des mathématiques 1970-1990* (N. Balacheff, M. Cooper, R. Sutherland, & V. Warfield Eds. & Trans.). Dordrecht, The Netherlands: Kluwer.

Chazan, D. (1993a). High school geometry students' justification for their views of empirical evidence and mathematical proof. *Educational Studies in Mathematics, 24*, 359-387.

Chazan, D. (1993b). Instructional implications of students' understandings of the differences between empirical verification and mathematical proof. In J. Schwartz, M. Yerushalmy, & B. Wilson (Eds.), *The geometric supposer: What is it a case of?* (pp. 107-116). Hillsdale, NJ: Erlbaum.

Chevallard, Y. (1985). *La transposition didactique* [The didactical transposition]. Grenoble, France: Editions La Pensée Sauvage.

Chevallard, Y. (1991). *La transposition didactique* [The didactical transposition] (2nd ed.). Grenoble, France: Editions La Pensée Sauvage.

Choi, S. (1996). Students' learning of geometry using computer software as a tool: Three case studies. (Doctoral dissertation, University of Georgia, 1996). *Dissertation Abstracts International, 58-02A*, 406.

Clements, D., & Battista, M. (1994). Computer environments for learning geometry. *Journal of Educational Computing Research, 10*, 173-197.

Clements, D. H, Sarama, J., Yelland, N., & Glass, B. (2008). Learning and teaching geometry with computers in the elementary and middle school. In M. K. Heid & G. W. Blume (Eds.), *Research on technology and the teaching and learning of mathematics: Vol. 1. Research syntheses* (pp. 109-154). Charlotte, NC: Information Age.

Cobb, P., Wood, T., Yackel, E., & McNeal, B. (1992). Characteristics of classroom mathematics traditions: An interactional analysis. *American Educational Research Journal, 29*, 573-604.

Confrey, J. (1995). A theory of intellectual development, part III. *For the Learning of Mathematics, 15*, 36-45.

de Villiers, M. (1991). Pupils' needs for conviction and explanation within the context of geometry. In F. Furinghetti (Ed.), *Proceedings of the 15th Conference of the International Group for the Psychology of Mathematics Education* (Vol.1, pp. 255-262). Assisi, Italy: Program Committee of the 15th PME Conference.

diSessa, A., & Abelson, H. (1986). Boxer: A reconstructible computational medium. *Communications of the ACM, 29*, 859-868.

Douady, R. (1985). The interplay between different settings. Tools-object dialectic in the extension of mathematical ability. In R. Streefland (Ed.), *Proceedings of the 9th International Conference for the Psychology of Mathematics Education* (pp. 33-52). Utrecht, The Netherlands: State University of Utrecht.

Duval, R. (1995). Geometrical pictures: Kinds of representation and specific processings. In R. Sutherland & J. Mason (Eds.), *Exploiting mental imagery with computers in mathematics education* (pp. 142-147). Berlin, Germany: Springer-Verlag.

Duval, R. (1998). Geometry from a cognitive point of view. In C. Mammana & V. Villani (Eds.), *Perspectives on the teaching of geometry for the 21st century* (pp. 37-52). Dordrecht, The Netherlands: Kluwer Academic.

Duval, R. (2000). Basic issues for research in mathematics education. In T. Nakahara & M. Koyama (Eds.), *Proceedings of the 24th Conference of the International Group for the Psychology of Mathematics Education* (Vol. 1, pp. 55-69). Hiroshima, Japan: Hiroshima University.

Edwards, L. (1992). A comparison of children's learning in two interactive computer environments. *Journal of Mathematical Behavior, 11,* 73-81.

Edwards, L. (1998). Exploring the territory before proof: Students' generalizations in a computer microworld for transformation geometry. *International Journal of Computers for Mathematical Learning, 2,* 187-215.

Falcade, R., Mariotti, M., & Laborde, C. (2004). Towards a definition of function. In M. Johnsen Hoines & A. B. Fuglestad (Eds.), *Proceedings of the 28th Conference of the International Group for the Psychology of Mathematics Education* (Vol. 2, pp. 367-374). Bergen, Norway: Bergen University College.

Fishbein, E. (1993). The theory of figural concepts. *Educational Studies in Mathematics, 24,* 139-162.

Flanagan, K. (2001). *High school students' understandings of geometric transformations in the context of a technological environment.* Unpublished doctoral dissertation, Pennsylvania State University, University Park.

Frerking, B. (1994). Conjecturing and proof-writing in dynamic geometry. (Doctoral dissertation, Georgia State University, 1994). *Dissertation Abstracts International, 55-12A,* 3772.

Freudenthal, H. (1973). *Mathematics as an educational task.* Dordrecht, The Netherlands: Reidel.

Fuglestad, A. B. (2004). ICT tools and students' competence development. In M. Johnsen Hoines & A. B. Fuglestad (Eds.), *Proceedings of the 28th Conference of the International Group for the Psychology of Mathematics Education* (Vol. 2, pp. 439-446). Bergen, Norway: Bergen University College.

Furinghetti, F., & Paola, D. (2003). To produce conjectures and to prove them within a dynamic geometry environment: A case study. In N. A. Pateman, B. J. Dougherty, & J. T. Zilliox (Eds.), *Proceedings of the Joint Meeting of the International Group for the Psychology of Mathematics Education and the North American Chapter* (Vol. 2, pp. 397-404). Hawaii: University of Hawaii, College of Education, CRDG.

Gawlick, T. (2000). Eine Studie zum Einfluß des Einsatzes von Dynamischer Geometrie-Software im anwendungsorientierten Geometrieunterricht. In M. Neubrand (Ed.), *Beiträge zum Mathematikunterricht 2000. Vorträge auf der 34. Bundestagung für Didaktik der Mathematik vom 28.2. bis 3. März 2000 in Potsdam* [A study of the influence of elements of dynamic geometry software in application-oriented geometry instruction] (pp. 213-216). Hildeheim, Franzbecker.

Gawlick, T. (2002a). Differential effects of dynamic geometry software on the acquisition of basic geometric notions. In A. D. Cockburn & E. Nardi (Eds.),

Proceedings of the 26th Annual Conference of the International Group for the Psychology of Mathematics Education (Vol. 2, pp. 2-416 – 2-421). Norwich: University of East Anglia, School of Education and Professional Development.

Gawlick, T. (2002b). On dynamic geometry software in the regular classroom. *Zentralblatt für Didaktik der Mathematik, 34*, 85-92.

Goldenberg, E. P. (1995). Rumination about dynamic imagery. In R. Sutherland & J. Mason (Eds.), *NATO ASI Series F: Vol. 138. Exploiting mental imagery with computers in mathematics education* (pp. 202-224). Heidelberg, Germany: Springer-Verlag.

Goldenberg, E. P. (2001). Getting Euler's line to relax. *International Journal of Computers for Mathematical Learning, 6*, 215-228.

Goldenberg, E. P., & Cuoco, A. (1998). What is dynamic geometry? In R. Lehrer & D. Chazan (Eds.), *Designing learning environments for developing understanding of geometry and space* (pp. 351-368). Mahwah, NJ: Erlbaum.

Goldenberg, E. P., Cuoco, A., & Mark, J. (1998). A role for geometry in general education. In R. Lehrer & D. Chazan (Eds.), *Designing learning environments for developing understanding of geometry and space* (pp. 3-44). Mahwah, NJ: Erlbaum.

Guin, D. (1996). A cognitive analysis of geometry proof focused on intelligent tutoring systems. In J. -M. Laborde (Ed.), *Intelligent learning environments: The case of geometry* (pp. 82-93). Berlin, Germany: Springer-Verlag.

Hadas, N., & Hershkowitz, R. (1998). *Proof in geometry as an explanatory and convincing tool.* In A. Oliver & K. Newstead (Eds.), *Proceedings of the 22nd Annual Conference of the International Group for the Psychology of Mathematics Education* (Vol. 2, pp. 25-32). Stellenbosch, South Africa: University of Stellenbosch.

Hadas, N., & Hershkowitz, R. (1999). *The role of uncertainty in constructing and proving in computerized environment.* In O. Zaslavsky (Ed.), *Proceedings of the 23rd Conference of the International Group for the Psychology of Mathematics Education (PME 23)* (pp. 57-64). Haifa: Israel Institute of Technology.

Hadas, N., Hershkowitz, R., & Schwarz, B. (2000). The role of contradiction and uncertainty in promoting the need to prove in dynamic geometry environments. *Educational Studies in Mathematics, 44*, 127-150.

Hanna, G. (1998). Proof as explanation in geometry. *Focus on Learning Problems in Mathematics, 20*, 4-13.

Harada, K., Gallou-Dumiel, E., & Nohda, N. (2000). The role of figures in geometrical proof-problem solving—students' cognitions of geometrical figures in France and Japan. In T. Nakahara & M. Koyama (Eds.), *Proceedings of the 24th Conference of the International Group for the Psychology of Mathematics Education* (Vol. 3. pp. 25-32). Hiroshima, Japan: Hiroshima University.

Healy, L. (2000). Identifying and explaining geometrical relationships: Interactions with robust and soft Cabri constructions. In T. Nakahara & M. Koyama (Eds.), *Proceedings of the 24th Conference of the International Group for the Psychology of Mathematics Education* (Vol. 1, pp. 103-117). Hiroshima, Japan: Hiroshima University.

Hershkowitz, R., & Schwarz, B. (1999). Reflective processes in a technology-based mathematics classroom. *Cognition and Instruction, 17*, 65-91.

Hillel, J., & Kieran, C. (1987). Schemas used by 12-year-olds in solving selected Turtle Geometry tasks. *Recherches en Didactique des Mathématiques, 8*, 61-102.

Hillel, J., Kieran, C., & Gurtner, J. (1989). Solving structured geometric tasks on the computer: The role of feedback in generating strategies. *Educational Studies in Mathematics, 20*, 1-39.

Holland, G. (1994). Intelligent tutorial systems. In R. Biehler, R. W. Scholz, R. Sträßer, & B. Winkelmann (Eds.), *Didactics of mathematics as a scientific discipline* (pp. 213-223). Dodrecht: Kluwer.

Holland, G. (2001). Wissensbasierte Experten in einem dynamischen Geometriesystem. In H. -J. Elschenbroich, T. Gawlick, & H. -W. Henn (Eds.), *Zeichnung—Figur—Zugfigur* [Knowledge-based experts in a dynamic geometry system] (pp. 103-112). Hildesheim, Berlin, Germany: Franzbecker. German version retrieved January 4, 2006, from http://www.uni-giessen.de/~gcp3/geolog.htm

Hollebrands, K. (2002). The role of a dynamic software program for geometry in high school students developing understandings of geometric transformations. In D. Mewborn (Ed.), *Proceedings of the 24th annual meeting of the North American Chapter of the International Group for the Psychology of Mathematics Education* (pp. 695-706). Columbus, OH: ERIC Clearinghouse for Science, Mathematics, and Environmental Science Education.

Hollebrands, K. (2003). High school students' understandings of geometric transformations in the context of a technological environment. *Journal of Mathematical Behavior, 22* , 55-72.

Hölzl, R. (1994). *Im Zugmodus der Cabri-Geometrie. Interaktionsstudien und Analysen zum Mathematiklernen mit dem Compute*r [The drag mode of Cabri-Geometry. Investigation and analysis of mathematics learning with the computer]. Weinheim, Germany: Deutscher Studien Verlag.

Hölzl, R. (1995). Eine empirische Untersuchung zum Schülerhandeln mit Cabri-géomètre [An empirical study of student activity with Cabri-Geometry]. *Journal für Mathematik-Didaktik, 1/2*, 79-113.

Hölzl, R. (1996). How does the dragging affect the learning of geometry? *International Journal of Computers for Mathematical Learning, 1*, 169-187.

Hölzl, R. (1999). *Qualitative Unterrichtsstudien zur Verwendung dynamischer Geometrie-Software* [Qualitative instructional studies of use of dynamic geometry software]. Augsburg, Germany: Habilitation Universität Augsburg.

Hölzl, R. (2001). Using dynamic geometry software to add constrast to geometric situations: A case study. *International Journal of Computers for Mathematical Learning, 6*, 63-86.

Hoyles, C. (1998). A culture of proving in school mathematics. In D. Tinsley & D. Johnson (Eds.), *Information and communication technologies in school mathematics* (pp. 169-181). London: Chapman and Hall.

Hoyles, C., & Healy, L. (1997). Unfolding meanings for reflective symmetry. *International Journal of Computers for Mathematical Learning, 2*, 27-59.

Hoyles, C., Noss, R., & Kent, P. (2004). On the integration of digital technologies into mathematics classrooms. *International Journal of Computers for Mathematical Learning, 9*, 309-326.

Hoyles, C., & Sutherland, R. (1990). Pupil collaboration and teaching interventions in the Logo environment. *Journal für Mathematik-Didaktik*, *90*, 324-343.

Hoyos, V. (2002). Coordinating mediation of activity in the learning of geometrical transformations. In D. Mewborn (Ed.), *Proceedings of the 24th annual meeting of the North American Chapter of the International Group for the Psychology of Mathematics Education* (Vol. 2, pp. 707-716). Columbus, OH: ERIC Clearinghouse for Science, Mathematics, and Environmental Science.

Jackiw, N. (2001). The Geometer's Sketchpad (Version 4.0) [Computer software]. Emeryville, CA: Key Curriculum Technologies.

Jahn, A. -P. (2000). New tools, new attitudes to knowledge: The case of geometric loci and transformations in dynamic geometry environment. In T. Nakahara & M. Koyama (Eds.), *Proceedings of the 24th Conference of the International Group for the Psychology of Mathematics Education* (Vol. 1, pp. 91-102). Hiroshima, Japan: Hiroshima University.

Jahn, A-P. (2002). "Locus" and "trace" in Cabri-géomètre: Relationships between geometric and functional aspects in a study of transformations. *Zentralblatt für Didaktik der Mathematik*, *34*, 78-84.

Jones, K. (1996). Coming to know about dependency within a dynamic geometry environment. In L. Puig & A. Gutierez (Eds.), *Proceedings of the 20th annual conference of the International Group for the Psychology of Mathematics Education* (Vol. 3, pp. 145-151). Valencia, Spain: University of Valencia.

Jones, K. (1999). Students' interpretations of a dynamic geometry environment. In I. Schwank (Ed.), *Proceedings of the First Conference of the European Society for Research in Mathematics Education* (Vol. 1, pp. 249-258). Osnabrück, Germany: Forschungsinstitut für Mathematikdidaktik.

Jones, K. (2000). Providing a foundation for deductive reasoning: Students' interpretations when using dynamic geometry software and their evolving mathematical explanations. *Educational Studies in Mathematics, 44*, 55-85.

Kadunz, G. (2002). Macros and modules in geometry. *Zentralblatt für Didaktik der Mathematik*, *34*, 73-77.

Kakihana, K., Shimizu, K., & Nohda, N. (1996). From measurement to conjecture and proof in geometry problem. In L. Puig & A. Gutierez (Eds.), *Proceedings of the 20th annual conference of the International Group for the Psychology of Mathematics Education* (Vol. 3, pp. 161-168). Spain: University of Valencia.

Kaput, J. (1992). Technology and mathematics education. In D. Grouws (Ed.), *Handbook of research on mathematics teaching and learning* (pp. 515-556). New York: Macmillan.

Kaput, J. (1995). Creating cybernetic and psychological ramps from the concrete to the abstract: Examples from multiplicative structures. In D. Perkins, J. Schwartz, M. West, & M. Wiske (Eds.), *Software goes to school: Teaching for understanding with new technologies* (pp. 130-154). New York: Oxford University Press.

Keskessa, B. (1994). Preuve et plans des signification: une hypothèse [Proof and signification plans: an hypothesis]. *Recherches en Didactique des Mathématiques, 14*, 357-391.

Koedinger, K. (1998). Conjecturing and argumentation in high-school geometry students. In R. Lehrer & D. Chazan (Eds.), *Designing learning environments for developing understanding of geometry and space* (pp. 319-347). Mahwah, NJ: Erlbaum.

Koedinger, K., & Anderson, J. (1990). Abstract planning and perceptual chunks: Elements of expertise in geometry. *Cognitive Science, 14,* 511-550.

Koedinger, K., & Anderson, J. (1993a). Effective use of intelligent software in high school math classrooms: Artificial intelligence in education. In S. Ohlsson (Ed.), *Proceedings of the World Conference on Artificial Intelligence in Education* (pp. 241-248). Charlottesville, VA: Association for the Advancement of Computing in Education.

Koedinger, K., & Anderson, J. R. (1993b). Reifying implicit planning in geometry: Guidelines for model-based intelligent tutoring system design. In S. P. Lajoie & S. J. Derry (Eds.), *Computers as cognitive tools* (pp. 15-46). Hillsdale, NJ: Erlbaum.

Kordaki, M., & Potari, D. (2002). The effect of area measurement tools on students strategies: The role of a computer microworld. *International Journal of Computers for Mathematical Learning, 7,* 65-100.

Kortenkamp, U., & Richter-Gebert, X. (2001) Decision complexity in dynamic geometry. In D. Wang (Ed.), *Proceedings of ADG 2000, Lecture Notes in Artificial Intelligence 2061* (pp. 167-172). Heidelberg, Germany: Springer-Verlag.

Kuntz, G. (1999). Une classe bousculée par les nouvelles technologies relate son expérience [A class overturned by new technologies recounts its experience]. *Association des Professeurs de Mathématiques de L'Enseignement Public, 422,* 308-312.

Kynigos, C., & Psycharis, G. (2003). 13-year-olds' meanings around intrinsic curves with a medium for symbolic expression and dynamic manipulation. In N. A. Pateman, B. J. Dougherty, & J. T. Zilliox (Eds.), *Proceedings of the Joint Meeting of the International Group for the Psychology of Mathematics Education and the North American Chapter* (Vol. 3, pp. 165-172). University of Hawaii, College of Education, CRDG.

Laborde, C. (1993). The computer as part of the learning environment: The case of geometry. In C. Keitel & K. Ruthven (Eds.), *Learning from computers: Mathematics education and technology* (pp. 48-67). Berlin, Germany: Springer Verlag.

Laborde, J. -M. (1999). Some issues raised by the development of implemented dynamic geometry as with Cabri-geometry, plenary address. In H. Brönnimann (Ed.), *Proceedings of the 15th European Workshop on Computational Geometry* (pp. 7-19). Sophia Antipolis, France: INRIA.

Laborde, C. (2000). Dynamic geometry environments as a source of rich learning contexts for the complex activity of proving. *Educational Studies in Mathematics, 44,* 151-161.

Laborde, J. -M. (2001). Zur Begründung der dynamischen Geometrie [Foundation of dynamic geometry]. In H. -J. Elschenbroich, T. Gawlick, & H. -W. Henn (Eds.), *Zeichnung—Figur—Zugfigur* (pp. 161-172). Hildesheim, Berlin: Franzbecker.

Laborde, C., & Capponi, B. (1994). Cabri-géomètre constituant d'un milieu pour l'apprentissage de la notion de figure géométrique [Cabri-geométrè constituting a milieu for learning the idea of geometric figure]. *Recherches en Didactique des Mathématiques, 14,* 165-210.

Laborde, J. -M., & Sträßer, R. (1990). Cabri-géomètre, a microworld of geometry for guided discovery learning. *Zentralblatt für Didaktik der Mathematik, 90*, 171-190.

Leron, U., & Hazzan, O. (1998). Computers and applied constructivism. In D. Tinsley & D. C. Johnson (Eds.), *Information and communications technologies in school mathematics* (pp. 195-203). London: Chapman and Hall.

Leung, A. (2003). Dynamic geometry and the theory of variation. In N. A. Pateman, B. J. Dougherty, & J. T. Zilliox (Eds.), *Proceedings of the Joint Meeting of the International Group for the Psychology of Mathematics Education and the North American Chapter* (Vol. 3, pp. 197-204). Hawaii: University of Hawaii, College of Education, CRDG.

Leung, A., & Lopez-Real, F. (2004). Theorem justification and acquisition in dynamic geometry: A case of proof by contradiction. *International Journal of Computers for Mathematical Learning, 7*, 145-165.

Mariotti, M. -A. (2000). Introduction to proof: The mediation of a dynamic software environment. *Educational Studies in Mathematics, 44*, 25-53.

Mariotti, M. -A. (2001). Influence of technological advances on students' math learning. In L. English, M. G. Bartolini Bussi, G. Jones, R. Lesh, & D. Tirosh (Eds.), *Handbook of international research in mathematics education* (pp. 695-723). Mahwah, NJ: Erlbaum.

Mariotti, M. -A., Laborde, C., & Falcade, R. (2003). Function and graph in DGS environment. In N. Pateman, B. Dougherty, & J. Zilliox (Eds.), *Proceedings of the 2003 Joint Meeting of the International Group for the Psychology of Mathematics Education the North American Chapter:* (Vol. 3, pp. 237-243). Hawaii: University of Hawaii, College of Education, CRDG.

Marrades, R., & Guttierez, A. (2000). Proofs produced by secondary school students learning geometry in a dynamic computer environment. *Educational Studies in Mathematics, 44*, 87-125.

Minsky, M., & Papert, S. (1971). *Research at the laboratory in vision, language and other problems of intelligence.* Cambridge, MA: MIT Press.

Noss, R., & Hoyles, C. (1996). *Windows on mathematical meanings.* Dordrecht, The Netherlands: Kluwer.

Noss, R., Hoyles, C., Healy, L., & Hölzl, R. (1994). Constructing meanings for constructing: An exploratory study with Cabri-geometry. In J. da Ponte, J. Matos, & J. Filipe (Eds.), *Proceedings of the 18th Conference of the International Group for the Psychology of Mathematics Education* (Vol. 3, pp. 360-367). Lisbon, Portugal: University of Lisbon.

Olive, J. (1991). Logo programming and geometric understanding: An in-depth study. *Journal for Research in Mathematics Education, 22*, 90-111.

Olivero, F. (2002). *The proving process within a dynamic geometry environment.* Unpublished doctoral dissertation, University of Bristol, United Kingdom.

Olivero, F., & Robutti, O. (2002). How much does Cabri do the work for the students? In A. D. Cockburn & E. Nardi (Eds.), *Proceedings of the 26th annual conference of the International Group for the Psychology of Mathematics Education* (Vol. 4, pp. 9-16). Norwich, United Kingdom: University of East Anglia, School of Education and Professional Development.

Parzysz, B. (1988). Knowing versus seeing: Problems of the plane representation of space geometry figures. *Educational Studies in Mathematics*, *19*, 79-92.

Pegg, J., & Davey, G. (1998). Interpreting student understanding in geometry: A synthesis of two models. In R. Lehrer & D. Chazan (Eds.), *Designing learning environments for developing understanding of geometry and space* (pp. 109-136). Mahwah, NJ: Erlbaum.

Pesci, A. (2000). The properties of necessity and sufficiency in the construction of geometric figures with Cabri. In T. Nakahara & M. Koyama (Eds.), *Proceedings of the 24th Conference of the International Group for the Psychology of Mathematics Education: Vol. 4* (pp. 73-80). Japan: University of Hiroshima.

Pratt, D., & Ainley, J. (1996). Construction of meanings for geometric construction: Two contrasting cases. *International Journal of Computers for Mathematical Learning*, *1*, 293-322.

Pratt, D., & Davison, I. (2003). Interactive whiteboards and the construction of definitions for the kite. In N. A. Pateman, B. J. Dougherty, & J. T. Zilliox (Eds.), *Proceedings of the Joint Meeting of the International Group for the Psychology of Mathematics Education and the North American Chapter* (Vol. 4, pp. 31-38). Hawaii: University of Hawaii, College of Education, CRDG.

Robert, A. (1998). Outils d'analyse des contenus mathématiques à enseigner au lycée et à l'université [Tools for analyzing mathematical content for teaching at the lycee and the university]. *Recherches en didactique des mathématiques*, *18*, 139-190.

Rolet, C. (1996). *Dessin et figure en géométrie: analyse et conceptions de futurs enseignants dans le contexte Cabri-géomètre* [Drawing and figure in geometry: future teachers' analysis and design in the context of Cabri-geométrè]. Unpublished doctoral dissertation, University of Lyon, France.

Sanchez, E., & Sacristan, A. I. (2003). Influential aspects of dynamic geometry activities in the construction of proofs. In N. A. Pateman, B. J. Dougherty, & J. T. Zilliox (Eds.), *Proceedings of the Joint Meeting of the International Group for the Psychology of Mathematics Education and the North American Chapter* (Vol. 4, pp. 111-118). Hawaii: University of Hawaii, College of Education, CRDG.

Santos, M., Aguero, E., Borbon, A., & Paez, C. (2003). Students' use of technology in mathematical problem solving: Transforming technological artifacts into mathematical tools. In N. A. Pateman, B. J. Dougherty, & J. T. Zilliox (Eds.), *Proceedings of the Joint Meeting of the International Group for the Psychology of Mathematics Education and the North American Chapter* (Vol. 4, pp. 119-126). Hawaii: The University of Hawaii, College of Education, CRDG.

Saraiva, M. J. (1992). Students' understanding of proof in a computer environment. In W. Geeslin & K. Graham (Eds.), *Proceedings of the 16th Conference of the International Group for the Psychology of Mathematics Education* (Vol. 2, pp. 290-297). Durham, NH: University of New Hampshire.

Scher, D. (2001). *Students' conceptions of geometry in a dynamic geometry software environment*. Unpublished doctoral dissertation, New York University.

Schumann, H. (1994). Der Computer als interaktives Konstruktionswerkzeug im Geometrieunterricht der Sekundarstufe I: Planung, Durchführung und Ergebnisse einer Medienvergleichsuntersuchung [The computer as interactive construction tool in secondary school geometry instruction: Planning, implementation, and results of a median comparison investigation]. In K. P. Müller (Ed.), *Beiträge zum Mathematikunterricht 1994. Vorträge auf der 28. Bundestagung für Didaktik der Mathematik vom 28.2. bis 4.3.1994 in Duisburg* (pp. 346-349). Bad Salzdetfurth, Germany: Franzbecker.

Schumann, H. (2003). Computer aided treatment of 3d-problems in analytic geometry. *Zentralblatt für Didaktik der Mathematik, 35,* 7-13.

Schuster, W. (1993). Der Satz von Napoleon im Falle des Vierecks [Napoleon's Theorem for the case of quadrilaterals]. In K. P. Müller (Ed.), *Beiträge zum Mathematikunterricht 1993. Vorträge auf der 27. Bundestagung für Didaktik der Mathematik vom 22.3. bis 26.3.1993 in Freiburg/Schweiz* (pp. 335-339). Bad Salzdetfurth: Franzbecker.

Schwartz, J., & Yerushalmy, M. (1987). The Geometric Supposer: An intellectual prosthesis for making conjectures. *College Math Journal, 18,* 58-65.

Sinclair, M. (2003). Some implications of the results of a case study for the design of pre-constructed, dynamic geometry sketches and accompanying materials. *Educational Studies in Mathematics, 52,* 289-317.

Skemp, R. (1976). Relational understanding and instrumental understanding. *Mathematics Teaching, 77,* 20-26.

Smith, C. (2002). Designing tasks to explore dragging within soft constructions using Cabri-géomètre. In A. D. Cockburn & E. Nardi (Eds.), *Proceedings of the 26th annual conference of the International Group for the Psychology of Mathematics Education (PME 26)* (Vol. 4, pp. 4-217 – 4-224). Norwich, England: University of East Anglia, School of Education and Professional Development.

Smyser, E. (1994). The effects of the Geometric Supposers: Spatial ability, van Hiele levels, and achievement. *Dissertation Abstracts International, 55-06A,* 1498. (UMI No. AAI9427802)

Stevenson, I., & Noss, R. (1998). Supporting the evolution of mathematical meanings: The case of Non-Euclidean Geometry. *International Journal of Computers for Mathematical Learning, 3,* 229-254.

Sträßer, R. (1992). Didaktische Perspektiven auf Werkzeug-Software im Geometrie-Unterricht der Sekundarstufe I [Didactic perspectives on tool software in secondary school geometry instruction] . *Zentralblatt für Didaktik der Mathematik, 24,* 197-201.

Sträßer, R. (2001). Chancen und Probleme des Zugmodus [Prospects of and problems with the drag mode]. In H. -J. Elschenbroich, T. Gawlick, & H. -W. Henn (Eds.), *Zeichnung—Figur—Zugfigur* (pp. 183-194). Hildesheim-Berlin: Franzbecker.

Sträßer, R. (2002). Research on dynamic geometry software (DGS)—An introduction. *Zentralblatt für Didaktik der Mathematik, 34,* 65.

Sutherland, R., & Balacheff, N. (1999). Didactical complexity of computational environments for the learning of mathematics. *International Journal of Computers for Mathematical Learning, 4,* 1-26.

Talmon, V., & Yerushalmy, M. (2004). Understanding dynamic behavior: Parent-child relations in dynamic geometry environments. *Educational Studies in Mathematics, 57,* 91-119.

Thompson, P. W. (1987). Mathematical microworlds and intelligent computer assisted instruction. In G. E. Kearsley (Ed.), *Artificial intelligence and instruction: Applications and methods* (pp. 83-109). Reading, MA: Addison Wesley.

Vadcard, L. (1999). La validation en géométrie au Collège avec Cabri-géomètre: mesures exploratoires et mesures probatoires [Validation in college geometry with Cabri-geométrè: exploratory measures and preliminary measures] . *Petit x, 50*, 5-21.

van Hiele, P. M., & van Hiele-Geldof, D. (1958). A method of initiation into geometry at secondary school. In H. Freudenthal (Ed.), *Report on methods of intiation into geometry* (pp. 67-80). Groningen, The Netherlands: J. B. Wolters.

Vérillon, P., & Rabardel, P. (1995). Cognition and artifacts: A contribution to the study of thought in relation to instrumented activity. *European Journal of Psychology in Education, 9*, 77-101.

Vygotsky, L. S. (1978). *Mind in society. The development of higher psychological processes.* Cambridge, MA: Harvard University Press.

Weth, T. (1995). Der Computer als Werkzeug in der Hand des Lehrers im Geometrieunterricht [The computer as tool in the hand of geometry students]. In K. P. Müller (Ed.), *Beiträge zum Mathematikunterricht 1995: Vorträge auf der 29. Bundestagung für Didaktik der Mathematik vom 6. bis 10. März 1995 in Kassel* (pp. 516-519). Hildesheim, Germany: Franzbecker.

Yerushalmy, M., & Chazan, D. (1990). Overcoming visual obstacles with the aid of the Supposer. *Educational Studies in Mathematics, 21*, 199-219.

Zbiek, R. M., & Hollebrands, K. (2006). A research-informed view of the process of incorporating mathematics technology into classroom practice by inservice and prospective teachers. In M. K. Heid and G. W. Blume (Eds.), *Research on technology and the teaching and learning of mathematics: Vol. 1. Research syntheses* (pp. 287-344). Charlotte, NC: Information Age.

CHAPTER 5

TECHNOLOGY AND CALCULUS

David Tall, David Smith, and Cynthia Piez

Of all the areas in collegiate mathematics, calculus has received the most interest and investment in the use of technology. Initiatives around the world have introduced a range of innovative approaches from programming numerical algorithms in various programming languages, to use of graphic software to explore calculus concepts, to fully featured computer algebra systems such as Mathematica (Wolfram Research, 2005), Maple (Maplesoft, 2005), Derive (Texas Instruments, 2005), Theorist (no longer available, replaced by LiveMath, 2005), and Mathcad (MathSoft, 2005). The innovations arose for a wide range of reasons—some because a traditional approach to calculus was considered fundamentally unsatisfactory for many students, others because "technology is available, so we should use it." Most innovators had a pragmatic approach, trying out new ideas to see if they worked. Some began with a theory that formulated how the enterprise should work, others formulated their theories in the light of successive years of experience.

Technology brought with it new market-driven factors in which large companies cooperated with educators to develop new tools. The first round of materials development produced a competitive situation, often with the main objective being to get the materials adopted. The early years of using technology in calculus were characterized by hopeful

Research on Technology and the Teaching and Learning of Mathematics:
Vol. 1. Research Syntheses, pp. 207–258
Copyright © 2008 by Information Age Publishing

enthusiasm and based on little documentation about the true success of the new ideas. The system was complex, and the wider effects of the changes would take several years to become apparent. Opinions were many and informed observations few. Over recent years, evaluations of reforms and research on the learning of calculus have begun to provide some answers about the effects of using technology in teaching and learning calculus—effects that may be positive, negative, or neutral (Ganter, 2001; Hurley, Koehn, & Ganter, 1999).

Our main aim is to report on what this research has to say to the community of mathematicians, educators, curriculum builders, and administrators. We include an analysis of the conceptual learning of calculus to put the research results in perspective. Our chapter addresses the wide range of students with different needs and aspirations who take calculus, the views of mathematicians, and the needs of society in this changing technological age.

In an article addressed to the mathematical community, Schoenfeld (2000) formulated some broad principles about the mathematics education research enterprise. He emphasized that there are no "theorems" in mathematics education that can be used to build up a theory in the way that is familiar to mathematicians, but there are issues of replicability, explanatory power, and predictive power that can be of value in reflecting on teaching and learning mathematics. These issues should be kept in mind when considering the results from research.

THE CULTURAL CONTEXTS OF THE CALCULUS

Calculus is a rich subject with a varied cultural history. It serves not only as a basis for mathematical modeling and problem solving in applications, but also as a natural pinnacle of the beauty and power of mathematics for the vast majority of calculus students who take it as their final mathematics course.

Calculus is only 350 years old. But in those three and one-half centuries it has been enriched by new perceptions and belief structures of successive generations, starting with the original conceptions of Leibniz and Newton on infinitesimals and limits. Currently we have a range of modern formal methods, from intuitive dynamic approaches to numerical, symbolic, and graphic approaches, culminating in theories ranging from formal epsilon-delta analysis, which banishes infinitesimals, to nonstandard analysis, which fully endorses them. The result is a wide range of viewpoints as to how the calculus should be conceived and taught. We therefore begin by considering some of these differing views to place our analysis in perspective.

The Views of Mathematicians

During the 1980s there arose among many mathematicians a growing concern for the quality of student learning in the calculus (Douglas, 1986). This led to the Calculus Reform movement in the United States proposing the integration of technology as one way to make the subject more meaningful to a broad range of students. Other countries, each in its own way, worked to integrate technology into their learning programs and their cultures. For example, periodic reviews of the curriculum in France turned attention to the use of technology in the transition to university mathematics (Artigue, 1990) and, in Britain, the Mathematics Association (1992) focused on the use of computers in the classroom.

The range of aspirations for a calculus reform course is exemplified by the following list of desirable characteristics summarized from the Mathematical Association of America's Subcommittee on Calculus Reform and the First Two Years (CRAFTY) (Roberts, 1996):

- Students should leave the course with a "sense of the role that calculus has played in developing a modern world view, the place it holds in intellectual as well as scientific history, and the role it continues to play in science" (p. 1).
- Students and instructors alike should find the applications real and compelling.
- Instructors should have high expectations for all students and should employ pedagogical strategies (e.g., cooperative learning, laboratory experiences) that engage students' interest and enable most to succeed.
- Students should learn to read and write carefully reasoned arguments at a level appropriate for their stage of development—intuitive at first, with rigor coming later for those who need it.

The CRAFTY committee observed:

A calculus course cannot be modernized simply by finding a way to make use of graphing calculators or computers. Neither should a modern course omit these tools where their use contributes to the goals of the course. Spelling checkers ... will not make a good writer out of a poor writer, and computer algebra systems will not make a good mathematician out of a poor one, but efficient practitioners of any art will make intelligent use of all the tools that are available. (p. 2)

The Calculus Reform provoked a vigorous debate among mathematicians. Some (e.g., MacLane, 1997; Wu, 1996) put the case for rigor and precision in mathematical thought, while others (e.g., Mumford, 1997) downplayed the emphasis on formal proof and advocated meaningful experiences to give insight into essential ideas. A vigorous correspondence ensued in the *Notices of the American Mathematical Society*, advocating a range of personal opinions based on professional experience rather than empirical research. These comments often focused on different mathematical approaches to the subject:

- "In praise of epsilon/delta." Norwood (1997) suggested that the students' problem with epsilon-delta analysis lies not in the use of Greek letters but in the students' failure to understand subtraction or absolute value.
- "Use uniform continuity to teach limits." Lax (1998) put forward the view that it was necessary to reduce the emphasis on quantification and keep the key concept of continuity closer to students' experience with functions.
- "Defining uniform continuity first does not help." Briggs (1998) responded with the comment that the problem lies not in building a foundation for rigorous arguments, but in the need for sense-making.
- "Use convergence to teach continuity." Abian (1998) suggested that the notion of convergence of sequences of function values is more intuitive than any epsilon-delta argument.
- "Teach calculus with big O." Knuth (1998) proposed the use of more intuitive order-of-magnitude notions, starting with an initial use of an "A-notation" for "absolutely at most."

Pragmatic Issues

As the debate continued, students were voting with their feet and moving away from mathematics. Between 1994 and 1996, student applications to mathematics departments in the United States declined by 32% (Maxwell & Loftsgaarden, 1997). Similar crises were building in other countries. In Germany, between 1990 and 1999 there was a decrease of 20% in the number of students registering to study mathematics and a decrease of 35% enrolling in first-semester mathematics courses (Jackson, 2000).

Even among those who follow a major course in mathematics, there is evidence that students do not retain all their knowledge as time passes. Anderson, Austin, Barnard and Jagger (1998) administered a questionnaire focused on what were considered essential, simple, first-year concepts to a selection of final-year (third-year) mathematics majors from 15 British universities. Only about 20% of the responses were "substantially correct" and almost 50% of the responses did not contain anything "credit-worthy." These data challenge the belief that an undergraduate mathematics course builds a broad conceptual understanding of the full range of mathematics in the course. It is, however, consonant with the experience of mathematics professionals who have a powerful knowledge of the mathematics that they are currently researching, but who may be less facile with other areas of mathematics, which nevertheless they may be able to reconstruct in a small amount of time (Burton, 2004).

Most students studying calculus are not mathematics majors. Kenelly and Harvey (1994) reported that 700,000 students enrolled in calculus in the United States, including about 100,000 in Advanced Placement programs in high school. Twelve thousand eight hundred twenty students graduated in 1997 with bachelor's degrees in mathematics (National Center for Educational Statistics, 1999), less than 2% of the calculus cohort. In addition to provisions for this small—but vitally important—group, it is therefore essential to take account of the needs of the other 98%. Some of these move on to science and engineering programs, using calculus in very different ways from their peers in mathematics; for many others, calculus is their last experience of mathematics in their formal education.

THE CHANGING NATURE OF THE CALCULUS IN A TECHNOLOGICAL WORLD

Successive waves of new hardware and software have made predicting the future notoriously difficult. In the early 1970s, when computers were beginning to appear on the horizon, the Mathematical Association in the United Kingdom wrote, "It is unlikely that the majority of pupils in this age range will find [a computer] so efficient, useful and convenient a calculating aid as a slide rule or book of tables" (Mathematical Association, 1974). Such illusions were soon shattered, and slide rules and books of tables lingered for only a short time before they became obsolete. It is important therefore in analyzing calculus teaching and learning to be aware of the changing landscape.

Numerical Algorithms

The first microcomputers had the BASIC programming language built in, so the first wave of enthusiasm was to encourage students to program their own numerical methods. At that time there were too few computers available in the classroom to allow programming to become universal. Nevertheless, there was widespread belief that programming would encourage students to formulate (and perhaps formalize) mathematical ideas—in particular, they might program algorithms for limit, rate of change, Riemann sums, and solutions of differential equations. Working with highly able mathematics undergraduates at Cambridge, Harding and Johnson (1979) found very positive effects on conceptual understanding and mathematical problem solving through programming mathematical algorithms. For the broader range of students, however, there is the possibility that simultaneously programming algorithms and conceptualizing mathematics may impose a great cognitive strain.

Using True BASIC to program algorithms, Cowell and Prosser (1991) reported:

> The students largely agreed that the computer assignments were well integrated with the rest of the course, and that learning the necessary programming was easy, but they disagreed that the computer enhanced their interest in the course material, they disagreed that the computer should be dropped and they were divided on whether the computer assignments were a valuable part of the course. (pp. 152–153)

In England, the Mathematical Association committee reporting on the use of computers (1992) saw the use of short programs as a definite way to improve instruction, producing *132 Short Programs for the Mathematics Classroom*. But such moves failed to take root, as other languages, such as Logo, came and went, and more powerful software environments were introduced. By the new millennium, the use of programming as a part of mathematics instruction had waned (Johnson, 2000).

New languages designed to use explicit mathematical constructions in the syntax, such as ISETL (Interactive SET Language), have been developed to introduce concepts of (finite) sets, functions, and quantifiers, through programming. Dubinsky and his colleagues (Asiala, Cottrill, Dubinsky, & Schwingendorf, 1997; Cottrill, Dubinsky, Nichols, Schwingendorf, Thomas, & Vidakovic, 1996) have reported learning gains in conceptualizing calculus using a carefully constructed learning sequence, which will be considered in detail in the following section, "Understanding of the Calculus—A spectrum of approaches."

Graphic Visualizations

In the early 1980s, high-resolution graphics brought new graphical approaches to the teaching of calculus that were designed to help students visualize mathematical ideas. There was soon considerable evidence that a visual approach employing graphs helped students to gain a wider conceptual understanding without adversely affecting their ability to cope with the corresponding symbolization (e.g., Heid, 1988; Beckmann, 1988). But on the debit side there also was evidence that the drawing of graphs involved quite subtle techniques in choosing an appropriate domain and range to give a suitable picture. Viewed in different windows with different scales on the axes, graphs could often look very different and the pictures drawn may fail to give a true and complete picture of the function of interest (Goldenberg, 1988).

Enactive Control

In 1984 the "mouse" was introduced to give the computer an enactive interface. Instead of having to type in a line of symbols, the user could now select and control the display by intuitive hand-movements. This allowed a completely different approach to learning that encouraged active exploration rather than writing procedural computations. For instance, Function Probe (Confrey, 1992; Confrey and Maloney, 2008; Smith & Confrey, 1994) allows graphs to be manipulated enactively, using the mouse to transform graphs by translating, stretching, reflecting. Such an approach treats the graph as a single object to be transformed and has the potential to relate physical movement to algebraic translations. More generally, an enactive interface allows the user to conceptualize mathematics based on underlying human perception, for instance, a first-order differential equation such as $\frac{dy}{dx} = \frac{x}{y}$ tells us the slope at each point (x, y), so a computer program can be designed to show a small line segment of a curve with the given slope (Figure 5.1). By "pointing and clicking," the line segments can be joined end to end to show a solution curve. This gives cognitive support for the insight that there is a unique solution through each point and that the solution as a whole is built up by following the direction given by the equation.

More generally, for many mathematical concepts, an enactive interface may be designed to give a "sense" of the idea that fits with our human perception. For instance, Nemirovsky, Tierney, and Wright (1998) have developed the use of motor detection devices that capture body motion or the movement of a mechanism such as a pendulum in three dimensions and graph it in real time. In this way, the transition between physical action and mathematical representation is being bridged. More generally, software with an enactive interface can be designed that provides intuitive support for ideas that have the potential both to be used in applications

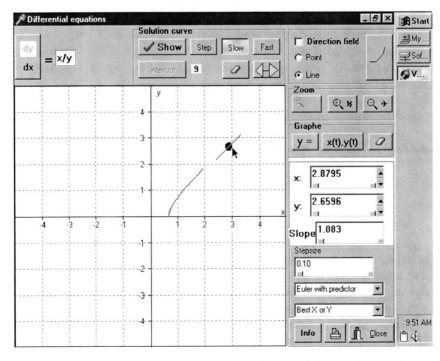

Figure 5.1.   Enactive software to explore the solutions of differential equations (Blokland, Giessen, & Tall, 2000).

of calculus and also to provide a basis for the later development of formal theory (Tall, 2001).

Computer Algebra Systems

The next stage introduced the power of computer algebra systems, bringing with it the possibility of removing the "drudgery" of symbol manipulation to allow students to concentrate on formulating solutions that could be carried out by computer algorithms (e.g., Davis, Porta, & Uhl, 1994b; Heid, 1988; Palmiter, 1991). The research literature will be considered later to seek evidence for this viewpoint. Essentially, we will find that well-designed approaches using computer algebra systems can produce considerable gains. On the other hand, students learn from what they *do*; if they press buttons in a computer algebra package without focusing on underlying conceptual ideas, they may simply learn which buttons to press (Monaghan, Sun, & Tall, 1994). In such a case, they may use the computer algebra systems to simplify an expression to a standard form. They will still need the flexibility to recognize and interpret the resulting symbolism when it is written in different ways.

Newer Technologies

Technology continues to develop at an astonishing pace, migrating from large mainframes to desktop calculators to portable calculators and portable computers that can be carried and used anywhere, anytime. The Internet allows information and software to be passed around the globe. Programs in *Java* (Sun Microsystems, 2005), *Flash* (Macromedia 2005a), or *Shockwave* (now part of *Director MX*, Macromedia, 2005b) can be ported between different hardware environments, allowing a single program to run on a wide range of machines. Computer algebra systems such as Mathematica and Maple provide the facility to write text explanations with graphical displays that can be modified and investigated experimentally. Multimedia interactive software grows ever more sophisticated, offering the learner a variety of facilities including explanatory text, spoken words, video, and interactive software to explore mathematical processes and concepts. Assessing the nature of learning with technology continues to focus on a moving target.

UNDERSTANDINGS IN THE CALCULUS—
A SPECTRUM OF APPROACHES

Traditional calculus, prior to the arrival of technology, focused on building symbolic techniques for differentiation, integration, and the solution of differential equations, complementing them where appropriate by static pictures of graphs to illustrate the phenomena involved. Technology can provide dynamic pictures under user control that can offer new insights into concepts not only in terms of traditional epsilon-delta analysis, but also in terms of more recent theories of nonstandard analysis. For instance, by highly magnifying a graph, the resulting picture may reveal that the graph is "locally straight." (Technically, the magnified picture will *look* like a straight line because of the size of the pixels.) Formally, using nonstandard analysis, in a precise technical sense, the "standard" part of the graph under infinite magnification (neglecting higher order infinitesimals) is a real straight line (see Tall, 2002 for details). Using a computer representation of the graph, by plotting a moving secant line through two close points on the graph, the learner may visualize the changing slope globally as a function rather than building it up point by point.

How does this affect the learning of calculus concepts? Those mathematicians who wish to build mathematics as a formal system may distrust visualization as containing hidden deceptions, and hence consider a visual approach lacking in rigor and precision. The formal approach, however, involves manipulation of a highly complex epsilon-delta definition with several nested quantifiers. Anecdotal observations from mathematics instructors are corroborated in empirical research that documents the extreme difficulty in using the formal limit as a foundation for teaching the calculus (Davis & Vinner, 1986; Williams, 1991).

On the other hand, a dynamic visual approach to the limit concept also has built-in conceptual difficulties. Research has shown that students imagine not only the *process* of tending to a limit, but they have a mental *concept* of a variable tending to zero as "arbitrarily small" (Cornu, 1991). Monaghan (1986) notes that, if a sequence, such as $\left\{\frac{1}{n}\right\}$, consists of a sequence of terms that tend to zero, then the mind is likely to imagine a "generic limit," which is a limiting object having the same properties as all the terms. For instance, the generic limit of $\left\{\frac{1}{n}\right\}$—which might be written by the student as $\left\{\frac{1}{\infty}\right\}$—may be conceived as a quantity that is infinitesimally small, but not zero. In the same way, every term of the sequence 0.9, 0.99, 0.999, ... is strictly less than 1, so the limit 0.999 ... may be considered as a quantity that is strictly less than one.

This view of a limiting process has a long history going back at least to the law of continuity of Kepler and Cusa, which Leibniz re-expressed in a letter to Bayle of January 1687: "In any supposed transition, ending in any terminus, it is permissible to institute a general reasoning, in which the final terminus may also be included" (quoted in Klein, 1972, p. 385). Lakoff and Núñez (2000) repackaged the same idea in a linguistic form as "the Basic Metaphor of Infinity" in which "processes that go on indefinitely are conceptualized as having an end and an ultimate result." The principle also has a biological basis in which a finite brain considering an ongoing process linking always to a particular brain structure will continue to use the link for the "ultimate result." The consequence is the mental image of variable quantities that are "arbitrarily small, but not zero" or functions that get "arbitrarily close to, but not equal to" a given limiting value. This natural product of human thought processes led to serious difficulties in the history of mathematics, requiring very subtle definitions to give satisfactory formal proofs.

Even when care is taken with the formal definitions, teaching mathematics can be subverted by the natural underlying human belief structure. Wood (1992) found that a sizeable minority of mathematics majors in their second year of analysis was able to hold simultaneously the two beliefs that "there is no *least* positive real number" but "there is a *first* positive number." Closer analysis revealed students using not one, but (at least) *two* models of the real numbers. One model uses decimals and reflects the student's dominant experience of numbers represented to a finite number of places that are naturally discrete, just as numbers on a computer are discrete. For instance, if numbers were represented to only four decimal places, then after 0.0000 comes 0.0001, then 0.0002, and so on. Likewise a computer with finite floating point arithmetic has a precise least positive number given by a single digital bit in some floating point representation. A natural extension for the human mind is to believe that after the "infinite decimal" 0.000...0 comes 0.000...1 (with an infinite number of zeros, followed by a 1, which might be written as 1 − 0.999...), which is the "first" positive number. The alternative continuous model of the real number line cannot have a "least positive" number because if a is positive, then $\frac{a}{2}$ is also positive but smaller.

Lakoff and Núñez (2000) formulate this beautifully by describing the real numbers as a "metaphorical blend" of two quite different metaphors, one a visual geometric metaphor of the "real line" that one can, in the mind's eye, trace with a finger, and another as a numerical metaphor building up from counting and measuring number activities. There is also a third metaphor, which is different again, described formally as a complete ordered field. These different metaphors, considered to be mathematically identical are cognitively very different. For instance, numerically a point has no size, but geometrically they stand together to give an interval of nonzero length.

Faced with a conflict between formalism and visual structure, formal mathematicians, in true Bourbakian style, distrust visualization as containing subtle aspects that conspire to deceive so they rely totally on the formal theory. However, many of their students and their colleagues in other fields have a "metaphorical blend" view of numbers that includes such anomalies. There are two ways out of this dilemma. One is to take a purely formal view and deal exclusively with mathematical symbols and quantified statements; this has proved to be notoriously difficult for the majority of students. The other is to educate visual intuition so that it is sound enough to build upon. For instance, Tall (1993, 2001) proposes ways in which visual ideas are translated directly into formal definitions to give mental images of formal concepts that can later be translated into formal proofs. Both strategies have been implemented using technology, leading to quite different approaches to the calculus. Both are also widely used by professional mathematicians in their research.

A Symbolic Approach to Calculus Using a Mathematical Programming Language

An approach to constructing mathematical concepts with both symbolic and psychological underpinnings has been designed by Dubinsky, a mathematician and a dedicated student of the theory of Jean Piaget. Dubinsky's approach uses the mathematical programming language ISETL in a carefully designed sequence of activities based on Piaget's theory of reflective abstraction. He and his colleagues have formulated a theory of cognitive development with the acronym APOS (Action-Process-Object-Schema):

> An action is any physical or mental transformation of objects to obtain other objects. It occurs as a reaction to stimuli which the individual perceives as external. It may be a single step response, such as a physical reflex, or an act of recalling some fact from memory. It may also be a multistep response, but then it has the characteristic that at each step, the next step is triggered by what has come before, rather than by the individual's conscious control of the transformation.... When the individual reflects upon an action, he or she may begin to establish conscious control over it. We would then say that the action is interiorized, and it becomes a process.... [Then] actions, processes and objects ... are organized into structures, which we refer to as schemas. (Cottrill, et al., 1996, p. 171)

Using this theory, Cottrill and colleagues (1996) formulated a "preliminary genetic decomposition" of the limit of a function f as the input value, x, approaches a as follows:

1. The action of evaluating the function f at a few points, each successive point closer to a than the previous point.
2. Interiorization of the action of Step 1 to a single process in which $f(x)$ approaches L as x approaches a. [This step was modified later in the paper in the light of empirical research to refer to the coordination of *two* processes, as "$x \rightarrow a$," and "$f(x) \rightarrow L$."]
3. Encapsulate the process of Step 2 so that, for example, in talking about combination properties of limits, the limit process becomes an object to which actions (e.g., determine if a certain property holds) can be applied.

4. Reconstruct the process of Step 2 in terms of intervals and inequalities. This is done by introducing numerical estimates of the closeness of approach, in symbols, $0 < |x - a| < \delta$ and $|f(x) - L| < \varepsilon$.

5. Apply a quantification schema to connect the reconstructed process of the previous step to obtain the formal definition of limit ... applying this definition is a process in which one imagines iterating through all positive numbers, and, for each one called ε, visiting every positive number, called δ this time, considering each value, called x in the appropriate interval, and checking the inequalities. The implication and the quantification lead to a decision as to whether the definition is satisfied.

6. A completed ε-δ conception applied to specific situations (Cottrill et al., 1996, p. 174).

This detailed analysis allowed the researchers to study the development in great detail, leading to the recognition of the need for an extra initial step in which $f(x)$ is evaluated at a single point near, or equal to, a, before focusing on the process of calculating numeric values as x approaches a. More significantly, the research revealed, in the context of an x-y coordinate system, that the limiting process, "as $x \rightarrow a$, so $f(x) \rightarrow L$" can be analyzed cognitively into two separate processes, one in which x approaches a, the other in which y approaches L, with these two processes being coordinated by the application of the function f.

This patient build-up of a concept through specific actions, routinized as a process, then encapsulated as an object, has a cost. In the first version of the development,

> There were no students who progressed to the point where we could ask questions that indicated their thinking relevant to the last two steps of the preliminary genetic decomposition. We repeat them in the revised version, although they might be dropped for the present because there is no evidence for them. (Cottrill et al., 1996, p. 187)

In other words, this approach may give a sound *process* conception of the limit, but the empirical evidence does not reveal examples extending this to an understanding of the epsilon-delta definition.

Other research has similarly underlined the difficulty of the formal definition. Knowing of the subtle problems found by Wood (1992) using decimal numbers and mentioned previously, Li and Tall (1993) designed an approach to limits of sequences through numerical programming for a class of preservice (primary and secondary) school teachers. This involved gaining experiences intended to be a foundation for the limit concept. For instance, to get a better approximation to the limit of a sequence, say to eight decimal places instead of four, it is (usually) necessary to go further along the sequence to find the terms stabilizing to eight decimal places. This was translated into the $\varepsilon - N$ limit definition in the form "to get the limit within accuracy ε, you will need to find a suitable value of N for the limit to be given to that accuracy." However, such an approach had almost *no* effect on the students' belief that "nought point nine repeating" is strictly less than one. In addition, an attempt to study more general sequences had an unforeseen side effect. The students were invited to consider the sum of the series whose nth term is "$\dfrac{1}{n^2}$ if n is prime, $\dfrac{1}{n^3}$ if it is not prime and even, and $\dfrac{1}{n!}$ if n is not prime and odd." The complexity of calculating the sum of this series to 1,000 or 10,000 terms was such that it took considerable time on the computers being used. This phenomenon led half the class to believe that the sequence would not tend to a limit even though they could see that it is bounded above via the comparison test. They reasoned that the sum would continue to increase slowly so that any specified value might, after a long time, be exceeded. When introduced to the completeness axiom, these students refused to accept it because they did not believe that it was true. Their belief is reasonable. There is only one complete ordered field, namely the real numbers. But the students believe that their mental number line contains infinitesimals (quantities that are arbitrarily small) (Cornu, 1983; Tall, Gray, Crowley, McGowen, Pitta, Pinto, et al., 2001), and such a number system is definitely *not* complete. A similar obstacle arises naturally in the second stage of Dubinsky's genetic decomposition where $f(x)$ approaches L as x approaches a. Calculating numerical values of $f(x)$ for x near a evokes discrete numerical values, while continuous motion of a variable x getting "arbitrarily close" to a evokes an image of arbitrarily small infinitesimal quantities (Cornu, 1991).

While many students have difficulties with infinitesimals on the one hand and quantifiers on the other, there is a small number of students who learn to handle the formal definition. Pinto (1998) found that successful mathematics majors were able to handle the definition in at least two distinct ways (reported in Pinto & Tall, 1999). One is the evident *formal* way, working with the definition and deducing the properties and theorems from the definitions and previously proven theorems. However, there is an alternate route, reminiscent of the work of more visually motivated mathematicians, often including geometers and topologists. This she termed a *natural* approach, building up meaning for the definition by working on one's own personal imagery. Some natural thinkers were able to build formal theory developing from their imagery, but others believed that their imagery was sufficient proof in itself and that formal proof was unnecessary. (For instance, if a_n gets close to a, and b_n gets close to b, then clearly $a_n + b_n$ must get close to $a + b$ without any further need of proof.)

One natural thinker did not wish to learn the definition by rote. He wanted a meaningful interpretation and saw the limit of a sequence in a picture in which the terms a_1, a_2, ... were plotted in the Cartesian plane over x-values 1, 2, ..., with the limit L marked as a horizontal line and the prescribed interval $L - \varepsilon$ to $L + \varepsilon$ marked as horizontal lines at distance ε above and below the limit line. For this value of ε, he sought a value of N so that, from this point on, all the points of the sequence a_n for $n > N$ lay within the horizontal lines $L \pm \varepsilon$. Not only did he use the picture to "see" the definition, he also built up the definition sequentially from this imagery and used the imagery to guide his later development.

His natural approach caused him to be often in a state of excitation as he constantly wrestled with his imagery. However, the theory he developed caused him continually to update his relationships with his other ideas, giving him a rich schema of intuitions and deductions that he could use to predict and prove new theorems. He was therefore successful, first by developing visual imagery that supported the definition, then using this imagery to underpin formal proof. He therefore may be considered a *natural formalist*, using natural imagery for thought experiments, then modifying them to underpin formal theory.

On the other hand, another student, following a formal route, remembered the definition through repetition and use. Once he was able to write it from memory, he was able to begin to use it to deduce properties in a formal manner. His knowledge of analysis was quite separate from his informal knowledge, which he distrusted and did not regard as an appropriate way to build up mathematical theory.

Thus, students can learn formal mathematics successfully in different ways. No single approach is suitable even for those who are successful. In addition to manipulating symbols and performing complex calculations, technology can provide a visual way to encourage natural thinking to support formal theory for those students who prefer a natural approach. For formal thinkers, even though it does not provide formal support for their axiomatic theory, it may still provide a complementary way of looking at the overall structure of ideas to solve problems.

An Embodied Visual Approach Using Local Straightness

A "natural" approach to calculus is to build on the dynamic visual idea of local straightness. This is at almost the opposite end of the spectrum from a symbolic-numeric programming approach. Whereas the ISETL approach based on APOS is designed to encapsulate a programmed process (of limit, derivative, or integral) as a mental object, a locally straight approach *begins* with an explicit visual image of a graph that "magnifies to look straight." This is consonant with the theory of Lakoff and Núñez (2000) that human thought is embodied in our natural human perception and action. Embodied foundations of the calculus include not only visual aspects but also other bodily sensations such as those that come from manipulating objects onscreen using a mouse. An embodied approach builds on fundamental human senses. We will see that it provides a foundational approach to the calculus that can be an end in itself, but it may also offer a natural way of leading to a formal, theoretical approach in terms of either traditional epsilon-delta analysis or nonstandard analysis using infinitesimals.

A "locally straight" approach has been followed in a range of curricula. For example, the School Mathematics 16–19 Project in Britain was designed to afford students who had limited algebra resources opportunities to look at a graph and to get the computer to sketch the graph of the changing slope of the curve. It is straightforward for students using these materials to guess that the derivative of x^2 with respect to x is $2x$, of x^3 is $3x^2$, and to conjecture the general pattern. A similar experimental approach extends to "seeing" the derivative of $\sin x$ and the derivative of $\cos x$, and even to finding the numerical value of k for which the derivative with respect to x of k^x is again k^x. This introduces an embodied meaning to mathematics. For instance, the derivative of $\cos x$ is *the additive inverse of* $\sin x$ not because an algebraic manipulation magically produces this result, but because the shape of the gradient of $\cos x$ looks the same as the graph of $\sin x$ "upside down."

Empirical evidence from written tests requesting students to draw the derivative of a function given graphically shows that this approach enables students to visualize and sketch the changing slope as a function with far greater insight than a corresponding student who has used only a paper-and-pencil symbolic approach (Tall, 1985).

In many calculus reform programs, the notion of "local straightness" is seen to be synonymous with "local linearity" (for example, see Dick & Edwards, 2008; Hughes-Hallett et al., 1994; Smith & Moore, 1996). Although the two ideas are mathematically equivalent, they are cognitively very different. Local straightness is an embodied visual conception that involves imagining the graph highly magnified to "see" how steep it is. Symbolism is not necessary at this point; it can be introduced at an appropriate stage with, or following, familiarization with the fundamental embodied concepts. Local linearity, however, requires symbolism from the very beginning to specify the linear function that is "the best linear approximation" to the graph near a particular point. While local straightness can suggest complementary visual ideas of nondifferentiability (in terms of "corners" on the graph at a point, or "wrinkles" over a range), local linearity concerns itself only with examples of functions that have a locally linear approximation at a point. The "locally straight" approach is therefore capable of far more sophisticated insights at an early stage. By magnifying wrinkled functions that remain wrinkled wherever they are magnified, it is possible to give a visual sense of a nowhere differentiable function, revealing the possibility of visualizing not only differentiability (local straightness), but also nondifferentiability (lack of local straightness).

The locally straight approach may also be used in a natural manner to build on dynamic technology-related perceptions to inspire formal definitions. For instance, we may begin with the idea of "stretching" a graph horizontally in a computer window while keeping the vertical scale constant (Figure 5.2).

In general, the value of $f(x_0)$ lies between $f(x_0) + \varepsilon$ and $f(x_0) - \varepsilon$, values that define the maximum and minimum height of a pixel, $f(x_0) \pm \varepsilon$, then to pull the graph flat means finding an interval $(x_0 - \delta, x_0 + \delta)$, so that the graph in this range lies within the vertical range $f(x_0) \pm \varepsilon$, and hence within a horizontal line of pixels. This gives the formal definition of continuity:

Given $\varepsilon > 0$, there exists $\delta > 0$, such that $|x - x_0| < \delta \Rightarrow |f(x) - f(x_0)| < \varepsilon$. The definition of continuity therefore arises by a natural process of stretching a graph horizontally to see if it becomes flat, rather than as a highly technical combination of three nested quantifiers. Such an approach can provide natural thinkers with mental images that can be used to lead to the formal manipulations of quantified statements to prove theorems. It can also be beneficial in giving a greater insight into sophisticated ideas that occur in mathematical analysis for those who are unlikely to be able to cope with the formal theory in its usual academic form. Tall (1993) employed a computer-based visual approach with pro-

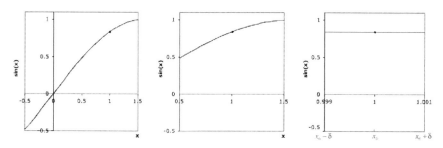

Figure 5.2.   Stretching the graph $y - \sin(x)$ horizontally about $x_0 = 1$, keeping the vertical scale constant.

spective secondary mathematics teachers who were expected to struggle with formal analysis. After instruction, they were able to discuss a wide range of concepts and principles in a "natural" manner. These included the idea of a function that is nowhere differentiable (because it is a fractal that nowhere magnifies to look straight) and yet it is continuous because the graph "pulls flat." A formal definition of continuity was developed and linked to visual ideas that (a) the area under a continuous function is a differentiable function, (b) the derivative of the area function is visibly the original function, and (c) the solution of a first-order differential equation involves knowing the slope of a curve and following the direction it specifies.

A visual approach was used to "see" that the function describing the area under a continuous function has a derivative equal to the original function. Working together in a group, the students suggested spontaneously that the area under a continuous nondifferentiable function is a function that will be differentiable once but not twice. This provides an existence proof that such an approach can give insights into highly subtle formal ideas that are totally out of reach of most students following a traditional course. The use of an embodied perceptual approach therefore offers not only the possibility of a deep-seated human meaning of subtle formal concepts, but also has the additional possibility of extending these ideas naturally towards a formal approach.

A Pragmatic Locally Linear Approach Using Graphic, Numeric, and Symbolic Software

Most of the approaches taken in the texts that implemented calculus reform (such as Hughes-Hallett, et al., 1994, or Smith & Moore, 1996) use the idea of local linearity, with a pragmatic choice of numeric, symbolic, and graphic representations, using computing technology (computers and/or graphic calculators and/or computer algebra systems) to approach ideas from a range of different viewpoints. As the reforms have progressed, the role of verbal representation has been raised to an explicit level, formulated in a "rule of four" that encourages the use of verbal, numeric, symbolic, and graphic representations to give a fuller sense of the concepts involved. New ideas are often introduced via specific contextual problems, using technology, to situate the concepts in a practical context. Some approaches, such as that of *Calculus&Mathematica* (*C&M*) (Davis, et al., 1994a, 1994b), use the power of a dynamic, computer-based text to explain concepts associated with numeric and graphic representations. On the other hand, *Calculus Using Mathematica* (Stroyan, 1993) is an approach based on student programming in Mathematica. A major factor in many of these reforms is a new atmosphere of collaborative group work, using technology to encourage active student exploration, discussion, and commitment to personal construction of meaning.

THE ROLES OF TEACHER AND LEARNER

Use of technology does not occur in a vacuum. Hence, before we analyze the research on the effects of using particular technologies in (primarily collegiate) calculus courses, we examine research on some of the ways that teachers and students can influence those effects.

The Role of the Teacher

In approaches using technology, the teacher plays a significant role in how the technology is used in learning. Keller and Hirsch (1998) noted that students' preferences for numerical, graphical, or symbolic representations in part reflect the instructional preference. Kendal and Stacey (1999) report the effect of teacher "privileging," in which the use of representations in teaching differential calculus affected the types of questions students were able to answer successfully on a test, as well as the way students approached finding solutions to problems. (For additional discussion of privileging, see Zbiek & Hollebrands, 2008). In their research, three teachers, who agreed to teach the same syllabus to high school students in Australia with a TI-92 calculator, also helped design the materials that were used.

Observations of the classrooms indicated that Teacher A enthusiastically used the computer algebra system at every opportunity and took primarily an algebraic (symbolic) approach. Teacher B was more reserved and underpinned the work with paper-and-pencil calculations, making some connections between concepts being discussed and graphs. Teacher C was enthusiastic about the calculator, using it more often to provide graphical insight. Their characteristics as observed by the researchers are given in Table 5.1.

Table 5.2 shows the teachers' expectations of their students' work before the course began. These suggest links between the perceptions of the individual teachers and their teaching characteristics.

Students were given a written test to assess their understandings and were asked to record when and how they used the calculator. An item-by-item analysis of student responses is given in Table 5.3.

Although the classes had similar means on the test (24.1, 26.7, and 27.9, respectively), students from the different classes answered different

Table 5.1.   Researcher's Categorization of Teaching Characteristics

Teacher Characteristics	Teacher A	Teacher B	Teacher C
Teaching style	Direct instruction	Guided discovery	Guided discovery
Direction of lesson	Followed lesson plan	Controlled exploration	Open exploration
Attitude to using CAS	Enthusiastic	Reserved	Enthusiastic
Structured lesson around calculator use	Mostly	Sometimes	Mostly
Used algebraic explanations	Very often	Very often	Often
Used graphical explanation	Sometimes	Sometimes	Often
Used both algebraic and graphical explanations	Rarely	Sometimes	Often

Table 5.2.   Teacher Predictions of Student Success

Teacher Predictions	Teacher A	Teacher B	Teacher C
Algebraic competence	Moderate	Higher	Moderate
Graphical competence	Moderate	Moderate	Higher
With new technology	Likely to succeed	Will probably succeed	Very likely to succeed

questions correctly. Class A students were most successful on questions that were procedural in nature, while Class C students were more successful with questions requiring conceptual understanding. The success with conceptual problems appeared to be connected to the use of a graphical approach along with an algebraic approach. It is interesting to note that, although a number of procedural questions could have been performed (or checked) on the TI-92, there were many students in classes B and C who did not use the TI-92 to check them. According to the researchers, "there is no simplistic conclusion that greater use of CAS leads to better results" (p. 236).

It is clear that teachers will adopt a variety of approaches to teaching, with some of the decisions about those approaches being based on their

Table 5.3. Summary of the Behavior and Success of Students on the Written Test

Student Behavior	Class A	Class B	Class C
Use of calculator	Most frequent	Least frequent	Frequent
Decision to use calculator	Too frequent	Discriminating	Discriminating
Preferred approach	Algebra by calculator	Algebra by hand	Graphical with calculator
Algebraic proficiency	Moderate by hand	Higher by hand	Lower by hand
Graphical skills	Lower	Moderate	Higher
Procedural competence	Good	Good	Good
Conceptual understanding	Lower	Moderate	Moderate-higher

beliefs about their students' abilities. These approaches will affect what students do with the technology and thus what they learn. For example, Class C students were able to use a graph to answer some questions in place of using a symbolic approach. Some teachers might be comfortable with students being able to solve a calculus problem without using symbols, while others may require symbolic work as well. This study can provide insights into how teachers (or curriculum developers) might adapt their teaching (or materials) depending on the goals for the course.

The Role of the Student

Students learning calculus encounter not only specific difficulties (such as difficulties dealing with the limit concept) but also a range of factors that are common to many environments. The Committee on Developments in the Science of Learning of the (U.S.) National Research Council (NRC) summarized research on learning in *How People Learn* (Bransford, Brown, & Cocking, 1999) and in a companion handbook for bridging the divide between research and practice (Donovan, Bransford, & Pellegrino, 1999). In brief, in order for learning to take place, the handbook suggests:

- Students' initial understandings must be engaged.

- To develop competence, students must have a deep knowledge base, understand in a conceptual framework, and organize for retrieval and application.
- Students must monitor progress toward goals.

Research on student *approaches* to learning (Bowden & Marton, 1998; Entwistle, 1987; Entwistle & Ramsden, 1983; Ramsden, 1992) tells us that deep learning approaches are quite different from surface learning approaches, and a given student—whatever his or her "learning style"— may exhibit different approaches simultaneously in different courses. These student-selected "coping strategies" are often determined, at least in part, by expectations set by the instructor, consciously or unconsciously. Rhem (1995) has summarized the work of Entwhistle, Ramsden, Marton, and their collaborators. He notes that surface learning is encouraged by excessive amounts of material to be covered, lack of opportunity to pursue subjects in depth, lack of choice over subjects and/or method of study, and a threatening assessment system. On the other hand, deep learning (the organized and conceptual learning described in the NRC study but with specific points taken from Rhem's summary) is encouraged by interaction (peers working in groups), a well-structured knowledge base (connecting new concepts to prior experience and knowledge), a strong motivational context with a choice of control and a sense of ownership, and learner activity followed by faculty connecting the activity to the abstract concept.

These are especially important messages for those whose goals include teaching mathematics to a much broader audience than just those who intend to become mathematicians. Calculus reformers and others interested in using technology, whether aware of the learning research or not, found that their task was as much about pedagogy as about choice of tools. As will be seen in our review of empirical research, the projects that successfully demonstrated learning gains are, for the most part, the ones in which use of technology is embedded in a rich learning environment that often looks quite different from the traditional lecture-plus-homework-plus-test environment of the typical college or high school classroom.

ANALYZING EMPIRICAL RESEARCH

In the section titled Understanding in the Calculus—A Spectrum of Approaches, we considered a range of pedagogical approaches to the calculus using technology, from an embodied visual viewpoint to a programming approach in which students are encouraged to write algorithms for mathematical processes to be encapsulated as mathematical concepts.

Other pragmatic solutions enlist technology to utilize graphical, numerical, and symbolic representations for student exploration and active construction of knowledge. We turn now to a broad review of research on the role of technology in the learning of calculus.

Research on college-level calculus is of more recent vintage than research on teaching and learning mathematics in school. At this time, much of the research related to learning calculus in the presence of technology has been reported in dissertations and is not yet reported in refereed publications. These empirical studies draw on both quantitative and qualitative methodologies, and both are important in addressing questions about learning mathematics. Research questions related to comparison of control and experimental groups on achievement (or other measures of performance) have been investigated using quantitative methods. When research questions addressed understandings of concepts and problem-solving approaches, researchers typically used task-based interviews with students and analysis of transcripts and written work. A number of the studies that use primarily a qualitative methodology have only small numbers of subjects. While the results of these studies may not be generalizable, one function they serve is to act as existence proofs that, under certain conditions, a certain type of learning can occur.

Studies were located using Dissertation Abstracts, ERIC, and bibliographies using search terms such as Calculus and Computers, Calculus and Technology, Calculus and Calculators, Calculus and (Learning or Teaching). Copies of dissertations were requested via interlibrary loan or purchased. Not all dissertations identified were available via interlibrary loan and results from these studies are thus not summarized here.

Students' understandings of concepts of calculus such as limits, derivatives, and integrals have been explored in a number of studies (Bezuidenhout, 2001; Ferrini-Mundy & Lauten, 1994; Gonzalez-Martin & Camacho, 2004; Orton, 1983a, 1983b; Williams, 1991). These understandings were found to be procedural in nature, often limited to finding a symbolic derivative or evaluating an integral. Students appeared to have difficulties with problems that required them to interpret concepts or solve nonroutine problems. Many of the studies summarized here examined whether technology, either situated within a reform curriculum or as an add-on to a traditional curriculum, would enable students to develop deeper understandings or become better at solving problems.

Conceptual and Procedural Knowledge

The majority of the studies that will be discussed characterized student knowledge and learning using the notion of conceptual and procedural knowledge. Typical goals for a calculus course include mastering (mostly algorithmic) skills related to finding derivatives, integrals, and limits. The type of knowledge required to carry out these procedures can be characterized as *procedural knowledge* (Hiebert & Lefevre, 1986). A second type of knowledge important in the learning of mathematics is *conceptual knowledge*, which consists of links or webs of relationships and is the type of knowledge used in problem solving or in understanding how various representations can stand for a concept.

In a number of studies that used a quantitative methodology, researchers classified certain problems as being procedural in nature and others as representative of conceptual knowledge because they require students to draw on a variety of relationships. Student success on these problems was used as an indicator of a student's procedural or conceptual knowledge. An example of a problem that would require only procedural knowledge is finding the derivative of $f(x) = \sin(x^2 + 1)$. Tasks that require conceptual knowledge include graphing a function given the graph of its derivative function or finding $f'(2.5)$ and graphing the normal line at $x = 2.5$ (where x is the independent variable), given the graph of the function f and its tangent line at $x = 2.5$, as in Figure 5.3 (adapted from Hart, 1991).

Conceptual Knowledge

Some of the earliest studies that examined the role of technology in learning calculus (Heid, 1984/1985; Palmiter, 1991) involved the resequencing of material with the emphasis being the development of understandings of major concepts. Implicitly, traditional curricula assume that either students need to learn rules for procedures first and then use them to solve problems, or that there is a strong interdependence between the development of procedural and conceptual knowledge. The intent of changes in curriculum and inclusion of technology was to enable students to focus on development of conceptual knowledge through exploration of concepts via various representations and multiple examples, and by off-loading of procedural work. What was unknown was whether students could learn concepts prior to the development of procedural skills, and in what ways student understandings of concepts and procedures would be different from those of students in traditional courses.

Resequencing

Heid (1984/1985) used computers and software in a business calculus course to produce graphs and symbolic manipulations from which students were to reason in a problem-solving setting. Data were collected

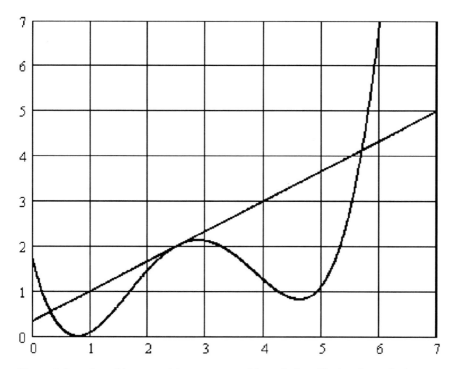

Figure 5.3.   A problem requiring conceptual knowledge: Find and graph the normal at $x = 2.5$.

from a traditional lecture class and two treatment classes. In the treatment classes the first 12 weeks were devoted to an in-depth development of meanings of concepts. Procedural skills were developed primarily during the last 3 weeks of the course. In one of the treatment sections simple by-hand procedures were shown as concepts were developed, and in the other section, focus on by-hand procedures was delayed until the end of the course. An interesting consequence of the delaying of development of procedural skills was that students were able to focus on the symbolic structure of functions, allowing them to better understand when and why they needed to use, for example, a derivative or an integral.

A total of 20 students from the various classes were selected to take part in 5 interviews (10 students from the treatment section and 4 from the control completed all 5 interviews). In order to investigate the nature of student understandings, it was necessary to develop a coding scheme that could help identify reasoning associated with deeper or better under-standing of concepts. Heid (1984/1985) examined interview transcripts for similarities and differences in reasoning and explanations involving concepts such as derivatives, integrals, limits and functions. Patterns were identified and used to construct a set of indicators that could be used to make a decision about a student's understanding. Experimental and control class interviews were analyzed separately and then compared to look for differences.

Heid defined eight indicators used to identify understanding of course concepts:

1. Individual students made a broader array of appropriate associations for the concept.

2. Within a single class there was a greater range of explanations of a given concept.

3. Individual students used certain calculus concepts to form conclusions about related concepts.

4. When individual students failed to remember a fact or formula they were able to reconstruct the appropriate conclusion from consideration of basic principles (often on their own initiative).

5. The wording or examples individual students used to explain concepts was unlike that appearing in the text or that used in class.

6. Individual students were able to use concepts in the analysis of applied situations.

7. Individual students were able to construct an embodiment of a concept which was unlike that covered in the text or in class.

8. Individual students made connections between concepts and their theoretical basis (p. 87).

The transcripts from the treatment sections and control section were analyzed separately using the indicators, and results were compared. Based on the analysis, students in the experimental sections exhibited deeper understandings of the derivative and its applications, as well as the other concepts. "The experimental class students provided a greater amount of evidence of conceptual understanding with each of the indicators" (p. 121). Mean scores from a common final examination (which did not allow use of the computer) for all groups were similar, and on problems that required computations the performance of the students in the experimental sections did not appear to be different from that of students in the traditional section. Common questions examining conceptual understanding were included on tests for all students and students from the experimental sections generally outperformed the students from the control sections on these questions. Not only did students in the experimental sections show greater understanding of concepts, their ability to complete computational problems was similar to that of students whose primary focus had been on developing skills and understanding necessary to carry out procedures.

A second early study examined this same question of whether the development of concepts could precede the development of skills. Palmiter (1991) used a computer algebra system to teach techniques of integration during a 5-week instructional period to students in an experimental section. Performance of these students on conceptual and computational exams was compared to performance of students in two traditional sections (who covered the same material during a 10-week period). On the conceptual exam the students in the experimental section scored significantly higher than those in the control groups. The experimental group also scored significantly higher on the computational exam on which students were allowed to use the computer.

These studies provide evidence that understanding of concepts and their applications can be developed prior to the acquisition of skills using technology to produce representations and examples for discussion and exploration. Students in the experimental sections of these studies developed better understandings of the concepts. Based on the indicators used by Heid (1984/1985), these understandings allowed the students to engage in reasoning to make sense of ideas, and to reconstruct ideas from basic principles when they forgot a piece of information. Students in these studies were able to develop the necessary procedural knowledge and in less time than was necessary in the control classes.

More recent studies investigated learning in a range of settings, from those with a high degree of integration of technology along with a change in pedagogy (for example, C&M) to those in which the text and teaching approach was traditional and students were asked to complete add-on activities. Findings from those studies are described next.

We looked at results from nine studies that used a quantitative instrument to examine differences in conceptual knowledge between experimental and control groups: Chappell and Killpatrick, (2003), Connors and Snook (2001), Cooley (1997), Cunningham (1991/1992), Estes (1990), Judson (1989), Melin-Conejeros (1992), Park (1993), and Schrock (1989/1990). Instruments used typically consisted of tests with a subset of questions categorized as assessing conceptual understanding. Five studies reported that the experimental group performed significantly better than the control group and four studies reported no significant difference in performance (Connors & Snook, 2001; Cunningham, 1991/1992; Judson (1989), Melin-Conejeros, 1992). Although a quantitative instrument was used in the study by Melin-Conejeros, it should be noted that in interviews conducted with students from both sections, students in the experimental section exhibited a better understanding of the concepts of asymptotes, concavity, limits of functions, continuity, and increasing and decreasing functions based on their explanations during tasks.

In the studies in which there was a significant difference in performance on conceptual items favoring the experimental groups, the instruction of the control groups appeared to be traditional in nature. In the experimental sections a greater emphasis was placed on the development of concepts, usually through use of technology in a curriculum that differed from the traditional curriculum. For example, the students in Park's (1993) study used *C&M*, and in Estes's (1990) study, students completed 11 extra assignments that engaged the students in exploration, generalization of ideas, and examination of concepts across various representations. Similar changes in curriculum and integration of technology can be found in the remaining seven studies as well.

In the studies that reported no significant differences there was often a limited implementation of technology and limited change in curriculum; or the studies involved the comparison of dissimilar types of curricula (traditional and reform). The only difference between the experimental section and the control section in the study by Melin-Conjeros (1992) was the use of *Derive* by students to do homework outside of class. The students in both sections completed similar homework and *Derive* was not used in the class during instruction. This use of technology is limited in nature and does not provide opportunities for the instructor to develop concepts during class time, nor are students necessarily engaged with tasks that use technology to provide both various representations and opportunity to explore ideas.

Judson (1989) restructured material on the concept of derivative and its applications in a business calculus course using Maple. The same lecture examples were used in both the control and experimental sections, and students were assigned the same homework. Students in the experimental section completed a computer assignment outside of class to motivate a topic to be covered in class. Results from examination of subportions of a common final exam showed no significant difference in overall achievement, or in skills, concepts, or applications. The nature of the experimental version of the course did not differ from that of the control sections except during the learning of this one topic.

The study by Connors and Snook (2001) compared results from a common final examination of students who learned the material using an HP 48G graphing calculator and students who used TI-89 calculators. Both calculators perform symbolic operations such as differentiation, although the HP 48G could not be used to evaluate limits. All sections used the same text and syllabus. The TI-89 users performed significantly better on only one of eight conceptual items due to the fact that they "could graph the function defined by an integral on their calculator and then analyze the resulting graph" (p. 107). So the difference in calculator type did not affect the development of understanding of concepts between these two groups. A separate set of questions focused on application of concepts and the TI-89 users performed significantly better on five of the six questions. This leads to questions about how or why the use of different types of calculators could result in differences in answering applied questions that require students to interpret the question and carry out correct procedures.

Students in the experimental and control sections of Cunningham's (1991/1992) study used the same text and completed the same homework and tests, and both groups had instruction that emphasized the development of concepts. The computer was used to perform symbolic manipulation in the experimental section to off-load procedural work. The statistical analysis suggested that the students in both groups developed similar understandings, so the use of a CAS to do computations did not result in development of deeper understandings. Because there was not a control group that received traditional instruction, it is not clear whether the understandings these students developed were in any way different from those of students in a more traditional course.

The studies by Judson (1989) and Melin-Conjeros (1992) provide some evidence that significant differences in development of understanding may depend both on the level of integration of the technology and the degree to which activities and instruction focus on conceptual development, although more research is needed to support such a claim. Chappell and Killpatrick (2003) compared the performance of calculus students ($n = 300$) in control and experimental sections in which both groups completed the same Maple-based laboratories, and instruction in the classrooms involved use of a graphing calculator. (No information was provided on the nature of the Maple laboratories.) Instruction in the control sections was "procedure-based," with the instructor providing a brief overview of material followed by introduction of definitions and procedures. The experimental section was "concepts-based," with students engaging in activities requiring explanations and problem solving via various representations. Concepts were introduced informally by the instructor, then linked to more formal conceptions, and then followed by development of skills. As in earlier studies conducted during the previous two decades (Heid, 1984/1985; Estes,1990; Palmiter, 1991; Park, 1993), the students in the concepts-based sections significantly outperformed those in the other sections on the instrument used to assess conceptual understandings, and no significant difference in performance was reported between the two groups on procedural skills.

Wells (1995/1996) compared the development of conceptual understanding in three types of calculus classes. The first type consisted of traditional sections. The second type was an Honors course that combined use of graphing calculators with ongoing assignments that included problems that either required or built conceptual understandings and were writing-intensive. The third type of course had a traditional lecture portion and weekly sessions during which students worked collaboratively on worksheets. After controlling for confounding variables, Wells found that there were significant differences in the conceptual understandings in favor of students in the Honors course. Her belief was that it was the "consistent emphasis on concepts and the connections between and among concepts and procedures throughout the course" (p. iii). Both in this study as well as in Chappell and Killpatrick (2003) the significant differences in conceptual understandings appear to be linked to the approach to instruction. Combining the results of this and the Kendal and Stacey study (1999), we see that if the goal is to enhance conceptual understanding, technology use alone is not enough. Technology as an add-on to a traditionally taught class may not lead to any changes in learning.

Results regarding the development of higher order skills are, however, sometimes nuanced. Keller and Russell (1997) describe a preliminary study investigating students' performances on three different types of problems: simple computations such as evaluating a specific integral or finding a derivative, multistep problems such as finding a maximum, and complex problems formulated in a manner that requires information to be translated into appropriate mathematical form. In the preliminary study with a small number of students, they found that students using TI-92 calculators in a supportive group-oriented classroom context outperformed students who had access to other types of calculators on all three forms of problems. However, a later large-scale study (Keller, Russell, & Thomson, 1999) showed a significant difference ($p < 0.001$) in performance on one step and multistep problems, but not in complex problems.

Studies that used qualitative research methods such as interviews provide insights into the understandings developed by students in technology-enhanced curricula. Porzio (1994/1995) examined how different approaches to instruction affected students' use of multiple representations of concepts in problem solving. One group used graphing calculators along with a graphing-enhanced calculus textbook, and the other group used the *C&M* curriculum. The C&M students were better able to discuss connections between various representations of a concept and could describe how to use representations for solving a problem. These differences were attributed to the C&M students' active engagement with problem-solving situations that required them to use various representations in conjunction with each other and with problems that explicitly asked them to draw conclusions about connections. This was in contrast to the experiences the students using graphing calculators had listening to the instructor talk about the connections, and completing homework problems that did not require them to elaborate on or use these connections.

Park (1993) also conducted a comparative study that involved students in a *C&M* curriculum. Her control group consisted of students in traditional sections. C&M students, during interviews, made more and stronger connections between many ideas including the relationships between derivative, instantaneous rate of change, slope of the curve, and tangent line. They could reconstruct formulas when they forgot them, and they used graphs and visual thinking in their explanations. Similar to the Heid (1984/1985) study, Park found that C&M students were able to explain concepts using their own language and concluded that they had developed greater conceptual understanding than students in the control group.

Ellison (1993/1994) used TI-81 calculators and *A Graphic Approach to the Calculus* (Tall, 1990) to develop the concept of the derivative. Interviews with 10 students in this noncomparison study investigated their understandings of important characteristics of derivatives. Ellison found that students did develop connections between a number of ideas such as differentiability and local straightness of a curve, and of derivative as slope of curve, slope of tangent line, and as instantaneous rate of change. Six of the 10 students could produce the graph of the derivative function from a graph of a parent function, while only four could identify characteristics of a function from the graph of the derivative. A majority of the interviewees could state the formal definition of derivative but only half could connect the definition with a visualization of the slope of a curve at a point as the limiting value of the slopes of secant lines. However seven did link the tangent line to the notion of a limiting secant line. Ellison concluded that in situations in which technology was used to investigate limits it was important to help students interpret the outputs which are based on discrete values and realize that the theoretical tangent line or slope are never produced.

Crocker (1992) interviewed students from a course in which Mathematica was used to develop concepts and for problem solving. Students appeared to have formed an understanding of the relationship between the slope of a curve and the derivative. Crocker found that students who were characterized (by test results) as low-ability or middle-ability were more willing to use the computer to explore various solution paths than were high-ability students. The high-ability students often used only a single strategy to try to solve a problem and thus failed to solve it.

Procedural Knowledge

Reformed curricula shift emphasis from development of procedural skills and building of theoretical foundations to building understanding of concepts in the context of technology. Because the primary focus of traditional classrooms is on the development of by-hand procedures such as finding derivatives or indefinite integrals, concern is expressed about whether students will lose these skills if students learn calculus using technology. Early studies indicated that this is not the case, and later studies provided additional evidence.

We examined 12 studies for results related directly to the comparison of procedural skills between students in experimental sections and students in control sections (traditionally taught classes): Chappell and Kilpatrick (2003), Connors and Snook (2001), Cooley (1995/1996), Crocker (1993), Cunningham (1991/1992), Estes (1990), Galindo-Morales (1994), Keller (1993), Melin-Conejeros (1992), Park (1993), Schrock (1989/1990), and Soto-Johnson (1998). In these studies, test or quiz questions were categorized as testing for procedural skills, and work from students in the experimental and control sections was compared. In many of the studies, technology was not allowed on the test(s) so no advantage would be given due to its use. Ten studies reported no significant difference in performance between the two groups, and two studies reported that the students in the control groups significantly outperformed students in the experimental groups. In one study (Soto-Johnson, 1998) in which the control group outperformed the experimental group, the students from a Project CALC course spent half as much time studying infinite series as students in a traditional section or from a Mathematica-laboratory-enhanced section. The emphasis for the Project CALC students was on application of series as well as on exploration and explanation of concepts, and not on computation. These students made errors on some computational problems due to reliance on their calculators (instead of the formula) to find sums of geometric series, and thought the harmonic series converged due to the slow growth in terms (seen in a graph or table of values). The change in curriculum for Project CALC resulted in much less time spent on developing computational skills and on potential difficulties related to using technology to answer some types of questions leading to the differences in performance.

In looking across the studies, in some cases the experimental groups used the same textbook as the control groups with technology as an add-on either through laboratories or for assignments. Sometimes the difference between the two groups consisted of only five laboratories per semester. Other studies involved students enrolled in courses that had a significant change in the curriculum: a "reform" curriculum such as Calculus&Mathematica (at the University of Illinois or Ohio State University) or Project CALC (Duke University), a re-sequencing of material, or conceptually based instruction. The results from the studies indicate that generally there is no difference in development of procedural skills for students in traditional courses or those in any of the experimental courses with their wide variety of approaches to teaching and learning.

Overall Achievement

A number of studies compared overall achievement in control and experimental sections of calculus. Overall achievement was typically measured as a score on a common final exam taken by both groups. In interpreting results based on tests, it is important to keep in mind that some questions will favor students in a traditional course, others will favor those who have learned calculus in the presence of technology and/or with a change in curriculum, and still other items will be neutral. We located nine studies that examined overall achievement (Castillo, 1997/1998; Connors, 1995; Fredenberg, 1993/1994; Hawker, 1987; Judson, 1988; Melin-Conejeros, 1992; Padgett, 1994; Palmiter, 1991; Park, 1993). Three of the studies reported significant differences favoring the experimental classes, five reported no significant differences between the two groups, and one reported differences favoring the control group. These mixed results indicate that students in courses that have some degree of integration of technology are likely to do as well as students in a traditional course on a common final exam, and in some cases will outperform them.

Success in Subsequent Courses

Because calculus classes are often service courses for departments such as engineering, biology, and business, some of the studies already cited focused on courses designed for these majors. Other studies focused on courses whose intended audience was both mathematics and engineering majors. If the emphasis of the course is shifted away from a more theoretical foundation, will those students who go on to take more mathematics courses suffer as a consequence?

Cadena, Travis, and Norman (2003) compared final course grades of students from traditional calculus to those of students in a reform course (Hughes-Hallett, et al., 1994) to overall grades in subsequent mathematics, engineering, and science courses taken. The researchers normalized the values to adjust for the fact that students take differing numbers of subsequent courses "with each student contributing a fractional portion of their grade to the total grades received for all follow-up courses. The average percentages of grades were calculated and these values were used in the statistical analyses" (p. 214). They found no significant difference in the subsequent course grades between the two groups; students from the reform course did as well as students from traditional courses in subsequent courses that had Calculus I as a prerequisite.

The results of this study would support a "no harm" conclusion. What is the argument then for reform (typically technology-based) versus a traditional approach? This lies in the development of conceptual understandings, problem-solving abilities, and retention of knowledge and ability to apply it.

Roddick (2001) also studied student success in subsequent physics and engineering mechanics courses. The six above-average students in this comparison study enrolled in either a traditional course or a Calculus&Mathematica course. They were interviewed after they completed the calculus sequence and had enrolled in an engineering mechanics course. Responses from task-based interviews and achievement were compared, as were grades in subsequent courses. A significant difference was found in the grades for an Introduction to Differential Equations class that favored the traditional students. This appeared to be related to the fact that students spent less time in the C&M course calculating integrals. A significant difference was found favoring the C&M students in the first of a series of three calculus-based physics classes. And, when the top third of the C&M students (in terms of achievement level) were compared to the top third of traditional students, their achievement levels in Introductory Physics 1, Introductory Physics 2, and Introduction to Mechanics were significantly better than those of the traditional students. The results, then, are mixed for student performance in later courses.

Because the Roddick study was conducted one to two quarters after the calculus course, and perhaps before some of these ideas and skills were revisited in subsequent courses, the results provide some indication about the retention of knowledge. Roddick found that the two groups of students reasoned differently while explaining their work on tasks such as finding extrema of a function, determining which of two given graphs was the function and which its derivative, and finding the value of a definite integral, given the graph of a function. The C&M students typically used reasoning that could be categorized as drawing on conceptual knowledge, and the traditional students' responses drew more on procedural knowledge.

In examining responses to the two questions, What is a derivative? and What is an integral?, Roddick found the traditional students to have responses that were linked to specific applications of derivatives and integrals, while the C&M students' "responses were more general in nature and not linked to a specific example" (p. 177). In summary, she says "these responses represent each student's overall understanding of derivative and integral, and will likely have a great impact on how they apply such understanding in future problems involving calculus" (p. 177). If knowledge is linked to specific examples, there may be difficulties that arise in applying this knowledge to new situations or in problem solving. This may account for student success (or lack thereof) in later courses.

Bookman (2000) both reports and reflects on a study conducted earlier (see Bookman & Friedman, 1998, 1999) when Bookman was the evaluator for Project CALC at Duke University. The subjects of the study were Calculus I and II students in 1990-91, 78 in Project CALC (PC) and 182 in traditional calculus (TC). (Initially, the incoming students were assigned to sections randomly, but University policy allows students to switch sections and courses during the first two weeks of classes.) Technology plays an important role in the Project CALC course, but it is only one of many ways in which the course differs from the traditional one, including goals, pedagogy, and emphases in subject matter. In 1993 and 1994—the students' junior and senior years—Bookman collected data on the PC and TC subjects that included their grades in all courses with a calculus prerequisite or corequisite or that normally follow one or two semesters of calculus: mathematics (beyond Calculus III), physics, engineering, economics, and computer science, as well as specific courses in Introductory Biology, Organic Chemistry, and Public Policy Analysis. After controlling for SAT scores and performance in Calculus I and II, Bookman found that the traditionally taught students had better grade-point averages in these courses (in both their junior and senior years) by an average of 0.2 on a 4-point scale, a statistically significant difference. However, when the specific courses in biology, chemistry, and public policy were excluded, this difference disappeared. Also, there was no significant difference in upper-level mathematics courses alone. In addition, 23% of the PC students took more than two mathematics courses beyond Calculus III, as opposed to 13% of the TC students, a statistically significant difference. There are reasons local to Duke that can account for the slightly surprising performance of the TC students in biology, chemistry, and public policy, such as large numbers of the more conservative, risk-averse students (disproportionally premedical students) leaving the PC sections during the drop-add period. Bookman notes on reflection—and based on his follow-up interviews with seven matched pairs of the students—that course grades are a relatively poor proxy for understanding performance in subsequent courses. However, course grades appear to be the only large-scale measure available, and the inadequacy of these as measures reinforces the importance of focused interviews as a means of getting better information about student performance.

The effects on performance in later courses of various approaches have been researched in a major study involving over 2000 students. Armstrong and Hendrix (1999) compared students from courses following three different approaches to Calculus I and II: a traditional approach (Ellis & Gulick, 1991), the approach of *Calculus Using Mathematica* (Stroyan, 1993), and the approach taken by the Harvard Calculus Consortium (Hughes-Hallett, et al., 1994).

Calculus Using Mathematica is a computer-intensive, project-based course for honors students, quite different from the traditional courses that currently follow it, and also involving students in more programming than does Calculus&Mathematica. It attracted students with marginally better ACT scores, and its students performed marginally better in subsequent courses. Students who switched from this course in Calculus I to a different course in Calculus II performed significantly worse in later courses. The researchers attribute this in part to the fact that those students switching to other courses were already having difficulty and continued to have difficulty in their new courses. There was no significant difference in the later performance of students who switched from Calculus I to Calculus II in either direction between the traditional approach and the Harvard approach. For the majority of students who stayed with the same approach in both calculus courses, there was no statistically significant difference in performance on subsequent courses regardless of which approach they followed in Calculus I and Calculus II. The authors concluded that this justifies the teaching of traditional and reform courses concurrently as alternatives. In particular, they refute the opinion of critics who blame reformed calculus when their students "can't differentiate" or "never learned to integrate" (Armstrong & Hendrix, 1999, p. 98).

A word of caution should be expressed here. The research does not say there is no difference between the two approaches, only that there is no statistically significant difference in the marks attained on subsequent examinations. Wells (1995/1996), in a broad review of calculus research, noted that procedural items can give the impression that "most" students can be successful in the material covered, whereas more conceptually based items will reveal a broader range of success in understanding. If there is a qualitative difference, this may not be apparent statistically in the marks awarded for performance on traditional examinations. Mathematicians, in their desire to set examinations on which students can perform satisfactorily after following traditional courses, may therefore set questions that place more emphasis on procedural competence than on deeper mathematical understanding.

Although there is a broad consensus that students using technology do not score significantly differently from traditional students in pure mathematics exams, there is other evidence that those who use technology and go on to courses requiring problem-solving skills have better conceptual tools to formulate and solve problems (Meel, 1995/1996; Roddick, 1998).

Nonroutine Problem Solving

Meel (1995/1996) compared students from honors sections in third semester calculus, traditional versus Calculus&Mathematica. Students engaged in task-based interviews designed to examine their understanding of definitions and approaches to solving nonroutine problems. They also completed questions, on which technology was not allowed, that required them to differentiate, integrate, and find limits. Producing explanations of limits and derivatives was difficult for both groups. The C&M students scored significantly lower on questions related to definitions (not unexpected, since this is not emphasized in the *C&M* curriculum), and on conceptual problems. They were, however, more flexible in their ability to solve problems. They used technology to explore a problem and then used the results to plan a way to approach the problem. "The C&M students' greater adaptability [afforded by the technology] created opportunities to re-examine their own thinking, to question if the line of thinking being used made sense in light of the resultant evidence, and to proceed further toward the solution" (p. 189). This was in contrast to the students from the traditional section who did not examine their assumptions and did not change problem-solving strategies even when an answer was obviously incorrect.

The C&M students scored significantly lower on problems that were presented with text only versus those that were presented with text and a pictorial component. The traditional students did just as well on either presentation. As in other studies, the C&M students performed as well as the traditional students on procedural problems. However, on conceptual problems they scored significantly lower. Meel comments that this discrepancy may be due to the scoring rubric for these particular problems, which favored answers that were "consistent with formalized conceptualizations of limit, differentiation, and integration" (p. 184). Since C&M does not take a formal approach, that would disadvantage this group of students. Their explanations were often specific to certain cases or had errors, while the traditional students could provide more general, formal explanations. This result is in contrast to what Roddick (1997/1998) found. This may be due to an instructor placing an emphasis on more formal definitions at Roddick's institution, or perhaps the continuing use and exposure to the concepts in later courses, or the use of a less rigorous rubric.

How Students Use Technology in Learning or Problem Solving

Girard (2002) examined how college students used a graphing calculator to solve problems involving limits and derivatives. The course she designed and taught drew on notions developed by Tall (1990) in *A Graphic Approach to the Calculus* on local linearity, and it incorporated visualization in learning of mathematics. Students completed five researcher-designed laboratories that were add-ons to a course using a traditional text. These laboratories were designed to develop intuitive approaches to concepts and to encourage students to make connections across representation types and to make interpretations.

Girard found that students used technology in a variety of ways while solving problems. In a limit problem that was unfamiliar to the students, they used it as a tool for exploration, and they reached an impasse if they tried to stay with only the algebraic representation. It appeared that students were more willing to try to solve an unfamiliar problem due to the opportunities afforded by the technology (e.g., providing a graph or numerical data to examine). For familiar problems, if students chose to use the calculator, it was as a tool for verification and confirmation. In general, students who were successful on tasks usually used two representations together, algebraic and either graphical or numerical. One of Girard's recommendations is that "the curriculum must promote the use of numerical and graphical representation by having teachers model the use of those representations; and additionally students need to be regularly assigned tasks to include more discovery when using graphing calculators" (p. 179).

Forster and Mueller (2001) examined a similar question through responses on the Tertiary Entrance Exam of Calculus in Australia, a large-scale public exam. Students could use graphing calculators, including the HP 38G, which has limited symbolic capabilities. Some items on the test required students to show by-hand steps, and none specifically required the use of a calculator. Six of 19 questions were identified as ones on which students might choose to use a calculator that had graphing capability and student responses on those questions were examined. Subsequent interviews with students elaborated on how the calculator was used and what errors were made.

The researchers observed a number of difficulties encountered by the students: "Analysis ... indicates that interpretation and transcription of graphs are major areas of difficulty for many students" (p. 47), including recognizing asymptotic behavior (both vertical and horizontal) from the graph produced by a calculator, noting points of discontinuity, and correctly copying graphs from the calculator screen. Many students chose to use a symbolic approach to problems, even when those problems might be more quickly solved by producing a graph with the calculator. It was not clear that the students used the calculator even for checking answers, since incorrect answers often went uncorrected, although the error could have been found by examining a graph or numerical data.

These students were found to underutilize the technology and to have difficulty correctly interpreting graphical information. The researchers predict that, with time and increasing familiarity with when and how technology can be used to solve problems, the technology will be used more for verification and exploration.

Kidron and Zehavi (2002) report on the use of animation with Mathematica to provide visualization of the process of convergence of Taylor polynomials to a function. The students in the study were high school students (ages 16 to 17), "studying at the highest level" (p. 207). They used the software first to develop the definition of a Taylor polynomial of degree n for f at $x = 0$. Then the software was used to examine errors in values of the approximating polynomial for values of x close to 0 by plotting the remainder $R_n(x)$ as a function of x. Animation was then used to visualize "the dynamic *process* of the different polynomials approaching a given function" (p. 211), for changing values of n.

The research question was "To what extent did the use of dynamic graphics help the students develop a formal understanding of the limit concept?" (p. 216). Students were asked to describe and interpret animations and to build new animations. They used the animations for visual confirmations of the notion of a limit and were encouraged to develop ways of reasoning about expected and unexpected results. The objective was to relate the visual behavior of the error term $R_n(x)$ as n increased to the formal limit concept relating error ε to the corresponding value of n. On a written test, some students, but not all, were able to develop a formal definition related to limits. It appeared that "remembering the dynamic graphics was a source of trouble" (p. 225) and, while they recognized that there was a relationship between an epsilon and a delta in the definition, this process was reversed for some of them who gave a value in the domain of the function (a delta) and asked to find an epsilon (the error).

Studies of Technology-Based Reform Courses

To an increasingly greater extent, research studies on the use of technology in the calculus cover a wide range of considerations—to such an extent that attempting to summarize them would lose much of the subtle detail that makes them so distinctive. Most focus on implementations of a specific approach, often compared with a traditional course. A few focus on more general aspects, such as the effects of taking particular calculus courses on success in subsequent courses. Some papers make useful distinctions between various aspects of reform, in the curriculum (change in content of the syllabus) as opposed to the pedagogy (change in teaching strategies) (Lefton & Steinbart, 1995). In addition, we would place a high premium on the changes that occur in the learner. Here there is a wide spectrum of aspects, including the balance of learners' conceptual and procedural understandings, their abilities to communicate mathematical ideas, their abilities to use technology productively, their development of problem-solving strategies, and their flexibility in coping with new situations. In this section we review a number of these more general aspects, referring the reader to the original papers for finer subtleties.

Two different studies concerning Calculus&Mathematica (Lefton & Steinbart, 1995; Park & Travers, 1996) yield similar conclusions. The philosophy of the course (using technology as a toolbox for measurement, both exact and approximate) gives the opportunity for a new curriculum that emphasizes the underlying meaning by building on prototypical examples, at the same time eliminating the epsilon-delta definition from the curriculum and de-emphasizing formal proof. The pedagogy eliminates lectures and introduces the exploration of concepts through Mathematica notebooks and discussion of ideas. Park and Travers (1996) suggest that "the C&M course allows the students to spend less time on computation and better direct their efforts to conceptual understanding" (p. 175). The comparison of the performance of students in these courses with that of students following a traditional approach consistently reveals a higher degree of conceptual understanding and problem-solving ability, together with more positive attitudes towards technology and mathematics. The changes in the learner arise through a combination of both new curriculum and new pedagogy. Lefton and Steinbart (1995) found that client departments were "overwhelmingly supportive," because *Calculus&Mathematica* reflected "the way our colleagues actually used the calculus" (pp. 93–94). The response of the mathematics department was "lukewarm," a view that may reflect a response to changing the emphasis to inductive reasoning rather than proof, plus the perception of the increased effort involved in changing to the use of new technology.

A modification of the course using Maple instead of Mathematica showed some differences in perceived outcome. Aldis, Sidhu, and Joiner (1999) used Calculus & Maple in two classes studying differential equations at the Australian Defence Force Academy over a seven-week period. Both classes experienced difficulty with Maple syntax in the time available but were appreciative of the group work and small-class aspects. The authors hypothesized that a longer exposure to Maple could reduce the difficulties with syntax. Based on their explicit experience, they suggested:

> key concepts in a course should be *introduced* through a CAS. This would allow students to explore ideas without the hindrance of specific notation or technical terms and to develop a memorable, visual impression. Once introduced, the mathematical concepts could be followed up in small-group lectures and non-computer activities. (Aldis, et al., 1999, p. 186)

Such a conclusion is consistent with an embodied approach to the calculus that was discussed earlier in this article, using multimedia tools to enable students to begin by gaining insights into the concepts before tackling the detail of the more powerful symbolism. Indeed, the approach of *Calculus & Mathematica* has a deep underlying philosophy that builds concepts in a manner that is meaningful to the students in their own terms.

Similar conclusions arise with the Project CALC materials using Mathcad (Bookman & Friedman, 1998). Again there is a commitment to both new curriculum and new pedagogy using computer laboratories for cooperative learning. The Project CALC students performed significantly better than traditional students on problems that could be solved by pencil, paper, and scientific calculator. Some of the test items, such as word problems that required translation into mathematical form, were more appropriate for the Project CALC students than for those following the traditional course because the Project CALC students encountered such problems on a daily basis. However, the manner in which the students in the Project CALC group responded shows the ability of the reform course to raise awareness and success in achieving higher order learning goals.

Using Mathcad as an environment for computer-aided learning, Vlachos and Kehagias (2000) report positive effects of the reform course that led to their decision to implement the approach in all sections of their business calculus. Mathcad offers a combination of text, graphics, numeric, and symbolic facilities in a free-form environment within which the authors found it particularly easy to design their course. The improvement in student performance on standard tests was shown by comparison with a standard approach on those tests. The researchers noted their subjective experiences of improvement in attitudes, enthusiasm, systematic study, flexibility in using the representations, and personal "empowerment," by which weak students could "survive" and strong students have the opportunity to excel. They also noted several potentially negative factors, including the possible "overhead" in teaching specific computer skills, the possibility of the study degenerating into "computer gaming," the possible effects on later courses with very different traditional content, and the disorientation that may occur for both students and instructors caused by the radical change in approach.

DRAWING CONCLUSIONS

As we stated at the outset, a review of the research does not, and cannot, give definitive answers to whether reform courses using technology are "better" in general. There are no "theorems" in mathematics education as there are in mathematics. However, our journey through the research literature has produced some consistent themes that may be of benefit for those designing curricula and more generally for those seeking a deeper understanding of the issues.

First, a single opinion based purely on a particular philosophical viewpoint, be it from formal mathematics, crusading reformers, practical users, or anyone else, needs to be seen not only in its own context, in which it may have considerable substance, but also in a wider framework in which other views have their own validity.

In this chapter we have aimed at presenting a broader framework under the following headings:

- *Cultural contexts of the calculus.* Our purpose here was to generate a sense of the wider range of viewpoints.

- *The changing nature of the calculus in a technological world.* By reviewing the changes over recent years, we gave a perspective to show how the situation continues to change, so that our analysis continues to consider a moving target.

- *Understanding the calculus—a spectrum of approaches.* Different approaches are possible in the calculus, and they lead to different cognitive issues. A spectrum of approaches to the calculus was formulated, from a human-embodied approach to a formal mathematical viewpoint, with technology being used for dynamic, enactive visualization, conceptual programming, and the pragmatic use of a variety of technological resources involving symbolic, numeric, and graphic representations.

- *The roles of teacher and learner,* in which we considered ways in which the teacher can affect the learning, including teacher behaviors that encourage students to pursue surface rather than deep learning.

- *Analyzing empirical research,* in which we conducted a broad review of research studies and related them to the other themes of the chapter.

In this journey, a number of themes arise. The most important is the role not just of the technology, but the manner in which the technology is used. Clearly the skill of using software such as Mathematica or Maple is a valuable resource in its own right. However, the way in which technology is introduced and the purposes for doing so are both extremely important. Research studies to date—both on learning in general and on learning mathematics with or without technology—lead us to several conclusions:

1. The development of the understanding of major concepts of calculus can precede procedural skill development by using technology and an appropriate pedagogical approach. Procedural skills can develop quickly, and focus can shift to aspects of functions that lead to different procedures.

2. Results from quantitative comparison studies indicate that, in general, students in the various types of experimental sections, in general, did as well as students in traditional sections on questions examining procedural skills. More time spent on development of understanding of concepts, whether through resequencing of material or not, does not affect typical procedural skill development and indicates that less time could be spent on skill development.

3. Interpretations of results generated using technology and concepts such as convergence of infinite series should be discussed and compared to those from by-hand procedures.

4. Results from quantitative comparison studies that examined conceptual understanding were mixed, with experimental sections either performing the same as or better than control sections. Since it would seem that more time spent on concept development should result in better conceptual understandings, it is important to look at the studies in which there were no significant differences. Results from the Melin-Conjeros (1992) study point to difficulties with using only test items to make statements about student understanding. Other studies had treatments that involved the use of technology as an add-on without a significant change in pedagogy, which may result in no significant difference in learning.

5. In comparison studies that examined differences in pedagogy between sections that all integrated technology, differences in performance appeared linked to an approach that focused on concept development. The addition of technology without a corresponding change in curriculum does not appear to harm students, but may not lead to any significant gains in learning.

6. Results from qualitative studies indicate that students in various experimental sections developed more and better connections related to major concepts such as derivative and integral. Students were better able to explain ideas, especially using their own lan-

guage, and could often solve problems by drawing on conceptual knowledge and could also use procedural methods.

We next offer our observations about the implications of the available research—supplemented by our personal experiences and professional judgments—for continued renewal of calculus instruction.

1. Curricula need to be rethought periodically from the ground up, taking into consideration the tools that are available. It is not enough to think of clever ways to present calculus as the content was understood in the mid-twentieth century, when the available tool set was quite different, as was the intended audience.

2. Much of the effort that goes into design of a technology-based curriculum can be squandered if one does not at the same time rethink the design of the pedagogy in the light of research showing the effectiveness of active-learning strategies and distinguishing between effective and ineffective ways to stimulate deep learning approaches. It is not enough to adopt a new book or even a new book-plus-software package.

3. Our tools for assessing student learning—whether for purposes of assigning grades or for evaluating effectiveness of our curricula—need to be consistent with stated goals for each course and with the learning environments in which we expect students to function. It is not enough to continue giving timed, memory-based, multiple-choice, no-technology examinations.

4. If we are serious about calculus understanding for everyone with a "need to know"—not just the potential replacements for the mathematics faculty—then we need to plan our curricula, pedagogy, and assessments for effective learning of the skill sets and mental disciplines that are needed by a technology-literate public in the twenty-first century. It is not enough to keep using ourselves as "model learners."

5. Revision of curricula, pedagogy, assessment tools, and technology tools means nothing without concurrent professional development, both preservice and in-service, to keep faculty up to date with the required skills, knowledge, attitudes, and beliefs. It is not enough to continue acting as though an advanced degree is evidence of adequate preparation to teach.

REFERENCES

Abian, A. (1998). Use convergence to teach continuity [Letters to the Editor]. *Notices of the American Mathematical Society, 45*, 358-359.

Aldis, G. K., Sidhu, H. S., & Joiner, K. F. (1999). Trial of calculus and Maple with heterogeneous student groups at the Australian Defence Force Academy. *International Journal of Computer Algebra in Mathematics Education*, *6*, 167-189.

Anderson, J., Austin, K., Barnard, T., & Jagger, J. (1998) Do third-year mathematics undergraduates know what they are supposed to know? *International Journal of Mathematical Education in Science and Technology*, *29*, 401-420.

Armstrong, G. M., & Hendrix, L. J. (1999). Does traditional or reformed calculus prepare students better for subsequent courses? A preliminary study. *Journal of Computers in Mathematics and Science Teaching*, *18*, 95-103.

Artigue, M., (1990). *Enseigner autrement les mathématiques en deug A Premiere Année, Principes et Realisations* [Teaching mathematics in an alternative way in deug First Year, principles and realizations]. IREM de Lille, France.

Asiala, M., Cottrill, J., Dubinsky, E., & Schwingendorf, K. (1997). The development of students' graphical understanding of the derivative. *Journal of Mathematical Behavior*, *16*, 399-431.

Beckmann, C. E. (1988). Effect of computer graphics use on student understanding of calculus concepts. *Dissertation Abstracts International*, *50*(05), 1974. (UMI No. 8910117)

Bezuidenhout, J. (2001). Limits and continuity: Some conceptions of first-year students. *International Journal of Mathematical Education in Science and Technology*, *32*, 487-500.

Blokland, P., Giessen, C., & Tall, D. O. (2000). Graphic Calculus for Windows [Computer software]. Retrieved November 4, 2005 from http://www.vusoft.nl

Bookman, J. (2000). Program evaluation and undergraduate mathematics renewal: The impact of calculus reform on student performance in subsequent courses. In S. Ganter (Ed.), *Calculus renewal: Issues for undergraduate mathematics education in the next decade* (pp. 91-102). New York: Plenum Press.

Bookman, J., & Friedman, C. (1998). Student attitudes and calculus reform. *School Science and Mathematics*, *98*, 117-122.

Bookman, J., & Friedman, C. (1999). The evaluation of Project CALC at Duke University 1989-1994. In B. Gold, S. Keith, & W. Marion, (Eds.), *Assessment practices in undergraduate mathematics* (MAA Notes No. 49) (pp. 253-256). Washington, DC: Mathematical Association of America.

Bowden, J., & Marton, F. (1998). *University of learning: Beyond quality and competence in higher education*. London: Kogan Page.

Bransford, J. D., Brown, A. L., & Cocking, R. R., (Eds.). (1999). *How people learn: Brain, mind, experience, and school*. Washington, DC: National Academy Press.

Briggs, A. W. (1998). Defining uniform continuity first does not help [Letters to the Editor]. *Notices of the American Mathematical Society*, *45*, 462.

Burton, L. (2004). *Mathematicians as enquirers*. Dordrecht, The Netherlands: Kluwer Academic Press.

Cadena, J., Travis, B., & Norman, S. (2003). An evaluation of reform in the teaching of calculus. *Mathematics and Computer Education*, *37*, 210-220.

Castillo, T. (1998). Visualization, attitude and performance in multivariable calculus: Relationship between use and non-use of graphing calculator (Doctoral dissertation, The University of Texas at Austin, 1997). *Dissertation Abstracts International*, *59*(02), 438.

Chappell, K. & Killpatrick, K. (2003). Effects of concept-based instruction on students' conceptual understanding and procedural knowledge of calculus. *Primus, 13*, 17-37.

Confrey, J. (1992). Function Probe. [Computer software]. Santa Barbara, CA: Intellimation Library for the Macintosh.

Confrey, J., & Maloney, A. (2008). Research-design interactions in building Function Probe software. In G. W. Blume & M. K. Heid (Eds.), *Research on technology and the teaching and learning of mathematics: Vol. 2. Cases and perspectives* (pp. 183-210). Charlotte, NC: Information Age.

Connors, M. A. (1995). Achievement and gender in computer-integrated calculus. *Journal of Women and Minorities in Science and Engineering, 2*, 113-121.

Connors, M. A., & Snook, K. (2001). The effects of hand-held CAS on student achievement in a first year college core calculus sequence, *International Journal of Computer Algebra in Mathematics Education, 8*, 99-114.

Cooley, L. A. (1996). Evaluating the effects on conceptual understanding and achievement of enhancing an introductory calculus course with a computer algebra system (Doctoral dissertation, New York University, 1995). *Dissertation Abstracts International, 56*(10), 3869.

Cooley, L. A. (1997). Evaluating student understanding in a calculus course enhanced by a computer algebra system. *PRIMUS, 7*, 308-316.

Cornu, B. (1983). *Apprentissage de la notion de limite: conceptions et obstacles* [Learning the notion of limit: Concepts and difficulties]. Unpublished doctoral dissertation, University of Grenoble, Grenoble, France.

Cornu, B. (1991). Limits. In D. O. Tall (Ed.), *Advanced mathematical thinking* (pp. 153-166). Dordrecht, The Netherlands: Kluwer Academic Press.

Cottrill, J., Dubinsky, E., Nichols, D., Schwingendorf, K., Thomas, K., & Vidakovic, D. (1996). Understanding the limit concept: Beginning with a coordinated process scheme. *Journal of Mathematical Behavior, 15*, 167-192.

Cowell, R. H., & Prosser, R. T. (1991). Computers with calculus at Dartmouth. *PRIMUS, 1*, 149-158.

Crocker, D. A. (1993). Development of the concept of derivative in a calculus class using the computer algebra system Mathematica. In L. Lum (Ed.), *Proceedings of the fourth annual International Conference on Technology in Collegiate Mathematics* (pp. 251-255). Reading, MA: Addison Wesley.

Cunningham, R. F. (1992). The effects of achievement of using computer software to reduce hand-generated symbolic manipulation in freshman calculus (Doctoral dissertation, Temple University, 1991). *Dissertation Abstracts International, 52*(07), 2448.

Davis, B., Porta, H., & Uhl, J. (1994a). *Calculus&Mathematica*. Reading MA: Addison Wesley.

Davis, B., Porta, H., & Uhl, J. (1994b). *Calculus&Mathematica*: Addressing fundamental questions about technology. In L. Lum (Ed.), *Proceedings of the fifth annual International Conference on Technology in Collegiate Mathematics* (pp. 305-314). Reading MA: Addison Wesley.

Davis, R. B., & Vinner, S. (1986). The notion of limit: Some seemingly unavoidable misconception stages. *Journal of Mathematical Behavior, 5*, 281-303.

Dick, T. P., & Edwards, B. S. (2008). Multiple representations and local linearity—Research influences on the use of technology in calculus curriculum reform. In G. W. Blume & M. K. Heid (Eds.), *Research on technology and the teaching and learning of mathematics: Vol. 2. Cases and perspectives* (pp. 255-276). Charlotte, NC: Information Age.

Donovan, M. S., Bransford, J. D., & Pellegrino, J. W. (Eds.). (1999). *How people learn: Bridging research and practice.* Washington, DC: National Academy Press.

Douglas, R. G. (Ed.). (1986). *Towards a lean and lively calculus* (MAA Notes No. 6). Washington, DC: Mathematical Association of America.

Ellis, R., & Gulick, D. (1991). *Calculus, one and several variables.* Fort Worth, TX: Saunders.

Ellison, M. (1994). The effect of computer and calculator graphics on students' ability to mentally construct calculus concepts (Doctoral dissertation, University of Minnesota, 1993). *Dissertation Abstracts International, 54*(11), 4020.

Entwistle, N. J. (1987). *Understanding classroom learning.* London: Hodder and Stoughton.

Entwistle, N. J., & Ramsden, P. (1983). *Understanding student learning.* London: Croom Helm.

Estes, K. A. (1990). Graphics technologies as instructional tools in applied calculus: Impact on instructor, students, and conceptual and procedural achievement (Doctoral dissertation, University of South Florida, 1990). *Dissertation Abstracts International, 51*(04), 1147.

Ferrini-Mundy, J., & Lauten, D. (1994). Learning about calculus learning. *Mathematics Teacher, 87,* 115-121.

Forster, P.A., & Mueller, U. (2001). Outcomes and implications of students' use of graphics calculators in the public examination of calculus. *International Journal of Mathematical Education in Science and Technology, 32,* 37-52.

Fredenberg, V. (1994). Supplemental visual computer-assisted instruction and student achievement in freshman college calculus (Doctoral dissertation, Montana State University, 1993). *Dissertation Abstracts International, 55*(01), 59.

Galindo-Morales, E. (1994). Visualization in the calculus class: Relationship between cognitive style, gender, and use of technology (Doctoral dissertation, The Ohio State University, 1994). *Dissertation Abstracts International, 55*(10), 3125.

Ganter, S. L. (2001). *Changing calculus: A report on evaluation efforts and national impact from 1988 to 1998* (MAA Notes No. 56). Washington, DC: Mathematical Association of America.

Girard, N. (2002). Students' representational approaches to solving calculus problems: Examining the role of graphing calculators (Doctoral dissertation, The University of Pittsburgh, 2002). *Dissertation Abstracts International, 63*(10), 3502.

Goldenberg, E. P. (1988). Mathematics, metaphors, and human factors: Mathematical, technical, and pedagogical challenges in the educational use of graphical representation of functions. *Journal of Mathematical Behavior, 7,* 135-173.

Gonzalez-Martin, A., & Camacho, M. (2004). What is first-year mathematics students' actual knowledge about improper integrals? *International Journal of Mathematical Education in Science and Technology, 35*, 73-89.

Harding, R. D., & Johnson, D. C. (1979). University level computing and mathematical problem-solving ability. *Journal for Research in Mathematics Education, 10*, 37-55.

Hart, D. (1991). Building concept images: Supercalculators and students' use of multiple representations in calculus. *Dissertation Abstracts International, 52*(12), 4254. (UMI No. 9214776)

Hawker, C. (1987). The effects of replacing some manual skills with computer algebra manipulations on student performance in business calculus. *Dissertation Abstracts International, 47*(08), 2934. (UMI No. 8626590)

Heid, M. K. (1985). An exploratory study to examine the effects of resequencing skills and concepts in an applied calculus curriculum through the use of the microcomputer. (Doctoral dissertation, University of Maryland, 1984). *Dissertation Abstracts International, 46*(06), 1548.

Heid, M. K. (1988). Resequencing skills and concepts in applied calculus using the computer as a tool. *Journal for Research in Mathematics Education, 19*, 3-25.

Hiebert, J., & Lefevre, P. (1986). *Conceptual and procedural knowledge: The case of mathematics.* Hillsdale, NJ: Erlbaum.

Hughes-Hallett, D., Gleason, A. M., et al. (1994). *Calculus.* New York: John Wiley and Sons.

Hunter, M., Monaghan, J. D., & Roper, T. (1993). The effect of computer algebra use on students' algebraic thinking. In R. Sutherland (Ed.), *Working papers for ESRC algebra seminar.* London: Institute of Education.

Hurley, J. F., Koehn, U., & Ganter, S. L. (1999). Effects of calculus reform: Local and national. *American Mathematical Monthly, 106*, 800-811.

Jackson, A. (2000). Declining student numbers worry German mathematics departments. *Notices of the American Mathematical Society, 47*, 364-368.

Johnson, D. C. (2000). Algorithmics and programming in the school mathematics curriculum: Support is waning—Is there still a case to be made? *Education and Information Technologies, 5*, 201-214.

Judson, P. T. (1988). Effects of modified sequencing of skills and applications in introductory calculus (Doctoral dissertation, The University of Texas at Austin, 1988). *Dissertation Abstracts International, 49*(06), 1397.

Judson, P. T. (1990). Elementary business calculus with computer algebra. *Journal of Mathematical Behavior, 9*, 153-157.

Keller, B. A. (1993). Symbol sense and its development in two computer algebra system environments (Doctoral dissertation, Western Michigan University, 1993). *Dissertation Abstracts International, 54*(11), 5704.

Keller, B. A., & Hirsch, C. R. (1998). Students' preferences for representations of functions. *International Journal of Mathematical Education in Science and Technology, 29*, 1-17.

Keller, B. A., & Russell, C. A. (1997). Effects of the TI-92 on calculus students solving symbolic problems. *The International Journal of Computer Algebra in Mathematics Education, 4*, 77-97.

Keller, B. A., Russell, C. A., & Thompson, H. (1999). A large-scale study clarifying the roles of the TI-92 and instructional format on student success in calculus. *The International Journal of Computer Algebra in Mathematics Education, 6*, 191-207.

Kendal, M., & Stacey, K. (1999). Varieties of teacher privileging for teaching calculus with computer algebra systems. *The International Journal of Computer Algebra in Mathematics Education, 6*, 233-247.

Kenelly, J. W., & Harvey, J. G. (1994). New developments in Advanced Placement Calculus. In A. Solow (Ed.), *Preparing for a new calculus* (MAA Notes No. 36) (pp. 46-52). Washington, DC: Mathematical Association of America.

Kidron, I., & Zehavi, N. (2002). The role of animation in teaching the limit concept. *The International Journal of Computer Algebra in Mathematics Education, 9*, 205-227.

Kline, M. (1972). *Mathematical thought from ancient to modern times*. Oxford, England: Oxford University Press.

Knuth, D. E. (1998). Teach calculus with big O [Letters to the Editor]. *Notices of the American Mathematical Society, 45*, 687-688.

Lakoff, G., & Núñez, R. E. (2000). *Where mathematics comes from: How the embodied mind brings mathematics into being*. New York: Basic Books.

Lax, P. D. (1998). Use uniform continuity to teach limits [Letters to the Editor]. *Notices of the American Mathematical Society 45*, 6.

Lefton, L. E., & Steinbart, E. M. (1995). Calculus&*Mathematica*: An end-user's point of view. *PRIMUS, 5*, 80-96.

Li, L., & Tall, D. O. (1993). Constructing different concept images of sequences and limits by programming. In I. Hirabayashi, N. Nobda, K. Shlgematsu, & F. -L. Lin (Eds.), *Proceedings of the seventeenth international conference of the International Group for the Psychology of Mathematics Education* (Vol. 2, pp. 41-48). Tsukuba, Ibaraki, Japan: University of Tsukuba. (ERIC Document Reproduction Service No. ED383536)

LiveMath. (2005). LiveMath (Version 3.5) [Computer software]. Retrieved November 4, 2005 from http://www.livemath.com/products/

MacLane, S. (1997). On the Harvard Consortium Calculus [Letters to the Editor]. *Notices of the American Mathematical Society, 44*, 893.

Macromedia. (2004a). Flash 8 [Computer software]. Retrieved November 4, 2005 from http://www.macromedia.com/mobile/?promoid=CUOM

Macromedia. (2004b). Director MX [Computer software]. Retrieved November 4, 2005 from http http://www.macromedia.com/software/director/

Maplesoft. (2005). Maple 10 [Computer software]. Retrieved November 4, 2005 from http://www.maplesoft.com/products/maple/demo/index.aspx

Mathematical Association. (1974). *Mathematics 11–16*. Leicester, United Kingdom: Author.

Mathematical Association. (1992). *Computers in the mathematics curriculum: A report of the Mathematical Association*. Leicester, United Kingdom: Author.

Maxwell, J. W., & Loftsgaarden, D. O. (1997). Recent trends in graduate admissions in mathematics departments. *Notices of the American Mathematical Society, 44*, 213-216.

MathSoft. (2005). Mathcad 13 [Computer software]. Retrieved November 4, 2005 from http://mathsoft.com/solutions/calculation_management_suite/mathcad .asp

Meel, D. E. (1996). A comparative study of honor students' understandings of central calculus concepts as a result of completing a Calculus&Mathematica or a traditional calculus curriculum (Doctoral dissertation, University of Pittsburgh, 1995). *Dissertation Abstracts International, 57*(01), 142.

Melin-Conejeros, J. (1992). The effect of using a computer algebra system in a mathematics laboratory on the achievement and attitude of calculus students (Doctoral dissertation, University of Iowa, 1992). *Dissertation Abstracts International, 53*(07), 2283.

Monaghan, J. D. (1986). *Adolescents' understanding of limits and infinity.* Unpublished doctoral dissertation, Warwick University, U.K.

Monaghan, J., Sun, S., & Tall, D. O. (1994). Construction of the limit concept with a computer algebra system. In J. P. da Ponte & J. F. Matos (Eds.), *Proceedings of the eighteenth international conference of the International Group for the Psychology of Mathematics Education* (Vol. III, pp. 279-286). Lisbon, Portugal: University of Lisbon. (ERIC Document Reproduction Service No. ED383537)

Mumford, D. (1997). Calculus reform—For the millions. *Notices of the American Mathematical Society, 44,* 559-563.

National Center for Education Statistics (1999). *Digest of educational statistics 1999.* Retrieved January 30, 2001 from http://www.nces.ed.gov/pubs2000/Digest99/ d99t255.html

Nemirovsky, R., Tierney, C. & Wright, T. (1998). Body motion and graphing. *Cognition and Instruction, 16,* 119-172.

Norwood, R. (1997). In praise of epsilon/delta [Letters to the Editor]. *Notices of the American Mathematical Society, 44,* 1429.

Orton, A. (1983a). Students' understanding of differentiation. *Educational Studies in Mathematics, 14,* 235-250.

Orton, A. (1983b). Students' understanding of integration. *Educational Studies in Mathematics, 14,* 1-18.

Padgett, E. E. (1995). Calculus I with a laboratory component. (Doctoral dissertation, Baylor University, 1994). *Dissertation Abstracts International, 55*(09), 2754.

Palmiter, J. R. (1991). Effects of computer algebra systems on concept and skill acquisition in calculus. *Journal for Research in Mathematics Education, 22,* 151-156.

Park, K. (1993). A comparative study of the traditional calculus course vs. the Calculus&Mathematica course. (Doctoral dissertation, University of Illinois at Urbana-Champaign, 1993). *Dissertation Abstracts International, 54*(01), 119.

Park, K., & Travers, K. J. (1996). A comparative study of a computer-based and a standard college first year calculus course. *CBMS Issues in Mathematics Education, 6,* 155-176.

Parks, V. W. (1995). Impact of a laboratory approach supported by *Mathematica* on the conceptualization of limit in a first calculus course (Doctoral dissertation, Georgia State University, 1995). *Dissertation Abstracts International, 56*(10), 3872.

Pinto, M. M. F. (1998). *Students' understanding of real analysis.* Unpublished doctoral dissertation, Warwick University.

Pinto, M. M. F., & Tall, D. O. (1999). Student constructions of formal theory: Giving and extracting meaning. In O. Zaslavsky (Ed.), *Proceedings of the twenty-third international conference of the International Group for the Psychology of Mathematics Education* (Vol. 4, pp. 65-73). Haifa, Israel: Technion, Israel Institute of Technology. (ERIC Document Reproduction Service No. ED436403)

Porzio, D. T. (1995). The effects of differing technological approaches to calculus on students' use and understanding of multiple representations when solving problems (Doctoral dissertation, The Ohio State University, 1994). *Dissertation Abstracts International, 55*(10), 3128.

Ramsden, P. (1992). *Learning to teach in higher education.* London: Routledge.

Rhem, J. (1995). Deep/surface approaches to learning: An introduction. *National Teaching and Learning Forum, 5,* 1.

Roberts, A. W. (Ed.). (1996). *Calculus: The dynamics of change* (MAA Notes No. 39). Washington, DC: Mathematical Association of America.

Roddick, C. D. (1998). A comparison study of students from two calculus sequences on their achievement in calculus-dependent courses (Doctoral dissertation, The Ohio State University, 1997). *Dissertation Abstracts International, 58*(07), 2577.

Roddick, C. D. (2001). Differences in learning outcomes: Calculus&Mathematica vs. traditional calculus. *PRIMUS 11,* 161-184.

Schoenfeld, A. H. (2000). Purposes and methods of research in mathematics education. *Notices of the American Mathematical Society,* 641-649.

Schrock, C. S. (1990). Calculus and computing: An exploratory study to examine the effectiveness of using a computer algebra system to develop increased conceptual understanding in a first-semester calculus course (Doctoral dissertation, Kansas State University, 1989). *Dissertation Abstracts International, 50*(07), 1926.

Smith, D. A., & Moore, L. C. (1996). *Calculus: Modeling and application.* Boston: Houghton Mifflin.

Smith, E., & Confrey, J. (1994). Using a dynamic software tool to teach transformations of functions. In L. Lum (Ed.), *Proceedings of the fifth annual International Conference on Technology in Collegiate Mathematics* (pp. 225-242). Reading, MA: Addison-Wesley.

Soto-Johnson, H. (1998). Impact of technology on learning infinite series. *International Journal of Computer Algebra in Mathematics Education, 5,* 95-109.

Stroyan, K. D. (1993). *Calculus using Mathematica.* Boston: Academic Press.

Sun Microsystems. (2005). Java [Computer software]. Retrieved November 4, 2005, from http://java.com/en/download/index.jsp

Tall, D. O. (1985). Using computer graphics as generic organisers for the concept image of differentiation. In L. Streefland (Ed.), *Proceedings of the ninth international conference of the International Group for the Psychology of Mathematics Education* (Vol. 1, pp. 105-110). Utrecht, The Netherlands: State University of Utrecht. (ERIC Document Reproduction Service No. ED411130)

Tall, D. O. (with Blokland, P., & Kok, D.). (1990). *A graphic approach to the calculus.* Pleasantville, NY: Sunburst.

Tall, D. O. (1993). Real mathematics, rational computers and complex people. *Proceedings of the fifth annual International Conference on Technology in College Mathematics Teaching* (pp. 243-258). Reading, MA: Addison-Wesley.

Tall, D. O. (2001). Cognitive development in advanced mathematics using technology. *Mathematics Education Research Journal, 12*, 196-218.

Tall, D. O. (2002). Natural and formal infinities. *Educational Studies in Mathematics, 48*, 199-238.

Tall, D. O., Gray, E. M., Crowley, L., DeMarois, P., McGowen, M., Pitta, D., et al. (2001). Symbols and the bifurcation between procedural and conceptual thinking. *Canadian Journal of Science, Mathematics and Technology Education, 1*, 81-104.

Texas Instruments. (2005). Derive 6 [Computer software]. Retrieved November 4, 2005, from http://education.ti.com/us/product/software/derive/features/features.html

Vlachos, P., & Kehegias, A. (2000). A computer algebra system and a new approach for teaching business calculus. *The International Journal of Computer Algebra in Mathematics Education, 7*, 87-104.

Wells, P. (1996). Conceptual understanding of major topics in first semester calculus: A study of three types of calculus courses at the University of Kentucky (Doctoral dissertation, University of Kentucky, 1995). *Dissertation Abstracts International, 56*(09), 3493.

Williams, S. (1991). Models of limit held by college calculus students. *Journal for Research in Mathematics Education, 22*, 219-236.

Wood, N. G. (1992). Mathematical analysis: A comparison of student development and historical development. Unpublished doctoral dissertation, Cambridge University, United Kingdom.

Wolfram Research. (2005). Mathematica 5.2 [Computer software]. Retrieved November 4, 2005, from http://wolfram.com/products/mathematica/index.html

Wu, H. (1996). The mathematician and the mathematics education reform. *Notices of the American Mathematical Society, 43*, 1531-1537.

Zbiek, R. M., & Hollebrands, K. F. (2008). A research-informed view of the process of incorporating mathematics technology into classroom practice by inservice and prospective teachers. In M. K. Heid & G. W. Blume (Eds.), *Research on technology and the teaching and learning of mathematics: Vol. 1. Syntheses* (pp. 287-344). Charlotte, NC: Information Age.

CHAPTER 6

THE LEARNING OF MATHEMATICS AND MATHEMATICAL MODELING

Helen M. Doerr and Dave Pratt

The phrase "mathematical modeling" covers a broad range of theoretical and practical orientations to the teaching and learning of mathematics. In this chapter, we will attempt to synthesize the breadth of research on mathematical modeling and to analyze the equally broad role of technology in this research. In the first section of the chapter, we focus on the research on the learning of mathematics through modeling from two perspectives: epistemological and psychological. The second section describes the various roles that technology plays in supporting student learning through mathematical modeling. The third and final section of the chapter concludes with an analysis of the relationship between the theoretical perspectives on modeling and the use of technological tools within that research, and includes suggestions for further research and for tool development and instructional design.

Research on Technology and the Teaching and Learning of Mathematics:
Vol. 1. Research Syntheses, pp. 259–285

EPISTEMOLOGICAL PERSPECTIVE

Nearly all of the research on learning through mathematical modeling is grounded in some variation of an epistemological perspective that begins with an examination of the relationship between an experienced or "real" world and a model world. Collectively, this work suggests two epistemological underpinnings to mathematical modeling: first, that the model is separate from the world to be modeled and, second, that modeling is a cyclic, iterative process. The epistemological stance that separates the experienced world of phenomena from the constructed world of the model is in one sense artificial and in another sense at the crux of modeling. This separation is not a naïve, modern day version of a Platonist worldview wherein reality is directly represented in a mathematical model. Modeling does not attempt to promote or "preserve the fiction that there is an absolute and unproblematic distinction between the world and our apprehension of it" (Lehrer, Horvath, & Schauble, 1994, p. 219). Rather, as Skovsmose (1990) argues, our perceptions and observations are grounded in some theoretical framework, which then influences the structuring of reality that leads us to the construction of any particular model. The essence of this epistemological stance is that the world of phenomena and the model world co-construct each other.

The coconstruction of the experienced world and the model world is evidenced by the ways in which models are projected back into the experienced world. A now-classic example of this is the invention of the calculus by Newton and Leibniz, which in turn created an experience of the world governed by the laws of Newtonian physics. More modern examples of models that have helped construct reality are cellular automata, chaos theory, the concept of fractal dimension and the accountant's spreadsheet. The notion that reality is structured by the models that humans create is of significant importance from a scientific as well as a social and political perspective. As an example, Skovsmose (1990) points out that the Cobb-Douglas function for national production includes only labor force and capital investment. Therefore, ecological costs are always out of the question when discussing the economy according to this model. Thus, any claims about the economic system based on this model are claims about the conceptual system that only allowed consideration of labor force and capital investment in the first place and hence necessarily exclude ecological issues from the discussion. As Ogborn and Mellar (1994) point out, an economic model can affect the very outcome it forecasts (p. 18). Thus, the separation of the real world of phenomena and the mathematical world of the model is in some sense an artificial separation or a separation of degrees.

At the same time, the separation of phenomena and model is at the crux of the meaning of model. As Lehrer, Horvath, and Schauble (1994) argue, this separation between phenomena and model arises because models are fundamentally structural analogs between two systems. A model is a system of objects, relationships, and rules whose behavior resembles that of some other system. Modeling is the activity of mapping from one system to another. This activity is driven by the need to describe, predict, or explain some particular phenomena of interest to the modeler. Elements from the real world of the experienced phenomena are selected, organized, and structured in such a way that they can be mapped onto a model world. This model world necessarily simplifies and distorts some aspects of the real world while maintaining other features and allowing for manipulations of these features (or objects) in accordance with the rules of the model world. These manipulations lead to the descriptions, predictions, or explanations that are the goals of the modeling activity.

The second epistemological stance that grounds research and practice related to mathematical models is that modeling is a cyclic or iterative process. The source of this iteration comes from the attempts at validation in the real world of the outcomes of the manipulations of the objects in the model world. This validation can take several different forms. In some cases, the validity of outcomes is simply measured against the criteria of usefulness for some particular purpose. In other cases, validity is determined by comparison to other models or to other experienced phenomena or to predicted data. The outcomes of the validation process result in either a satisfactory model or generate another cycle of modeling activity. The cyclic nature of this modeling paradigm is generally presented in variations of the simplified form suggested in Figure 6.1 (National Council of Teachers of Mathematics, 1989; Giordano, Weir, & Fox, 1997; Galbraith & Clatworthy, 1990; Edwards & Hansom, 1989; Niss, Blum, & Huntley, 1991). This view of modeling is suggestive of the terms horizontal mathematization and vertical mathematization, used by the Dutch researchers in the tradition of Realistic Mathematics Education (Treffers & Goffree, 1985). Horizontal mathematization refers to the movement from the "real world" to the "model world." The notion of vertical mathematization in the Dutch tradition refers to activities in which mathematical elements are put together, organized, and structured into elements that are often more abstract than they were in their original form. This is close in meaning to the vertical arrow where transformations take place. In the Realistic Mathematics Education tradition, this transformation can lead to more formal and more abstract mathematical structures. Here, the transformations are intended to lead primarily to solutions that can be interpreted in the real world; in some cases, that may also include the creation of mathematical structures.

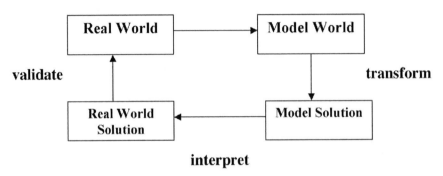

Figure 6.1.   The cyclic nature of the modeling process.

The cyclic notion of iteration implies that models are successively refined to better serve some purpose such as the understanding of an experienced system or predictions of behavior or explanations of causes or relationships. Some theoreticians (Forrester, 1987) call for a reconsideration of the structure of the model when the predicted behaviors are compared with other knowledge about the real world that is being modeled. Others, such as Black (1962) and Lesh (1981), include as part of the modeling process the explicit recognition of the introduction of simplifying assumptions and the later analysis of the validity and necessity of those assumptions. Niss (1989) argues that students should critically analyze and assess models, both those that they have constructed and those constructed by others. This analysis should include a critique of the mathematical relationships that are within the model as well as "the properties, qualities and bases of justification of the models as representations of given segments of reality" (Niss, 1989, p. 28). As noted earlier, Skovsmose (1990) argues that the comparison of the model with reality is inherently problematic: "A mathematical model is not a model of reality; it is a model of a conceptual system created by a specific interpretation, based on a more or less elaborated theoretical framework, and based on some specific interests" (p. 770). These arguments suggest that the development of a model needs to include the reflective and critical investigation that examines the assumptions and criteria used in the construction, application, and validation of the model.

Many of the researchers and teachers who use this cyclic paradigm tend to emphasize a view of mathematical modeling that is akin to applied problem solving. The focus is often on problem situations that arise in engineering (especially mechanics), physics, biology, and occasionally chemistry. Most of the reported work describes projects or curricular approaches that have been implemented in the secondary or tertiary schools (Fay & Joubert, 2002; Lawson & Tabor, 2001; Mandinach & Cline, 1994; Mintz, 1993; Osawa, 2002; Steed, 1992; vom Hofe, 2001). The findings are often reported in terms of student affect, engagement, and motivation, and in terms of the value of "real world" contexts to support these outcomes. The mathematics involved in these projects generally includes algebra, functions, regression analysis, calculus, differential equations, and stochastic processes. Numerous examples of the appeal of this kind of modeling can be found in the literature on mathematics instruction, which provides a litany of problems to be modeled by secondary or tertiary students (e.g., Bolte, 2002; Froelich, 2000; Sidhu & Carss, 2000; Swetz & Hartzler, 1991). The modeling process is generally described as a series of steps, similar to those shown in Figure 6.1, such as the following: Understand the particular phenomena to be modeled; define the context and constraints; identify the key variables; explicitly define the relationships among the variables; translate those relationships to an appropriate computer implementation; analyze and interpret the results; and then refine the model and one's understanding through an iterative process by repeating these steps (Edwards & Hansom, 1989). However, despite the richness of the problem contexts, the analysis of student learning through these steps in this literature is quite sparse.

PSYCHOLOGICAL PERSPECTIVE

A psychological perspective on the research on models and modeling more directly addresses issues related to the nature of the activities of learners when engaged in modeling tasks. Some researchers have rejected the implied linearity of steps in the modeling process (Bell, 1993; Lesh, Surber, & Zawojewski, 1983; Doerr, 1996a, 1996b; Lesh & Doerr, 2000; Lester & Kehle, 2003). These researchers argue that learners make many moves when engaged in the modeling process, often in no particular order, and that the process is characterized by many cycles and multiple stages. This view of the modeling process is represented by the nodes and the interconnections shown in Figure 6.2. While the modeling process necessarily begins with encountering the context of the problem situation, learners move among the nodes in no particular order, but with considerable revisiting and recycling from any given node to any other. Lesh and colleagues have found that learners often spent an overwhelming amount of time in refining their understanding of the problem. They posit a "spiraling model evolution [that] is characterized by the occurrence of repeated mapping cycles while simultaneously the qualitative level of

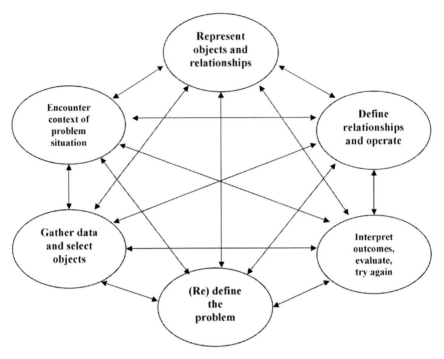

Figure 6.2.   A nonlinear view of the modeling process.

understanding increases" (1983, p. 132). Doerr and colleagues have illustrated the revisions and the increasing refinement of students' thinking as they cycle through interpretations of modeling tasks (Doerr, 2000; Doerr & English, 2003). Linn, diSessa, Pea, and Songer (1994) argue for a long-term perspective on the refinement and articulation of students' models as they develop their models into more sophisticated forms.

A second aspect that emerges from the psychological view of the learner and learning is the distinction between the use of an existing model created by an expert and the building of a model that reflects the learner's own emerging understandings of the phenomena. Many researchers have identified this distinction between running a prebuilt model and building a model (Clauset, Rawley, & Boedeker, 1987; Doerr, 1996a; Mandinach & Cline, 1989, 1994; Moar, Spensley, O'Shea, Singer, Hennessy, & Scanlon, 1992; Roberts & Barclay, 1988; Webb & Hassell, 1988). This distinction between using models and building models has also been described as the difference between exploratory modeling and expressive modeling (Bliss & Ogborn, 1989). According to these researchers, exploratory models are those models that are constructed by experts to represent knowledge in some content domain. Learners typically explore consequences of their actions within the boundaries of these content domain models. Typical activities include varying input parameters, observing changes in output, and explaining the consequences of certain actions and conditions. For example, some microworlds provide the student with a set of simulated, idealized worlds that embody the Newtonian laws of motion while allowing the student to explore the consequences of changes in the simulation's parameters and to reason about the relationship of the changes to the outcomes. A microworld permits the exploration of the consequences of "what if ..." for changes in variables and for extreme values of variables, while simultaneously putting the control for such questions into the hands of the learner and allowing for repeated investigations. Such microworlds provide the learner with the opportunity to explore a content domain through the testing of hypotheses and variation of parameters, the autonomy of self-directed inquiry, and interaction with dynamic, linked representations. As Bliss and Ogborn (1989) note, such exploratory models provide a way of asking, "Can you understand an expert's way of thinking about a problem?"

The modeling paradigm illustrated in Figure 6.2 is indicative of the activities involved in model *building*. Building a model (or expressive modeling) provides learners with the opportunity to express their own concepts and to learn through the iterative process of representing their ideas, selecting objects, defining relationships among objects, operating on those relationships, and interpreting and validating outcomes. Bliss and Ogborn (1989) describe such expressive models as providing a way of asking, "Can you understand your own way of thinking about a problem?" This is a significant shift in perspective from the activity of exploring a prebuilt model that necessarily embodies the intentions, concepts, and structures of an expert. The process of model building forces students to make explicit their own ideas about the relationships among objects and variables to examine, interpret, and validate the consequences of their ideas. For example, Confrey and Doerr (1994) found that a rich diversity of approaches was taken by different groups of students in conjecturing, refining, and confirming a set of relationships between the force acting on an object on an inclined plane and its component forces.

The Use of Technology in Supporting Student Learning in Modeling Activities

We wish to emphasize that the exploratory or expressive characteristic of modeling is a characteristic of the activity of the learner within a classroom setting, not an inherent characteristic of the tools used in modeling!

In this section, we will discuss the issue of the designers' intentions for the tools and then we will elaborate on how the same technological tool can be used, albeit quite differently, for either exploratory modeling or expressive modeling. We begin by examining the issue of the design of tools for students' modeling activities.

In her analysis of the problematic nature of the relationship between microworlds and the physical and mathematical phenomena that they are intended to embody or represent, Edwards (1998) draws a distinction between the design (or structural) characteristics of the microworld and the functional characteristics of the microworld as it is used as an element in a learning environment. From the structural point of view, the tool (in this case, a microworld) reflects the intentions of the developer with respect to the structure of some domain of mathematics or science. For example, according to Edwards, the "dynaturtle" environment (diSessa, 1982) reflects the Newtonian laws of motion and the Logo-based "House" microworld (Hoyles & Noss, 1992) embodies proportional figures. According to Edwards, a functional perspective on the microworld shifts the focus to how the tool is used. A learner could engage in manipulating objects, interpreting feedback, or using the objects to create new entities. Microworlds tend to be used as exploratory tools, although Edwards and others (Meira, 1995) point out that the meanings that learners make when working in such environments are not designed into the computer, but rather emerge through the social practices surrounding their use. Schecker (1993) proposes that model building (or expressive) software be recognized as a category of tools in its own right, and defines this new category as "context-free software tools that support the user in representing a part of the 'touch-and-show' reality in the form of an abstract, quantifiable system of parameters and their relationships (the *model*), which predicts the behavior of the real system" (p. 162).

He argues that, whereas simulation programs (such as microworlds) contain a prebuilt model, which the user is intended to explore or apply, model-building programs focus on developing the model itself. In categorizing such a family of software, Schecker claims that the use of such software enables the user to explore the consequences of his or her conceptual assumptions about the phenomenon, leading to a conceptual understanding of the physical domain. In a similar vein, O'Reilly, Pratt, and Winbourne (1997) contrast constructive tools—those designed for the learner to build with (and so essentially expressive)—and instructive tools—those intended to be made sense of by the learner (and so essentially exploratory). The approach by O'Reilly, Pratt, and Winbourne also envisions hybrid software that contains a mixture of expressive and exploratory tools.

We will return to the issue of the designer's intention for the technological tool when we discuss the pedagogical dimensions of modeling. For now, we will assume that exploratory or expressive modeling is a characteristic not of the tool but of the activity in which the learner engages with the tool. In this section, we will review research in which the apparently context-free spreadsheet is used to explore prepared models supplied by the teacher. We will examine the diversity of uses of dynamical geometry software, ranging from exploring a form of Euclidean geometry to expressing personal models of a drawing kit. In so doing, we intend to guard against a techno-centric approach, in which a software tool is assumed to have inherent properties for supporting learning, ignoring the crucial role played by the teacher or researcher in mediating that learning through structuring the task. As a constant reminder of this position, we will refer to the (tool, task) pair as the unit of analysis. Our synthesis of the literature will examine neither the tool (such as a spreadsheet) nor the task (such as modeling the length of a roll of paper) in isolation, but will consider these two dimensions as inseparable as the two sides of the same coin. We begin with our analysis of exploratory modeling activity.

Exploratory Models

In this section, we report on research about the exploration of models drawn from three domains of knowledge, namely physics (more specifically the laws of motion), probability, and geometry. Such diverse domains serve to illustrate that the issues raised by modeling through technology are pertinent across a wide spectrum of knowledge domains. A classic example of the use of exploratory models was provided by diSessa (1979) with the "dynaturtle." This Logo-based environment sought to enable students to work within a world that contrasted with the everyday world where objects appeared to slow down automatically. In the idealized computer world, Newton's first two laws as encapsulated in the formula $F = ma$ determined the motion of an object called a dynaturtle. Students could explore the implications of Newton's laws by attempting to control the dynaturtle. In so doing, students might find that an object would not slow down (or speed up) unless a force (to be programmed into the model by the student) provided an impulse. The intention was that students would experience conflict between their own mental model and the Newtonian model. Reflecting on these experiences, diSessa (1982) reports how students learning to control a Newtonian object reveal a robust Aristotelian expectation that things should move in the direction last pushed.

In addition, the evidence reported indicates a marked lack of influence of school physics in changing students' Aristotelian expectations.

White (1984) attempted to build on diSessa's pioneering work by designing games with specific goals aimed at focusing the students' attention on specific aspects of Newtonian dynamics. In her study, 32 science students (average age of 16.4 years) used a series of motion-based games. The students were tested before and after using these games and compared to a control group who did not play the games. The improvement in performance of the students who played the games was found to be statistically significant. There was evidence that playing the games improved understanding of Newton's laws. For example, many of the students who had played the games knew intuitively that the direction of motion after the application of an impulse was not in the direction of the impulse but was dependent on the initial velocity. Such an intuition contrasted with intuitions for similar situations in the pretest. Subsequent analysis provided some justification that the corrected thinking might be attributable to the game playing itself. The force and motion experiments involved the design of specialized environments, which contained elements that behaved according to a predetermined model, in this case as defined by Newton's first and second laws of motion. Notwithstanding the White experiment, evidence that students construct a link between a microworld experience and the real world is rare. This is a problematic aspect of much research with microworlds, namely the lack of evidence for any claim that the students reasoned better about real-world phenomena, even when they reasoned appropriately within the microworld.

Similar approaches have been used elsewhere in very different knowledge domains. Pratt (2000) reports on work in which he iteratively designed a stochastic *domain of abstraction*, which was an environment intended to support the testing of conjectures about the behavior of various stochastic *gadgets* (for example, coins, dice, and spinners). In this sense, the tools incorporated the laws of probability, although, of course, the children may have expectations of the behavior of these gadgets that do not conform to such laws. He worked with thirty-two 10-year-old children. The research iterated between phases of software design and clinical trials in which children used the tools provided. The report indicates that these children held a number of naïve ways of thinking about randomness that were nevertheless identifiable as similar to expert-like thinking. For example, the children sought out features of unpredictability, uncontrollability, fairness, and irregularity in trying to identify random phenomena. However, the children's ideas about randomness were abstracted from their experience of the short term; they did not refer to long-term properties of randomness where pattern emerges, at least in an aggregated and proportional sense. The children applied these naïve ideas even when trying to make sense of long-term behavior.

The gadgets went beyond their real-world counterparts in that they could be opened up to reveal tools that the children could use to explore and change their behavior. In fact, some of these gadgets were presented in broken form. The task for the children was to use the tools to mend the broken gadgets. In so doing, the children revealed their understanding of randomness and how that understanding changed during interaction with the gadgets. Underpinning each gadget was the same mathematical model, essentially the laws of probability, but each gadget appeared at the observation level as distinct. The research reports how a new intuition, constructed to explain the behavior of one gadget, was insufficiently robust for making sense of a new situation, even though that new situation was mathematically similar. Nevertheless, these children were able to use the new intuitions when other means of making sense of behavior were seen to lack explanatory power. Indeed, Pratt (2000) reports that the new intuitions seemed to gain increased power as they were found to be consistently useful in their ability to explain more and more situations. In other words, when a child explores a given model, an intuition for some aspect of that model may lie dormant when that same child explores another instance of a model that is superficially different. However, further activity may cause that intuition to be reused if other sense-making methods fail to provide explanatory power.

The laws of motion and the laws of probability have something in common: They both can be seen as representing mathematical models, abstracted from phenomenological behavior. The creation of computer-based microworlds (or domains of abstraction) demands a reverse-modeling process in which objects and tools, and perhaps the models themselves, are realized as manipulable on-screen entities, in some sense recognizable as the everyday phenomena from which the model was first abstracted. Pratt (1998) has referred to this process as *phenomenalizing*. In Figure 6.3, the traditional process of mathematical modeling cycles between the two elements in the top left corner. However, the model itself serves as the basis for creating models to be explored through the process of phenomenalizing. Exploration of the microworld can lead to the creation of mental models or abstractions as represented by the two elements in the bottom right corner of Figure 6.3.

The connections among phenomena, model, and microworld are fairly clear in the case of Newton's laws and probability. The relationship between phenomena and some other mathematical domains may also exist but is more abstruse. For example, how should we think about the family of dynamical geometry software in relation to modeling? Laborde and Laborde (1995) regard geometry as a partial modeling of space. Dia-

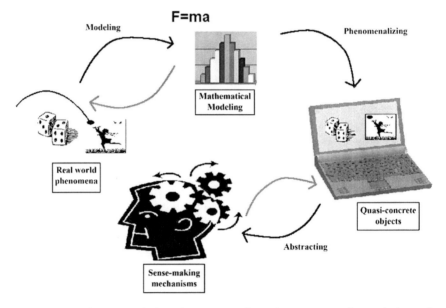

Figure 6.3.   Phenomenalizing, the process of creating on-screen instantiations of mathematical models, is in a sense the reverse of mathematical modeling.

grams play an ambiguous role in geometry and space; in the former they are theoretical constructs, while in the latter, as material objects, they offer properties that can be perceived. In phenomenalizing Euclidean geometry through the design of dynamical geometry software, a new type of entity is invented, the figure. A figure, constructed in dynamical geometry, has many of the perceptual qualities of a material diagram but at the same time has within itself embedded the geometric relationships of a theoretical diagram. In contrast to a theoretical diagram, those relationships as realized in dynamical geometry are "physically" manipulable (for example, by dragging). The role of the figure in relation to space and geometry seems analogous to that of virtual dice to real world games of dice and probability, and to that of the turtle or dot in motion simulations.

The Labordes propose that student learning in such an environment is supported in three principal ways:

1.   When a diagram is dragged, its behavior is dependent only on the software realization of the geometric relationships (and on the learner's choice of trajectory), allowing predictions of behavior to be tested more precisely by the learner. Thus a conjecture that a

particular relationship is invariant can be tested fairly thoroughly by dragging the diagram around the screen and into places where the relationship is tested to its extreme.

2. Second, learners are encouraged to experiment by the open-ended nature of the software. Whereas in the first point, the learner is regarded as already having a conjecture to be tested, more open exploration of a diagram may raise curiosity about some coincidental behavior leading to the formation of a conjecture.

3. Finally, learners are able to repeat experiments to test their validity across varying circumstances. A relationship that appears to hold in one diagram may or may not be true when certain factors are changed. The facility to try out ideas systematically may help the learner who is attempting to pin down the domain of validity for the relationship.

Several authors claim that the geometry, as encapsulated in such software, is epistemologically different from Euclidean geometry. For example, consider a geometric object whose construction is based on two other already existing objects. When the original objects are dragged around the screen by the mouse, the newly constructed object will maintain its relationship with the original two objects. This is one of the most important features of dynamical geometry software since it enables the learner to focus on invariant features of the construction. However, the newly constructed object cannot be dragged in a similar way. There is a functional dependence between the original objects and the newly constructed object that is, in effect, appended to the Euclidean properties of the construction. Hölzl (1996) discusses how a different geometry emerges out of the design and use of Cabri-géomètre (Laborde & Bellemain, 1988). This "computational transposition" (Balacheff, 1993) inherent in the phenomenalizing process described above leads to a new form of geometry, whose epistemological validity might be challenged. This issue is explored in more detail within this volume in the chapter on secondary geometry (Hollebrands, Laborde, & Sträßer, 2008).

The examples drawn from physics, probability, and geometry all involve the exploration of models created in environments specially designed for learning purposes. Some research has been based on tools, designed for commercial purposes but adapted to educational contexts. The most evident example is in the exploration of models built into a spreadsheet. Molyneux-Hodgson, Rojano, Sutherland, and Ursini, (1999) analyzed the results of a Mexican/British project in which spreadsheets were used as a mathematical modeling tools. They worked with two groups of 16- to 18-year-old science students, one group from Mexico and one from Britain. The students explored a range of science-based models relating to diffusion, chemical equilibrium, and the effect of collisions on momentum. The researchers concluded that the spreadsheet approach helped Mexican students to appreciate and use graphical and numerical representations while the English students were helped in a similar way on symbolic algebraic representations. The evidence suggests that exploring spreadsheet models might encourage facility in a widened set of representations.

This section has considered three illustrative themes, each involving the exploration of models drawn from contrasting domains of knowledge. Across domains of knowledge, some common conclusions can be drawn:

- Modeling can change the nature of mathematical objects. The process of phenomenalizing a domain of knowledge has epistemological and psychological implications. The exploratory models offer a particular perspective on a mathematical domain that exploits the opportunities offered by, but at the same time limited by, the digital nature of a computer. As a result, the technology-based model may not be a faithful representation of the conventional mathematical domain, but may, to a greater or lesser extent, represent a new domain of knowledge with its own particular opportunities for learning. Such opportunities appear to be offered through the possibility of manipulating the model, or objects dependent upon the model, in quasi-scientific ways. In this sense, phenomenalized mathematics can be explored and can be seen to be explored.

- We have discussed evidence that students can abstract within the modeling context. Some (tool, task) pairs promote the testing of conjectures by situating the tools in an investigative task. The knowledge abstracted is apparently constituted within the technology-based models, a process of modeling we call *intraconstructive*.

- There is however little evidence that students can abstract beyond the modeling context. Some theoretical models that conceive of conceptual change as deeply dependent on the situation would predict that *extra-constructive* modeling is unlikely or even impossible. The lack of evidence of extra-constructive modeling may however simply reflect a lack of research effort in this direction.

Expressive Models

In this section, we try to draw a distinction between research about the exploration of models and research in which the learners are building their own models. The intention in the activity on which this research is based is that students use given context-free tools to build their own models of reality, thus expressing their own thinking about that reality.

One of the earliest examples of a context-free modeling tool is STELLA (isee systems, n.d.), Structural Thinking Experimental Learning Laboratory. STELLA utilizes a systems dynamics approach in which it is supposed that complex phenomena can be better understood by examining how the system behaves and changes over time. By providing a graphical interface, STELLA operationalizes the process of identifying the characteristics of the system, specifying the interrelated relationships between variables. Such relationships will be deterministic and are likely to involve feedback loops as the effect of one or more relationships feed back into the dynamics of those same relationships. The claims for systems dynamics modeling through programs like STELLA have been extensive, ranging from a claim that STELLA offers the ability to empower students to solve problems that would otherwise be too difficult (or even impossible) to solve to a claim that STELLA provides a sort of conceptual map that helps to shift the focus of the learner from working with formulas to more conceptual reasoning (Niedderer, Schecker, & Bethge, 1991). In a review of the last ten years of development of STELLA, Doerr (1996b) outlines both these claims and the evidence to date in their support.

> There is some evidence to support the claim that systems dynamics software such as STELLA can support students in solving more complex, realistic problems .... Nonetheless, one must be cautious about any broad conclusions concerning students' learning given the limited scope and extent of educational research to date. (p. 219)

Doerr acknowledges that the software supports multiple approaches to problems and the expression of student conceptions. According to Doerr, the research on STELLA has identified a number of pressing issues and areas for further research. She argues that there is a need to understand the new role of the teacher as facilitator, for research on how students might be assessed, and on how student thinking evolves over extended use of context-free systems dynamics software. Doerr also emphasizes the need for research on how students validate their models.

In one of the few studies of preservice teachers' understanding of models, Zbiek (1998) studied validation strategies in a different context, curve fitting, an activity in which learners attempt to model a situation by representing it graphically. Zbiek worked with 13 prospective secondary mathematics teachers. She gave these prospective teachers a number of tasks, including one in which they were required to collect data and then model the time it takes for a skateboard to travel the length of a ramp as a function of the height of that ramp. The participants had available several software tools including curve fitters and other graphing utilities. Zbiek recorded the strategies used. The strategies were diverse. At one extreme, the subjects worked algorithmically by employing a tool that simply fed back a chi-square statistic for the *goodness of fit* of the proposed model. They validated their models according to which gave the highest goodness of fit. At the other extreme, some students paid little or no attention to the tools provided. Most students used mixed strategies, leaning towards one or the other of these two extremes. For example, one group was not totally dependent on the tools provided but allowed the tool to limit the set of possible curves that might fit the situation. Zbiek claims that "the modeler's degree of dependence on the tool determines the extent to which the modeling is algorithmic or artful" (p. 198).

Vitale (1995) has argued (in particular with diSessa over his use of the dynaturtle) that students are unlikely to learn about the physics of motion by manipulating on-screen objects that could have been programmed to obey arbitrary dynamical laws. Vitale argues that the exploration of pre-built models may allow a learner to appreciate the way a given algorithm unfolds, learning that Vitale would not want to undervalue, but does not necessarily support a belief in how the phenomena themselves behave. Vitale places emphasis upon activity away from the computer before using programming tools (Logo in particular) through which the learner builds a model (perhaps many models) of the phenomenological experience. Vitale's approach appears to offer insight into the nature of a model, an insight that perhaps would have benefited those of Zbiek's students with algorithmic tendencies, by de-mystifying the process of validation.

In another context, programming has also led to insights about the nature of a model. Resnick's (1994) work involves the use of StarLogo (MIT Media Lab Learning and Common Sense Group), which, like STELLA, enables the modeling of complex behavior. However, in contrast to STELLA, StarLogo models the behavior of individual elements of the system, on the basis that interesting but complex behavior can result from the multiple interaction of many relatively simple behaviors. Resnick reports on potential for new insights to be gained by a shift of perspective from a centralized mindset to one involving complex parallelism. He describes two students who were building a model of a traffic jam, using StarLogo. Their early attempts created a system that seemed to fit with the reality of traffic jams when several cars and a radar trap were involved. Traffic jams appeared as the cars slowed down for the radar trap (which the cars could detect). Resnick asked them what would happen if the radar trap were removed. They predicted that the jams would disappear and the cars would become roughly equidistant. In fact, the traffic jams continued. The effect of a few slow moving cars was to bring about traffic jams in the system as a whole, despite the lack of any explicit causal factor. Resnick claims that such experiences have the potential to change the mindset of people using such software. We observe that the difficulty of programming in a parallel environment such as StarLogo has precluded widespread use of the software, making it unlikely that significant advances in learning will occur using such software. Similar to the critique of dynaturtle offered by Vitale, we note that there is little evidence offered that the investigation of StarLogo models provides insight into the behavior of the phenomena being modeled. It would appear that the person who gains most is the person who creates the model. In more recent work, Wilensky has made significant enhancements to the StarLogo programming interface that allow for more flexible environments to be created (Wilensky, 2003).

Earlier, we discussed how spreadsheets have been used to allow learners to explore prepared models. However, the more frequent use of spreadsheets in the research literature has been in instances in which no prebuilt model was offered but the spreadsheet was used instead as an expressive tool. In one such experiment, Matos (1995) describes a class of tenth-grade students working on a problem in which they were required to model the length of paper in a paper roll. They were provided with spreadsheets and a collection of paper rolls. Matos analyzed the progress made by the students in terms of four identifiable stages. Initially, they formed images of the paper roll that seemed to be partly based on prior experience of spreadsheets and partly on their experience of rolling paper into such rolls. They next envisioned the paper roll as a series of concentric circles in which the radii belonged to an arithmetic progression. In the second stage, the students began to create tables and relations on the spreadsheet. They were able to express the length of paper in each wrap using the formula for the circumference of a circle and they were able to compute the total length by summing the lengths from each wrap. In the third stage, the students attempted to validate their model against a formula that they had been given for the number of wraps. There was in fact a mismatch between the prediction for the number of wraps based on the given formula and that predicted by their model. The students searched for explanations of the mismatch in terms of the paper running out in the real situation. They did not test the validity of their model by checking their results against reality (for example by unrolling a paper roll and making measurements). Matos proposes that the students' initial model of concentric circles, once translated onto a spreadsheet, had taken on a reality of its own. This proposal is consistent with the fourth stage of progress in which the students explored the model by asking "what happens if" questions, varying parameters in the spreadsheet. For example, they explored, entirely within the spreadsheet model, whether doubling the radius doubled the length of paper. Matos concludes that, as an empirical environment, the spreadsheet was essentially an expressive mediation tool between reality and mathematics but became in fact their conceptual version of reality.

The students that Matos observed appear to have been confident in their use of spreadsheets even to the extent that he believes knowledge of spreadsheets influenced their thinking about the model at the earliest stages of modeling. Wild (1996) problematizes the question of just how expressive spreadsheets can be as modeling tools. He describes work with a small group of slightly younger students (12 and 13 years old). The children previously had been taught how to use a spreadsheet. They worked on a problem involving the making and selling of mince pies in order to raise funds. The spreadsheet was to be used to decide how many mince pies to make and what price to charge in order to make a minimum profit. Wild describes in detail the work of one girl who chose to work with specific known quantities, first with paper and pencil, then on the spreadsheet, in order to reason about the relationships between variables. Only at the last stage did this girl introduce symbolic representations, even though the spreadsheet template with which she was working encouraged such an approach. Wild concludes that the spreadsheet probably helped her to develop her thinking from being situation-specific towards being general and symbolic, but detailed study of her progress indicates a number of tensions between her mental model and the requirements of the spreadsheet. In discussing the work of the class as a whole, Wild points out that a number of children were not able to resolve such tensions. For them, the spreadsheet was not at all expressive as there was too large a mismatch between the students' mental models and the nature of a spreadsheet model. Wild summarizes: "Not only might some children's mental models be somewhat incompatible with their computer modeling but the tension so caused might not lead to stronger and more accurate mental models on the part of the learner" (p. 19).

Pratt and Ainley (1997) place the nature of the task at the center of the modeling process. They describe two episodes. In one, a class of children (age 8 and 9 years) independently from their teachers discovered Cabri-géomètre on their portable computers. They produced a series of wonderfully imaginative and detailed drawings but they did not use the construction tools that might have involved the children in geometric (rather than simply spatial) thinking. In contrast, the second episode describes the work of a class of 11- and 12-year-olds. They were given the task of making a drawing kit for their younger reading partners. The nature of the task was such that the children needed to engage with the notion of construction in building their models. Pratt and Ainley argue that it is not enough that the modeling tools have expressive power (as found by the students in Wild, 1996). The task has to be carefully chosen to suggest a purpose to the children such that, in pursuing that purpose, they are likely to engage with the key mathematical or modeling ideas.

The task element of the (tool, task) pair is foregrounded by the preceding research by suggesting that children's construction of purpose for the task shapes the modeling activity that takes place. The centrality of the task element in the (tool, task) pair may offer insight into an issue that seems to run through this section on expressive modeling activity. It seems that model validation is problematic. There appears to be limited research in this area. What research exists seems to suggest that, when students engage in computer-mediated expressive modeling, there is a tendency for the computer version of the model to become the dominant reality. Students may use the computer tools algorithmically or without ongoing reference to the reality from which the models were initially abstracted. Research on how tasks might encourage not only model building but also validation activity is required. Furthermore, there is a need to look more closely at the complex relationship between the task, the nature of the expressive tools, and the type of thinking that emerges. Our reading of the literature seems to indicate that careful analysis of how the purpose for the task is constructed by the students might signal how task design might promote validation activity. We believe that validation as an activity is intrinsically linked to the need to reveal the potential and the limitations of a model, and if validation activity is to be spontaneous then students must have a reason for wanting to pursue such a direction. Any such reason will inevitably be wrapped up in their construction of the purpose for the activity as a whole.

DISCUSSION

In the previous sections, we have made a distinction between research on exploring given models and research on expressing models. We should reflect a little on this distinction. We are struck by the fact that there is a commonality about the whole endeavor, as played out by designers, researchers, and learners, but that the actors carrying out the enterprise change depending on whether the emphasis for student activity is placed on exploration or expressiveness. Let us consider this idea in more detail. There are four separable arenas of activity (see Figure 6.4). The phenomenological arena marks out that territory of *real* experience, where events can be observed or perceived through our senses. The mathematical arena incorporates mathematical knowledge made up of the relationships and objects (such as axioms, theorems, proofs, and concepts) and models expressed using that language. The virtual arena includes the models that are programmed into a computer, which might be representations (and here we refer explicitly to representations "out there" as opposed to mental representations) of large-scale mathematical systems, like geometry or Newton's laws, or they might be small-scale, for example a spreadsheet solution to a specific problem involving a few interconnected formulas. The creation of such virtual instantiations is closely connected to, but not the same as, their counterparts in the mathematical arena. Finally, the mental arena includes cognitive schemes or, less grandly, the pieces of knowledge such as intuitions or schema that might be coordinated to generate a mental model.

In Figure 6.4, we set out the activity across these arenas in the two cases of exploratory and expressive modeling. On the left side of Figure 6.4, we see an abbreviated form of Figure 6.3. The modeling process has created culturally accepted models of phenomena that exist in the mathematical arena. Designers create phenomenalized versions of these models that can be manipulated and explored by students. The only process carried out by those students is the final stage of abstracting (through use) situated understandings about the behavior of the embedded virtual models. The reader should note that the connecting lines, representing activity, are bidirectional though this is only of real interest in the case of the bottom line where it is clear that situated abstractions are not created in simple ways but through extended interaction within the virtual arena.

On the right side of Figure 6.4, we set out a corresponding schematic for expressive modeling. In this case, the students carry out the modeling activity. Since the representation when technology is employed tends to live directly inside the computer, we have incorporated the mathematical arena into the virtual arena. Evidence seems to suggest that validation often takes place solely within the virtual arena, and hence we do not show the connector back to the phenomenological arena. In exploratory modeling, the natural starting point for activity is in the virtual arena. In contrast, the natural starting point for expressive modeling is in the phenomenological arena. And yet we argue that each type of modeling has its own set of difficulties:

1. If the student begins activity in the virtual arena, how can he or she be helped to make connection with the mental arena or to the mathematical arena? We have offered some evidence as to how students can construct situated abstractions but research in this field has not adequately answered Vitale's earlier question in which he queried how students could learn about Newton's laws by playing with tools that may from their perspective bear no relation to Newton's laws. Exploratory modeling seems to facilitate situated understanding, but just what is the relationship between that situated understanding and the experiential world of real phenomena?

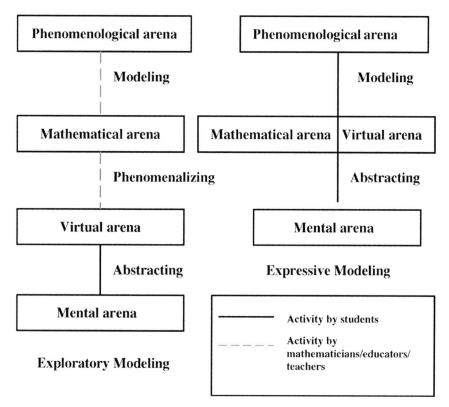

Figure 6.4.   An activity map for two approaches to modeling.

2. If the student begins in the phenomenological arena, as in expressive modeling, how can he or she be expected to make mathematical models of situations that they might not yet understand? What sort of support structures might be needed in order to allow some sort of iterative process to converge on increasingly "useful" or valid models? A further question here relates to how the student connects back to the phenomenological arena; we have already stated that there is remarkably little evidence related to students' validation of their models.

In searching for answers to the preceding questions, it is worth bearing in mind a cautionary tale that can be inferred from two separate pieces of research. Cuoco (1995) analyzed how computational media might support the learning of functions. In terms of the above analysis, he envisioned his students beginning in the mathematical arena. He found it necessary to develop three different pieces of software to address the learning of functions according to the nature of the individual student's prior conception of function. Meira (1998) worked with eighth-grade students in the same mathematical domain, using physical apparatus and a computerized input-output machine. Meira concludes in a similar vein that *transparency* is not an attribute of tools (physical or virtual) but a measure of access to knowledge and activities. It seems then that if we wish to help students connect the phenomenological, virtual, and mental arenas, we may have to employ a range of software tools, depending upon the students' current knowledge.

There is evidence to suggest that when exploring prepared models, such as might be programmed into a microworld, students appear ready and able to work within the virtual arena, and to make abstractions pertaining to that situation (Noss & Hoyles, 1996). They may appropriate the virtual arena to the extent that it becomes for them a sort of virtual reality. There is as yet little evidence to suggest that students are able to connect the mental abstractions to the mathematical arena. There is a need for research into whether and how students make use of abstractions or cognitive models constructed from virtual activity when they are active in the mathematical or phenomenological arenas.

IMPLICATIONS

Our synthesis of the literature reveals four main areas to which research should be directed.

- There is a need for classroom-based research on modeling. The current domination of rhetoric and how-to articles restricts the ability of researchers to build on prior effort in extending knowledge of modeling. In reporting such research, it is essential that rich descriptions of the task and the setting are elaborated so that the impact of the (tool, task) pair can be better understood.
- There is a need for research on teacher's knowledge about modeling. The teacher is clearly influential in how any modeling activity develops. It is reasonable to suppose that the teacher's own appreciation of modeling is likely to be a particularly significant factor in that development. Yet we were able to find just one study that reported data in this area.
- There is a need to understand how students' intraconstructive modeling might influence reasoning about phenomena. We envisage teaching programs designed to help students make connections between their exploration of virtual models and real

phenomena. Research studies that explore how students make those connections would need to be linked to the teaching programs in such a way that data captured during activity would reveal the nature of such meaning-making.

- We need to appreciate more deeply the relationship between the design of tasks and tools and the modeling activity that ensues. In particular, we need to understand how the (tool, task) pair might encourage validation activity.

Finally, we state again that technological tools for modeling are not inherently exploratory or expressive. There is plenty of evidence that shows how software tools can be used for many different purposes, and we argue that it is more profitable to think in terms of the (tool, task) pair. We have examples of (tool, task) pairs that elaborate exploratory modeling in which intraconstructive modeling took place. We have relatively few examples of (tool, task) pairs that elaborate expressive modeling. As discussed above, there is a need to develop (tool, task) pairs that explicitly aim to help the child to link intraconstructive modeling to phenomena. We imagine that it would be easier to design the task element with such an aim in mind if the design of the tool and task elements happened hand-in-hand. The design of (tool, task) pairs needs to take seriously the issue of supporting the student in validation activity; consideration of the purpose of the task as might be constructed by the student may prove profitable in this respect.

REFERENCES

Balacheff, N. (1993). Artificial intelligence and real teaching. In C. Keitel & K. Ruthven (Eds.), *Learning from computers: Mathematics education and technology* (pp. 131-158). Berlin, Germany: Springer.

Bell, M. (1993, April). *Modeling and the uses of mathematics in the K-6 curriculum.* Paper presented at the K-12 Modeling and Simulation Conference, Boston, MA.

Black, M. (1962). *Models and metaphors: Studies in language and philosophy.* Ithaca, NY: Cornell University Press.

Bliss, J., & Ogborn, J. (1989). Tools for exploratory learning. *Journal of Computer Assisted Learning, 5,* 37-50.

Bolte, L. (2002). A snowflake project: Calculating, analyzing and optimizing with the Koch snowflake. *Mathematics Teacher, 95,* 414-419.

Clauset, K., Rawley, C., & Boedeker, G. (1987). STELLA: Software for structural thinking. *Collegiate Microcomputer, 5,* 311-319.

Confrey, J., & Doerr, H. M. (1994). Student modelers. *Interactive Learning Environments, 4,* 199-217.

Cuoco, A. (1995). Computational media to support the learning and use of functions. In A. A. diSessa, C. Hoyles, R. Noss, & L. Edwards (Eds.), *Computers and exploratory learning* (pp. 79-107). Berlin, Germany: Springer-Verlag.

diSessa, A. A. (1979). Dynamics: Learning physics with a Dynaturtle. In S. Papert, D. Watt, A. diSessa, & S. Weir (Eds.), *Final report of the Brookline Logo Project. Part II: Project summary and data analysis* (pp. 6.1-6.20). Cambridge: Massachusetts Institute of Technology.

diSessa, A. A. (1982). Unlearning Aristotelian physics: A study of knowledge-based learning. *Cognitive Science, 6*, 37-75.

Doerr, H. M. (1996a). Integrating the study of trigonometry, vectors and force through modeling. *School Science and Mathematics, 96*, 407-418.

Doerr, H. M. (1996b). STELLA ten years later: A review of the literature. *International Journal of Computers for Mathematical Learning, 1*, 201-224.

Doerr, H. M. (2000). How can I find a pattern in this random data? The convergence of multiplicative and probabilistic reasoning. *Journal of Mathematical Behavior, 18*, 431-454.

Doerr, H. M., & English, L. D. (2003). A modeling perspective on students' mathematical reasoning about data. *Journal for Research in Mathematics Education, 34*, 110-136.

Edwards, L. (1998). Embodying mathematics and science: Microworlds as representations. *Journal of Mathematical Behavior, 17*, 53-78.

Edwards, D., & Hansom, M. (1989). *Guide to mathematical modeling*. Boca Raton, FL: CRC Press.

Fay, T., & Joubert, S. (2002). Dimensional analysis: An elegant technique for facilitating the teaching of mathematical modelling. *International Journal of Mathematical Education in Science and Technology, 33*, 280-293.

Forrester, J. (1987). Lessons from system dynamics modeling. *Systems Dynamics Review, 3*, 136-149.

Froelich, G. (2000). Modeling soft-drink packaging. *Mathematics Teacher, 93*, 478-488.

Galbraith, P., & Clatworthy, N. (1990). Beyond standard models—Meeting the challenge of modelling. *Educational Studies in Mathematics, 21*, 137-163.

Giordano, F., Weir, M., & Fox, W. (1997). *A first course in mathematical modeling* (2nd ed.). Pacific Grove, CA: Brooks/Cole.

Hölzl, R. (1996). How does 'dragging' affect the learning of geometry? *International Journal of Computers for Mathematical Learning, 1*, 169-187.

Hoyles, C., & Noss, R. (1992). A pedagogy for mathematical microworlds. *Educational Studies in Mathematics, 23*, 31-57.

Hollebrands, K., Laborde, C., Sträßer, R. (2008). Technology and the learning of geometry at the secondary level. In. M. K. Heid & G. W. Blume (Eds.), *Research on technology and the teaching and learning of mathematics: Vol. 1. Research syntheses* (pp. 155-206). Charlotte, NC: Information Age.

isee systems. (n.d.). STELLA [Computer software]. Lebanon, NH: Author.

Laborde, C., & Laborde, J. (1995). What about a learning environment where Euclidean concepts are manipulated with a mouse? In A. A. diSessa, C. Hoyles, R. Noss, & L. Edwards (Eds.), *Computers for exploratory learning* (pp. 241-262). Berlin, Germany: Springer-Verlag.

Laborde, J. -M., & Bellemain, F. (1988). Cabri Geometry [Computer software]. Grenoble, France: Cabrilog Innovative Math Tools.

Lawson, D., & Tabor, J. (2001). Stopping distances: An excellent example of empirical modelling. *Teaching Mathematics and its Applications, 20*, 66-74.

Lehrer, R., Horvath, J., & Schauble, L. (1994). Developing model-based reasoning. *Interactive Learning Environments, 4*, 218-232.

Lesh, R. (1981). Applied mathematical problem solving. *Educational Studies in Mathematics, 12*, 235-264.

Lesh, R., & Doerr, H. M. (2000). Symbolizing, communicating, and mathematizing: Key components of models and modeling. In P. Cobb, E. Yackel, & K. McClain (Eds.), *Symbolizing and communicating in mathematics classrooms: Perspectives on discourse, tools, and instructional design* (pp. 361-383). Mahwah, NJ: Erlbaum.

Lesh, R., Surber, D., & Zawojewski, J. (1983). Phases in modeling and phase-related processes. In J. C. Bergeron & N. Herscovics (Eds.), *Proceedings of the fifth annual meeting of the International Group for the Psychology of Mathematics Education-North American Chapter* (Vol. 2, pp. 129-136). Montreal, Quebec, Canada.

Lester, F., & Kehle, P. (2003). From problem solving to modeling: The evolution of thinking about research on complex mathematical activity. In R. Lesh & H. M. Doerr (Eds.), *Beyond constructivism: Models and modeling perspectives on mathematics problem solving, learning and teaching* (pp. 501-518). Mahwah, NJ: Erlbaum.

Linn, M. C., diSessa, A., Pea, R. D., & Songer, N. B. (1994). Can research on learning and instruction inform standards for science education? *Journal of Science Education and Technology, 3*, 7-15.

Mandinach, E., & Cline, H. (1989). Applications of simulation and modeling in precollege education. *Machine-Mediated Learning, 3*, 189-205.

Mandinach, E., & Cline, H. (1994). *Classroom dynamics: Implementing a technology-based learning environment.* Hillsdale, NJ: Erlbaum.

Matos, J. F. (1995). The spreadsheet as a tool for mathematical modeling: A case study. In A. A. diSessa,, C. Hoyles, R. Noss, & L. Edwards (Eds.), *Computers and exploratory learning* (pp. 48-62). Berlin, Germany: Springer-Verlag.

Meira, L. (1995). The microevolution of mathematical representations in children's activity. *Cognition and Instruction, 13*, 269-313.

Meira, L. (1998). Making sense of instructional devices: The emergence of transparency in mathematical activity. *Journal for Research in Mathematics Education, 29*, 121-142.

Mintz, R. (1993). Computerized simulation as an inquiry tool. *School Science and Mathematics, 93*, 76-80.

MIT Media Lab Learning and Common Sense Group. StarLogo [Computer software]. Cambridge, MA: Author.

Moar, M., Spensley, F., O'Shea, T., Singer, R., Hennessy, S., & Scanlon, E. (1992). Two uses of computers in science teaching: Horizontal motion simulation and simulation building. In E. DeCorte, M. C. Linn, H. Mandl, & L. Verschaffel (Eds.), *Computer-based learning environments and problem solving* (pp. 429-443). Berlin, Germany: Springer-Verlag.

Molyneux-Hodgson, S., Rojano, T., Sutherland, R., & Ursini, S. (1999). Mathematical modeling: The interaction of culture and practice. *Educational Studies in Mathematics, 39*, 167-183.

National Council of Teachers of Mathematics. (1989). *Curriculum and evaluation standards for school mathematics.* Reston, VA: Author.

Niedderer, H., Schecker, H., & Bethge, T. (1991). The role of computer-assisted modelling in learning physics. *Journal of Computer Assisted Learning, 7*, 84-95.

Niss, M. (1989). Aims and scope of applications and modelling in mathematics curricula. In W. Blum, J. Berry, R. Biehler, I. Huntley, G. Kaiser-Messmer, & L. Profke (Eds.), *Applications and modelling in learning and teaching mathematics* (pp. 22-31). Chichester, West Sussex: Ellis Horwood Limited.

Niss, M., Blum, W., & Huntley, I. (Eds.). (1991). *Teaching of mathematical modelling and applications.* New York: E. Horwood.

Noss, R., & Hoyles, C. (1996). *Windows on mathematical meanings: Learning cultures and computers.* London: Kluwer Academic.

Ogborn, J., & Mellar, H. (1994). Models: Their makers, uses and problems. In H. Mellar, J. Bliss, R. Boohan, J. Ogborn, & C. Tompsett (Eds.), *Learning with artificial worlds: Computer-based modelling in the curriculum* (pp. 16-26). London: Falmer Press.

O'Reilly, D., Pratt, D., & Winbourne, P. (1997). Constructive and instructive representation. *Journal of Information Technology for Teacher Education, 6*, 73-92.

Osawa, H. (2002). Mathematics of a relay—Problem solving in the real world. *Teaching Mathematics and its Applications, 21*, 85-93.

Pratt, D. (1998). *Meanings in and meaning for a stochastic domain of abstraction.* Unpublished doctoral dissertation, University of London, England.

Pratt, D. (2000). Making sense of the total of two dice. *Journal for Research in Mathematics Education, 31*, 602-625.

Pratt, D., & Ainley, J. (1997). The construction of meanings for geometric construction: Two contrasting cases. *International Journal of Computers for Mathematical Learning, 1*, 293-322.

Resnick, M. (1994). *Turtles, termites, and traffic jams: Explorations in massively parallel microworlds.* Cambridge, MA: MIT Press.

Roberts, N., & Barclay, T. (1988). Teaching model building to high school students: Theory and reality. *Journal of Computers in Mathematics and Science Teaching, 8*(1), 13-16, 24.

Schecker, H. P. (1993). The didactic potential of computer aided modeling for physics education. In D. L. Ferguson (Ed.), *Advanced educational technologies for mathematics and science: NATO Conference, June 1990* (pp. 165-207). Berlin, Germany: Springer-Verlag.

Skovsmose, O. (1990). Reflective knowledge: Its relation to the mathematical modelling process. *International Journal of Mathematical Education in Science and Technology, 21*, 765-779.

Sidhu, L., & Carss, M. (2000). Dynamics modelling activities. *Australian Senior Mathematics Journal, 14*, 15-31.

Steed, M. (1992). STELLA, a simulation construction kit: Cognitive process and educational implications. *Journal of Computers in Mathematics and Science Teaching, 11*, 39-52.

Swetz, F., & Hartzler, J. (Eds.). (1991). *Mathematical modeling in the secondary school curriculum: A resource guide of classroom exercises*. Reston, VA: National Council of Teachers of Mathematics.

Treffers, A., & Goffree, F. (1985). Rational analysis of realistic mathematics education: The Wiskobas Program. In L. Streefland (Ed.), *Proceedings of the ninth annual conference of the International Group for the Psychology of Mathematics Education* (Vol. 2, pp. 97-121). Utrecht, The Netherlands: OW&OC.

Vitale, B. (1995). From local to global: Programming and the unfolding of local models in the exploratory learning of mathematics and science. In A. A. diSessa, C. Hoyles, R. Noss, & L. Edwards (Eds.), *Computers and exploratory learning* (pp. 45-58). Berlin, Germany: Springer-Verlag.

vom Hofe, R. (2001). Investigations into students' learning of applications in computer-based learning environments. *Teaching Mathematics and its Applications, 20*, 109-119.

Webb, M., & Hassell, D. (1988). Opportunities for computer based modeling and simulation in secondary education. In F. Lovis & E. D. Tagg (Eds.), *Computers in education, Proceedings of the IFIP TC3 First European Conference on Computers in Education—ECCE 88, International Federation for Information Processing* (pp. 271-277). Amsterdam, The Netherlands: Elsevier Science.

White, B. Y. (1984). Designing computer games to help physics students understand Newton's Laws of Motion. *Cognition and Instruction, 1*, 69-108.

Wild, M. (1996). Mental models and computer modelling. *Journal of Computer Assisted Learning, 12*, 10-21.

Wilensky, U. (2003). Statistical mechanics for secondary school: The GasLab multi-agent modeling toolkit. *International Journal of Computers for Mathematical Learning, 8*, 1-41.

Zbiek, R. M. (1998). Prospective teachers' use of computing tools to develop and validate functions as mathematical models. *Journal for Research in Mathematics Education, 29*, 184-201.

CHAPTER 7

A RESEARCH-INFORMED VIEW OF THE PROCESS OF INCORPORATING MATHEMATICS TECHNOLOGY INTO CLASSROOM PRACTICE BY IN-SERVICE AND PROSPECTIVE TEACHERS

Rose Mary Zbiek and Karen Hollebrands

There is ample evidence that use of various forms of technology may enhance student understanding of mathematics. The key to enriched understanding lies not only in the skillful development of the technology but also in how that technology is used by and with learners. Teachers therefore play a central role in the technology-based mathematics learning experiences of children of all ages. In this chapter we examine the literature on teachers teaching and learning mathematics with mathematics technology.

Research on Technology and the Teaching and Learning of Mathematics:
Vol. 1. Research Syntheses, pp. 287–344
Copyright © 2008 by Information Age Publishing

ORGANIZING PERSPECTIVE

We ground this discussion of the literature in the goal of teaching mathematics better through the use of mathematics technology. Teachers move along a continuum from nontechnology stances to incorporating technology extensively and well in their teaching of mathematics. The journey for some may begin before their preservice experience as learners of mathematics with technology in the spirit discussed in other chapters of these volumes. Others start as learners of mathematics and technology in their preservice experience. Yet others begin as active teachers challenged to change their existing practices. In any of these scenarios, teachers are learners who move toward deeper understanding of what it means to use mathematics technology effectively with students.

We organized this review of the literature to describe this learning process and the factors that influence it. Because there are too few studies in several areas to provide a comprehensive view, this organization serves as a tool for thinking about the literature. More formal analyses of the literature were not feasible. Some techniques, such as a meta-analysis, were impossible; many studies were qualitative investigations. The purposes, contexts, goals, and conditions of the studies typically varied too greatly within any one type of technology for an organization by technology type to make sense. In addition, several studies blended various forms of technology in instructionally sound or empirically practical ways that precluded identifying the roles and effects of each particular type of technology.

We start the chapter by describing ways to view the concerns of teachers and to consider the modes of technology use teachers exhibit as they move along a learning continuum. We then describe how classroom practice may appear within various modes in terms of the roles that teachers may take. When available in our sources, we include the teachers' or lessons' intentions. We address the affordances or opportunities offered by technology, and how teachers' roles and technology affordances in practice affect students. We turn next to teachers' understandings and conceptions of mathematics, of technology, and of learning and teaching. These are factors that influence teachers' practices and how they proceed as learners along the continuum. In return, teachers' efforts to use technology influence these understandings and conceptions in a synergistic relationship. We close by noting the constraints that impede teacher learning and the supports that facilitate teacher growth as savvy professionals in technology-using mathematics classrooms. Our concluding comments include a note on how technology may differ from other innovations in teaching.

SELECTION OF LITERATURE

We chose literature that had teachers and teaching mathematics with technology as the foci of empirical studies. There are several points about teachers and teaching, technology, and the studies that underlie our decisions about papers to include. The studies had to investigate an aspect of mathematics teaching or had to have the mathematics teachers as subjects. The mathematics content or the teachers' focus could be elementary, middle, high school, or preservice education. We found it important to include studies focusing on both practicing teachers and prospective teachers. We are troubled by the scarcity of studies in our literature corpus involving elementary teachers and prospective elementary teachers.

Given the broad meaning of technology, we focused on mathematics technology that also is cognitive technology (Pea, 1987) used to do mathematics as well as for mathematics instruction. Cognitive technologies are those mediums that help "transcend the limitations of the mind (e.g., attention to goals, short-term memory span) in thinking, learning, and problem-solving activities" (Pea, 1987, p. 91). This general view of technology seemed consistent with the chapters on student understanding. The focus on cognitive technology clearly represented the bulk of the literature we found. We also note that much of the literature on teachers involved the function concept and geometric topics. Many of the function studies used computer algebra systems (CASs) and graphing tools. Dynamic environments dominate the geometry studies. The dominance of these types of technology may reflect the centrality of function and geometry or the applicability of those tools to the K-12 curriculum as well as the interests of the broader teacher education, technology education, and mathematics education fields at the time of the studies. In contrast, some popular areas for research on students' understanding and learning did not appear as part of the literature on teachers and teaching. For example, programming is hardly mentioned in this chapter. We omitted noncognitive technologies, including most drill-and-practice software and tutorials.

We emphasized empirical work in this chapter. We included syntheses of several studies when those syntheses were clearly tied to the empirical work and offered insights not only into the studies but also into how the collection of studies informs teaching mathematics with technology. Authors of these papers typically were researchers heavily involved in the studies.

We began with refereed journal articles. To tap the most current work and to reflect norms in different countries and research communities, we included chapters in books on technology in teaching mathematics and proceedings of conferences. Technical reports on mathematics teaching with technology projects and dissertations offered detailed descriptions that enriched our discussion of how teachers work with technology.

From this body of literature we build a story of teachers as learners using mathematical technology as tools in their classrooms and in their own mathematical work. In all cases, we include as much detail about the technology used, the instructional intentions, and the learning goals as we could glean from the literature. We borrow useful definitions, such as that of mathematics technology, from Heid and Blume (2008).

A DEVELOPMENTAL PROCESS: CONCERNS AND USES

We think about learning to teach mathematics with technology as a developmental process. The literature suggests that teachers involved in this process have concerns and exhibit particular ways of drawing technology into their practice. In this section, we describe how we think about these issues in ways that are helpful both to understand the literature and to develop research-based interventions to assist teachers in this process. Our perspective draws on the Concerns-Based Adoption Model (CBAM) (Hall & Hord, 1987, 2001) and on the PURIA vision (Beaudin & Bowers, 1997). The CBAM includes Levels of Use and Stages of Concerns expressed by individuals who are adopting a new innovation and the PURIA view includes different ways in which an individual may be using technology. Combining these perspectives allows us to respect teaching with technology as an innovation that elicits both affect and action, although most studies focused on actions with little attention to affect.

Concerns of Teachers

Concerns are the affective aspect of implementing technology in teaching. There were variations in the details, but teachers' concerns generally changed as teachers became more knowledgeable about the use of technology. Hall and Hord (1987, 2001) described the Stages of Concerns through which teachers or others pass when they encounter innovations. Three of Hall and Hord's Stages of Concern—personal concerns, management concerns, and consequence concerns (i.e., concerns about student learning)—help us to organize research insights about teachers' concerns regarding technology use.

Types of Concerns

Personal Concerns

Teachers expressed *personal concerns* about how the technology would affect them personally as teachers in their own classrooms. For example, teachers using a variety of computer software packages with elementary and middle school students in New Zealand were concerned about how to arrange the classroom and place themselves physically in the room (Thomas, Tyrell, & Bullock, 1996). Other teachers, studied by Wiske and Houde (1993), who were using the Geometric Supposer (Schwartz & Yerushalmy, 1988) with high school geometry students, initially expressed concern about whether they had the time and knowledge to deal effectively with the demands of the technology within a classroom environment. In addition to logistics and planning concerns, the need for personal, managerial, and professional control arose as issues with which teachers struggled (McDougall, 1996). These middle school teachers, who were using The Geometer's Sketchpad (Jackiw, 1992) to teach a unit on construction, expressed concerns about having personal control, which manifested itself in how they viewed themselves as the mathematical authority in the classroom. One of the four teachers McDougall studied exhibited some trepidation about revealing to students her lack of complete knowledge of the mathematical relationships the students were discovering. For this teacher, there was fear about changing the role of the teacher from one who was viewed as the sole mathematical authority to one who was a coconstructor of knowledge.

Management Concerns

Management concerns such as having control of and managing technology-enabled classroom environments arose as another significant issue. Some researchers reported that when teachers incorporated some types of technology the teachers felt out of control. For example, teachers who adopted a guided-discovery approach to teaching high school geometry with the aid of the Geometric Supposer were reported as feeling unsure about which students were learning what (Lampert, 1993) because students were able to use the technology to pursue their own correct or incorrect conjectures. These concerns may have been heightened by the combination of a guided-inquiry approach with the use of an exploratory software environment. In our view, the need of these teachers in Lampert's study to know which conjectures students were pursuing so they could manage the classroom may have influenced the ways in which they structured technology-based activities. Those teachers who perceived a greater need for control might have created activities that were less open-ended and more directive in terms of how technology should be used.

The ways in which teachers use technology seemed related to concerns about management and may also be connected to *concerns about consequences* that are related to their goals for student learning. Tharp, Fitzsimmons, and Brown Ayers (1997) found that teachers who held rule-based conceptions of mathematics teaching and learning were more likely than their peers to use a highly structured approach to the use of the graphing calculator in precalculus. Rule-based high school teachers interviewed by Akujobi (1995) were more likely than their colleagues to reserve any use of computer software for remediation or for drill and practice. However, in one large-scale survey conducted on middle school and high school teachers' use of computers in Missouri it was reported that teachers rarely used the computers for purposes other than drill and practice (Manoucherhri, 1999). In terms of specific technologies, teachers' views of graphing calculators may influence the ways in which they use them. Jost (1992) found that teachers who perceived the graphing calculator as a computational tool stressed content-oriented goals and viewed learning as listening. Teachers who viewed graphing calculators as instructional tools stressed student-centered goals, used interactive teaching approaches, and viewed learning as student-centered. However, the ways in which teachers use technology in their classrooms does not seem directly related to how they may have experienced using technology as a learner (Fleener, 1995). Zbiek (1995) reported that although a teacher of first-year algebra enjoyed and valued open-ended explorations with technology in her own learning she did not feel comfortable allowing her students to engage in such tasks. As a result, she provided detailed directions for technology use to fulfill her need for an orderly classroom. Timmerman (1998) found similar results in her study of elementary in-service teachers. One teacher, Susan, valued working with the microworld Toys (Olive & Steffe, 1994c) as a learner, but as a teacher she became frustrated because she had little control over and interaction with her students as they used the microworld in pairs. Using a classroom set of calculators fit more easily into her pedagogical style since she could direct the mathematical activities and have all students working on the same task at the same time.

Technology Concerns

Concerns about how the technology affected teachers personally and concerns about management seemed to take priority over and perhaps to precede concerns about learning. Thomas and colleagues (1996) reported it was not until the elementary, middle, and high school teachers they studied were familiar with the technology and had created ways to incorporate it into their teaching that teachers focused their concerns on how technology could be used to engage students in exploring mathematics. Findings from several research studies (e.g., Beaudin & Bowers, 1997; Tharp, et al., 1997; Wiske & Houde, 1993) suggest there may exist stages through which teachers pass or a level of comfort and familiarity with the technology and curriculum before they are able to focus on students and what they are learning.

Potential for Stages

A theme that arose from the literature was that the concerns of teachers when incorporating new technologies in their mathematics teaching changed as teachers became more familiar with the technology that they were using (Brill, 1997; McDougall, 1996; Tharp et al.,1997; Thomas et al.,1996; Wiske & Houde, 1993). While there were some differences in the number of concerns researchers identified and the importance these researchers placed on the concerns, there seem to be some commonalities among teachers' concerns about technology use that researchers identified. This observation suggested there might be stages of concerns through which teachers pass in the long process of incorporating technology into practice.

Wiske and Houde (1993) examined the nature and progression of teachers' concerns as teachers incorporated the Geometric Supposer in their classrooms. Wiske and Houde categorized concerns using Hall and Hord's (1987) Stages of Concern about innovations in teaching. They grouped these stages within the four different clusters of concerns initially described by Fuller and her colleagues (Fuller, 1973; Fuller & Brown, 1975; Fuller, Brown, & Peck, 1967; as cited in Hall & Hord, 1987): Unrelated concerns, Self concerns, Task concerns, and Impact concerns. Unrelated concerns are not related to teaching or learning. Self concerns are focused on the teacher using the technology to gain personal understandings of what it can and can not do. Self concerns also revolve around teachers' beliefs about whether they possess the knowledge needed to use technology in the classroom and how its use will affect them personally. Task concerns are focused around selecting appropriate tasks and managing the use of technology in the classroom. Impact concerns are focused on understanding what impact the technology will have on students, determining how to collaborate with others who are using technology, and thinking about how the use of technology may affect the curriculum. Impact concerns seem to consider the effects of technology broadly by considering technology's impact on students, on other teachers, and on the curriculum. Thus, it seems there is a discernible pattern to teacher concerns. Although a lack of affect research focused on technology use with and by teachers precludes additional elaboration, we note that Hall and Hord's (2001) summary includes the types of concerns found in the technology literature.

Modes of Use

Many studies provide insights into what teachers do with technology on their own and in their classrooms. In addition to Stages of Concern, the model developed by Hall and Hord (1987, 2001) includes Levels of

Use in the complex developmental process teachers undergo as they learn about innovations such as technology. In addition to three levels of nonuse, Hall and Hord describe five different levels of use: Mechanical, Routine, Refinement, Integration, and Renewal. Generally, use of an innovation begins with a *mechanical use* for which the person may closely follow a user guide to complete specific activities and may not have in mind long-range plans for how the innovation may be used next week or next month. For example, consider the innovation of using graphing calculators in the precalculus classroom. At this first level, a teacher may try a set of graphing-calculator lessons using prescriptive handouts without considering how or if at all the calculators will be used in future lessons. After employing the innovation for some time the person may develop some patterns and *routines* for using it. At this level, the teacher may establish patterns for distributing and collecting the calculators and methods for performing mathematical tasks such as graphing or curve fitting. The teacher may have longer-range plans for calculator use and these plans may be stable or unchanging. At the next level, users may *refine* their use of the innovation with a focus on their clients. For example, the graphing-calculator lessons are revised to match the local students' needs. At the level of *Integration* teachers may recommend the innovation to their colleagues so that through a collective effort they can extend the positive effects of the innovation to a larger population of students. The graphing-calculator lessons become part of what other precalculus teachers use. The last level, *Renewal,* occurs when teachers make major changes or modifications in their use of the innovation to improve the outcomes. Graphing calculator use in our example would be mandated in all precalculus courses and would infiltrate the rest of the high school mathematics program.

Hall and Hord's (1987, 2001) model has been used frequently to study and facilitate innovation and it seems helpful in understanding technology use for innovation in large form. Using Levels of Use however was not as helpful in discussing the intertwined components of learning to teach mathematics with technology. In what Beaudin and Bowers (1997) described as the PURIA (Play, Use, Recommend, Incorporate, Assess) model, we found a perspective that allowed for explicit consideration of teachers' needs to learn the technology, to learn to do mathematics with technology, to use the technology with students, and to attend to student learning as a guide for innovation. Table 7.1 contains Beaudin and Bowers' "stages" and our descriptions. We choose to refer to the "stages" as "modes" because we do not view PURIA as a formal stage model. We consider PURIA a useful tool to understand the literature and to work with teachers learning to teach with technology. Our elaborated versions of the descriptions by Beaudin and Bowers (1997) extend their version to tech-

Table 7.1.   The Elaborated and Extended PURIA Model

PURIA Mode	Nature of Activity During the Mode
<u>Pl</u>ays with the technology	Uses technology for no clear mathematical purpose.
<u>Us</u>es technology as personal tool	Uses technology in doing mathematics of one's own design. May be using it as a learner of mathematics but not using it in a classroom setting and not using it with students.
<u>R</u>ecommends technology to others	Recommends use to a student, a peer, or a small group of students or peers. This likely is not in a formal classroom setting and it is not an integrated part of instruction.
<u>I</u>ncorporates technology into classroom instructions	Integrates the technology into classroom instruction. This occurs to varying degrees.
<u>A</u>ssesses students' use of technology	Examines how students use the technology and what they learn from using it.

nology beyond CAS. We also broaden the Recommends mode to include teachers working together, teachers working with "experts," and teachers working with individual students or small groups of students. The resulting PURIA modes reflect the teacher becoming familiar with the technology as a tool for doing mathematics in the Play and Use modes. The growth during these modes includes the transition of the technology as the developer's tool into the teacher's instrument for doing mathematics, a crucial aspect of learning to use technology captured by the notion of instrumental genesis (Guin & Trouche, 1999; Trouche, 2000). In the Incorporate and Assess modes, the teacher's attention turns, implicitly or consciously, toward the use of the technology as a pedagogical tool, including the development of instructional orchestrations (Trouche, 2000) or elaborated plans regarding use of technology in the social dimensions of classrooms. The Recommends mode seems marked by a transition between mathematical and pedagogical aspects of the technology.

The first two modes suggest that teachers use the technology, playfully at first and then in a more structured manner, for their own personal use prior to using it with students. After teachers are knowledgeable about the tool, they may share ideas with colleagues or recommend that their students use it in limited ways outside of main classroom activities. This initial limited use may provide teachers with the confidence needed to incorporate the use of the tool into classroom practice. After the technology has been incorporated, the teacher may feel ready to assess what students are learning with the technology involved. The modes in this model echoed clearly the three categories of concerns we observed in the literature: how to use technology personally, how to manage technology use in the classroom, and how to assess student understanding that emerges concomitant with student use of technology.

The PURIA model shares many similarities with Hall and Hord's (1987, 2001) Levels of Use but we find it more appealing for several reasons. First, the PURIA Play and Use modes seem more mathematically oriented than the Mechanical, Routine, and Refinement Levels from the Levels of Use framework. Further, the literature suggested the importance of the Play Mode and the distinction between Use and Incorporate (e.g., Moreira & Noss, 1995; Pagnucco, 1994). For example, although the elementary teachers using Turtle Math (Clements & Meredith, 1994) in their fifth-grade classrooms were provided with a support person to meet with them after school to provide technical assistance and to teach demonstration lessons, they expressed a preference to "play around with" the software on their own (Sarama, Clements, & Henry, 1998, p. 138). The researchers respected the need for teachers to play with the software but they stated that "without appropriate guidance (e.g., written materials, tutoring), 'playing' may be unproductive" (p. 140). That is, the researchers seemed to believe that the teachers might not move from the Play Mode to the Incorporate Mode if they were not provided with adequate support and guidance and suggested that a blending of the two approaches (personal play and supporting materials and personnel) was needed. Other literature underscores the difficulty of transition from personal use to classroom use. For example, Pagnucco (1994) describes "Peter" as a self-taught computer science instructor involved in Project Litmus who used a spreadsheet for grading. Project Litmus engaged K-12 teachers in exploring the possibilities of new technologies for doing mathematics and for teaching mathematics. The project did not prescribe classroom materials but did advocate a discovery-oriented, active-learning stance. Teachers in the project were encouraged to try to develop their own lessons and ideas (Stallings, 1995). Pagnucco notes Peter was "very comfortable, prepared, satisfied, and confident" (p. 66) in his personal technology use. However, Peter rated his use of technology for instructional purposes much less favorably in terms of comfort, preparation, and satisfaction. We see Peter as one who definitely used technology for personal needs, although his technology play was not documented. However, he was struggling with incorporating technology in his classroom. Similar comfort with personal use but concern over instructional use also were voiced by Carol and Donna, the middle school and elementary teachers also involved in both Project Litmus and Pagnucco's study. These observations underscore the difficulty of the move from Play to Incorporate, despite encouraging environments.

The literature also evidenced the critical role of the Recommend mode as teachers worked together formally and informally or as they worked with individual students or with small groups of students. Engagement in technology use with small groups may help teachers like Peter, Carol, and Donna to use technologies in whole-class work. Evidence that this type of use has preceded technology use with an entire class arises in several studies. For example, Stallings (1995) documents a Recommend mode in how Diane came to incorporate graphing calculators in her classroom. In Diane's words: "I had a Calculus student who had a graphing calculator. I think it was Casio or something, and he would come out and we would play with it. We would try to figure out what it was." (Stallings, 1995, p. 67). In a study of the impact of a teacher-enhancement project, Almekbel (2000) reported that experienced teachers noted that they loaned graphing calculators to students, implying the teachers thought this was an important part of their growth within the project. The teachers also thought the project contributed to use of technology in instruction by fostering interactions between participating teachers and with nonparticipating teachers. Almekbel's descriptions suggest these interactions may be indicative of teachers in the Recommend mode. The data from other studies implicitly suggest an absence of Recommend mode while reporting a negative classroom experience with technology. In a study of teacher learning within the context of implementing Advanced Placement Statistics, VanNetta (2000) quotes Mr. Keppler, a teacher with 31 years of experience: "When I did the residual plot and analysis for exponential regression, I had really done it in advance so I knew exactly what to do on the calculator. But when I presented it in class, they got very lost" (p. 312). Work in the Recommend mode situated between his personal use mode and his classroom implementation mode, in our view, could have provided Mr. Keppler the opportunity to move from intense concentration on his technology use to closer consideration of how to engage his class in mathematics.

It is possible for some teachers to progress very little within a mode. Some studies reported little change over time in the ways in which teachers used technology (e.g., Kendall & Stacey, 2001) while others reported great strides (e.g., Piliero, 1994; Tharp et al.,1997; Thomas et al., 1996; Zbiek, 1995).

CLASSROOM PRACTICE

The concerns and modes teachers experience as they incorporate technology in the classroom are embodied in their evolving classroom practice. For in-service teachers, this includes the decisions they make daily in their classrooms as they relate to students, technology, and mathematics content. Preservice teachers manifest their practice through prepractice discussions of classroom events and through tutoring sessions, via microteaching experiences, and in student teaching as they work with individuals, small groups, or whole classes. This section outlines the roles that teachers have in technology-using classrooms and discusses what teacher questioning and technology contribute to the classroom experience, and connects classroom practice to its potential effects on students.

Teacher Roles

Several researchers sought to capture the roles and responsibilities of teachers using mathematics technology in their mathematics classrooms. We start by looking at the roles in general and then focus on teacher questioning of students as a particularly important aspect of classroom practice with technology use.

Possible Roles Emerge

Key among those researchers who delineated teacher roles in technology-using mathematics classrooms are Fraser, Burkhardt, Coupland, Phillips, Pimm, and Ridgway (1988), Farrell (1996), and Heid, Sheets, and Matras (1990). Farrell (1996) used videotapes of six precalculus classrooms to determine the extent to which teachers in these classrooms assumed Manager, Task Setter, Explainer, Counselor, Fellow Investigator, and Resource roles while using graphing technologies. Farrell adapted these roles for teachers from the Systemic Classroom Analysis Notation (SCAN) developed by Fraser and colleagues (1988). In contrast, Heid and colleagues (1990) developed their list of roles from observations of teachers who were using a combination of graphing utilities, table generators, curve fitters, and symbolic manipulators in first-year algebra classrooms. Farrell explicitly considered how teacher roles manifested themselves in the graphing calculator-using precalculus classrooms and how these manifestations compared with those of the same teachers in non-technology-using classrooms. Heid and colleagues wrote about teacher responsibilities and challenges as well as roles in classrooms in which teachers and students used both a graphing program and a symbolic manipulator. We have chosen to recast these responsibilities and challenges here as roles[1] because these responsibilities are enacted through roles in the classroom. For our purposes, the roles we identified are not necessarily distinct. We use them as tools to help researchers, teacher educators, professional development providers, and others to think about the learning process and how teachers' practice may evolve as they become more adept at incorporating technology in teaching mathematics.

In combining the lists of roles from Farrell (1996) and Heid and her colleagues (1990), we find some overlap among categories. We also find some aspects missing, due perhaps to the state of technology and technology use in mathematics teaching at the time of these studies. Our final list of roles and our revised descriptions include the following, listed alphabetically:

- *Allocator* of time (presented as responsibility and challenge in Heid et al., 1990): The teacher is working with the time requirements of the school as well as orchestrating time for accommodating the needs of individual students.

- *Catalyst and Facilitator* (Heid et al., 1990): The teacher facilitates the introduction of a new problem or real-world context and the discussion of various solutions so that the lesson reaches an appropriate close.

- *Collaborator* (Heid et al., 1990) or *Fellow Investigator* (Farrell, 1996): The teacher is initially unfamiliar with both the problem and the solution and therefore is a true participant in mathematical learning.

- *Counselor* (Farrell, 1996; part of the Technical Assistant role in Heid et al., 1990): The teacher is familiar with the problem and is able to advise and assist students when they ask for teacher input. This role includes playing the devil's advocate as well as providing encouragement or serving as a stimulator or diagnostician. [We would include here the part of the description by Heid and colleagues of Technical Assistant that involves the teacher working with students on their problem-solving difficulties.]

- *Evaluator* of student learning (presented as responsibility and challenge in Heid et al., 1990): The teacher uses informal and formal assessments of different types to describe individual students' emerging understandings with and without technology.

- *Explainer* (Farrell, 1996): The teacher demonstrates, establishes the context, focuses the classroom direction, and serves as a rule giver and knowledge source.

- *Manager* (Farrell, 1996): Teacher serves as tactical manager, director, and authoritarian. [We add this as general classroom management work and less related to the instructional and learning issues than Allocator of time.]

- *Planner and Conductor* of classroom activities (presented as responsibility and challenge in Heid et al., 1990): The teacher plans and implements with-technology and without-technology activities, and chooses among whole-class, small-group, or individual settings as needed. This includes selection, chronology, and creation of curriculum materials and technology tools. [We believe this role subsumes managing work for and across groups of students, a phenomenon that Farrell (1996) observed more in technology-using classrooms than in technology-free settings.]

- *Resource* (Farrell, 1996): The teacher represents a system to be explored and functions as a giver of factual information. [We see this as different from Technical Assistant in that the teacher as a Resource simply possesses information to share but students have to ask an appropriate collection of questions of the teacher in order to obtain relevant information. We also distinguish Resource from the following roles in which the teacher's role is to engage students in mathematical work and not merely to provide information.]

- *Task Setter* (Farrell, 1996): The teacher is a questioner and decision maker who also sets the examples and strategies.

- *Technical Assistant* (part of the Technical Assistant role noted in Heid et al., 1990): The teacher helps students with hardware and software difficulties. [As Heid and her colleagues noted, teachers as Technical Assistants must be problem solvers. They must determine the nature of the technology-related difficulty and generate and choose from among possible solutions.]

Farrell studied how roles assumed by teachers, students, technology, manipulatives, and textbooks when technology was in use differed from when it was not in use. The comparisons were based on codes of 5-minute segments of videotape. A role was coded either as present or not present during each segment. Farrell compared the number of segments containing any instance of the role as a percentage of the total number of segments. Her results indicate that the teachers, with or without the technology, functioned as Managers in nearly 100 percent of the 5-minute segments. This omnipresent nature of Manager may explain why Heid and her colleagues seemingly did not attend to this role. Interestingly, Farrell found low incidence of Resource (5%) and Fellow Investigator (17%) when technology was in use and similarly low incidence (3% and 6%, respectively) when no technology was in use. The role of Counselor occurred rather infrequently during nontechnology-use segments (19%) as compared to during technology-use segments (43%). This finding is similar to that of Rochowicz (1996), who found that instructors reported that they perceived that the teacher takes on a role that we would describe as Counselor when calculators and computers are incorporated into the calculus classroom.

The roles of teachers have also been documented implicitly if not explicitly in other research. Stallings (1995) reported on Monica, a first-year algebra teacher in Project Litmus. In Monica's description of her workload, we describe how her roles as Planner and Implementer were far more intense when technology was involved. However, Monica also believed she became better at planning for technology use as she gained experience. Piliero (1994) reported the different tensions over roles felt by a teacher using Function Probe (Confrey, 1991). That teacher described her personal struggle as one in which she wanted to be a "guider" [our Counselor] but acted more as a "troubleshooter" [Technical Assistant]. The desire to be a Fellow Investigator arises for Nan, an algebra teacher in a study by Barnes (1994). She valued having graphing calculators in hand so she and her students could share the struggle and learn together. Similarly, Doerr and Zangor (2000) observed the teacher assuming the role of Facilitator and Catalyst. Among other things, these researchers considered the relationship of teacher roles, knowledge, and beliefs to students' graphing calculator use. Using Texas Instruments TI-82/83 calculators and calculator-based laboratory devices (CBLs) with pre-calculus students, the teacher encouraged student control of the class-room calculator. This in turn inspired student initiative and student-led discussion. However, Doerr and Zangor in their report focused more on the roles of the calculator and did not elaborate further on other teacher roles.

All of the contexts cited thus far involved function as a key feature. However, these roles do not appear to be limited to algebraic function contexts. For example, based on their study of middle school students using Cabri (Baulac, Bellemain, & Laborde, 1994), Hoyles and Jones (1998) suggested that the teacher must create an environment in which students' thinking is valued and students are encouraged to reason about properties of figures rather than about the appearance of the drawings. This implies that the teacher would take on a combination of roles, including Counselor as well as Catalyst and Facilitator. Further, there is evidence that these roles begin prior to classroom teaching experience. Galindo (1995) noted that preservice teachers using The Geometer's Sketchpad during a workshop assumed the role of facilitator [our Counselor]. This is consistent with the observations of Zbiek (1998) in working with preservice teachers using curve fitters during modeling activities. Several of these preservice teachers made and shared their observations about potential models with the intent of challenging others' current mathematical understandings and conclusions. They naturally assumed the role of Counselor.

While the roles of teachers within a technology-present classroom may emerge in the context of teaching, it is possible to draw teachers' attention to and make them aware of the many roles a teacher may take on as that teacher learns to use technology. Within the context of a mathematics education course, Timmerman (1998) reported "Susan's interactions with the 'tools' of the course including the TIMA microworlds (Olive & Steffe, 1994a, 1994b, 1994c) engaged her in reflecting and making explicit her conceptions of both teacher and student roles when teaching and learning mathematics with tools in her classroom" (p. 470). Susan lamented having only one computer in the classroom for her course project with fourth-grade students. While a few students worked with the TIMA environment, Susan worked with the remaining students. She thought this situation made it impossible for her to have opportunities to assess student understanding in the TIMA environment. Although neither Susan nor Timmerman identifies any student and teacher roles by name, we see Susan struggling with her desire to take a Counselor role and work closely with the TIMA-using students at odds with the decision she made in her Planner role given access to only one computer. Providing opportunities for teachers to reflect on technology-based activities may encourage teachers to make explicit their conceptions of both teacher and student roles when teaching and learning mathematics.

Although the roles in the list we compiled seem to arise in multiple settings, it is important to note that researchers found substantial differences in the blends and depths to which individual teachers assume these roles in actual classroom settings. The variations across teachers are consistent with our view of technology incorporation as a developmental learning process in at least two ways. Some variance may come from the teacher-learners being in different modes. Variance within any one mode is unavoidable as teachers construct their own understandings of teaching mathematics with mathematics technology.

Questioning in Practice

One of the key components of several of the teacher roles is questioning. Questioning can be used as a teacher's tool for effecting a technology-rich classroom environment conducive to students' mathematical activity and learning. For example, Doerr and Zangor (2000) documented aspects of teacher questioning in a precalculus course that drew heavily on mathematical modeling and required Texas Instruments TI-82/83 calculators and CBLs. As a Facilitator, the teacher asked questions that

diverted students' attention from the tool computation to the interpretations of the tool results and to mathematical justifications of results. The
nature of this questioning was essential in creating a classroom environment in which the calculator was not the ultimate authority.

Teachers' views of the role of questions in assessment formats as well as
in classroom discourse also may serve to focus and perhaps narrow students' mathematical activity. Heid, Blume, Zbiek, and Edwards (1999)
document the questioning techniques used by LeAnne, Sara, and Bill as
they learned to generate and use interviews to assess student understanding in a first-year algebra course. These teachers used interviews to verify
whether students' thinking and solutions matched the teacher's standard
rather than to elicit the students' emerging understandings and strategies. The teachers focused to various degrees on whether the students
could use the technology in particular ways and did not explore other
aspects of student understanding. The potential net effect was limiting
students' technology approaches and mathematical reasoning in favor of
checking basic technological skills and verifying fundamental terminology. This effect may be enhanced by the use of lab sheets—written directions for students to follow as they work with technology. The use of these
guiding directions arose in several studies and contexts (e.g., Cates, 1998;
Stallings, 1995; Zbiek, 1995) as ways of managing students' productivity
in exploratory settings. This contrasts with Piliero's (1994) description of
Tara, a 10-year veteran teaching precalculus. Using Function Probe and
specially designed curriculum materials, Tara moved from management
issues in September to mathematical issues by January. Her growth in
questioning followed a parallel course as she learned how to balance
being too directive with giving too little direction. Watching a video of her
questioning interaction with one student during a stimulated-recall session assured her that she was able to generate good questions. This
implies, of course, that she recognized truly good questions but needed
the video to show her the reality of her classroom. It seems that new technology may elicit new questioning styles, but teachers who reach a sense
of mastery of the technology may return to a stable use of less open-ended
questions, unless they are able to observe and reflect on their own classroom practices.

Particular questioning techniques or teachers' conceptions of questioning may be counterproductive in both teachers' and students' technology
work. An example comes from individual interviews and classroom observations with LeAnne, an experienced teacher (Zbiek, 1995). LeAnne
described questioning as a way to get students to understand; she juxta-
posed questioning with "telling students what to do" when she talked
about her teaching and when she reacted to written descriptions of scenarios involving other teachers. Her questioning of students in the CAS-

based algebra course she was teaching for the first time as well as in the geometry course that she had taught for years often had the funneling tendency noted by Steinbring (1992). LeAnne began with one question and then asked increasingly more guiding questions and continued in this way until students gave her desired answer. Questions LeAnne asked of her students as they worked on generalization tasks allowed overarching conclusions to be based only on a few examples. Her questioning of herself as she did mathematics embodied a slightly different narrowing effect. For example, in a problem she solved during a task-based interview she was satisfied that graphs of functions of the form $f(x) = a^x + \dfrac{b}{x} + c$ were "two hyperbolas" (see images in Figure 7.1) given her consideration of only four sets of parameter values representing changes in only one of the three parameters: $a = b = c = 1$; $a = 2$ and $b = c = 1$; $a = -2$ and $b = c = 1$; and $a = -1$ and $b = c = 1$ (Zbiek, 1995, p. 217). The questions LeAnne asked of herself seemed to focus on what could be said about the examples she had and not on how other examples might help refine her conclusions.

Funneling and failure to probe technology-generated results seem to narrow the mathematics students, experience with technology. Ironically, questioning patterns may hinder rather than facilitate exploration, reasoning, and conceptual understanding—three often-expressed teacher goals for using technology.

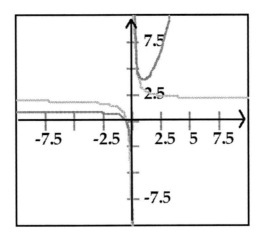

Figure 7.1.   Graphs of $f(x) = a^x + \dfrac{b}{x} + c$ for $a = b = c = 1$ and for $a = 2$ and $b = c = 1$.

Technology Affordances

The roles of the teacher and the nature of teacher questioning may be influenced by what technology affords. The blend of affordances and roles seems crucial in advancing the mathematical experience of students.

Technology Involved in Studies. Affordances vary greatly with the different genres of mathematics technology. The products in studies of teachers doing mathematics or teaching with technology range widely. Common tools include graphing utilities (including graphing calculators), computer algebra systems, and dynamic environments for geometry. Use of simulation environments, data collection devices, spreadsheets, and web applications seem less frequent. Several studies involve concurrent use of two or more forms of technology.

Affordances of That Technology. We find it helpful to think about the affordances offered by technology as falling into two very broad categories: those shared by many types of technology, and those limited perhaps to a particular genre of technology. Affordances shared by many types of technology typically involve features (e.g., programming, user-defined line thickness or color, cutting and pasting) that are very similar across different software packages or across different types of hardware. These affordances shared by many types of technology are different from affordances based on features that are found mainly in one type of technology (e.g., collecting motion data and storing it as lists). Of course, there may be affordances relative to specific tools, but product-specific features seem better articulated in the context of the chapters of these volumes focused on the development of those technology products.

A particular affordance shared by many types of technology is related to the ability to capture and replay students' work. This typically arises through a history screen or related feature that is very easy for teachers and students to learn to use. Mariotti and Bussi (1998) noted this affordance as they studied high school teachers and their use of Cabri in teaching ninth-grade students. The researchers suggest that the technology allowed teachers to help students to focus on the process of constructing rather than on the production of a drawing that appeared correct. Students could be asked what commands mean and to predict the results of implementing history screen lines. In essence, Cabri's "history" command enabled the teachers to engage students in interpretation and prediction games, which may have encouraged students to reason about the construction process rather than to focus only on the constructed product. The history screen on Derive similarly has been used to help teachers communicate with students (Lumb, Monaghan, & Mulligan, 2000) and thus to assist teachers in their roles as Counselor. In fact, the absence of the history feature may have negative effects in the classroom. Zbiek

(2001) describes a teacher of first-year algebra, LeAnne, using Calculus T/L II (Child, 1991), a computer algebra system that can record student actions but not in an easily retraceable form. The teacher's frustration in trying to see what students had done was a factor contributing to her creation of worksheets for students to follow. Using these sheets, the teacher replaced students' open-ended mathematical explorations with scripted key-pressing exercises. The resulting lack of student exploration conflicted with the teacher's goal for students to become fluent in using multiple representations to solve problems and explore function properties. The absence of the history feature in this classroom hampered the teacher's desire to work as Collaborator, as Counselor, as Technical Assistant, and as Evaluator of student learning.

Dragging is another built-in feature of technology that may be used as an instructional tool. While this feature may be most well known for its use to explore and test properties of figures created with dynamic geometry programs, it is also present in other types of technology. For example, dragging allows time efficiency and error reduction in some CAS environments. Rather than entering tedious commands to add $2x$ to both sides of the equation, $8 - 2x = 5x - 3$, the user may highlight "$2x$" in the equation and use the mouse to drag the expression to the right side of the equation, yielding more quickly $8 = 7x - 3$. The 10th-grade teacher in Pagnucco's (1994) study frequently used Maple's dragging capability for algebraic simplifications. Pagnucco reported that the teacher believed dragging helped him to understand simplification and assumed the same would be true for his students.

A technology affordance with a different slant is the existence of environments with multiple, linked representations of function. Other chapters of these volumes elaborate on how this technological feature as used by students may enhance their mathematical understanding. Lachance (1999) reported teacher learning inspired by the linked representations in Function Probe. Despite her in-service teachers' difficulty with the early version of the software, the teachers still reported new mathematical insights about transformations of function graphs. Bowers and Doerr's (1998) report on the use of SimCalc[2] by prospective teachers in college courses and during tutoring sessions suggests that these prospective teachers may have taken on a type of Collaborator role when given linked representations. An important feature of SimCalc is that it provides not only links among different types of representations (e.g., simulation and graph) but also among graphic representations of the same phenomenon and bidirectional links (e.g., change in a graph results in a change in a literal expression and vice versa). Through activities with SimCalc, the prospective teachers deepened their conceptual understanding of familiar calculus relationships such as the Fundamental Theorem of Calculus and the Mean Value Theorem. The prospective teachers then created lesson plans on these ideas and used them with students in tutoring sessions. Insights came to the prospective teachers not only as they did activities as mathematics learners in college classrooms but also as they implemented and reflected on lessons in the tutoring sessions. The prospective teachers were not exactly co-learners with the students during the tutoring sessions but rather took roles of asynchronous Collaborators, learning through their own work and through what the students did but not necessarily assuming strict learner roles during the tutoring session.

An example of an affordance that may be particular to a genre of technology is the "click-on" definition of variable in a spreadsheet. Dugdale (1994) described how K-12 teachers used this feature to define variables quickly and easily as they developed recursive models with Excel. The ability to click on a cell and have the technology immediately associate that cell's contents with the value of a variable allowed the teachers, and perhaps particularly the primary grade teachers, to create sophisticated models. The teachers developed classroom activities for Grades 2 through 12 on these spreadsheet models. Dugdale noted that most of these activities involved students *using* rather than *creating* the files. The interesting point here is that the affordance of the technology in this case, probably unlike the history screen or the representation links, is an affordance that may not be apparent to the students. Children using the spreadsheet models may never use the click-on method to define a variable yet they may benefit mathematically from its use by their teachers.

Technology affordances influence teacher roles as well as teacher understanding. The history screen example from Zbiek (1995) suggested how affordances might influence teacher roles. Although any new insights of teachers may be due as much to how they are taught or the materials they use as to the technology, Dugdale (1994) and Pagnucco (1994) reported teachers learning familiar mathematics more deeply due to affordances of technology-implemented definitions and dragging. There also appears to be a connection among roles, affordances, and teacher learning. LaChance's (1999) teachers learned mathematics in their roles as Planners and Conductors of technology-based activities. Bowers and Doerr's (1998) prospective teachers learned mathematics when they were acting as asynchronous Collaborators during tutoring sessions and college courses. While these observations seen as examples of teachers learning from practice may not seem unique to technology settings, they do suggest the importance of having teachers plan, implement, and reflect on lessons as part of how they learn mathematics as well as how they learn about technology affordances.

Student Effects

We noted how teacher roles and technology affordances impact the classroom environment and the mathematical activities that students encounter. Consideration of classroom practice is incomplete and unsatisfying without looking at the effects of classroom practice on students. However, the literature involving classrooms using technology frequently reports outcomes in the absence of descriptions of classroom events and teachers' actions and roles. This is particularly true of comparison studies that typically compare the treatment (technology-using) class with a control ("traditional" non-technology-using) class and sometimes with an alternative technology-using class. There may be indications of the curriculum used, the technology employed, and tests or other instruments involved. However, data collection limitations due to time and resources, or pagination limitations and preferences of most journals and proceedings, preclude inclusion of the details of the teaching. The impact of technology use on student understanding gleaned from these studies appears in the first six chapters of this volume. In this section we focus only on direct connections between students' outcomes and teachers' actions, intended or unintended.

A particularly rich collection of studies conducted in Australia by Kendal and Stacey (1999, 2000, 2001) offers a very engaging example of how research can inform the relationship of classroom practice, particularly in light of teacher roles and technology affordances, to its effects on students' understandings and actions. Three teachers used CAS in a unit revolving around multiple representations of differentiation in a high school calculus course. The teachers coplanned the lessons yet differed in how they carried out their roles in the classrooms. The differences included differences in how teachers "privilege" (i.e., use most frequently and give priority to) symbols or graphs, concepts or skills, and by-hand techniques or by-technology methods. As a result, students in different classes seemingly had different cognitive experiences based on the differences in their classroom exposure. Written tests and interviews indicated that students learned similar amounts based on total scores on tests but they did not develop understandings of the same things to the same depth. For example, students whose teacher favored procedures scored high in this area but low in concepts. Students used various representations in patterns similar to the patterns of representation privileging they encountered in the classroom. Student reports of their CAS use indicated that different classes approached any given problem in considerably different ways, with two of the three classes making considerably more accurate and appropriate use of the CAS. In short, the teachers' actions seemingly had direct impact on how the students subsequently did mathematics as well as on how the students used the technology. This issue is particularly important in thinking about open-ended mathematics technology that provides students with multiple ways of solving problems and representing concepts. Privileging, done either explicitly or unconsciously, defeats the purpose of the teacher who values this open-ended environment.

This series of related reports suggests that, at least for CAS use with high school students in differential calculus courses centered on representations, teachers' implicit choices regarding uses of technology can affect substantially what students learn. Further, differences among teachers matched with differences in problem approaches between classes are very difficult to ascertain if data collected involve only final answers to mathematical questions. Teacher choices may have additional manifestations in technology classes. For example, Stallings (1995) suggested that one of her teachers had two geometries coexisting: one on the computer and one in class. The researcher compared this to the two arithmetics of the teacher in Havita (1988). In both studies, there was one set of rules for doing mathematics with technology and another set of rules for doing mathematics without technology.

Conclusion for Classroom Practice Section

Changes in the roles teachers assume, in the affordances of technology on which they capitalize, and in the effects teachers' roles have on their students are critical aspects of classroom practice. Practice however exists in a synergistic relationship with characteristics of the teacher and the teacher's environment. What happens in the classroom is influenced by and has an influence on the teacher's knowledge and perceptions of technology, of mathematics, and of learning and teaching. We address these areas in the next three sections of this chapter.

TECHNOLOGY

The ways in which technology is integrated into teachers' classrooms is influenced by their conceptions of technology, mathematics, learning, and teaching. And, teachers' conceptions of technology, mathematics, and teaching influence the ways in which technology is integrated into their practices. Several studies examined teachers' conceptions of and beliefs about mathematics technology, the ways in which teachers used (or did not use) technology, and teachers' knowledge of technology. While some studies focused only on the teacher, others looked at the effects of the teacher's conceptions, beliefs, use of technology, and knowledge on students' learning.

Teacher Conceptions

Teachers' conceptions, beliefs, knowledge, and use of technology seemed to influence the activities they created for their students who were using technology to learn mathematics. Noss, Hoyles, and Sutherland (1990) observed in-service high school teachers as they participated in a series of workshops. They found that the teachers tended to project their own views about computers onto their students. This tendency suggests that teachers who believe that it is necessary, in their own learning with technology, to know all of the technological steps to be successful might structure activities for students that provide them with all of the technological steps. This seems consistent with a need to be told what is right mathematically. Pagnucco (1994) described one participant's views of technology after she was engaged in an in-service mathematics project that focused on the use of computer and calculator technology to support a problem-oriented approach to teaching. Donna was a first-year teacher who thought calculator use could be limited to learning activities followed by computer games to reinforce skills. Donna needed to understand the software but was unlikely to experiment with it on her own. She panicked at the notion of having to generate original ideas. Wanting others to tell her whether a mathematical idea is valid suggests Donna had an authoritarian view of mathematics. It seems unlikely that Donna would generate inquiry-based tasks. Open-ended and challenging teacher-developed tasks were absent in other studies. Heid and her colleagues (1999) found that some first-year algebra teachers viewed the computer algebra systems as the content of the curriculum rather than as a tool for learning mathematics. These teachers constructed interviews that "tested" whether students had mastered certain CAS strategies (e.g., zooming with graphs) rather than probing students' understandings of mathematics.

Bottino and Furinghetti (1996) examined conceptions that practicing high school mathematics teachers held about technology when they were confronted with a change in the mathematics curriculum, as a result of the requirement to include the use of computers and computer resources (programming languages as well as mathematics technology) within mathematics classes. Bottino and Furinghetti's analysis identified four different conceptions of technology that were held by teachers who were using computers in their classrooms: *formative* conceptions, *pragmatic* conceptions, *service-subject* conceptions, and *technological* conceptions. Teachers who held a *formative* conception used the technology in ways that focused students on concepts that were common to both mathematics and the computer (e.g., variable, algorithm). Teachers who held a *pragmatic* conception of technology focused on motivating students to use technology by highlighting the practical usefulness of its use in everyday life. Teachers who held a *service-subject* conception of technology emphasized the practical applications of technology and those who held a *technological* conception focused on the technology as a subject without necessarily connecting it to mathematics, like the teacher-interviewers that "tested" CAS-skill mastery (Heid et al., 1999). Bottino and Furinghetti's findings might be influenced by their context and by the particular uses made of computers. Their teachers were not given a choice about whether or not to incorporate technology. Rather, they were directed to include its use and had to find ways in which this could be done. Noss and colleagues (1990) described this type of use as reactive (using technology in reaction to changes prescribed by someone else). However, Bottino and Furinghetti found that some teachers they studied used the computer proactively. That is, the teachers knew in advance what they wanted to do in their classroom and they used the computer as a tool to assist in meeting their goals. It would be interesting to know the extent to which the proactive users had previously played with the technology or used it as their personal tools and the extent to which the reactive users did not. Such information would suggest that proactive users reached the PURIA Incorporate mode of use whereas reactive users might have been forced to function as if they were at that mode without having the appropriate earlier learning experiences.

Other researchers have suggested that preservice teachers who viewed the teacher as the authority in the classroom also tended to treat technology as curriculum. They provided students with explicit directions about how to use technology when they used it in their mathematics classrooms (Turner & Chauvot, 1995). They also believed that it was necessary for students to fully understand mathematical ideas before exploring them with technology. It is possible that for this reason they also believed that technology could only be used with upper-level high school mathematics students. It is possible that these teachers also had narrow conceptions of mathematics (i.e., mathematics is confined to what is in the textbook) and so they viewed the computer as a delivery tool rather than a tool for investigating mathematics (Noss et al., 1990). Diana, a primary school teacher who viewed mathematics as applying procedures quickly and accurately, perceived the use of Logo and the computer as a separate subject she was required to teach rather than a tool that could be used to enhance the teaching of mathematics (Moreira & Noss, 1995). Drier (2001) reported that the prospective middle school and high school mathematics teachers she studied entered a course that focused on the learning and teaching of mathematics with technology, with the view that technology could only be used after students had learned mathematical concepts in by-hand settings. Fine and Fleener (1994) conducted interviews with preservice elementary teachers and reported similar results. They found that the preservice teachers' perceptions of when calculators should be used were connected to the way they viewed the technology. Those who viewed the technology as a computation tool for doing mathematics rather than an instructional tool for learning mathematics were more likely to believe that technology should be used after students have learned the concepts or skills by hand. When the prospective middle school and high school teachers Drier studied had opportunities, as learners of mathematics, to experience ways in which technology could be used to broaden their own understandings, their views about its use before or after by-hand skills had been taught changed. Using technology as a mathematics learner and reflecting on that experience from the perspective of a teacher seemed to be critical activities that influenced these prospective teachers' views about the use of technology in mathematics classrooms. Similar findings arose in other studies that focused on secondary teachers (e.g., Lachance, 1999).

Focusing on conceptions of success rather than on conceptions of the change, Ruthven and Hennessy (2002) examined secondary mathematics teachers' perceptions about factors they attributed to successful use of computers and computer resources (graphing calculators or graphing programs, spreadsheets, Logo, software accompanying textbooks) in their classrooms. The teachers who were interviewed represented seven different types of schools. The researchers identified ten operational themes (italicized in this paragraph) they used to describe teachers' perceptions of features of technology that supported their successful use of computers in the classroom. These themes often appeared in conjunction with each other. They included teachers' association of computer use with an improvement in student motivation (*motivation improved*) and an enhancement of the classroom setting because of the change in venue that was required when computers were used (*ambience enhanced*). It is likely that these themes were also related to the teachers' observation that students experienced *intensified engagement* while working with computers. Teachers also noted that the use of technology might increase participation of students because it can *alleviate restraints* by performing tasks that students cannot perform and *facilitate routines* by quickly executing tasks that might otherwise require an extensive amount of time for students to complete. Teachers also noted that the feedback offered by different computer resources may allow students access to information that enables them to correct their own errors, which may also encourage students to persist and work without requiring the assistance of the teacher (*tinkering assisted*). Teachers also commented that students' *attention* was *raised* because students could focus on broader ideas without being distracted by tedious tasks. Teachers also perceived that mathematical *features* were *accentuated* by the visual representations provided by the technology. They also associated computer use with the ability to assist students in developing ideas (*ideas established*) and claimed that computer use enabled teachers to maintain the pace of instruction and create a productive classroom (*activity effected*). These operational themes were sometimes related to the ways in which teachers discussed their pedagogy. The researchers identified two pedagogical themes: *investigation promoted* and *consolidation supported*. Teachers described how technology promoted an investigational approach to teaching and also noted that specific programs that were written for the curriculum supported their goal of consolidating what students had learned by providing students practice and reinforcement.

Effects on Students

While several researchers have focused on teachers' personal uses of technology, others have examined the effects of teachers' uses of technology on students. Doerr and Zangor (2000) found that the ways in which a precalculus teacher used technology in her classroom influenced how students in the classroom perceived of and used technology in their learning of mathematics, as teacher and students implicitly negotiated roles and uses of technology. The teacher's familiarity with and knowledge of the Texas Instruments TI-82/83 calculators and her flexible use of these tools contributed to an environment in which students felt free to make use of the graphing calculator in a variety of ways. Students did not simply use the calculator in ways that were dictated by the teacher. This is in contrast with the findings of Kendal and Stacey (1999) who reported that, in general, students used a CAS calculator in ways that were similar to how it was used by their instructor. A variety of factors may account for these different findings (e.g., type of technology, duration of use, familiarity with the technology, and external assessments).

Doerr and Zangor identified five different patterns in students' use of the technology: computational tool, transformational tool, data collection and analysis tool, visualizing tool, and checking tool. While it is probably not surprising that students used the calculator to perform calculations, collect and analyze data, use visual methods to fit functions to data, find appropriate viewing windows, solve equations, and check results or predictions, its use as a transformational tool seemed quite novel. As a transformational tool, the task was changed because of the calculator. For example, the teacher focused students on understanding the meaning of the functions they were generating in the problem-solving context. This action redirected students' attention from computing to interpreting. The students directed the calculators to do the computing and the students' task then became one of interpreting. Doerr and Zangor also noted that the teacher believed that the results produced by technology could not always be trusted. This seemed to contribute to a classroom environment in which interpretations of technological results and justifications were encouraged.

Conclusion for Technology Section

Teachers' conceptions of technology influence how the technology is used in the classroom. Evidence such as explicit technology-use directions and quizzing students on technology skills suggest that both in-service teachers and prospective teachers tend to fixate on the teaching of technology rather than the use of technology as a tool for mathematics and as a tool for teaching mathematics. These events seem to be documented in studies in which teaching with technology is an innovation and the teachers are prepared to use the technology as their own tool. These teachers may be transitioning from the personal-use mode of use to the recommending-to-student mode of use or they may be forced to act as if in the implementation mode of use in the PURIA model. In any case, it may be natural for teachers who are in these beginning modes of using technology to believe that their needs as users of technology are the same as the needs of their students who are learners with technology (Noss et al., 1990).

MATHEMATICS CONCEPTIONS AND UNDERSTANDINGS

A teacher's practice and how the teacher moves through different modes or needs seem to be related to the teacher's mathematics. Rather than recapitulate the body of literature on teachers' knowledge, conceptions, perceptions, and attitudes involving mathematics, we focus here on those studies that are directly related to teaching mathematics with technology. The literature about teaching mathematics with technology underscores the teacher's conception of school mathematics as a key issue in how a teacher's practice evolves with technology use in the classroom. We also include teachers' understandings of mathematics with technology. The literature does not tightly connect this area of teacher understanding to teacher practice, but it is clear from existing studies (e.g., Doerr & Zangor, 2000; Zbiek, 1998; Zbiek & Glass, 2001) that prospective teachers' understandings of mathematics may be influenced through technology use in their own mathematics learning.

Conceptions of School Mathematics

Teachers have particular conceptions of what mathematics is. More crucial to technology use is what they think school mathematics is or should be. These conceptions of school mathematics influence the content they teach with technology and the ways technology is used in the classroom.

Conception Effects. Tharp and colleagues (1997) noted, among participants in a Virginia telecourse on calculators in mathematics and science, that teachers in Grades 6 through 12 with rule-based views of mathematics used procedural approaches with graphing calculators in their classrooms. This analysis of questionnaires and journals also indicated that these teachers thought calculators would not help and could possibly hinder instruction. In the classroom, the rule-based teachers were much more likely than their peers to control carefully the use of graphing calculators. This control took the form of discouraging exploration and discovery while replacing inquiry activities with lectures. Akujobi (1995) found a similar pattern while examining how teachers' knowledge and beliefs about teaching and learning mathematics influence their use of technology. High school mathematics teachers holding conceptual views of mathematics supported technology use in their classrooms. However, their colleagues with rule-based views of mathematics avoided technology use and relegated it solely to remediation and drill-and-practice purposes. Tharp and her colleagues ascribe this change to the teachers' desires to be in control of the classroom and to avoid the embarrassment. The teachers were frustrated and threatened when students found uses for the calculator that were unknown by the teachers. We would describe these rule-based teachers as abdicating a Technical Assistant role and avoiding a Collaborator role while resorting to an Explainer role.

A different kind of control of technology use occurred at the college level for Luci, a teaching assistant observed by Slavit and Yeidel (1999). She was asked to incorporate five Web-based outside-class activities in her precalculus course. Luci assigned the activities but did not incorporate the web experiences in her class discussion. Her students found these activities isolated from their classroom learning experiences. Slavit and Yeidel attributed Luci's control of technology use in the classroom to the conflict between the conceptual focus of the Web work and the procedural work that Luci believed was the essence of the course. In each of these studies, the instructor's conflict between the perceived mathematics to be taught (e.g., content coverage, symbolic manipulation) and the mathematics of the technology-based activities (e.g., problem solving, investigation, alternate notation systems) results in potential underincorporation of technology in the classroom.

Luci seemed to have a view of mathematics similar to that of the rule-based teachers in Tharp and colleagues (1997). Like the grade 6-12 teachers, she retained an Explainer role. However, Luci seemed to make her decisions against technology-based lessons as the Planner of classroom activities while the other teachers made theirs after having been the Conductor of calculator-using lessons.

The PURIA model may help to explain this difference between Luci and the other rule-based teachers. Despite having an expert mentor during the classroom trials, Luci was forced to act at the Incorporate mode without having sufficient opportunity to play, to use the web tools for her own goals, and to try the materials with a few students. Luci's case suggests that prematurely requiring technology use may be minimally productive if not counterproductive. In contrast, the calculator telecourses experienced by the teachers in Tharp and colleagues (1997) provided time for the teachers to learn to use the tool and to try things with small groups of students before and while being asked to use it in their classrooms. Their change in views about the value of the calculator for instruction may be related to positive experiences they had at the first two PURIA modes. Importantly, they noted that teachers with initially rule-based views of mathematics retained these views despite changes in their views of the calculator's value in instruction.

Changing Conceptions. As suggested by Tharp and her colleagues, teachers' views of mathematics matter. Teacher conceptions of school mathematics influence the mathematics students encounter with technology as well as what they do with technology during the learning process. Further, one might expect a dual relationship here; experience in teaching with technology would influence teacher conceptions of school mathematics. Lampert (1993) describes how teachers using the Geometric Supposer in their classrooms changed their view of what had to be in the geometry curriculum as well as the order in which the topics needed to unfold. Their changes seemed to be influenced strongly by the thinking they saw their students doing with the technology in the classroom. In contrast, Heid and colleagues (1999) note the difficulty that teachers of first-year algebra had in letting go of their traditional values and expectations. What they valued from the traditional curriculum continued to dominate, at least implicitly, what they wanted students to know, despite their adoption of a technology-intensive curriculum and their use of atypical assessment formats. Part of their hesitation to change their views extensively may be due to what they were teaching. They seemed to possess strong convictions about beginning algebra and how students needed a particular type of experience at this level for success in later courses. These two studies, showing how experiences in seeing how students work with technology influence teacher conceptions of what matters in a course, are very situation-dependent.

In the situations described by Lampert and by Piliero (1994), it is clear that teachers' views of school mathematics are susceptible to change through exposure to students' learning and doing mathematics with technology. It would seem that teachers' understanding would deepen as they use technology in their classrooms. However, this may not be true for teachers at all modes. If teachers with strong traditional values continue to limit or discourage mathematics technology use in their classrooms as Tharp and colleagues (1997) and Akujobi (1995) suggested, there might be less likelihood that their students will encounter atypical mathematics with technology. There would be an absence of rich classroom events that would challenge the teachers' traditional views. In cases in which students and teachers are struggling to use the technology to achieve the mathematical goals the teachers believe they could reach without technology, the classroom technology trials could have a negative effect. This seems to support the PURIA model proposed by Beaudin and Bowers (1997). Teachers would need to have opportunities to Play with the technology and to see rich results from students to whom they Recommend the use of technology before teachers are ready for Incorporate. The teachers' early observations of rich results may be sufficient impetus, particularly if paired with apposite curriculum materials, to help teachers reconceptualize school mathematics in ways that make their classroom use of technology richer and thereby more successful.

Understanding of Mathematics (With Technology)

It seems obvious that teachers' understanding of mathematics with technology would also affect their classroom practice. In reports of studies such as those by Heid and colleagues (1999) and by Doerr and Zangor (2000) are general indications that teachers' knowledge of mathematics influences what tasks teachers choose and how they plan and implement them in the classroom and in assessment settings. Like Heid and her colleagues, Akujobi (1995) provided evidence that high school mathematics teachers' knowledge of mathematics combines with their educational goals, their beliefs about teaching and learning, and their perceptions of the potential of technology in education. There is also evidence that technology use may enhance teacher understanding of mathematics.

Not Drawing on Existing Understanding and Past Experience. One might expect prospective and in-service teachers—like many other mathematics learners and doers—not to draw immediately and well on mathematics from their existing knowledge and past experiences. Several studies document this phenomenon in the presence of technology in several areas that suggest aspects of function understanding to address in teacher education and professional development.

Perhaps due to ease in conducting mathematics learning studies on campus and with one's own students in one's own technology-equipped classroom or computer lab, the bulk of the research on teachers' mathematical understanding with technology involves preservice teachers. Research involving prospective teachers indicates they do not readily draw upon the mathematical ideas that should be familiar to them from their mathematics courses. For example, Bowers and Doerr (1998, 2001) presented potential secondary mathematics teachers with activities using SimCalc. In this multi-linked-representational microworld, the prospective teachers were able to see visual illustrations of distance-velocity-acceleration relationships and to manipulate graphs of distance, velocity, or acceleration versus time. In the tasks, they needed to work with areas under graphs and relationships between velocity and distance that embodied the Fundamental Theorem of Calculus and the Mean Value Theorem. However, the prospective teachers were surprised that the relationships existed and they did not see them as embodiments of these two central theorems from their recent calculus courses. A parallel lack of connection expected among representations arises with in-service secondary mathematics teachers studied by Weigand (1991). Given a Turbo Pascal (Borland, 1989) program to assist them in generating models of iterative relationships, only a few teachers recognized the relations among solutions of $f(x) = x$, the stagnating value of the sequence, the fixed point, and the intersection of the graph with $y = x$. They did not see these as various representations of the fixed-point phenomenon. It is important to note that Weigand's study of the status of student and teacher understanding was not designed to be a learning activity for the participants.

More fundamental mathematical understandings needed in school mathematics and major mathematical principles encountered across many courses also may be inaccessible to prospective teachers as they engage in mathematics with technology. Zbiek (1998) described unsophisticated strategies devised and accepted by several prospective teachers using software to fit functions to data. Students using these strategies seemed to ignore the fact that a point on the graph of a function represents an input value of a function and its corresponding output value. They accepted, as models for real-world situations, functions whose graphs denoted infinitely many points whose coordinates would have no

meaning in the situations they tried to represent. In contrast, other prospective teachers drew on function characteristics (e.g., increasing/
decreasing, asymptotes, intercepts) to defend or generate models. A few
also drew on mathematical constructs (e.g., ratio and proportion) that
were at most tangentially related to an aspect of the situation they were
modeling without seeming able to relate that construct to the bigger picture (e.g., one student suggested that the ratio $y{:}x$ for one (x, y) data-pair
models the whole situation even if the ratio does not hold for a second
data pair). As in this ratio case, some accepted examples as proof. They
claimed a model was "even better" if they showed two or more data points
were consistent with the model they generated using only one data point.

There are similar examples among in-service teachers of the absence of
mathematical understandings we see among prospective teachers. As a
teacher of first-year algebra, Sara (Heid, 1995) found little use for function notation. She often replaced expressions like "$f(x)$" with a symbol like
"f" and thus changed a function rule into an equation and then treated
the function as a process rather than an object (e.g., Breidenbach, Dubinsky, Hawks, & Nichols, 1992). She avoided function notation use with the
CAS despite the importance the function notation had to the proper definition of a function in the CAS environment. She also confused the independent   variable   and   parameters   in   parameter   explorations.
Unfortunately, her understanding of function did not seem to improve
over the year of CAS using and teaching. This is somewhat different from
the case of one of her peers teaching the same curriculum at another
school. LeAnne (Zbiek, 1995) had not taught algebra prior to this study.
She learned to explore function families via parameter explorations and
became very agile in her use of technology. She fluently connected representations although she did not always have the appropriate vocabulary to
describe what she saw. However, her work was marked by conclusions
based on very few cases and devoid of symbolic reasoning about why these
conclusions would be reasonable. Due largely to her deeper understanding of the mathematics involved, LeAnne's interviews with students were
richer than those developed and used by Sara (Heid et al., 1999). This
mixed evidence about how teachers struggle to find their mathematics
leads to questions about what mathematics they learn when they work
with mathematics technology.

*Learn New Mathematics (and About Mathematics) From Technology-Based
Activities.* The combination of Sara's and LeAnne's cases suggests that
teachers sometimes, but not always, learn substantial mathematics as they
use technology with tasks designed for them and as they work through
tasks designed for their students. While this may happen in other settings, such as manipulative use, the potential for learning with mathematics technology may be different due to the increased ease to produce

multiple representations, quick access to numerous examples, and unexpected events within a single software environment. After teaching an exponential functions unit with Function Probe, Tara displayed richer problem-solving methods and fluency in moving among multiple representations (Piliero, 1994). She was more decisive in her action and more confident in her explanations. Research with prospective teachers seems to support the potential for teacher learning as well as suggest ways in which that learning may be facilitated. For example, Bowers and Doerr (2001) observed the intense changes in their prospective teachers' understanding of calculus concepts and principles. The researchers concluded that SimCalc was an effective environment for eliciting perturbations. The prospective teachers, however, were surprised that the relationships existed. This inability to see known mathematics in alternative settings extended to in-service teachers may help to explain why the teachers working with Wiske and Houde (1993) missed opportunities to discuss concepts and ideas as their students used The Geometric Supposer in an inquiry-based high school geometry course.

Surprising outcomes and unexpected "technology events" seemed to cause Bowers and Doerr's (2001) prospective teachers to develop deeper understandings of mathematics. The researchers remarked about the importance of the prospective teachers explaining these events for the prospective teachers' learning. This process of observing an unexpected technology outcome and creating new understandings while reasoning mathematically to explain the event is at the heart of the "shaky conjecture" notion proposed by Zbiek and Glass (2001). They conjecture that a user will most likely reason extensively and deeply when confronted with a technology-generated result that conflicts with the user's personal mathematical expectations. This conjecture is based on their observations of several prospective teachers using The Geometer's Sketchpad to investigate parameter effects on graphs of functions defined by equations of the form $y = \dfrac{a}{1 + be^{cx}} + d$. Like other participants in the study, Katie had only to drag a point to change the value of a, b, c, or d. As she dragged the points, there were several occasions on which she was surprised by the extent to which the results on the screen did not match her expectations. For example, she conjectured that graphs associated with negative values of a will be reflections of graphs associated with positive values of a. When they were not, she proceeded to unravel the mathematical situation, using supplemental lines and symbolic reasoning to explain why a sign change in the numerator of the fraction would not yield the mirror image for the graph. Her reaction to this technology-based surprise led to her deeper understanding of this function and to her enhanced ability to reason in other parameter explorations.

The fact that Katie was an honors student near the end of a rigorous undergraduate mathematics program further supports the earlier observation about the lack of connection between existing knowledge and technology work. Even the best-prepared and most capable students do not draw immediately on their existing mathematical understanding when working in a novel technology setting. Katie, for example, did not immediately consider that only part of the expression $\dfrac{a}{1 + be^{cx}} + d$ was negated when the sign of a changed and she did resort to limits in order to explain the graphical effects she saw. Katie found some connections to existing knowledge (e.g., changing the sign of the numerator of a fraction changes the sign of the fraction) more difficult than others (e.g., limits are useful in determining end behavior). Perhaps unsurprisingly, she drew on the idea from her calculus course before drawing on the idea from her earlier experiences. This example suggests teachers working in technology environments need experience in drawing on ideas across the K-16 curriculum.

Another potential for enriching teacher understanding of mathematics through technology-based experiences is capitalizing on the mathematical experience of teacher peers. For example, the prospective teachers' naïve views of curve fitting documented in Zbiek (1998) became progressively more sophisticated when a peer challenged their strategy and they listened to his description of a more robust method. Listening to these alternatives also challenged some of the prospective teachers to reevaluate their conceptions of school mathematics as predominantly correct-answer-oriented procedures. Influential peer exchanges also happen when experienced teachers use technology. Barnes (1994) presented an account of a high school teacher, Nan, and her colleagues using graphing calculators. They were looking at graphs of a function and its inverse and trying to determine why the inverse graph did not appear as they expected it would. Nan's realization that the graphs had to be reflection images in $y = x$ not only moved the group mathematically but it also provided a positive example. In Nan's words, "The calculators and our thinking about a problem can really work together" (Barnes, 1994, p. 124).

Providing prospective teachers and in-service teachers with opportunities to do mathematics with technology seems to be an important part of their learning to teach mathematics with mathematics technology. Observations of the outcomes of discussions like the one in which Nan participated seem to argue that the role of co-investigator with other teachers in mathematics learning situations as well as with students in their classrooms may be key to the continued development of deeper understanding of seemingly fundamental mathematics. The studies reviewed here suggest (a) that particularly useful tasks may be those that create situations in which teachers encounter unexpected results, and (b) that these tasks need to be followed by opportunities for the teachers to investigate the situation and to explain and discuss the events. These experiences may be the essence of powerful interventions during the personal use PURIA mode.

Conclusion for Mathematics Conceptions and Understandings Section

Drawing on mathematical understandings in classroom settings is an essential part of doing and teaching mathematics with technology. Research results illustrate that it is difficult for teachers to draw on mathematical ideas that should be part of their recent, or less recent, past mathematical experiences. However, instances from research do suggest the types of tasks and subsequent discussions that can help teachers to develop deeper understanding.

LEARNING AND TEACHING

How teachers believe learning occurs and how they envision teaching related to learning influence greatly their concerns and modes as they work to teach mathematics with technology. In addition, the research suggests that views of student ability rather than views of student learning may be an issue. The few studies that closely link practice with teaching acts suggest that teachers' conceptions and knowledge of mathematics and technology remain very influential for student learning.

What is Teaching?

Teachers in the studies of mathematics-technology use talk about teaching as "facilitating," but the tensions between their words and actions underscores how difficult it is for teachers to assume a Facilitator role. One example is found in Heid and colleagues' (1999) description of first-year algebra teachers using computer algebra systems for the first time. The teachers used the terminology of facilitating *student learning*. However, it seemed that the teachers, in practice and subsequent conversation, were intent on facilitating an *outcome* of *student expression of correct answers* rather than a *process* of *student construction of deep understanding*. Evidence of this perspective included the teachers' interview questions that targeted students' expressions of valid final answers rather than probed students' vague mathematical claims and unspoken problem solution paths. These teachers often entwined facilitating with questioning. An example arose as one of the three teachers in Heid and colleagues (1999), LeAnne, critiqued a teaching episode from a hypothetical classroom (reported in Zbiek, 1995). She praised the teacher for asking questions that led students to the correct final answer without "giving away" that answer. LeAnne compared this style positively to what she saw as her facilitative teaching; she noted, "I ask them questions for them to think through what the answer should be" (p. 216). This desirability of leading questioning is not consistent with the Facilitator role envisioned by Heid and colleagues (1999) and the Counselor role documented by Farrell (1996). However, this style of teacher questioning is sometimes effective for reaching the teachers' goals and addressing the teachers' concerns at the time. Getting students to answers rather than having students articulate their strategies and reasons simply may be part of some teachers' normal questioning style. From a PURIA perspective, it makes sense for this questioning to be natural as teachers move into new modes of technology use. It is a way for "right answers" to be made public, ensuring teachers moving into Recommend and Incorporate modes that the students are using the tool correctly.

What About Students?

Evidence suggests that teachers know their students' mathematical tendencies and that teaching practices are influenced by this knowledge. For example, teachers may know how their students work in technology environments. Teachers also may be able to predict how their students will respond to mathematical tasks. The three high school calculus teachers who were described in Kendal and Stacey (1999) accurately predicted their students' relative success with different representations and CAS use on a test designed by the research team. Part of the predictability may come from the teachers' potential beliefs that students know only what they have been taught. However, there is also learning that occurs outside of what has been taught and learning in this arena may be accentuated when students use technology. Strong evidence of this belief is seen in the teachers of first-year algebra studied by Heid and her colleagues (1999).

Teachers also seem to attend to affective reactions of students and respond to these reactions in different ways. Steve was one of the CAS-using high school calculus teachers and co-authors in the Lumb and colleagues (2000) team. He reported breaking from his initial technology focus when he feared his students were bored. Attention to students' affective responses also seemed to apply when students were learning beginning algebra with computer algebra systems. Similarly, Sarama and colleagues (1998) reported that elementary teachers perceived that the software program, Turtle Math, did not contain enough "bells and whistles" and other such features to inform students about whether their answers were correct or incorrect. The teachers felt that these features were needed to sustain student interest and support student learning. However, the students described the software to the designers as fun and did not mention the need to have game-like features the teachers thought were necessary. Bill (Heid et al., 1999) feared that he made students too uncomfortable if he asked them questions that were not readily answered. He altered his interview questions to include less demanding questions in order to retain a high level of student comfort. This tendency to ask what students know also seemed to be associated with Bill's view of knowing. Bill's language suggested he believed knowing was binary-valued: Either *you know it* or *you don't know it*. Students would naturally be uncomfortable if asked about those things in the "*you don't know it*" category.

A pattern of rule-based view of mathematics and attention to student affect during participation in an extended series of professional development sessions is not unique to Bill. Tharp and colleagues (1997) suggested that rule-based teachers may focus more on students' affective reactions to the use of calculators rather than on the mathematical understandings that students were developing as they worked with the technology. These researchers studied mathematics, science, and other teachers of grades 6-12 who participated in a series of professional development sessions. In contrast to those teachers, Steve (Lumb et al., 2000), a member of a collegial team, did not seem to focus as narrowly on student affect, nor did he seem to focus solely on skill development. Steve wanted to use a CAS for algebra and calculus topics with his A-level students in order "to relieve students from 'tedious' calculations" (p. 227). This combination of studies suggests that one's view of mathematics and attention to student affect are intertwined in the process of learning to teach with mathematics technology. Perhaps seeing positive student affect during the PURIA Recommendation mode is a key factor in teachers changing their views of mathematics during their attempts to implement technology.

There also is a possibility that teachers' projections of their self-perceptions heavily influence their ongoing attention to student affect. This seems to have been reflected in the interviews designed, conducted and interpreted by all three teachers studied by Heid and her colleagues (1999). For example, Sara pointed out that she could not imagine students quickly acquiring CAS competency or facility. She herself struggled to use the tool. LeAnne was uncomfortable when asked about something she had not previously encountered. She believed students needed exposure in order to understand and therefore would interview students only about things and with tasks very close to what they had done in class. She thought students needed verification and reinforcement and altered her questioning to ensure success. LeAnne expressed similar ideas about herself when she was doing mathematics. Both LeAnne and Sara expected students' experiences to parallel their personal experiences.

Modest portions of data seem to suggest that teachers make technology-related decisions based on what they perceive to be the ability of their students and avoid things that they think are beyond their abilities. Teacher B (Kendal & Stacey, 2000, 2002) thought his CAS-using high school calculus students were less able than students in other classes. He chose to focus on symbolic representations, noting that the students may be confused if faced with the variety of CAS symbolic representations. Teacher B used CAS graphs to help student understanding but thought the tool's symbolic manipulation capability was an intrusion in the (traditional) curriculum. LeAnne (Zbiek, 1995) believed her average-at-best students in a first-year-algebra course needed help learning how to use the CAS. She provided very detailed directions for solving classes of mathematical problems. Both Teacher B and LeAnne adapted the technology use to match their perceptions of student ability. In at least one other case (Kwak, 1994), high school teachers opted not to use technology with low-ability students due to these teachers' concerns about managing guided discovery lessons. Teachers in Austrian technical colleges also thought less-able students would not benefit from Texas Instruments TI-92 use. However, they attributed the problem not to managerial issues but to these students' inability to see the theory behind the technology work (Skarke & Koenig, 1998).

The idea that teacher's knowledge of student factors plays into what teachers and students do in the classroom is not new. Its presence in teaching with technology does suggest something about how one might support teachers moving through the PURIA modes. For example, if teachers project their own struggles with technology and feeling of incompetence on students, it is very important that the teachers have positive experiences in their use of technology during the earliest play and personal use modes of their technology experience. It may also suggest that teachers would monitor affect as well as intellect during the final PURIA mode of assessing students' use of technology.

How Are Students Affected?

We found very few studies that tried to match carefully particular aspects of teacher performance with specific student outcomes. The work reported by Kendal and Stacey (1999, 2000, 2002) illustrates nicely how teachers' classroom practices can influence not only the final scores of students on posttests, but also how students approach a problem in a technology-supported setting. Their three teachers, Teachers A, B and C, participated in the development and implementation of lessons that incorporated computer algebra systems in a high school unit on derivatives with a focus on multiple representations. Classroom observations suggested Teacher B focused on concepts and intuitions. He stressed symbolic representations and by-hand processes but allowed students free use of CAS-generated tables and graphs. The representations and strategies that these teachers privileged in the classroom remained consistent over time (Kendal & Stacey, 2002). Students in the three classes achieved similarly in terms of overall score on the posttest on differentiation. However, the methods students chose and the particular items students answered reflected the emphasis they experienced in the classrooms. Based on analysis of interview data (Kendal & Stacey, 1999), there appears to be a tendency—though not an exact match—between the representations and methods privileged by teachers in the classroom and the approaches used by their students. Students in Teacher B's classroom were more likely to use symbolic methods, members of another class favored CAS methods, while the third class made heavy use of graphical methods, each paralleling the representations that dominated in their respective classrooms.

The consistent nature of the privileging in the studies about these three teachers suggests the teachers had either reached a comfortable practice or that they had stagnated. Kendal and Stacey, however, describe other aspects of the classrooms that suggest some components of the teachers' circumstances did change somewhat over the two years. For example, Teacher B consistently emphasized symbolic forms and by-hand work. Believing that his class during the second year was less mathematically able, he thought they would not succeed with multiple representations, justifying his emphasis on one representation. The evidence suggests Kendal and Stacey's teachers were at the PURIA level of incorporating technology into the classroom and curriculum. However, it may be true that teachers can remain at this Incorporate mode for a long time. Perhaps this mode may be marked by drastic changes at first and then the emergence of a relatively stable practice until the teachers' practice is perturbed by observations of student abilities. Assessing students' understandings at the next PURIA mode may provide the perturbation needed for subsequent rounds of changes once incorporation has been natural for the teachers. With this thought in mind, it would be interesting to know the reactions of Teachers A, B, and C to the student data reported by Kendal and Stacey and to see how, if at all, this information might impact the teachers' privileging patterns.

Teaching Experience

Teaching experience arises as a factor in two ways: comparisons of more and less experienced teachers and observations about long-term teachers. Experience using technology and teaching mathematics may be related to the types of technology tasks teachers create for students. For example, Laborde (2001) examined the tasks that were generated by teachers who had a range of experience in teaching mathematics and using a dynamic geometry program (Cabri) during a 3-year project. The teachers included a novice teacher who had extensive experience using technology, two experienced teachers who were familiar with technology but had never incorporated it into their teaching, and one experienced teacher who was not familiar with technology. Laborde classified the tasks that were generated by the teachers into four different categories depending on how Cabri was used: (a) to produce more quickly a paper-and-pencil drawing that could be used to solve the problem, (b) to assist students in generating conjectures, (c) to increase the level of thinking that is needed by students to complete the task using technology instead of paper and pencil, and (d) to create a problem that is only meaningful in the technological environment and can be solved by using technology. At the beginning of the project, a novice teacher who had extensive experience in using technology was the only teacher to create tasks of the first type. All four teachers created tasks of the second type and few of the tasks were of the third or fourth type. It was not until the end of the project that all teachers, except the novice teacher experienced with technology, created tasks of the third and fourth types. Laborde suggests that it is easier for teachers to adapt paper-and-pencil tasks to technology use, but much more difficult to create novel technological tasks that are different in nature from what one might do with paper-and-pencil.

At least three case studies mentioned in this chapter involved individual teachers, each with over 20 years of classroom experience, although there is no documentation of the quality of those experiences. Doerr and Zangor (2000) shared the story of a teacher using Texas Instruments TI-82/83 calculators and CBLs in two precalculus classes for lessons on rate of change and transformations of exponential and trigonometric functions. These lessons seemed to be very successful. The high school teacher in Zbiek (1995) used CAS with her first-year algebra students. These lessons seemed moderately successful from the teacher's perspective but increasingly teacher-directed from the researcher's perspective. Heid (1995) suggests that another teacher's lessons in first-year algebra were not always mathematically constructive. In fact, this teacher's conceptions of mathematics and tentative use of the technology seem to have destined particular lessons to be only minimally successful. This combination of case studies indicates success with technology in the classroom is not immediate for those with substantial teaching experience. This parallels the finding of Churchill (1985) who conducted a study of teachers' attitudes toward the use of technology in elementary mathematics classrooms. After conducting a series of workshops with preservice and inservice elementary teachers, she noted that teaching experience did not make a difference in attitude. The cases also support the idea that incorporation of technology is a learning process along a continuum, with varying degrees of success. It is essential that we recognize that these studies—or any other studies—therefore are only snapshots of practice at particular times along that continuum.

The case studies of veteran teachers may be useful in understanding the impacts of the concerns and modes through which teachers pass and how those modes affect classroom activity and student understandings. Using the PURIA model, it seems that Heid's teacher, Sara, was being forced prematurely to function at the incorporation mode. We claim her use of the technology suggested that she still needed to use the CAS as a personal tool to understand CAS-generated results and to develop her technology skills. Growth also might have occurred if she were working individually or recommending its use to students and others. These other users could have, in turn, helped her to see the fallacies in her CAS entries and interpretations, fallacies which otherwise continued to be part of her technology-present mathematics and part of what she shared with her students in this premature incorporation setting. The PURIA modes may also help us to understand why a veteran teacher may experience turmoil when starting a technology-based innovation (e.g., Piliero, 1994). The nature of the early modes also helps us to see this teacher's first attempts at incorporating technology in the classrooms as "now I feel like a rookie again" (Heid & Zbiek, 1995, p. 655). This phrase seems to capture the sense of experienced teachers as they return to the mode of child-like play with the technology and then struggle to use the tool on their own. That "first-year teacher" feeling of insufficiency may diminish further as teachers work with a few students, leaving teachers feeling more prepared to incorporate technology more extensively into their classrooms.

Conclusion for Learning and Teaching Section

Several studies suggest that teacher conceptions and beliefs about learning and about students influence what teachers do in the classroom. The modest subset of technology and teaching literature that captures teachers' classroom practice and associates it with student learning suggests that a teacher's classroom use of technology corresponds to students' strategies for solving mathematical problems. The teachers who were novices in teaching and in using technology created tasks that were peripheral to the curriculum and restricted the tools students could use while working with the technology (Laborde, 2001). The quite varied experiences that veteran teachers have with their first attempts at introducing a technological innovation imply the usefulness of a modes-of-use view of the teachers' learning process. Consideration in the next section of the barriers and constraints to using technology in the mathematics classroom will add to researchers' and others' ability to understand the learning context and to support teachers' learning in all modes.

EXTERNAL FACTORS: SUPPORTS AND CONSTRAINTS

The process of learning to use technology occurs within a context larger than the teacher and the classroom. The extent to which technology was integrated within a classroom was influenced not only by factors internal to the teacher, such as concern and needs of teachers, but was also influenced by external factors. External factors include influences on the teacher (i.e., preservice and in-service professional development) as well as environmental factors (e.g., availability of technology, external testing, support systems, time, materials). This section presents findings from research that focused on environmental factors affecting teachers' use of technology in classrooms.

When teachers are incorporating the use of technology in their teaching, an important supporting factor is ready access to technology and experienced support staff (Kwak, 1994; Olive & Ramsay, 1999; Thomas et al., 1996). Thomas and colleagues (1996) found that implementing the use of computers with a variety of mathematics software programs in the teaching of mathematics in elementary through high school classrooms was best accomplished with constant teacher access to computers and the availability of experienced users of computers to offer assistance. Watson (1993, as cited in Monaghan, 1997) claimed that a support staff for mathematics teachers needed to include more than teacher colleagues who were also using technology in their classrooms. He found that having high-end effective users within a school did not always carry over to other teachers, even when these teachers were supportive colleagues. Like the absence of collegial support, teacher isolation may be a major constraint (McDowell, Wiske, Browne, Holland, & Saunders, 1987, as cited in Piliero, 1994). Additionally, Becker (1993) reported that teachers in mathematics and in other subject areas benefited in a variety of ways if school districts rather than individuals were involved in making decisions about incorporating technology in classrooms. In these situations, teachers were provided with a greater number of professional development opportunities and there were more higher-order thinking software programs available for teachers to use, particularly at the high school level. In at least one workshop setting, it seems that the facilitators most appreciated by mathematics teachers were experts that connected mathematics and technology events to students and classrooms and that allowed teachers to share their own expertise (Lachance, 1999). Experts, peers, and students are the others with whom the teacher experiences the Recommendation mode. They may also be key agents in connecting the teacher's growing technological competence with ideas for the classroom integration.

Other factors that influenced the extent to which teachers made use of technology in their classrooms were related to time constraints (e.g., Barnes, 1994; Kwak, 1994; Piliero, 1994). The early PURIA modes require time to experiment with the technology and time to learn how to use it. The absence of time for these experiences has been a factor discouraging technology use (Schrum, 1993, cited in Stallings, 1995). For teachers comfortable with technology play, the earlier modes may be more natural and the later modes may reflect teachers' technological playfulness. For example, Mr. Flack and Mr. Vine in Kwak (1994), with playful views of technology, generate and incorporate interesting technology-using materials in their practice.

Time concerns also take other forms. Almekbel (2000) reported that experienced teachers taking part in a teacher-enhancement project reported that the short length of their secondary-school mathematics classes hindered their effective use of calculator-based laboratories. These teachers needed longer class meetings in order for students to have adequate time to use the technology to conduct the technology-based mathematics explorations. External evaluation imposes another time constraint. In England, some teachers did not make extensive use of a computer algebra system with their A-level mathematics students because they felt pressured to teach to a formal assessment that was administered to all students (Lumb et al., 2000). Stallings (1995) reported similar teacher tensions regarding assessments. The teachers and students felt that time spent on learning the technology would take away from time that could be used to teach to the test. This finding suggests the importance of aligning assessment with instruction. Teachers may do this internally within their own classrooms in the Assess mode but they need an external assessment system that accommodates their innovations.

In addition to time constraints, other researchers found that teachers attributed their low use of technology to logistics. Bowers and Schuller (1997, as cited in Beaudin & Bowers, 1997) reported that 85% of teachers at schools with CAS do not use it in teaching because of logistical reasons versus 15% who do not use it because of their ideological opposition. The main reasons that teachers provided for not using CAS were lack of awareness and/or confidence in using CAS (44%), the need to create new lessons and work schemes in order to include CAS (22%), and the absence of adequate lab space (19%). Teachers also report the need to be prepared or trained for many things at once (Stallings, 1995). The concurrent demands of several initiatives may be another type of logistical constraint.

Despite logistical constraints teachers may continue to use technology. For example, Ms. Mayer in Kwak (1995) struggled to have access to the Geometric Supposer. She borrowed other teachers' classroom computers, and arranged for students to use the software in their free time. She incorporated technology in her geometry class despite the potential barriers. It could be that her play, her own use, and her use with groups of four or five students provided her desired evidence that the benefits exceeded the difficulties. An alternative reason for continuing despite difficult logistics is seen in the middle school first-year algebra teacher in the Cates (1998) study. Mrs. Rowland was moved by the need to prepare students for the future: "if I don't at least try to introduce my students to the graphing calculator, I am doing them even more of an injustice than having them learn along with me" (p. 62). This seems to be the spirit of the teacher who moves beyond the Use modes to the Recommendation and Integration modes.

The availability of technology, as well as the availability of curriculum materials that capitalize on that technology, seemed to be an important component for successful implementation of technology. The potential for different technology use in different materials may explain why one teacher would have very different technology use patterns in one course versus another. For example, Barnes (1994) described a high school mathematics teacher, Rachel, who felt more comfortable incorporating computer and calculator technology in her Advanced Algebra III class instead of in her Algebra I class because the Advanced Algebra III textbook was written to take advantage of computing tools. Graham and Thomas (2000) report the very positive response to technology use from the grade 9 teachers with whom they worked. The researchers provided an early-algebra module that introduced students to graphing calculators and built on a press/see/explain pattern for activities. Students would *press* keys as directed, *see* what appeared on the screen, and *explain* how the calculator might arrive at those results. One interesting feature was "screen-snaps," an activity in which students were given a screen dump such as one containing the symbolic expression $A + B$ evaluating to 0 and A/B evaluating to -1 (see Figure 7.2) and requested to replicate the screen on their calculators. Dugdale (1994) describes a project in which teachers developed spreadsheet models that they felt would be appropriate for

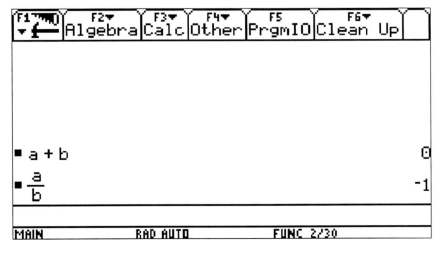

Figure 7.2.   Sample output given to students in a press/see/explain pattern.

their students, ranging from Grade 2 to Grade 12. Over a period of 3 to 6 hours, these teachers explored sample spreadsheet models provided by Dugdale's team and then generated their own models and lessons. It seems that the positive teacher reaction may relate to the extent to which the materials or workshops met the needs of teachers moving through the PURIA modes of use. Teachers had the opportunity to play with the technology and to use it on their own as well as think about implementing it with perhaps only a few students or for only a few days. Using technology for only a few days may be analogous to recommending it to a few students. Interestingly, the materials that teachers across the studies saw as useful with students were prepared files rather than activities in which students would generate their own files. When generating materials, however, it may be easier for teachers to generate materials for a lab than for a one-computer classroom (Stallings, 1995).

Other teachers, however, were unable to match technology use to their textbook use (Piliero, 1994; Kwak, 1994). Teachers also were unable to find written curriculum materials needed to support their technological work, and many resorted to creating their own written materials (Lumb et al., 2000; Monaghan, 2000). Monaghan (2000) studied thirteen teachers who were incorporating information and communication technology (ICT)—which included algebraic, spreadsheet, and geometry software packages—into their mathematics classes. Initially, all but two of the teachers included ICT while still closely following the mathematics textbook. Several months later, three other teachers found the textbook to be inappropriate, and all five teachers had difficulty locating curriculum materials that would match what they wanted to do with ICT. Many teachers created their own worksheets to supplement their technological lessons. Teachers using the Geometric Supposer and a guided-inquiry approach also had to rely on creating their own materials to accompany students' technological work or use those that were made available to them by the researchers. A limiting factor that seemed to contribute to teachers' use (or nonuse) of technology appeared to be related to the availability of written curriculum materials that were aligned with the technology they were using.

The supplementary written materials teachers created to accompany what students were doing with technology varied widely. Lumb and colleagues (2000) reported that teachers struggled with developing CAS-using calculus activities for students. One teacher relied on his own worksheets to "ensure control over students' work" and claimed that the textbook mathematics was different from the CAS mathematics. The other teacher tried two different books (one "traditional" and one "investigational") and rejected them because he felt that the tasks were not sufficient for his goals. Many of the supplementary materials teachers provided focused only on the technology and not on the mathematical ideas. Monaghan (2000) reported that teachers created worksheets that focused directly on the technology (e.g., technological commands available) and emphasized what technological procedures to follow to solve mathematical tasks. One teacher, reported by Kendal, Stacey, and Pierce (2002), seemed to view the mathematics done by CAS differently from mathematics done by hand. This teacher wrote calculus board notes with the paper-and-pencil method in one column and the CAS method in another column without making connections between the two columns. In the CAS-method column, keystrokes rather than mathematical terminology (e.g., F2 rather than "solve") were used. Students then did not use CAS effectively in their own work as evidenced on tests given by researchers and compared to other CAS-using classes. Slavit and Yeidel (1999) found that for one teacher who included in-class discussions that focused on goals of (rather than procedures for doing) technological activities students engaged in outside of class, students found the technological activities to be meaningful and connected to what they were learning in class. Research seems to suggest that it is important for curriculum developers to offer support to teachers by creating materials that make connections between the technology and the curriculum and that incorporate technology into mathematical activities. This enhances the likelihood that technology will be seen as a means for fostering students' mathematical understandings rather than as a subject devoid of mathematical meaning. It seems that differences in how teachers perceive and compensate for the absence of written materials may be due in part to their experiences within the PURIA modes. Rich experiences in any mode may lead to a better understanding of the types of materials and tasks that facilitate learning and teaching mathematics with technology.

Many studies identified external factors (e.g., accessibility of technology, time constraints, training, support personnel, curriculum materials) that influence the extent to which technology is integrated into mathematics classrooms and viewed these factors as controllable. It is important to note that even factors external to the teacher are perceived differently by the individual teacher depending upon his or her beliefs and conceptions about mathematics, technology, and teaching, and therefore the situation is not easily altered (Sarama et al., 1998).

Other teacher perceptions and setting characteristics may be factors. Piliero (1994) suggested that teacher perceptions of student effort might constrain technology use. Observations of lack of effort may enhance the teachers' already increased levels of stress and frustration as they try to change classroom events. Issues of courses and grade level corresponded to differences in graphing calculator use found by Milou (1998). The researcher's survey of southeastern Pennsylvania teachers indicated significantly greater use by second-year algebra teachers than by first-year algebra teachers. Perhaps not surprisingly then, 100% of the high school teachers but only 56% of the middle school teachers reported graphing calculator use in their schools. These cases suggest that PURIA mode movement may be related to the type and range of courses teachers are teaching.

CHAPTER CONCLUSION

Teaching mathematics with mathematics technology is a learning process. Models and concepts such as the PURIA modes may be useful in helping us to understand not only how teachers' understandings grow but also why teachers' personal technology use and classroom practice may differ greatly. Substantial evidence suggests there is a complex relationship among a teacher's classroom practice and his or her interconnected knowledge and perceptions of mathematics, technology, learning, and teaching. There is also a suggestion that particular characteristics of a technology-using practice may impact student mathematical thinking and problem solving.

Glimpses of the complexity of teachers learning to teach mathematics arise in several studies. This is nicely summarized by a quote from Charles (in Stallings, 1995), who in the midst of change separates the experience into two steps, developing some computer knowledge, and incorporating it in one class to start. Charles describes this guess-and-test philosophy:

> Just try to find something on your own, and do your own experimentation and play, and say, "Well maybe that'd be something." I'm still learning things. It's a growing process, but you've got to feel comfortable yourself and competent. And then you try it on your students, and it excites them, fine. If they think it's –. If you get a worse reaction than you did the old way, then you through [sic] it out and say, "Well, that's just going to make learning more difficult because they shut down even quicker because they don't learn with that approach." So it's a matter of just guessing and checking, you know, [like] factoring. We guess to see if it's going to do, and either refine, change, throw out, try something else. It's by personal experience, [a] professional [way of] seeing things. (Stallings, 1995, pp. 80-81)

Charles captures the need to play with technology, use it as one's tools, try it with students, and continually refine the classroom use. He also notes implicitly the role of assessment, his views on learning, the role of student affect, and the iterative nature of teacher knowing.

Technology Versus Other Innovations

For experienced teachers like Charles, the use of technology in teaching mathematics is an innovation in teaching mathematics. For prospective teachers, the use of technology is an innovation in learning mathematics and a change from how they have seen mathematics taught. It likely is not a surprise that much of this chapter reports concerns, insights, constraints, and supports that are reminiscent of the incorporation in teaching and learning mathematics of other innovations, such as manipulatives or cooperative groups. However, incorporating technology in one's practice is different from other innovations. There are issues beyond mere technophobia and beyond the difficulty of keeping up with the rate at which the technology itself changes.

Technology has significant implications for the content that is taught and the understandings that arise, as evidenced in other chapters in these volumes. The problem of how much of which skills students acquire can call into question the very essence of the curriculum. There is also curricular tension surrounding the time taken from curricular goals and spent in learning to use the technology. Technology offers new ways in which teachers may capture and replay student work, thus suggesting good ways to assess students' understandings. The small screens and personal nature of some technologies may challenge teachers' informal assessment techniques.

Technology may be perceived as more of a black box than other innovations. For example, while a teacher may not be familiar with using particular physical manipulatives such as Dienes blocks or a classroom structure such as group learning, the teacher still recognizes the physical object or arrangement and does not wonder extensively about what is "inside it." The fact that mathematics technology can "do" a certain range of mathematics makes this technology a mathematical mystery in ways that other innovations are not. Exploratory technology may be particularly challenging in that one may use it in so many ways, and how to get students started with it may not be clear. The many avenues that students can take and the rapidity with which students may pursue alternatives leads to a breadth of potential in the classroom that may be as overwhelming as it is invigorating. Perhaps the biggest difference between technology and other innovations is technology can quickly assume, or open to students, roles in the classroom that were once the exclusive domain of teachers.

Research Needs

To address the challenge of teaching mathematics with technology, teachers, teacher educators, researchers, and others need the current research base to be extended in several ways. Research on students needs to be done to connect more clearly teaching events and teacher characteristics to the detail and variations in student performance and learning outcomes. Research reports need to provide description of teachers and teaching that occurs with technology in more detail than merely naming the type of technology involved. Possible venues for future research may be attempts to validate, refute, or refine the potential of the PURIA modes. Other studies should consider what students learn as the roles of teachers change with technology innovations. Studies that focus on additional grade levels, mathematical content, and types of technology may broaden the existing literature.

The research suggests that teacher educators, curriculum developers, researchers, and others need to be aware of what to expect when both prospective and in-service teachers are learning to teach with technology. There are several things that seem easy to expect. The intended curriculum will not be the implemented curriculum in the classrooms. The teachers are students, too. They project their attitudes, understandings, and beliefs about mathematics, technology, and teaching on their students. The role of curriculum materials, the role of students and learning, and the role of teachers and teaching are in a synergistic relationship with technology use.

Teachers need time and experience to move beyond "Should I use technology?" to "How should I use it?" to "How can I use it better?" This is an on-going learning process involving many supporting players. If teachers are to teach mathematics better with technology, all communities involved must work together. For example, curriculum development, professional development, and teacher education must be mutual partners in the change.

Curriculum materials must be consistent with an overall view of learning, including the call for higher-order thinking in Dunham and Hennessy (2008). Add-on or optional technology components for curriculum materials may add nothing to teaching and learning mathematics. The mathematics in the curriculum needs to be made explicit for teachers. The background information about the technology must be there, and the mathematical and curricular connections must be obvious. This may remove the potential for the technology to become the curriculum as teachers learn the technology. It also is important because teachers have neither the excess time to explore ideas nor the resources to draw immediately on their non-technology mathematics experiences. The PURIA modes are consistent with using "big tools" rather than disjoint technology pieces; teachers may need more time to learn a more complex technology before teaching initial lessons, but it may require less time in subsequent lessons for them to become comfortable using the technology as their personal tools. There is also a need, as noted by Clements, Sarama, Yelland, and Glass (2008), to help teachers to facilitate post-technology use discussions.

Based on the literature, strong professional development would give teachers time to play with technology and to become acquainted with it as their personal tool. However, workshops should never be about the technology in the absence of curriculum materials. Activities involving students' technology-based work should also be included for teachers to consider. An example is the use of the 6/5 bar in Olive and Lobato (2008). There should be opportunities for teachers to try the technology-based ideas with small groups of students prior to full-scale implementation. The implementation needs continued support and should not be rushed. Teaching with technology likely would be facilitated if prospective and in-service teachers learned mathematics with technology. Strong mathematics activities would involve mathematically valid but surprising technology results that force teachers as learners to engage in mathematical reasoning.

In addition, research and ideas—like those in the chapters of this volume—should be shared with teachers. Examples of useful constructs from this chapter are the ideas of privileging of particular representations, the affordances of different forms and genres of technology, and the roles that teachers may productively undertake in technology settings. It seems that these are also useful constructs for mathematics instructors, curriculum developers, technology developers, researchers, and teacher educators as they think about their roles in teaching and learning mathematics in the context of technology. In terms of the *Sabertooth Curriculum* (1939) noted in the preface of these volumes, the main implication is obvious: If we give teachers mathematical technology as nets, but provide no personal learning experiences and no support, we should not be surprised when they prefer to continue to catch their mathematical and pedagogical fish by hand.

NOTES

1.   We will also revisit some of the responsibilities and challenges near the end of this chapter as we discuss constraints and supports of technology incorporation.
2.   Information on SimCalc is available at http://www.simcalc.umassd.edu (Retrieved January 15, 2006).

REFERENCES

Akujobi, C. O. (1995). *Teachers' knowledge and beliefs about the use of computers in high school mathematics*. Unpublished doctoral dissertation, Michigan State University, East Lansing.

Almekbel, A. S. M. (2000). *The impact of a teacher enhancement program on 7th through 12th grade mathematics instruction with regard to curriculum, technology, and assessment*. Unpublished doctoral dissertation, Ohio University, Athens.

Barnes, D. E. (1994). *Secondary mathematics teachers' interactions with technology*. Unpublished doctoral dissertation, University of Georgia, Athens.

Baulac, Y., Bellemain, F., & Laborde, J. -M. (1994). Cabri II [Computer software]. Dallas, TX: Texas Instruments.

Beaudin, M., & Bowers, D. (1997). Logistics for facilitating CAS instruction. In J. Berry, J. Monaghan, M. Kronfellner, & B. Kutzler (Eds.), *The state of computer algebra in mathematics education* (pp. 126-135). Lancashire, England: Chartwell-York.

Becker, H. (1993). Instructional computer use: Findings from a national survey of school and teacher practices. *The Computing Teacher, 20*, 6-7.

Borland. (1989). Turbo Pascal [Computer software]. Scotts Valley, CA: Author.

Bottino, R., & Furinghetti, F. (1996). Emerging of teachers' conceptions of new subjects inserted in mathematics programs: The case of informatics. *Educational Studies in Mathematics, 23*, 59-97.

Bowers, J., & Doerr, H. (2001). An analysis of prospective teachers' dual roles in understanding the mathematics of change: Eliciting growth with technology. *Journal of Mathematics Teacher Education, 4*, 115-137.

Bowers, J. S., & Doerr, H. M. (1998). Investigating teachers' insights into the mathematics of change. In S. Berenson, K. Dawkins, M. Blanton, W. Coulombe, J. Kolb, K. Norwood, et al. (Eds.), *Proceedings of the twentieth annual meeting of the North American Chapter of the International Group for the Psychology of Mathematics Education* (pp. 789-795). Columbus, OH: ERIC Clearinghouse for Science, Mathematics, and Environmental Education.

Breidenbach, D., Dubinsky, E., Hawks, J., & Nichols, D. (1992). Development of the process conception of function. *Educational Studies in Mathematics, 23*, 247-285.

Brill, M. (1997). The relationships among components of elementary teachers' mathematics education knowledge and their uses of technology in the mathematics classroom. *Dissertation Abstracts International, 58*(08), 3050. (UMI No. 980789).

Cates, J. M. (1998). *The teacher's role in the utilization of the graphing calculator in teaching graphing linear functions in middle school Algebra I.* Unpublished doctoral dissertation, Florida State University, Tallahassee.

Child, J. D. (1991). Calculus T/L II [Computer software]. Pacific Grove, CA: Brooks Cole.

Churchill, L. D. (1985). *The effects of sequencing of computer-related training on elementary teachers' attitudes toward mathematics, mathematics instruction and computers in education.* Unpublished doctoral dissertation, University of Washington, Seattle.

Clements, D. H., Sarama, J., Yelland, N., & Glass, B. (2008). Learning and teaching geometry with computers in elementary and middle school. In M. K. Heid & G. W. Blume (Eds.), *Research on technology and the teaching and learning of mathematics: Vol. 1. Research syntheses* (pp. 109-154). Charlotte, NC: Information Age.

Clements, D., & Meredith, J. (1994). Turtle Math [Computer software]. Montreal, Quebec: Logo Computer Systems, Inc. (LCSI).

Confrey, J. (1991). Function Probe [Computer software]. Santa Barbara, CA: Intellimation Library for the Macintosh.

Doerr, H., & Zangor, R. (2000). Creating meaning for and with the graphing calculator. *Educational Studies in Mathematics, 41*, 143-163.

Drier, H. S. (2001). *Beliefs, experiences, and reflections that affect the development of techno-mathematical knowledge.* Paper presented at the meeting of the Society for Information Technology and Teacher Education, Orlando, FL.

Dugdale, S. (1994). K-12 teachers' use of a spreadsheet for mathematical modeling and problem solving. *Journal of Computers in Mathematics and Science Teaching, 13*, 43-68.

Dunham, P., & Hennessy, S. (2008). Equity and use of educational technology in mathematics. In M. K. Heid & G. W. Blume (Eds.), *Research on technology and the teaching and learning of mathematics: Vol. 1. Research syntheses* (pp. 345-415). Charlotte, NC: Information Age.

Farrell, A. (1996). Roles and behaviors in technology-integrated precalculus classrooms. *Journal of Mathematical Behavior, 15*, 35-53.

Fine, A. E., & Fleener, M. J. (1994). Calculators as instructional tools: Perceptions of three preservice teachers. *Journal of Computers in Mathematics and Science Teaching, 13*, 83-100.

Fleener, M. J. (1995). A survey of mathematics teachers' attitudes about calculators: The impact of philosophical orientation. *Journal of Computers in Mathematics and Science Teaching, 14*, 481-498.

Fraser, R., Burkhardt, H., Coupland, J., Phillips, R., Pimm, D., & Ridgway, J. (1987). Learning activities and classroom roles with and without computers. *The Journal of Mathematical Behavior, 6*, 305-338.

Galindo, H. (1995). Planning to teach geometry with the Geometer's Sketchpad. In D. Owens, M. Reed, & G. Millsaps (Eds.), *Proceedings of the seventeenth annual meeting of the North American Chapter of the International Group for the Psychology of Mathematics Education* (Vol. 2, p. 286). Columbus, OH: ERIC Clearinghouse for Science, Mathematics, and Environmental Education.

Graham, A., & Thomas, M. (2000). Building a versatile understanding of algebraic variables with a graphic calculator. *Educational Studies in Mathematics, 41*, 265-282.

Guin, D., & Trouche, L. (1999). The complex process of converting tools into mathematical instruments: The case of calculators. *International Journal of Computers for Mathematical Learning, 3*, 195-227.

Hall, G., & Hord, S. (1987). *Change in schools: Facilitating the process*. Albany: State University of New York Press.

Hall, G., & Hord, S. (2001). *Implementing change: Patterns, principles, and potholes*. Needham Heights, MA: Allyn & Bacon.

Havita, N. (1988). Sigal's ineffective computer-based practice of arithmetic: A case study. *Journal for Research in Mathematics Education, 19*, 195-214.

Heid, M. K. (1995). The interplay of mathematical understandings, facility with a computer algebra program, and the learning of mathematics in a technologically rich mathematics classroom. In D. Owens, M. K. Reed, & G. M. Millsaps (Eds.), *Proceedings of the seventeenth annual meeting of the North American Chapter of the International Group for the Psychology of Mathematics Education* (Vol. 2, pp. 221-225). Columbus, OH: ERIC Clearinghouse for Science, Mathematics, and Environmental Education.

Heid, M. K., & Blume, G. (2008). *Research on technology and the teaching and learning of mathematics: Vol. 1. Research syntheses*. Charlotte, NC: Information Age.

Heid, M. K., & Zbiek, R. M. (1995). A technology-intensive approach to algebra. *Mathematics Teacher, 88*, 650-656.

Heid, M. K., Blume, G., Zbiek, R., & Edwards, B. (1999). Factors that influence teachers learning to do interviews to understand students' mathematical understandings. *Educational Studies in Mathematics, 37*, 223-249.

Heid, M. K., Sheets, C., & Matras, M. A. (1990). Computer-enhanced algebra: New roles and challenges for teachers and students. In T. J. Cooney (Ed.), *Teaching and learning mathematics in the 1990s* (1990 NCTM yearbook) (pp. 194-204). Reston, VA: National Council of Teachers of Mathematics.

Hoyles, C., & Jones, K. (1998). Proof in dynamic geometry contexts. In C. Mammana & V. Villani (Eds.), *Perspectives on the teaching of geometry for the 21st century* (pp. 121-128). Dordrecht, The Netherlands: Kluwer Academic.

Jackiw, N. (1992). The Geometer's Sketchpad (Version 2.0) [Computer software]. Berkeley, CA: Key Curriculum Press.

Jost, K. L. E. (1992). The implementation of technology in the calculus classroom: An examination of teacher beliefs, practice, and curriculum change. *Dissertation Abstracts International, 53*(06), 1876. (UMI No. 9229677)

Kendal, M., & Stacey, K. (1999). Varieties of teacher privileging for teaching calculus with computer algebra systems. *International Journal of Computer Algebra in Mathematics Education, 6*, 233-247.

Kendal, M., & Stacey, K. (2000). Acquiring the concept of derivative: Teaching and learning with multiple representations and CAS. In T. Nakahara & M. Koyama (Eds.), *Proceedings of the 24th annual conference of the International Group for the Psychology of Mathematics Education* (Vol. 3, pp. 127-134). Hiroshima, Japan: Hiroshima University.

Kendal, M., & Stacey, K. (2001). The impact of teacher privileging on learning differentiation with technology. *International Journal of Computers for Mathematical Learning, 6*, 143-165.

Kendal, M., Stacey, K., & Pierce, R. (2002). L'influence des environnements de calcul formel sur les modes de travail des enseignants [The influence of algebra environments on teachers' ways of working]. In L. Trouche & D. Guin (Eds. & Trans.), *Calculatrices symboliques transformer un outil en un instrument du travail mathématique: Un problème didactique* (pp. 117-150). Grenoble, France: La Pensee Sauvage.

Kwak, E. (1994). *Instructional computers in high school mathematics reform: Its theory and practice.* Unpublished doctoral dissertation, The Ohio State University, Columbus.

Laborde, C. (2001). Integration of technology in the design of geometry tasks with Cabri-Geometry. *International Journal of Computers for Mathematical Learning, 6*, 283-317.

Lachance, A. M. (1999). *Promoting reform in mathematics education by building content knowledge, technological skills, and teacher community.* Unpublished doctoral dissertation, Cornell University, Ithaca, NY.

Lampert, M. (1993). Managing the tensions in connecting students' inquiry with learning mathematics in school. In D. Perkins, J. Schwartz, M. West, & M. Wiske (Eds.), *Software goes to school* (pp. 213-232). New York: Oxford University Press.

Lumb, S., Monaghan, J., & Mulligan, S. (2000). Issues arising when teachers make extensive use of computer algebra. *International Journal of Computer Algebra in Mathematics Education, 7*, 223-240.

Manoucherhri, A. (1999). Computers and school mathematics reform: Implications for teacher education. *Journal of Computers in Mathematics and Science Teaching, 18*, 31-48.

Mariotti, M., & Bussi, M. (1998). From drawing to construction: Teacher's mediation within the Cabri environment. In A. Olivier Alwyn & K. Newstead (Eds.), *Proceedings of the conference of the International Group for the Psychology of Mathematics Education* (Vol. 3, pp. 247-255). Stellenbosch, South Africa: Faculty of Education.

McDougall, D. (1996, July). *Mathematics teachers' needs in computer-based geometric environments.* Paper presented at the 8th International Congress on Mathematics Education, Seville, Spain.

Milou, E. (1998). *Attitudes toward and use of the graphing calculator in the teaching of algebra.* Unpublished doctoral dissertation, Temple University, Philadelphia, PA.

Monaghan, J. (1997). Teaching and learning in a computer algebra environment: Some issues relevant to sixth-form teachers in the 1990s. *The International Journal of Computer Algebra in Mathematics Education, 4,* 207-220.

Monaghan, J. (2000). *Investigating the move from the occasional to regular use of ICT in mathematics classes.* Retrieved May 9, 2005, from University of Leeds, Centre for Studies in Science and Mathematics Education Web site: http://www.esrcsocietytoday.ac.uk/ESRCInfoCentre

Moreira, C., & Noss, R. (1995). Understanding teachers' attitudes to change in a LogoMathematics environment. *Educational Studies in Mathematics, 28,* 155-176.

Noss, R., Hoyles, C., & Sutherland, R. (1990). Teachers' characteristics and attitudes as mediating variables in computer-based mathematics learning. In G. Booker, P. Cobb, & T. N. de Mendicuti (Eds.), *Proceedings of the fourteenth annual meeting of the International Group for the Psychology of Mathematics Education* (Vol. 1, pp. 175-182). Oaxtepex, Mexico: PME.

Olive, J., & Lobato, J. (2008). The learning of rational number concepts using technology. In M. K. Heid & G. W. Blume (Eds.), *Research on technology and the teaching and learning of mathematics: Vol. 1. Research syntheses* (pp. 1-53). Charlotte, NC: Information Age.

Olive, J., & Ramsay, A. (1999). *Technology and change in mathematics teaching: Three case studies of project LITMUS teachers.* Paper presented at the research presession of the 77th annual meeting of the National Council of Teachers of Mathematics, San Francisco.

Olive, J., & Steffe, L. (1994a). TIMA: Bars [Computer software]. Acton, MA: William K. Bradford.

Olive, J., & Steffe, L. (1994b). TIMA: Sticks [Computer software]. Acton, MA: William K. Bradford.

Olive, J., & Steffe, L. (1994c). TIMA: Toys [Computer software]. Acton, MA: William K. Bradford.

Pagnucco, L. A. (1994). *Mathematics teaching and learning processes in problem-oriented classrooms.* Unpublished doctoral dissertation, University of Georgia, Athens.

Pea, R. (1987). Cognitive technologies for mathematics education. In A. Schoenfeld (Ed.), *Cognitive science and mathematics education* (pp. 89-123). Hillsdale, NJ: Erlbaum.

Peddiwell, J. A. (1939). *The saber-tooth curriculum.* New York: McGraw-Hill.

Piliero, S. C. (1994). *The effects of a problem-based curriculum, multi-representational software, and teacher development on the knowledge, beliefs and practices of a secondary mathematics teacher.* Unpublished doctoral dissertation, Cornell University, Ithaca, NY.

Rochowicz, J. A. (1996). The impact of using computers on calculus instruction: Various perceptions. *Journal of Computers in Mathematics and Science Teaching, 15*, 423-435.

Ruthven, K., & Hennessy, S. (2002). A practitioner model of the use of computer-based tools and resources to support mathematics teaching and learning. *Educational Studies in Mathematics, 49*, 47-88.

Sarama, J., Clements, D., & Henry, J. (1998). Network of influences in an implementation of a mathematics curriculum innovation. *International Journal of Computers for Mathematical Learning, 3*, 113-148.

Schwarz, J., & Yerushalmy, M. (1988). The Geometric Supposer [Computer software]. Pleasantville, NY: Sunburst.

SimCalc Project. (1997). SimCalc [Computer software]. Dartmouth, MA: University of Massachusetts Dartmouth. Retrieved January 16, 2005, from http://www.simcalc.umassd.edu

Skarke, P., & Koenig, E. (1998). New perspectives in teaching mathematics due to the use of the TI-92 [CD ROM]. In C. Leinbach (Ed.), *Proceedings of the third international DERIVE and TI-92 Conference*, Gettysburg, PA.

Slavit, D., & Yeidel, J. (1999). Using web-based materials in large-scale precalculus instruction. *International Journal of Computers for Mathematical Learning, 4*, 27-50.

Stallings, L. L. (1995). *Teachers' stories learning to use computing technologies in mathematics teaching*. Unpublished doctoral dissertation, University of Georgia, Athens.

Steinbring, H. (1992). Epistemological investigation of classroom interaction in elementary mathematics teaching. *Educational Studies in Mathematics, 32*, 49-92.

Tharp, M. L., Fitzsimmons, J. A., & Brown Ayers, R. L. (1997). Negotiating a technological shift: Teacher perception of the implementation of graphing calculators. *Journal of Computers in Mathematics and Science Teaching, 16*, 551-575.

Thomas, M., Tyrrell, J., & Bullock, J. (1996). Using computers in the mathematics classroom: The role of the teacher. *Mathematics Education Research Journal, 8*, 38-57.

Timmerman, M. (1998). *Learning in the context of a technology-enriched mathematics teacher education course: Two case studies of elementary teachers' conceptions of mathematics, mathematics teaching and learning, and the teaching of mathematics with technology*. Unpublished doctoral dissertation, The Pennsylvania State University, University Park.

Trouche, L. (2000). Mastering by the teacher of the instrumental genesis in CAS environments: Necessity of instrumental orchestrations. *Zentralblatt für Didaktik der Mathematik, 34*, 204-211.

Turner, P., & Chauvot, J. (1995). Teaching with technology: Two preservice teachers' beliefs. In D. Owens, M. Reed, & G. Millsaps (Eds.) *Proceedings of the seventeenth annual meeting of the North American Chapter of the International Group for the Psychology of Mathematics Education* (Vol. 2, pp. 115-121). Columbus, OH: ERIC Clearinghouse for Science, Mathematics, and Environmental Education.

VanNetta, C. M. (2000). *Interpreting the advanced placement statistics curriculum in three high school classrooms: Case studies of teacher practice and teacher learning.* Unpublished doctoral dissertation, University of Maryland, College Park.

Weigand, H. (1991). Iteration sequences and their representations. *Educational Studies in Mathematics, 22,* 411-437.

Wiske, M., & Houde, R. (1993). From recitation to construction: Teachers change with new technologies. In J. Schwartz, M. Yerushalmy, & B. Wilson (Eds.), *The geometric supposer: What is it a case of?* (pp. 193-215). Hillsdale, NJ: Erlbaum.

Zbiek, R. (1995). Her math, their math: An in-service teacher's growing understanding of mathematics and technology and her secondary school students' algebra experience. In D. Owens, M. K. Reed, & G. M. Millsaps (Eds.), *Proceedings of the seventeenth annual meeting of the North American Chapter of the International Group for the Psychology of Mathematics Education* (Vol. 2., pp. 214-220). Columbus, OH: ERIC Clearinghouse for Science, Mathematics, and Environmental Education.

Zbiek, R. (1998). Prospective teachers' use of computing tools to develop and validate functions as mathematical models. *Journal for Research in Mathematics Education, 29,* 184-201.

Zbiek, R. M. (2001, July). *Influences on mathematics teachers' transitional journeys in teaching with CAS.* Paper presented at the Communicating Mathematics through Computer Algebra Systems Conference, Utrecht, The Netherlands.

Zbiek, R. M., & Glass, B. (2001). Conjecturing and formal reasoning about functions in a dynamic environment. In G. Goodell (Ed.), *Proceedings of the twelfth annual International Conference on Technology in Collegiate Mathematics* (pp. 424-428). Reading, MA: Addison-Wesley.

CHAPTER 8

EQUITY AND USE OF EDUCATIONAL TECHNOLOGY IN MATHEMATICS

Penelope Dunham and Sara Hennessy

Information technology has become an essential part of mathematics education in the schools. The dramatic growth in access to personal computing power has been called "the single most important catalyst for today's mathematics education reform movement" (Heid, 1997, p. 5). Along with the promises of technology, however, come concerns about inequities that arise from differential access and use and may result in unequal outcomes for various populations. The purpose of this chapter is to examine research on technology in mathematics education from the perspective of equity.

Two key principles in the National Council of Teachers of Mathematics (NCTM) *Principles and Standards for School Mathematics* (NCTM, 2000) reflect the focus of this chapter:

Equity: Excellence in mathematics education requires equity—high expectations and strong support for all students.

Technology: Technology is essential in teaching and learning mathematics; it influences the mathematics that is taught and enhances students' learning. (p. 11)

Research on Technology and the Teaching and Learning of Mathematics:
Vol. 1. Research Syntheses, pp. 345–418

Is it possible to implement both principles simultaneously? Can technology be integrated into mathematics instruction in an equitable way that gives equal access and support to all students? Early research (reviewed by Sutton, 1991) indicated that increased emphasis on technology-enhanced curricula could foster inequities and raise barriers to learning and achievement. Access to computers and calculators and patterns of use often varied by race, ethnicity, gender, and social class due to economic and societal pressures, producing differences in benefits between technology "haves" and "have-nots." More recent studies show that as technology levels of availability rise both in schools and in homes, access is inevitably becoming more equal in the Western world (Council of Ministers of Education, Canada [CMEC], 2000; Organisation for Economic Cooperation and Development [OECD], 2003; Kleiner & Lewis, 2003). Using educational technology may—inadvertently perhaps—alleviate some existing inequities and break down barriers by leveling the field for previously disadvantaged students (Dunham, 2000; Hickey, Moore, & Pellegrino, 2001; Hong, Toham, & Kiernan, 2000).

In this chapter, we briefly discuss the increasing importance of educational technology in the teaching and learning of mathematics, rationales for achieving equity in its use, and several frameworks for the meaning of equity. We then organize findings of studies on equity and technology in three sections: availability of resources, use of technology (desktop and portable computers, and calculators), and associated educational outcomes. The central question that pervades our analysis in each of these areas is:

- As access to information technology (IT) increases both in homes and in schools, are previous inequities being reduced or eliminated, or are they exacerbated?

The final section of this chapter presents implications of the studies, research-based suggestions for policies on technology access and use to achieve equity, a sampling of programs and policies already in place that facilitate equity in technology use, and suggestions for future research.

THE IMPORTANCE OF TECHNOLOGY AND EQUITY IN ITS USE

Electronic technologies have the potential to transform the teaching and learning of mathematics (Clements, 2000; Heid, 1997; Waxman, Williams, & Bright, 1994) and help to make higher level mathematics more accessible to students (NCTM, 2000). With technology, students can explore concepts; engage in experimentation; model problem settings; access more problem-solving tools; compute more efficiently; focus on conjecturing, decision making, and reasoning instead of on computation and manipulation; collect and analyze real-world data; and examine many examples from graphical, numerical, and algebraic perspectives (Clements, 2000; Dunham & Dick, 1994; Ellington, 2003; Guerrero, Walker, & Dugdale, 2004; Heid, 1997). Nonroutine uses of technology (e.g., exploring complex problems or developing number properties) can lead to significant gains in mathematical understanding and achievement (Clements, 2000; Ellington, 2003; Guerrero et al., 2004). "Cognitive technologies" (such as computer algebra systems, dynamical geometry programs, microworlds, and graphing calculators) afford students the opportunity to transcend limitations of conventional approaches and engage in reflection, and they enable teachers to implement more student-centered instruction (Heid, Blume, Hollebrands, & Piez, 2002; Pea, 1987). If educational technology can exert such a strong influence on teaching and learning then all students of mathematics deserve equal access to its benefits as a matter of fairness, and the equity argument is made.

Yet it is growing societal and economic pressures—more than instructional benefits—that have led to the rapid expansion of educational technology and the pervasive presence of the Internet in schools today. Efforts to provide for the technological needs of the workplace have fueled the change as shifts in demographics and economic demands have highlighted the need for developing the technological skills of all students (Sutton, 1991). The electronic revolution has made "digital literacy" (especially Internet experience) increasingly essential for a modern workforce and an informed citizenry; digital literacy is thus a life skill that must be available to all students (Wiburg, 2003).

Whether motivated by economic goals or pedagogical ones, schools face increased concerns about inequities in computer use. In a subsequent section, Equal Opportunity to Learn: Access, we offer evidence that populations have differential access to technology. Because of costs for equipment, technical support, and teacher training, students in economically advantaged schools often have more resources than students in less-advantaged schools (particularly in inner city and rural areas), creating inequities related to socioeconomic status (SES) (Becker, 2000a, 2000b; Swain & Pearson, 2003) and race (Page, 1998; Wenglinsky, 1998). Gender differences in technology interactions are evident; as the gap between the sexes for frequency of use narrows, girls continue to use computers in ways different from the ways boys do (Colley & Comber, 2003; DeBell & Chapman, 2003; Volman & van Eck, 2001). To a lesser degree, unequal access to and use of calculators in schools exists (Braswell, Lutkus, Grigg, Santapau, Tay-Lim, & Johnson, 2001; Burton, 1996; Strutchens & Silver, 2000).

Since the 1980s, the education community and government agencies have produced a host of programs to increase students' access to computing technology.[1] Although some progress has been made in addressing inequities of access between high- and low-income schools, between males and females, and among racial groups, differences still exist in the way that different populations interact with technology and in the outcomes of their interactions (DeBell & Chapman, 2003; Hedges, Konstantopoulos, & Thoreson, 2003; Looker & Thiessen, 2003; Wenglinsky, 1998). The importance of equity issues remains high. Some consider mathematical and digital literacy the new civil rights battleground for minority students (Ladson-Billings, 1997; Roy, 2000; Wiburg, 2003) and argue that society must strive to erase inequities in attaining that literacy. Robert Moses, founder of the Algebra Project,[2] called mathematical training critical to the future of disenfranchised communities and noted, "A great technological shift has occurred that places the need for math literacy front and center" (Moses & Cobb, 2001, p. 6). Others see technology (especially Internet use) as a means to alleviate past inequities by making more educational opportunities available to diverse populations (Smerdon, Cronen, Lanahan, Anderson, Iannotti, & Angeles, 2000).

Definitions of Equity

Croom (1997) states, "Equity in mathematics education implies fairness, justice, and equality for all students so that they may achieve their full potential, regardless of race, ethnicity, gender, or socioeconomic status" (p. 2). Wiburg (2003) frames the issue in economic and political terms, calling digital equity "the latest battle in the effort to keep access to education and political representation open to all—to avoid having a technological underclass that contributes to the economic and educational divides that already exist" (p. 114). Thus digital equity is a social justice construct that includes access to educational technology (machines, software, and support) as well as to high-quality curricular and pedagogical resources that provide opportunities for using technology to facilitate learning for all students.

Some researchers distinguish between *"equity"* as fairness and *"equality"* as sameness or lack of difference in some measurable index, for example, ratio of students to computers (Swain & Pearson, 2003; Wiburg, 2003). Fennema (1990), in the context of defining gender equity for mathematics teaching and learning, agrees that *equity* implies "fairness" and suggests three perspectives for evaluating it: (a) equity as equal opportunity to learn mathematics, (b) equity as equal educational treatment, and (c) equity as equal educational outcomes. Each of the categories can be assessed by quantitative measures. Fennema argues, however, that the third perspective is the one that most promotes fairness and justice in mathematics education, even if it conflicts with implementation of the first two.

In fact, if equal outcomes are a goal, equity and equality may conflict so that achieving equity may require inequality (Sutton, 1991). Reaching diverse populations who traditionally have not performed well or who have been underrepresented in mathematics in the past could necessitate *inequality* in terms of treatment in order to achieve fairness in outcomes. For example, several research studies indicate that girls perform better in cooperative learning settings, whereas boys succeed with individual learning and competitive situations (e.g., Littleton, Light, Joiner, Messer, & Barnes, 1992). The need for differential treatment is a significant, albeit discomforting, implication of this approach to equity.

We will use Fennema's three categories to organize research on digital equity in terms of: (a) availability of technology resources in and out of school, for various populations (equal opportunity to learn); (b) the amount and type of activities and interactions students experience with available technology, both in terms of curriculum and pedagogy (equal educational treatment); and (c) the effects of technology on students' mathematical understanding, performance, and attitudes (equal educational outcomes). We use Fennema's perspectives not as separate definitions of equity, but rather as three different lenses for viewing digital equity. While individuals may prefer one lens or another, each view has implications for the others. Equitable access to technology must occur before benefits accrue from its use, but access alone does not guarantee fair use. For many, the ultimate measure of fairness may be equal outcomes, but the way in which students and teachers use technology may determine what outcomes occur. Thus our review presents research findings from each of Fennema's viewpoints (in the respective sections Equal Opportunity to Learn: Access; Equity as Equal Treatment: Process Variables; and Equity as Equal Educational Outcomes: Effects of Technology Use) and makes connections among them wherever possible. We will focus on equity implications for groups identified by gender, race, ethnicity, socioeconomic status (SES), language, age, mental or physical ability, as well as by location (e.g., by country, state, urban/rural), but lack of research in some areas will preclude discussing all characteristics in each section.

Equal Opportunity to Learn: Access

To study the equity implications for mathematics instruction, we need to know what technology is available to students. This section describes students' physical access to resources—calculators, computer hardware, mathematical software, Internet connections, and instructional support—at home and in school. We also address teachers' access to technology. Because it is difficult to determine accurate data in a time of rapid growth in educational technology, we offer a "snapshot in time" from the most recent national surveys and government reports available at the time of publication and a discussion of historical trends from past studies.[3] Only a few studies in this section deal directly with technology for mathematics learning, but general access information sets the stage for describing equity implications that arise from differences in accessibility. We present results for computers and for handheld technology separately.

Comparisons of past research with recent data on computer and calculator access in schools show the following:

- Availability of all types of technology has increased dramatically in the last decade.
- Calculator access has increased steadily and is fairly equitable.
- Some previously reported inequities in access to computing technology have lessened.
- Pockets of inequity still exist—among countries, among racial and ethnic groups, among schools and regions, among socioeconomic groups, and between the sexes.
- Inequities similar to those mentioned in the previous item apply to home access, and these interact with access at school (where students with home experience tend to dominate).

Knowing how many computers or calculators are available in a school does not, of course, tell us how often, in what manner, and by whom the technology is used; those aspects are addressed in the section titled Equity as Equal Treatment: Process Variables.

Access to Computers and the Internet

School access. Spurred by public initiatives and personal interest, growth in computer access has developed rapidly. Sutton (1991), in a review of computer equity studies through the 1980s, found that computer implementation in the United States occurred at "an unprecedented rate for a new technology" (p. 475). In 1983 about half of American schools had no computers (Becker, 2000a); two decades later, virtually all U.S. public schools had computers and 99% were connected to the Internet in 2002 (Kleiner & Lewis, 2003). The ratio of students to instructional computers in U.S. public schools dropped from a national average of 6 to 1 in 1999 to a rate of 4 to 1 in 2002 (Kleiner & Lewis, 2003). A survey of 56,000 U.S. households in 2001 found that 81% of children aged 5-17 reported using a computer at school.

Similar increases in access occurred in other countries. Schools in Canada reported that in 1999, ratios of students to instructional computers were 9:1 for elementary schools, 8:1 in lower secondary schools, and 7:1 for upper secondary schools (CMEC, 2000). By 2000, the median rate for secondary students in Canada was 6:1 (OECD, 2003). Australian schools reported similar access figures; for example, in 2000 there were 5 students per instructional computer for secondary schools in Australia (OECD, 2003).

Statistics on computer use in British schools indicated that considerable change took place since the mid-1980s when over half of upper secondary students had never used a computer at school (Fife-Schaw, Breakwell, Lee, & Spencer, 1986). United Kingdom government figures for 2003 showed that the ratios of instructional computers to students were 8:1 in primary schools, 5:1 in secondary schools, and 3:1 in special schools[4] (Department for Education and Skills [DfES], 2003). The most technology-intensive countries in education have been the United States, Denmark, Norway, Finland, Iceland, United Kingdom, the Netherlands, New Zealand, and Sweden (OECD, 2003). These countries also have a genuinely uniform school computer environment, whereas Greece, Portugal, Bulgaria, and Romania are characterized by very wide distributions of the student-per-computer ratios between schools[5] (Eurydice, 2004: reporting the results of the Programme for International Student Assessment [PISA] and Progress in International Reading Literacy Survey [PIRLS] surveys in 2000 and 2001). International differences are thus compounded by inequities in computer access within nations, districts, and schools (Becker, 2000a; Eurydice, 2004; OECD, 2000).

Despite overall increases in access, demographic differences are evident (DeBell & Chapman, 2003; Looker & Thiessen, 2003). Past studies showed that boys often had greater access to computers (Butler, 2000; Dugdale, DeKoven, & Ju, 1998; Volman & van Eck, 2001), but some more recent studies show little or no difference in the percents of boys and girls who use computers in schools (DeBell & Chapman, 2003; Kleiner & Lewis, 2003; Looker & Thiessen, 2003). Older students have more access to computers than younger ones (Smerdon et al., 2000), and differences relative to race/ethnicity, socioeconomic status, and urbanicity persist (Looker & Thiessen, 2003). Students from predominantly White, high-SES schools or schools with low minority enrollment have more computers per school and lower student-per-computer ratios (Becker, 2000a; Braswell et al., 2001; Kleiner & Lewis, 2003; Smerdon et al., 2000; Tate, 1997) than schools with more minority and lower-SES students. Urban and rural schools often have fewer computers and greater student-per-computer ratios than suburban schools (Brush, 1999; Kleiner & Lewis, 2003; Looker & Thiessen, 2003). Minority children, overrepresented among poor children and in urban schools, thus may experience a confounding of racial and SES effects on equity (Ladson-Billings, 1997; Page, 1998; Waxman & Padron, 1994). Even when rates of access seem similar for high-income and low-income schools, computers in poorer schools and in schools with high minority enrollments are often outdated models with limited computing speed, lacking up-to-date external or internal memory devices, CD/DVD drives, or modems, and incompatible with newer software or peripherals (Becker, 2000a; Smerdon et al., 2000). Studies in Canada (Looker & Thiessen, 2003) and the United States (Kleiner & Lewis, 2003) also found limited technical support in rural and lower-SES schools, which were less likely to have a full-time trained computer specialist available.

School Internet connectivity. Although there has been little use of the Internet in mathematics teaching and learning,[6] Internet connectivity has become a measure of a school's technology access. There has been a marked increase in Internet connections in more developed countries (OECD, 2003). Surveys from 1994 to 2002 (using representative samples of 1000 schools each year) indicated that the percentage of U.S. public schools connected to the Internet jumped from 35% in 1994 to 99% by 2002, that 94% had broadband connections and 92% of instructional rooms were wired (Kleiner & Lewis, 2003). In Finland, similarly, there was nearly universal connectivity by 1999 (OECD, 2000). Portugal went from 30% to 100% secondary school connectivity within a single year (1998-99). In Canada, 88% of elementary students and 97% of secondary attended schools with Internet connections in 1999; access across the provinces was uniform (CMEC, 2000). In Great Britain, Internet connections also expanded rapidly; for example, in 2000, DfES (2002) reported that the percentage of primary schools with Internet access was five times higher (at 86%) than it was in 1998 (17%) (DfES, 2002) and has continued to rise. Indeed virtually every educational institution now enjoys access to on-line resources and the majority of its computers were connected to the Internet by 2002 (DfES, 2003); this is for the most part due to the government's National Grid for Learning (NGfL[7]) scheme. Other developed countries also have created infrastructures for digital learning, such as Sweden's "Schoolnet"—a heavily used, filtered information center. In Japan, the "Virtual Agency" connected virtually all schools by 2002[8] and intended to train all teachers and provide computers and high-speed Internet access in every classroom by 2005.

Inequities in Internet access indicate a "global digital divide" between poor and rich nations (OECD, 2003). For example, in 2001 nearly half of all people with Internet access were in the United States (175 million), where three in five Americans were Internet users compared to one in 25 in Russia, one in 150 in Iran, and one in 600 in Sudan (Moghaddam & Lebedeva, 2004). Similarly, poor schools and small schools have less access (Becker & Ravitz, 1998; Looker & Thiessen, 2003). Access in rural areas is often limited by having no local Internet provider (Looker & Thiessen, 2003). Some gaps are closing in the United States where access to Internet connections by locale was almost equivalent in 2002 for urban, rural, and suburban schools, and where 90% of smaller schools had Internet connections, compared to 100% of large schools (Kleiner & Lewis, 2003). An SES effect persists, however; in 2002, the ratio of students to computer with Internet access was 5.5:1 in high-poverty public schools[9] but 4.6:1 in more economically-advantaged schools (Kleiner & Lewis, 2003). The equity implications of the higher ratios for lower-SES students are made more severe by findings that the majority of disadvantaged children only have access to the Internet at school (DeBell & Chapman, 2003).

In Britain, in 2003 only half of all schools had the high-speed connections that they need for efficient Internet access (Office for Standards in Education [Ofsted], 2004a); primary schools especially still cannot afford it although connectivity was undoubtedly rising quickly (the government's aim was to connect all schools via broadband by 2006). The proposed implications of the NGfL connectivity scheme—equality of access irrespective of age, race, gender, type of school, and so forth—is still not fully realized. Although at least 90% of U.K. schools offered students some Internet access (British Educational Suppliers Association [BESA], 2003), in some schools, for cost reasons or parental fears about accessing unsuitable material, only older or selected students had Internet access (Valentine, Holloway, & Bingham, 2002). These kinds of differentiation within schools show that access and connectivity figures inevitably tell us only part of the story. Should Internet use become more common in mathematics classrooms, inequities in web accessibility could have significant implications for mathematics teaching and learning.

Teacher access. The vast majority of Australian, British, and U.S. teachers now have access to computing technology and the Internet at school and at home (detailed figures are provided by DfES, 2003; OECD, 2003; Smerdon et al., 2000). In Britain, only 33% of classroom teachers have a computer for their personal use at school although 93% of primary teachers and 85% of secondary teachers have home access (DfES, 2003). In Turkey, however, a survey of elementary and secondary teachers in four cities found that 41% had never used a computer (Cakiroglu, Cagiltay, Cakiroglu, & Cagiltay, 2001). Of course, concerns regarding teachers' use of educational technology go beyond access; issues of time, support, knowledge, and training all create significant barriers to limit access for teachers and hence their classroom use of technology (e.g., Becker, 2000a, 2000b; CMEC, 2000). (We discuss how teachers use technology in the section titled Equity as Equal Treatment: Process Variables.) As software and hardware develop rapidly, ongoing staff development is increasingly important for teachers' confidence in using technology (DfES, 2003; Smerdon et al., 2000) and for effective use of technology within the curriculum (Bright & Love, 1994; Schmidt, 1999). For example, a survey of over 4000 U.S. teachers indicated that instructors with better-than-average technical ICT[10] skills who regularly used computers for their own work engaged students in wider and more nonroutine classroom uses of computers when compared to teachers with minimal skills and limited use of computers (Becker, 2000b). Limited resources have consistently proved to be a barrier to teaching with technology; desktop machines can quickly become obsolete so that newer multimedia software will not run (Swain & Pearson, 2003; Wiburg, 2003), and clustering computers in labs rather than classrooms makes integrating technology into the mathematics curriculum more difficult (Ruthven & Hennessy, 2002). Becker (2000a) reported that teachers with at least five computers in their classrooms are much more likely to use computers frequently than teachers who share a computer lab. These data might reflect a phenomenon that teachers who most want to use computers negotiate greater classroom access (Wiburg, 2003); yet, it is the case that students are more likely to have access to computers in shared labs than in their classrooms. Data from the 2000 National Assessment of Educational Progress (NAEP) showed that 92% of Grade 8 students and 95% of Grade 12 students had access to computers in shared labs but only 52% and 43%, respectively, had computers available in the classroom at all times (Braswell et al., 2001). A survey of 4000 U.S. teachers in 10 subject areas found that only 2% of secondary mathematics teachers had at least one computer for four students in their classrooms and mathematics had the lowest percent among the ten (Becker, 2000b).

Home access. More children use computers and the Internet at school than at home (DeBell & Chapman, 2003; Looker & Thiessen, 2003), but differential access to home computers is an important equity issue because it can affect school use of technology (see Facer, Sutherland, Furlong, & Furlong, 2001) and perhaps mathematics achievement (see the section on Equity as Equal Educational Outcomes: Effects of Technology Use). Dugdale and colleagues (1998), for example, found that home access was more important for girls than boys; access to home computers predicted girls' early success in solving prealgebra problems with computers and increased the effect of computer course enrollment on their mathematical achievement, although the advantages diminished over time as those without home computers gained more experience. Others suggest that home use may have a greater effect on students' attitudes toward technology than school use (Kirkman, 1993) and/or gender (Comber, Colley, Hargreaves, & Dorn, 1997). Data on home access to computing technology show the same pattern of increasing availability seen for school computing (DeBell & Chapman, 2003; Looker & Thiessen, 2003). Yet, Becker (2000a) warns that "the digital divide separating children in socioeconomically advantaged homes from children in socio-economically disadvantaged homes is mammoth" (p. 56). Data from the U.S. Census Bureau's survey of 56,000 U.S. households in 2001 indicate that home access differs dramatically by income: Children in families with an annual income over $75,000 were far more likely to use computers at home (89%) than children from families with family incomes under $20,000 (31%) and were three times as likely to use home computers for schoolwork (DeBell & Chapman, 2003). Looker and Thiessen (2003) reported similar patterns of inequitable home access for Canadian children from lower-SES families and those living in remote rural areas. Children in families that can afford to provide support for and access to ICT outside of school may experience greater educational advances and achievement (Becker, 2000a; Wenglinsky, 1998). In Britain, the Screen-Play Project issued an even stronger warning after surveying 855 children aged 9-14: Children without computers at home are at a "significant disadvantage" and can be excluded from using technology at school. Students who are better experienced and more confident with home computers tend to dominate use of school machines, and the problem can be compounded by teachers choosing these students for computer-based tasks (Facer et al., 2001). Technologically competent secondary school students can be offered greater access, exacerbating the fluency gap and hence increasing rather than challenging the division between those with and without home access (Valentine et al., 2002). In sum, there is an *interaction between home and school access.*

As home access steadily rises in Britain and has reached 90% for households with school children (DfES, 2003), a significant SES-related digital divide is evident there, too. The Young People and ICT survey by the British government (DfES, 2002) found that computer ownership was highest at 91% among households in social grade AB (professional and managerial occupational groups within the conventional SES scale), with ownership for DE households (unskilled and semiskilled manual workers) significantly lower at 58%. Internet access is also far more prevalent in middle class (88%) than working class (61%) families (Livingstone & Bober, 2004). The British Household Panel Study (BHPS, 1998; Scales, 1999), which annually surveys a representative sample of 9,500 people, found that the number of home PCs and the availability of Internet access was lower for children of unemployed parents or single-parent households. DeBell and Chapman (2003) reported similar results in the United States. They also found that less home access to computers and the Internet was associated with lower education level for parents, with living in city centers, and with being physically or mentally disabled. In 1999, people with disabilities in the United States owned half as many computers as able-bodied people and only 10% used the Internet, despite the potential of the Internet for overcoming social isolation and mobility problems (Greene, 2000). International differences also affect home ownership and there is a strong correlation between national wealth as measured by Gross Domestic Product per capita and home access to computers; throughout Europe the latter figure varies from 20% (Eastern Europe) to over 90% (Nordic countries) of schoolchildren (Eurydice, 2004).

Ethnicity creates additional inequities in home access; in the United States, Hispanic and Black[11] children are less likely than other children to have computer and Internet access in the home. The percentages (by racial group) of students ages 5-17 reporting home computer use in 2001 were: Whites, 77%; Blacks, 44%; Hispanics, 41%; Asians, 76%; and Native Americans, 54% (DeBell & Chapman, 2003). Black students experienced a 39 percentage-point difference between school and home use, compared to less than a 7-point difference for White students. Increases in computer ownership for most minority groups have resulted in a slight narrowing of the gaps among Whites, Blacks, Hispanics and Native Americans[12], but great disparities remain. In the United Kingdom, the Young People and ICT survey showed that 79% of Whites owned a personal computer or laptop, compared to 77% of the Asian group and 67% of the Black/Other group (DfES, 2002).

Home use of computers in the United Kingdom is highly related to gender with boys owning and using computers significantly more than girls (Harris, 1999). A 2001 survey for the ScreenPlay Project found that 50% of boys had their own computer compared with 37% of girls (Facer, Furlong, Furlong, & Sutherland, 2003). The Computers in Education project, a survey of 20 countries in 1989 and 70,000 students in 10 countries in 1992, found that boys reported significantly greater home access in all countries but the United States; the largest gender differences in home and school use were reported in Germany, Austria, and Latvia (Reinen & Plomp, 1997). However timeline trends indicate a slow narrowing of the gap (Colley & Comber, 2003).

Access to Handheld Technology

Most school computers are desktop machines; for example, in the United Kingdom in 2003 there were 6 portable[13] computers per primary school and 29 per secondary school, compared with 25 and 191 desktop computers respectively (DfES, 2003). While around half of British schools consider that they are well equipped with desktops, less than 15% perceive that provision of portable computers is adequate (BESA, 2003). National initiatives have equipped students in certain areas or schools with portable computers, but there is no available information about other aspects of equity affecting access and use of portable computers. In contrast, the most affordable technologies for mathematics classrooms today are calculators, ranging from simple four-function models to sophisticated graphing calculators with computer algebra systems (CAS), dynamical geometry software (DGS), and statistics software. Despite a tendency to undervalue handheld technology (McChesney, 1995), we will see in the section titled Equity as Equal Treatment: Process Variables, that calculators are used more than computers for mathematics instruction in the middle and upper grades[14] (Ansell & Doerr, 2000; Braswell et al., 2001; Guerrero et al., 2004). In this section we describe the availability of these handheld computing tools in school and at home and some associated inequities. In the Equity as Equal Educational Outcomes: Effects of Technology Use section we make the case that regular access to calculators affects mathematics achievement outcomes.

School access. Today many state standards for the mathematics curriculum in the United States emphasize the importance of technology, particularly use of graphing calculators. A majority of elementary and middle school students and nearly all secondary students in the United States have access to some form of handheld computing technology (Ansell & Doerr, 2000; Dion, Jackson, Klag, & Wright, 2000). The type of calculator used by students differs by grade level and by type of mathematics course (Ansell & Doerr, 2000). This has equity implications because type of calculator used has been associated with differential achievement outcomes (Braswell et al., 2001).

Sparrow and Swan (2000) reported limited access to calculators in primary classrooms of Western Australia, England, and Japan. Although most secondary school students in a host of countries have calculator access, the degree of access varies significantly (Mathematical Association, 2002; Oldknow, 2000). Variation in national policies for calculator use create a potential area of inequity. A survey of calculator policies for 29 countries in Europe, Asia, North America, and South America found that approaches to calculators in class ranged from no encouragement of use in secondary schools through discretionary use, to established or compulsory use (Oldknow, 1997). Discrepancies in policy also affect national mathematics exams; in 1997, several countries (12 of 29 surveyed) allowed some use of calculators; four countries required some use; nine countries actively encouraged use, and only four banned it. The International Baccalaureate program, which serves 800 schools in 95 countries, now requires graphing calculators on exit exams for three of its four mathematics courses (Mathematical Association, 2002). In the United States, calculator use is allowed on all SAT[15] exams and graphing calculators are required for parts of the Advanced Placement exams for calculus and statistics; models with CAS functionality are permitted, provided they do not have a QWERTY-style keyboard (Dion et al., 2000). In a backlash against calculators, however, the California State Board of Education banned calculators from the tested curriculum[16] for Grades K-6 (Ralston, 1999). Similarly, in the United Kingdom, where calculators are compulsory in the National Curriculum, a major policy change in 2000 restricted the use of graphing calculators and CAS machines in "A" level examinations and coursework. However calculator use is now common starting at age 11 and there is a specific assessment objective at "A" level concerned with their use. While several countries (notably Australia and Austria) have recently integrated CAS in schools, a picture of inconsistent and inequitable provision remains. Calculator use on exams can affect outcomes and, thus, restrictions on use or type of calculator in assessments raise equity concerns if the restrictions are applied differentially (see the section on Equity as Equal Educational Outcomes: Effects of Technology Use).

There is little evidence of gender differences in calculator availability, and early inequities for minorities or low-income students at the secondary level seem to have disappeared by the end of the 1990s (Dion et al., 2001). (Within schools, however, calculator use can vary by grade level, ethnicity, and SES; see the section on Equity as Equal Treatment: Process Variables.) Some teachers have raised questions about equitable access with regard to cost (Bright & Love, 1994), but Bitter and Hatfield (1993) established that equity concerns about access for middle school students in a middle-to-low-income district were not applicable for inexpensive four-function calculators. Studies that address the impact of calculator technology on students with lower SES (e.g., Waxman & Padron, 1994) are discussed in the section on Equity as Equal Educational Outcomes: Effects of Technology Use.

Summary

Students' access to technology both at school and at home has increased astronomically over the last few years, particularly in the United States, Australia, and Great Britain, and, to a lesser degree, in many other economically-advantaged nations, but not in developing countries. Despite the reduction of some inequities in access to computers, the "digital divide" between the haves and have-nots is still apparent. However the situation is much more complex than this simplistic binary construct implies; it is construed instead as a "multidimensional continuum" along which students' needs and the types and locations of technologies available vary in a multitude of ways (Damarin, 2000). It is now recognized that there are, in fact, multiple divides varying in their nature, extent, and impact on disparate groups within society (British Education and Communications Technology Agency [Becta], 2001). A host of national initiatives has not yet eliminated substantial disparities in computer availability and Internet access that persist between richer and poorer nations and along racial, ethnic, gender, geographic, and socioeconomic lines.

Recent studies, however, have shown improvement for some groups and regions (Kleiner & Lewis, 2003; OECD, 2003). Calculator availability is widespread with few differences in access for different social groups, especially at the high school level. However, as handheld technology becomes more sophisticated with added functionalities that make it more costly, teacher fears about inequities in calculator access may increase as well. If using more expensive technology results in higher achievement, then inequities in access raise questions about fairness. Computer access is less equitable. Students located in poor areas are doubly disadvantaged by less access to technology both at school and at home and are unlikely, in the near future at least, to have access to computers at home. In the next section we show that these issues are related, and like gender and ethnic differences, can affect students' confidence levels and familiarity with technology, and hence their school experiences of using it, too. An interaction between home and school access is thus apparent.

Access to technology cannot be translated simply into the issue of who has use of a computer or calculator. Issues of updated equipment, technical support, teachers' expertise and training, and curricular choices affect students' access (Becker, 2000b; Guerrero et al., 2004). National and local policies forbidding or requiring technology in mathematics assessment also have an impact on calculator availability (Braswell et al., 2001; Burrill, Allison, Breaux, Kastberg, Leatham, & Sanchez, 2002). Because restrictions on calculator use in mathematics assessment differ, for example, by race (Strutchens & Silver, 2000), technology policies for exams raise equity issues. As national examinations include more technology-related sections, it is likely that those who have had regular access to the accepted technology will again have an advantage, creating more inequities for those with limited access.

EQUITY AS EQUAL TREATMENT: PROCESS VARIABLES

Even when technology is readily available, inequities related to access and experiences with using technology can still arise. In this section, we describe research findings concerning variables in the *process* of using technology: *how often* students use technology, *which* students use it, *when* they use it, *how* they interact with it when it is available, and *what* factors (physical, social, psychological and educational) influence the use of instructional technology. Differential experiences with technology can create barriers that reinforce differences among populations. The literature shows that:

- Technology is often underused and poorly integrated into mathematics curricula.
- Type and amount of technology use varies among schools and among subjects.
- Differential experiences can prevent some groups—minority, lower SES, inner-city, rural, disabled, and female students—from benefiting from the full potential of educational technology.
- Even when calculator access is generally high, equity issues arise from the variety of functionalities for different models, the effect of course selection on the kind of technology used, and equality of access to effective instruction with technology.
- Teacher characteristics (e.g., technology access, attitudes, expertise, and training) can determine instructional use and influence the extent of inequities among students.
- Portable technologies offer more equitable use than desktop technology, and their use diminishes gender differences in particular.
- Inequities in physical access at school are exacerbated by differential home access that is influenced by social factors including family computer cultures and parental support.
- Psychological factors including attitude, motivation, and confidence level influence participation, interaction with technology at school/home, and physical control, but—in general—not mathematical achievement.

Frequency of Use

Having physical access to technology does not imply frequent or appropriate use of it in the mathematics classroom. In fact, available technology is often underused, particularly in mathematics classrooms (Huang & Waxman, 1996; Huinker, 1996; Norris, Sullivan, Poirot, & Soloway, 2003). In a 1998 survey of 4,000 U.S. teachers by subject area, mathematics ranked near the bottom (ninth out of ten subjects) for frequent instructional computer use[17] (Becker, 2000b). While most frequent computer use occurred in computer or vocational classes, only 11% of secondary mathematics teachers reported that their students used computers frequently in class. A 2001 survey also found minimal instructional use of computers: 45% of almost 4000 K-12 teachers across all subjects reported using a computer with their students less than 15 minutes per week while only 18% reported instruction with computers for more than 45 minutes per week (Norris et al., 2003). Recent figures indicate that despite massive increases in provision of technology, less than one-third of British secondary schools (31%) report making "substantial" use of it in mathematics, while the figure for primary schools is 47%; just over half of all schools make "some" use and the remainder still make little or no use of it (DfES, 2003). The United Kingdom, Iceland, and the Netherlands are nevertheless the most regular computer users in Europe, where on average 64% of 15-year-olds claim to use a computer at school once or several times a month, and virtually half of pupils aged 9-10 "never/hardly ever" use the computer at school (Eurydice, 2004). Enormous international differences again arise with Greece, Bulgaria, Lithuania, and Slovakia being the lowest users of the 19 European countries surveyed.

Determining how and when technology is actually used is difficult. Studies like that of Huang and Waxman (1996) that use classroom observations are rare, and self-reported data can produce misleading or conflicting results, such as discrepancies between rates for teacher-reported and student-reported use.[18] Nonetheless, survey data can give us a sense of trends over time or across age groups. For example, data from the teacher questionnaires on the 2000 NAEP (Braswell et al., 2001) showed that the percent of students who had computers available at all times increased by at least 20 points since 1996, yet 26% of fourth-grade students and 52% of eighth-grade students had teachers who never used computers for mathematics instruction. By contrast, daily calculator use increased significantly from 1992 to 1996 but declined in 2000, and the percent of eighth-grade students allowed unrestricted use of calculators declined significantly between 1996 and 2000, from nearly half to just one third.

Analyses of the 1996 NAEP data raise equity concerns because frequency of technology use at home and in school (as reported by teachers and students) varied substantially by ethnicity and economic standing (Hedges et al., 2003; Strutchens & Silver; 2000). Children who qualified for free lunch programs and Black, Hispanic, and American Indian children were less likely than more economically advantaged White and Asian children to have home computers, but patterns of home use differed by grade level. In Grade 4, minority and poor children were more likely than advantaged students to use a home computer every day for schoolwork; in Grades 8 and 12, that pattern reversed. Hedges and colleagues concluded that disadvantaged students experienced progressively less academic computer use at home as they aged. School use in mathematics classes also showed differentiation by SES and ethnicity. Poorer students in Grade 8 were less likely to use computers every day and more likely to never use them. Across all levels, Hispanic students were far more likely than other groups to report that they never or rarely used computers for mathematics, and the gap increased with each grade. On the other hand, Black students in Grades 4 and 8 used computers frequently (at least weekly) more often than White or Asian students, but the gap closed by Grade 12.

The NAEP data show there were differences by ethnicity and economic status for calculator use as well. Strutchens and Silver (2000) reported that White students in Grade 4 were more likely than Black or Hispanic students to have teachers who reported using calculators for mathematics instruction at least weekly. In Grade 8, however, White students were more likely than Hispanic or Black students to have their own calculators and to have teachers reporting at least weekly use of calculators and unrestricted use in class; Black and Hispanic students were more likely to use school-supplied calculators and to have teachers who never used calculators in mathematics class. White students in Grade 8 also were more likely than Black or Hispanic students to have teachers that allowed calculators on tests, but there were no differences for unrestricted use in class or on tests in Grade 4 (Strutchens & Silver, 2000).

The longitudinal NELS data (Owens & Waxman, 1998) showed similar patterns of differentiated computer use. It is difficult, however, to draw conclusions about equity from these frequency-of-use data without information on the *type* of computer activities in which students are engaged. For example, Becker (2000a) found that teachers in low-SES schools reported the highest rate of frequent computer use by students in mathematics classes (24%) and teachers in high-SES schools had the lowest rate (6%), but the way the technology was used differed between the groups. We will discuss equity implications of these use patterns and the impact they have on mathematical achievement in the following sections.

Type of Technology Use by Population

Type of calculator use in schools runs the gamut from arithmetic computation to graphical analysis and symbolic manipulation (Burrill et al., 2002; Ellington, 2003; Heid et al., 2002). Sutton's (1991) review of technology research described a shift in computer use away from drill and computer-assisted instruction (CAI) toward more programming in the early 1980s, followed by a reduction in programming (particularly with Logo[19]) and an increase in computer-based tools (e.g., spreadsheets, databases, word-processors) in the late 1980s. However, Smerdon and colleagues (2000) reported that combined data from three national surveys showed that only half of the teachers in U.S. public and private schools who had access to computers used them for in-class instruction. For public school teachers who had computers at school, 61% reported assigning students to use word processing programs or spreadsheets; the next most popular uses were Internet research (51%), drill activities[20] (50%), solving problems and analyzing data (50%). Thus calculator or computer use for drill remained a major activity in many schools (Becker, 2000a, 2000b; Braswell et al., 2001; Manoucherhri, 1999; Wenglinsky, 1998).

Differential use patterns for educational technology within and among schools create inequities so that some groups do not experience the full potential of computers and calculators in mathematics education (Croom, 1997; Swain & Pearson, 2003; Wiburg, 2003). NAEP data indicated that, although Black students in Grade 8 used computers more frequently than other groups, they were also more likely to use the computers for drill and practice (26%) than White (14%) or Hispanic (14%) students. On the other hand, White students in Grade 8 were twice as likely (14%) as Black students (7%) to have teachers who used computers for mathematical simulations, applications or problem solving (Strutchens & Silver, 2000). NAEP data for eighth-grade students showed that type of calculator used varied by course with scientific and graphing calculators more prevalent in upper level courses (Braswell et al., 2001). Because the kind of technology a student uses determines what type of use is possible and can affect achievement (see the section on Equity as Equal Educational Outcomes: Effects of Technology Use), potential inequities in outcomes can develop from course selection and technology use.

Differences by ethnicity, social class, and ability. The impact of race and ethnicity in education is often confounded by economic or social status (Ladson-Billings, 1997). Consider, for example, the equity implications of the interaction between course selection and calculator type mentioned above. Poor and minority students remain underrepresented in some higher level mathematics courses such as calculus (Byrnes, 2003; Campbell, Hombo, & Mazzeo, 2000; Ndura, Robinson, & Ochs, 2003) in which more advanced types of calculators are often used, and calculator functionality can affect assessment outcomes, so there is potential for interaction of technology use with race and socioeconomic status. Despite increases in access to technology for minority and low-income students, economically disadvantaged students experience inequities in technology use as a result of a wider problem that was first identified by Habermann (1991) as the "pedagogy of poverty" (Ladson-Billings, 1997; Page, 1998; Roy, 2000; Waxman & Padron, 1994). Students in low-SES schools or classes often experience a narrow curriculum accompanied by low expectations and little demand for high performance, as a consequence of tracking[21] (ability grouping, known as "setting" in Britain). In the United States, minority and low-SES students are disproportionately assigned to low tracks, nonacademic programs that place an emphasis on remediation and basic skills reinforcement, and to special education classes (Arnold & Lassmann, 2003; Ortiz-Franco, 1999); opportunities to learn and develop higher order thinking skills are severely reduced (Byrnes, 2003; Swain & Pearson, 2003). Overrepresentation of low-SES students in the lower tracks is also a phenomenon in England (Boaler, 2002).

Mathematics instruction in such classrooms is dominated by skill acquisition featuring repetition and following of directions; the technology use that accompanies that instruction is similar: teachers of high-achieving classes use more types of intellectually complex software for reasoning while teachers of low-achieving classes use more tutorials and games for skill practice (Becker, 2000a; Swain & Pearson, 2003). Diem and Katims (2002) evaluated a seven-year effort to infuse technology throughout the curriculum of a high school serving minority at-risk students and concluded that most students were not using computers in ways that promoted higher order or critical thinking. In sum, ethnic minority and low-income students may experience educational technology as "meaningless, boring, and controlling" (Damarin, 1998, p. 13). White and more affluent students, on the other hand, use computers for programming, problem solving, and tool application (Becker, 2000a; Ladson-Billings, 1997; Page, 1998; Sutton, 1991; Swain & Pearson, 2003).

Page (1998) concluded that computer technology has not narrowed the gap between groups characterized by race, ethnicity, SES, and ability but widened it. Others support that view (see Hativa & Shorer, 2001), but some studies conclude that technology can reduce achievement gaps (e.g., Hong et al., 2000). Page's concerns are supported by data from NAEP indicating a pattern of higher proficiency scores for students whose teachers emphasized computers for reasoning and analytic problem solving (Braswell et al., 2001) and by Wenglinsky's (1998) findings that using computers for drill and practice greatly reduces the value of the computer experience.[22] Byrnes (2003), on the other hand, found more equitable technology use occurred in advanced courses and was associated with higher achievement outcomes for minority students. His regression analysis of 1992 NAEP scores for Grade 12 found that White, Black, and Hispanic high-achieving students (above the 80th percentile) reported equally high rates of calculator use: nearly four-fifths used calculators daily regardless of ethnicity. In a survey of 438 teachers, Becker and Ravitz (1998) reported that ability levels affected amount and type of Internet use. When the *same* teacher taught classes of different abilities, higher ability classes had more Internet opportunities than average classes;

moreover, the greater the difference in abilities between the classes, the more the top class was favored with access. In sum, grouping by ability reinforces inequities in technology use.

Effects of Teacher Characteristics on Equitable Use

Having technology in a school does not guarantee that it will be used effectively; rather it is primarily the teachers who determine whether to use technology and how it will be used (Diem & Katims, 2002; Hedges et al., 2003). In this section we examine the critical role of teachers' attitudes and beliefs about technology; their confidence, knowledge, and experience with it; and associated pedagogies. Studies show that these factors can affect the extent to which computers and calculators will be integrated into mathematics classrooms and curricula and strongly influence the ways in which students will use technology in school (Bright & Love, 1994; Fleener, 1995; Goos, Galbraith, Renshaw, & Geiger, 2003).

Teacher attitudes and beliefs. A complex web of beliefs about the nature of mathematics and the goals of mathematics education can work against the full inclusion of technology (Becker, 2000a, 2000b; Fleener, 1995; Schmidt, 1999). Teachers (and parents) fear that technology can hinder development of mathematical ability and that students will use calculators in particular as a crutch, losing basic skills (Bitter & Hatfield, 1993). Bright and Love (1994), for example, found that teachers in calculator workshops held common stereotypes about calculator use; some believed that higher ability students who had already mastered concepts could benefit from using calculators in problem solving but that lower ability students should only use calculators to check answers after working problems by hand. Chan (1989), in a survey of CAI use, reported that teachers in learning disability centers said that, "students of low ability enjoyed and needed drill and practice" (p. 113), but that these teachers had mixed opinions about the value of drill for bright students.

Teacher attitudes have particular equity implications for minority and low-income students because of tracking practices. Mathematics teachers' beliefs that drill-and-practice activities are more effective for lower achieving students, that children must first master basic skills before higher order thinking (Schmidt, 1999), and that poor and minority children lack the basics can affect the impact of educational technology for marginalized groups (Sutton, 1991; Waxman & Padron, 1994) since drill programs are associated with lower NAEP scores (Braswell et al., 2001). (See the section titled Equity as Equal Educational Outcomes: Effects of Technology Use, for NAEP outcomes and a discussion of benefits of CAI.) The effects of such beliefs are found in Oakes and Franke's (1999) study of the process of "detracking" in six racially-mixed schools. Teachers who developed successful curricula to achieve detracking in mathematics used more open-ended problem solving and less paper-and-pencil manipulation. Those teachers believed that computers, calculators, and manipulatives gave students functioning at low skill levels an opportunity to engage in higher order thinking without being held back by weak manipulation skills.

Teacher experience and training. Technology training offers one explanation for why teachers might use technology in diverse ways with different groups of students (Ryan, 1991; Swain & Pearson, 2003). The strongest and most creative users of technology tend to be teachers with technology expertise, who participate in professional development, and are professionally engaged with colleagues (Becker, 2000a, 2000b). Yet, Wenglinsky (1998) found that children from suburban schools were more likely than those from urban and rural schools to have teachers with recent (last five years) technology training—thus highlighting an equity issue related to urbanicity that could also interact with race and socioeconomic status. Because teachers with training are likely to request more access to computers, training can affect students' classroom access (Becker, 2000a). Teachers' experience with technology affects their beliefs, according to Milou (1999) who found that algebra teachers who were unsure how to use graphing calculators were more likely to report thinking that students would become too dependent on the machines and fail to master algebraic manipulation. Successful integration of technology requires teachers who are knowledgeable and enthusiastic about teaching with technology. Diem and Katims (2002) cited individual teachers as the biggest hurdle in a 7-year project to bring computers to at-risk students; they identified "business-as-usual instructors" (p. 28) who resisted educational technology, fearful that it would supplant rather than supplement and enrich their teaching. Teachers who do not fully integrate computer technology may lack confidence with the technology or may not be convinced of its usefulness because of inadequate or outdated training in educational use of technology (Manoucherhri, 1999). Fortunately, such teachers are by now in the minority. For example, in Britain around 90% have been trained to use technology and the vast majority are confident in using it in subject teaching (DfES, 2003). Nevertheless, school inspections indicate that despite significant government funding for training and resources, the development of ICT use to promote learning in mathematics remains "a weak and underdeveloped aspect of provision" (Ofsted, 2004b, p.4), whereas this is not the case in science. There is a pressing need to improve training, which should be ongoing, sensitive to teachers' individual learning styles, centered on subject content, matched to teachers' needs and comfort levels (Bright & Love, 1994; Diem & Katims, 2002; Ofsted,

2004a), and prolonged over time (Ryan, 1991). A survey by Castor (1994) indicated that teachers required five to seven years of training and experience with educational technology to feel confident and comfortable teaching with technology; it may take at least that long for most teachers to move from drill-and-practice software to more creative uses.

Pedagogical training plays a role, too. Wiburg (2003) suggests that a significant barrier to meaningful integration of technology is that many teachers do not know how to accommodate groups of students engaged in different tasks. Teachers trained to use technology in mathematics instruction are more likely to stress the appropriate use of calculators as problem-solving tools (Copley, Williams, Huang, & Waxman, 1994) to emphasize estimation, and to choose analytic software over drill programs (Becker, 2000a). However, those findings raise other equity issues; male teachers often have more experience with technology and greater interest in training to use computers than female teachers do. For example, Looker and Thiessen (2003) found that 81% of teachers in charge of ICT at senior high schools in Canada were men, providing role models of technology users for boys but not for girls.

Teachers' classroom practice. Adapting classroom practice and methods of instruction to better accommodate technology use by all students can improve the teaching of mathematics for disadvantaged students (Damarin, 1998; Roy, 2000). Technology can help in a number of ways: by increasing active, student-directed, and autonomous behavior; by giving more feedback; by promoting higher order thinking; by increasing problem-solving activities; by offering diversity in instructional approaches; and by changing teacher role to facilitator instead of knowledge deliverer (Clements, 2000; Waxman & Padron, 1994). Farrell's (1996) study of classroom behavior reported such changes in teacher roles while technology was in use: mathematics teachers in Farrell's study engaged in more inquiry while technology was in use, with less lecturing and explaining and more consulting as they monitored student investigations and motivated discussion. These behaviors are associated with greater interest and overall success in mathematics (e.g., Keller, Russell, & Thompson, 1999) and are consistent with practices that create more welcoming environments for female and minority students in mathematics classes (Butler, 2000; Jacobs & Becker, 1997; Waxman & Huang, 1997). Some educators have called such practices—especially those that include collaborative learning rather than competition and teacher as participant rather than dictator—"friendly pedagogies" and believe that the approaches can lead to supportive environments that include technology without sacrificing equity (Damarin, 1998; Roy, 2000).

Interactions With Computers

Technology is far more than a physical resource, and there is an abundance of research illustrating how it is intertwined with social factors that differentially affect interactions. Understanding the social factors that affect students' experiences with computers more generally can inform our understanding and interpretation of differential interactions with technology in mathematical instruction. These factors include physical access to machines, family computer cultures (Sutherland, Facer, Furlong, & Furlong, 2000), "psychological access" (Howlett, 1998), social identities and social exclusion (Valentine et al., 2002), encouragement (or discouragement) from others (Millard, 1997a), the setting (alone or with others) for technology use (Webb, 1985), and group composition for technology activities (Kutnick, 1997). These issues have a particular relationship with gender identity and are also connected with home access to technology. Since there is little hard data concerning how students in various groups interact specifically with mathematical software and technologies, in this section we summarize relevant potential inequities affecting students' interactions with computers in general and then the available findings specific to computers in mathematics instruction. Finally we turn to interactions with handheld technology.

Impact of home computer cultures on classroom teaching. The context of home computer use frames the interactions of children with technology, and it is far from uniform (Sutherland et al., 2000). Degree of integration into family life, extent of prioritization and parental understanding of the role of information technology in supporting children's learning, availability of hardware and software, and nature of adult role modeling of computer use vary enormously, posing a subtle source of potential inequity *within* the group of students with home access. This issue of parental support is closely related to both SES and gender and means that some students come to school with much more prior experience of—and crucially, confidence in—using technology than others. This prior experience is known to shape students' attitudes and interactions with technology at school and is very likely to affect their use of technology in mathematics, as we discuss later. The consequent impact upon teachers must not be underestimated; while they have often had to deal with a range of ability, technological capability now confounds the issue of differentiation. Adapting to all students' needs simultaneously can be nearly impossible and is a potentially demotivating factor in using technology in subject teaching, particularly at the secondary level (Hennessy, Ruthven, & Brindley, 2005). In addition to classroom demands, variation in accessibility of computers among children may mean that setting homework tasks involving technology further advantages those with home computers—who use them more often and in preference to school computers. Selwyn (1998) surveyed 983 students aged 16 to 19 and concluded that boys benefit here since greater home access gives them the freedom to work more effectively (often on more sophisticated machines) and thus produce better schoolwork.

Psychological and social factors in the gender divide. Howlett (1998) described the phenomenon of "psychological access," in which individuals' attitudes and confidence levels have a significant role (beyond levels of prior technology experience) in influencing their voluntary participation in the use of information technology. Resulting female exclusion strategies may be operating such that boys exclude girls and girls exclude themselves, and psychological access remains inequitable. For example, earlier work established that boys' enthusiasm for using computers is often accompanied by physical and verbal aggression in mixed-sex groups that, in turn, adversely affects the extent of use and enjoyment of computers by girls (Culley, 1988; Underwood, 1994). More recently, Klawe, Inkpen, Phillips, Upitis, and Rubin (2002) observed that given the opportunity, boys aged 10 to 14 using mathematical games tended to claim the computers and were grudging about girls' participation. Computer users also remain stereotyped as predominantly male,[23] and that perception can limit girls' interest and participation in technology activities. Even where use within lesson time is equivalent, boys often dominate school computer clubs and free access sessions (Siann & MacLeod, 1986; Howlett Sunley, 2006[24]). According to Underwood, "Boys, girls and computers are a dangerous combination... because the boys see themselves as the rightful and superior users of the technology" (1994, p. 9). Valentine and colleagues (2002) described how teenage girls in particular actively resist opportunities to develop technology skills, some to the extent that they might be labelled technophobic. The technology was perceived as threatening their identities, social relationships, and inclusion within their peer group culture.

Siann and Macleod (1986) stressed that if students are to view technology as a useful resource, then we must take steps to avoid alienating girls any further. Parents can provide girls with access to home computers and software tools, as well as with role models and encouragement. The importance of home access and adult modeling of opportunity is corroborated by a study of 190 students aged 11 to 14 by Millard (1997b). While actual computer provision appeared to be approximately equivalent, more than twice as many boys had computers situated in their own rooms; some boys acted as computer bouncers, restricting access by their sisters (a study of home Internet access by Livingstone and Bober indicated that this gap had narrowed only slightly by 2004). Millard claims that gender differences in the ownership and control of machines can be overcome by family-shared machines and computer-literate parents. In sum, students bring with them to school firm ideas about what aspects of computer literacy are most appropriate to themselves. The prevailing female culture rather than the culture of computing per se is the focus of some attempts to improve girls' participation and the productivity of their interactions with computers (Littleton & Hoyles, 2002). It is essential to recognize that technologies can reproduce or even magnify existing social relationships and deliberate efforts need to be made to avoid creating a digital underclass of girls as computers are increasingly deployed in schools (see the section titled Recommendations and Conclusion).

Economic and ethnic differences. From a survey of over 11,000 U.S. children, Becker (2000a) determined that the greatest predictors of type of home computer use were the following (in order): a child's age, functionality of the home computer, family computer expertise (especially parents' work experiences), and SES level. Children from low-SES families were much less likely to use home computers for e-mail, word processing, or educational software—what Becker calls "common, ordinary activities" (p. 63) for middle-class children. (One exception to this finding is the NAEP data (Hedges et al., 2003) showing that minority and poor students in Grade 4 are more likely than more-advantaged students to use a home computer for schoolwork.) Similarly, the BHPS (1998) showed that computers bought by middle-class parents for working at home quickly become tools for homework; everyday use in word processing, searching files, or surfing the Web was found to give children who were privileged with home access the confidence and easy familiarity with technology that makes learning more advanced applications easy. It also develops more advanced inquiry skills (OECD, 2000). Students from low-SES families may not develop skills for self-directed learning that are critical in exploiting information technology (OECD, 2000.). Thus the SES factor confounds the interaction between home and school access.

The disproportionate representation of minority children in economically disadvantaged homes also confounds SES inequities with ethnicity. Harrell (1998) asserted that diverse attitudes of different groups toward learning and toward computers in general will affect what and how they will learn. For example, students from different ethnic or home backgrounds may have different expectations about the role of the teacher and about responsibility for learning (Murphy, 1996). Springer, Stanne, and Donovan's (1999) meta-analysis showed that positive effects for achievement in small-group settings with computers were significantly greater for groups comprising mostly or exclusively African American or Latino students than for mostly White or mixed-race groups.

Group interactions. Some studies support the claim that computers and calculators can facilitate collaborative or small-group work and promote discussion and inquiry in mathematics classes (Ellington, 2003; Farrell, 1996; Goos et al., 2003; Heid et al., 2002). On the other hand, Doerr and Zangor (2000) found that private graphing calculator use by individuals inhibited communication in small groups; they found group work on a shared computer or whole-class demonstrations prompted more mathematical discussion and interaction among students. Working alone at computers can alienate girls in particular, whose superior social skills mean that they tend to enjoy and benefit from collaborating (Hoyles, 1988; Murphy, 1996; Underwood, 1994). Boys, by contrast, may fight for control, and they view collaboration as distracting from individual achievements (Sutherland & Hoyles, 1988). Successful group work appears to allow students to transcend gender stereotypes and allay the perception, particularly by girls, that computing is an unsociable activity (Pryor, 1995). Group composition also may affect the quality of student interactions with technology; while mixed-sex grouping can undermine the confidence and perceived competence of girls (Underwood, 1994), single-sex groupings prevent male domination and may reduce girls' apparent disadvantages (e.g. Littleton et al., 1992; Culley, 1988). These results are not uniformly supported by research, however (see Hughes, Brackenridge, Bibby, & Greenhaugh, 1988, for a conflicting result); ability and personality factors may be more important (Pryor, 1995). Springer, Stanne, and Donovan (1999), in a meta-analysis of 39 research studies on small-group learning in science, mathematics, engineering, and technology courses, found no significant differences in positive effect size for achievement between predominantly female groups and mixed-gender groups. Finally, Littleton and Hoyles (2002) reported similar learning gains in mathematics for both sexes working in groups with computers; structured activities characterized by balanced co-construction proved advantageous for learning and for preventing male dominance.

Interactions With Handheld Technology

Calculators and other portable technologies may provide different use patterns from those associated with desktop models. Robertson, Calder, Fung, Jones, and O'Shea (1995) reported that girls and boys displayed the same overall pattern of use of the Pocket Book (palmtop computer) for homework, for personal use, for different applications, and in different subjects. A survey of over 500 British students in the National Council for Educational Technology (NCET) portable computers scheme yielded no significant sex differences in the use of different features of the portables (Stradling, Sims, & Jamison, 1994).

The issue of male dominance is muted by the private and accessible nature of handheld technology in mathematics instruction which builds confidence and allows more independent investigation (Bitter & Hatfield, 1993; Dunham, 2000; Ruthven, 1996). Noting that boys dominated more when access to technology was limited, researchers from one NCET school observed that male computer experts lost their status when portables were used since girls quickly matched their expertise (Stradling et al., 1994). These findings suggest at least that these new technologies offer no advantages to boys, and they may be instrumental in overcoming girls' feelings of inadequacy and "learned helplessness" (Licht & Dweck, 1984).

Portable computers may offer more opportunities than desktop machines to address the ability differences that interact with equity issues. They support differentiated teaching through offering greater challenges than usual to average and below-average students while extending demands on the most able students (Bowell, France, & Redfern, 1994; Stradling et al., 1994). Studies of students with (and without) learning disabilities tend to converge on the conclusion that using portable computers increases student control, independence, and confidence in using technology and encourages more positive attitudes toward school work (e.g., NCET, 1993; Price, 1994).

Curriculum and Equity

Besides providing disadvantaged districts with technology, there must also be an effort to incorporate technology into the curriculum. The greatest gains from technology use occur in settings in which the instructional materials and the pedagogy are designed for the technology and technology is integrated into the curriculum (Burrill et al., 2002; Clements, 2000; Ellington, 2003; Heid, 1997). When handheld technology is used over a long period of time in conjunction with curricula that take full advantage of the technology, a classroom "culture" develops that has a positive impact on achievement, conceptual development, problem solving, as well as on teacher and student roles (Dunham & Dick, 1994; Farrell, 1996; Goos et al., 2003; Lagrange, 1999).

What changes should we anticipate in mathematics curricula if all students have access to age-appropriate technology, and what will be the impact of such changes on equity? Curriculum writers may resequence the order of concepts and skill development (Heid, 1988, 1997) to open up the traditional linear mathematics curriculum and make it possible for students with weak computational skills to take more advanced courses or to have access to more challenging mathematics (Horton, Lovitt, & White, 1992; Oakes & Franke, 1999). Technology-based mathematics curricula can feature more interesting, realistic problems because computers and calculators provide a wider range of problem-solving tools (e.g., Heid et al., 2002; Ruthven, 1996). There is also evidence that meaningful and socially relevant applications and real-world contexts are particularly attractive to minority students (Roy, 2000; Ortiz-Franco, 1999) and female students (Damarin, 1998; Siann & MacLeod, 1986). Where applications of technology-based work are concrete and practically useful, girls are reported to be as eager as boys to experiment with technology (Millard, 1997b). Technology also facilitates and complements Standards-based reform curricula (Boaler, 2002). Several studies found that technology-based constructivist and reform curricula improved mathematics achievement for at-risk and disadvantaged students (Hickey et al., 2001), reducing inequities related to ethnicity, SES, and linguistic differences (Boaler, 2002).

Past studies of curriculum effects on technology equity have often looked at the impact of software images, content, and approaches (Sutton, 1991). In education, there is an overwhelming bias toward production of software that is specifically male-interest oriented (Butler, 2000; Damarin, 1998). This culture understandably produces feelings of unease for women. For example, Littleton and colleagues (1992) found that altering the characters and setting of a computer game substantially increased girls' performance and motivation. Girls' preference for a female-stereotype version was significantly related to performance, but no such relationship emerged for boys (Joiner, Messer, Littleton, & Light, 1996). However, Volman and van Eck (2001) suggest that using gender-neutral figures is not a solution because boys and girls tended to assign male identities to genderless characters. Researchers recommend selecting classroom software and technology activities carefully for the way they construct male and female images, since these shape children's attitudes and perceptions of themselves and of computers (Culley, 1988; Littleton et al., 1992). Harrell (1998) recommends screening for racial or religious as well as sexist stereotypes in the way that characters are presented. Software and technology activities also need to avoid exclusion of particular groups by building on experiences of both boys and girls, and of different ethnic and religious groups, so that all students perceive the relevance of computing to themselves.

Summary

Physical access to technology does not necessarily mean full and effective use of that technology. Inequities can result from various factors: amount of use, type of use (e.g., programming vs. drill), nature of teachers' attitudes and knowledge, nature and quality of student interactions with technology, and nature of group dynamics in the presence of technology. Despite a clear indication that frequency of use is a critical factor in achievement, many students and teachers report limited use of calculators or computers in class. Some research demonstrates information technology as intertwined with social factors; students' interactions with technology are affected by gender and a complex mix of ethnicity, social class, and ability. Class and income differences interact with parental support and home access as key factors influencing educational technology use. Male and female students exhibit different interactions with technology in terms of physical control, activity choices, and group settings; gender-role socialization—linked to technology use within home, school, and peer cultures—operates here. Girls may continue to be disadvantaged in terms of actual and "psychological" access to desktop machines. Individual access to portable computers and calculators seems to create more equitable experiences for girls and may reduce male dominance. Other studies show that inequities resulting from the "pedagogy of poverty" and tracking practices often restrict minority and disadvantaged students' technology experiences to routine drill, whereas, in more affluent schools, the emphasis is on conceptual development activities.

Teacher beliefs and classroom practices, regional and school resource levels, and course selection patterns affect the kinds of equipment, software, and curricular materials that students use. The role of the teacher in the classroom can change dramatically when technology is incorporated. The classroom is more likely to be student-centered and group-centered, which promotes discussion and inquiry and creates a positive learning environment especially for female and minority students. For this environment to exist, however, teachers must have a positive attitude toward technology and its inclusion in lessons, be trained in the latest software and hardware, and be knowledgeable about pedagogical strategies for and pedagogical consequences of including technology in lessons. In practice, transformation of teaching practices seems to have affected only a minority of mathematics teachers so far (Becker, 2000b; Ofsted, 2004a).

EQUITY AS EQUAL EDUCATIONAL OUTCOMES: EFFECTS OF TECHNOLOGY USE

We have made the case in two of the previous sections, Equal Opportunity to Learn: Access, and Equity as Equal Treatment: Process Variables, that factors such as ability, gender, race, and SES create differential opportunities for students, affecting what technology is available to them and how they use it in school and at home. We now assert that unequal technology access and use can lead to unequal educational outcomes, including differences in mathematics achievement related to:

- frequency of technology use,
- amount of home access,
- type of software used,
- differential privileging associated with different calculator models, and
- differential attitudes toward mathematics and technology.

There is, however, evidence that some traditionally disadvantaged groups accrue benefits rather than deficits when technology is used in supportive teaching and learning environments. Frequent use of computers and calculators in creative ways may "level the playing field" by reducing prior inequities for marginalized groups.

The outcome measures that we review include mathematics achievement for skills and concepts, test results as affected by technology, student attitudes toward mathematics and technology, and student behavior in the classroom.

Mathematics Achievement With Technology-Aided Instruction

There is a well-established body of research showing that computer use can have a significant positive effect on student outcomes in mathematics achievement (Chan, 1989; Christmann, Lucking, & Badgett, 1997; Heid, 1997). Using computers for programming, simulations, topic development, and nonroutine problem solving promotes higher order thinking and can lead to gains in understanding and concept development (Becker, 2000a; Clements, 2000; Hickey et al., 2001); however, the most common use of computers in mathematics instruction is for drill and practice. CAI is effective in improving mathematics basic skills when it is used to complement classroom instruction, but there is some evidence that gains are not retained over time (Chan, 1989; Ryan, 1991).

There are some methodological difficulties to consider. Studies contrasting performance of "control" or comparison groups with that of an experimental group using technology are fraught with difficulties precisely because these complex factors (particularly teacher behaviors and pedagogy) are rarely accounted for or adequately matched. Fair comparison using test scores alone is therefore almost impossible (Dunham & Dick, 1994). Research by Hennessy, Fung, and Scanlon (2001) and by others has highlighted the integral role that technology can play in shaping mathematical activity; the resulting quandary about using technology in the tests themselves (e.g., Hammond, 1994) further muddies the water.

Equity implications of achievement measures are also complex. Although CAI is often assumed to benefit low-achieving students most, Hativa and Shorer (2001) reported significant differences in arithmetic gains for CAI instruction influenced by SES, ability, and gender. They found an interaction of ability with SES, favoring high achievers in the advantaged group, and an advantage for boys over girls. Other researchers have found an interaction with location; CAI was most effective in urban settings, then suburban schools, followed by the least achievement gains for students in rural schools (Christmann et al., 1997). These findings raise serious equity issues for disadvantaged and at-risk groups who experience more CAI and drill activities than more advantaged students.

Using calculators in nonroutine ways (to solve complex problems, to explore concepts) similarly leads to greater gains in mathematics achievement in a way that routine calculations do not (Guerrero et al., 2004). Meta-analyses comparing effect sizes from studies over two decades indicated that instruction with non-graphing calculators produced significantly higher achievement scores across most grades and ability levels on paper-and-pencil tests of basic skills, problem solving and conceptual understanding (Hembree & Dessart, 1986, 1992). Research reviews by Dunham and Dick (1994), Heid (1997) and colleagues (Heid et al., 2002) and Penglase and Arnold (1996) concluded that advanced handheld technology use could result in better understanding of function and graph concepts, improved problem solving, greater calculus readiness, and higher scores on achievement tests for algebra and calculus skills. Nonetheless, the link between mathematical achievement and use of technology—particularly frequent calculator use for young children—has been a topic of debate for the public as well as for researchers. Research indicates that frequent instructional work with calculators is necessary to get the maximum benefits from the technology (Burrill et al., 2002; Ellington, 2003) and is positively correlated with achievement on national and international exams (Braswell et al., 2001; Owens & Waxman, 1998; Strutchens & Silver, 2000; Tarr, Uekawa, Mittag, & Lennex, 2000). Others note that correlations at some grade levels (most notably, Grade 4) are negative (Braswell et al., 2001; Hembree & Dessart, 1987, 1992). It is important to note that correlations between student characteristics and achievement do not imply causality and that the data (even within a single study) can be contradictory. (See Hedges et al., 2003, for a discussion of correlation and causality relative to NAEP achievement data and calculator use.)

The 2000 NAEP mathematics results as reported by Braswell and colleagues (2001) show how complex the situation can be. The teacher data[25] showed no significant relationship between calculator use and student scores in Grade 4, whereas Grade 8 students whose teachers reported daily calculator use had the highest average scores. Significant positive relationships existed between average scores and frequent calculator use, unrestricted use, and use on exams. The student-reported data yielded similar results in Grades 8 and 12: Those students reporting daily use of calculators had the highest mean scores and non-users the lowest. The student data for Grade 4, however, produced the opposite results; those who used a calculator monthly scored highest while daily users (10% of the students) had the lowest average score.

The impact of calculator use on mathematics achievement is positively affected by length of exposure (Heid et al., 2002; Lagrange, 1999) and the nature of activities; greater emphasis on computation and drill is associated with lower achievement (Braswell et al., 2001). Moreover, students who use calculators regularly in creative and nonroutine ways over an extended period have a greater advantage (Dunham & Dick, 1994; Guerrero et al., 2003; Heid et al., 2002; Farrell, 1996; Lagrange, 1999). Ellington's (2003) meta-analysis of 54 calculator studies showed problem-solving skills improved when calculators were fully integrated with mathematics instruction and testing. These results raise equity concerns for minority and disadvantaged students who have limited calculator experience because of economic issues or teacher practices and beliefs. As Roy (2000) noted, limited technology resources can harm low-SES students in two ways: Disadvantaged students are denied access to curricular innovations that would benefit their understanding and achievement; and advantaged students who do have access to technology improve even more, widening the gap in achievement.

The type of software used and the nature of technology activities similarly play a substantial role in determining the advantages of computer-based learning (Heid, 1997; Sutton, 1991; Wenglinsky, 1998) and this too has equity implications. Differences between Black and White students in higher order uses of computers have already been discussed. Ability differences favoring low-achieving students and gender differences favoring boys in the effectiveness of skills-based drill software have also been cited in the literature (Sutton, 1991). However, the picture for technology-enhanced achievement is not entirely consistent, as two key British studies illustrate. First, a landmark study of portable use carried out in Northern Ireland was the Pupils' Learning and Access to IT (PLAIT) project. In contrast with many positive research results related to use of portables, this study detected no significant improvement in student performance on general mathematics tests after a year of using laptops (Gardner, Morrison, & Jarman, 1993). More recently, the follow-up ImpaCT2 research program involving 2100 pupils in 60 schools was the first large-scale study to assess the impact of technology use on individual pupil attainment in national tests (Harrison, Comber, Fisher, Haw, Lewin, & Lunzer, 2002). It attempted to overcome the methodological problems of earlier studies by controlling for SES and establishing reliable ways of measuring technology use. Few significant relationships between relative gain scores and level of use emerged, and there were none in mathematics at any age level. There was also no interaction between initial attainment levels and high technology use in any subject, thus pupils at particular ability levels were not advantaged or disadvantaged by high technology use. Two recent reports which review and summarize the complex findings of this and other key studies of achievement emphasize that teachers and their pedagogical approaches are "the crucial component" in the use of technology within education; use of technology across the curriculum and school leadership are further contributory factors, but much more needs to be learned about which types of use are most effective (Cox, Webb, Abbott, Blakely, Beauchamp, & Rhodes, 2003; Pittard, Bannister, & Dunn, 2003). The participation and approaches of different groups of students—and their impact—warrant further investigation, too (Volman & Van Eck, 2001).

Gender differences. Gender differences in overall mathematics achievement in the United States are small and have eroded over the last decade, according to NAEP and NELS data (Tate, 1997; Braswell et al., 2001). The 1999 NAEP long-term trend assessment in mathematics found no significant difference in average scores between boys and girls at any age (Campbell et al., 2000). Explanations for gender differences are complex, but increases in advanced course enrollment for older girls and increased exposure to more sophisticated uses of technology, especially graphing calculators, associated with advanced courses may be factors in the recent improvement (Campbell et al., 2000; Tate, 1997). Dugdale and colleagues (1998) also found that girls' enrollment in a computer course interacted with home computer use to affect achievement in prealgebra. Past studies have found significant gender-related differences in achievement associated with computer use (Sutton, 1991), although the differences often revealed interactions of gender with another characteristic. For example, in a study of effects of group composition for computer-based problem solving with 60 elementary students, boys scored higher than girls, and girls in mixed-sex groups outperformed girls in single-sex groups, whereas girls-only groups had the lowest level of achievement at the end of the term (Kutnick, 1997).

Several researchers have found that, with calculators, female students perform as well or better than male students (Boers & Jones, 1993; Ellington, 2003; Forster & Mueller, 2002). For example, Bitter and Hatfield's (1992) study of middle school students' achievement on the Iowa

Test of Basic Skills (ITBS) showed that boys outperformed girls when tested without calculators, but the reverse was true when the same students used calculators on a parallel form of the ITBS; female students had higher gain-scores and a higher average than the males. Forster and Mueller (2002), reporting on six years of data from university entrance exams in Australia, found that girls closed an achievement gap on the exam, and both male and female students using graphing calculators had overall superior achievement compared to groups not using graphing calculators. There were, however, some gender effects; girls outperformed boys at the lower end of the score range while boys dominated the higher scores, and girls did better on analytic solution methods while boys gained an edge on items with diagrams. Ruthven (1990) also found interactions between gender and calculator use: among calculator users, women scored higher than men on symbolizing of graphical items, whereas the reverse was true among non-calculator users. By contrast, men in both groups—with and without calculators—scored higher than women on graphical interpretation items (where graphing calculators provided no help). Ruthven conjectured that women using calculators gained confidence in graphing, reduced their levels of anxiety, and thereby increased their achievement levels on items for which graphing calculators were useful. Boers and Jones (1993), however, attribute achievement differences to a negative effect for male students using calculators rather than a positive one for female students (graphical analysis may lead to "deskilling" in algebra by removing the need to manipulate algebraic expressions). Forster and Mueller (2002) confirmed that observation in part. In their study of calculus entrance exam scores for Australian students, they reported that girls scored better than boys on items that required analytic solutions, but when boys in their study gained a significant advantage, it was on items for which graphs and diagrams featured in the solution method.

Ethnicity and class differences. Does technology use alleviate or exacerbate inequities in achievement measures for groups characterized by race, ethnicity, SES, and language differences? Page (2002) reported that students from low-SES elementary schools who used a technology-enriched curriculum made significant gains on standardized mathematics achievement tests and improved their self-esteem. Wenglinsky (1998) noted associations between the nature of technology use among racial and socioeconomic groups and differential outcomes in mathematics; the same correlations were found in the Office of Educational Research and Improvement (OERI) (2000) survey. Other research shows more benefits than deficits associated with computer use. Schacter and Fagnano's (1999) review of learning and achievement with technology more generally found that software based on socio-cultural theories about learning benefited ethnically diverse students in collaborative settings; the researchers observed improvements for students in learning, reflection, and project quality.

Outcome effects associated with calculator use by minorities and disadvantaged students show a generally positive pattern. Bridgeman, Harvey, and Braswell (1995) reported no differences in performance scores among four racial or ethnic groups (White, African American, Asian, Hispanic) for those who reported using calculators on the SAT-M.[26] Waxman, Huang, and Padron (1994) found that after one year of instruction with calculators, Hispanic middle school students with limited English proficiency who reported using calculators "daily" or "3 to 4 times a week" scored significantly higher on a problem-solving test than students who used calculators less frequently. Siskind (1995) reported similar results in a study of the effects of scientific calculator use on mathematics achievement in a rural South Carolina school with high minority enrollment. Byrnes (2003) found that high-achieving minority students used calculators as frequently as White students and more frequently than low-achieving minority students.

Ability differences. Some studies show that technology use can reduce achievement gaps for lower ability students (Harskamp, Suhre, & van Streun, 2000; Hong et al., 2000). By contrast, Hativa & Shorer (2001) claim that computer-based drill instruction produces the greatest benefits for higher-ability and SES-advantaged students. We will discuss this issue at length in a later section.

Effects of Calculator Technology on the Assessment Process

The greatest benefits for students taught with calculators are seen when students have access to technology during the assessment process (Ellington, 2003). Choosing to use technology can give students advantages of time and accuracy (Forster & Mueller, 2002). Thus testing with calculators can have equity implications for haves and have-nots. Research confirms that the performance of students tested with calculators is correlated with prior testing experience with calculators and with the type of technology a student uses on tests (Bridgeman et al., 1995; Dunham, 2000; Heid, 1997; Morgan & Stevens, 1991). Therefore, inequities in calculator access prior to and during assessment may aggravate differences in outcomes and limit the effectiveness of technology instruction.

The 1996 NAEP surveys of teacher practices indicated some inequities in the use of calculators for testing for racial groups. Although there was no difference across White, Black and Hispanic groups in Grade 4 for the percent of students whose teachers reported calculator use on tests, by

Grade 8 White students were significantly more likely (72%) than their Black or Hispanic peers (51% and 56%, respectively) to have teachers who permitted use of calculators on tests (Strutchens & Silver, 2000). Several studies have observed that students with prior experience with using technology during instruction can use calculators more effectively on tests such as the SAT-M and they achieve higher scores (Bridgeman et al., 1995; Greenes & Rigol, 1992; Usnick, Lamphere, & Bright, 1995). Burton (1996) suggested that differences in performance related to calculator experience may have gender and racial implications for groups with limited access to technology, but that those should diminish over time. Ensuring prior test experience with calculators for women and minorities could reduce inequities. Dion and colleagues (2001) found that in-school calculator policies for calculator use on exams varied by calculator type (scientific vs. graphing) and course level. Rates at which graphing calculators were always permitted on tests increased by course difficulty: from 22% for Algebra I to 54% for Precalculus/trigonometry.

Inequalities created by the type of calculator used were evident in the 2000 NAEP results. Students who used scientific calculators in Grade 8 had higher scores than those who used simpler models. For Grades 8 and 12, graphing calculator use was more positively correlated with achievement than was scientific calculator use (Braswell et al., 2001). In addition, the capabilities of CAS calculators can have a significant impact on mathematics performance (e.g., Keller et al., 1999) and this raises serious equity issues, especially for exams. In sum, the wide range of functionalities in calculator models affects achievement outcomes and means that they can differentially privilege students (Dunham & Dick, 1994; Morgan & Stevens, 1991).

Bitter and Hatfield (1992) concluded that the greatest factor limiting full implementation of calculators is policy forbidding their use on standardized tests. Making technology available in a testing situation, however, changes the difficulty level and accessibility of some assessment items. If the questions are not adjusted to reflect the capabilities of the available technology, one runs the risk of failing to assess achievement or understanding of mathematical concepts adequately. On the other hand, when students have access to calculators or computers with different capabilities, inequities can arise because of technology-dependent items.

Dion and colleagues (2000) reported that the College Board believes national tests should reflect classroom practice and that, to align with NCTM Standards, calculator use on exams is appropriate. However, the College Board had several concerns about equitable policy; the concerns involved cost (with obvious implications for low-income students), features of different calculator models, availability of calculators in classrooms, availability of appropriate instruction on calculator use, and whether policies allowed, required, or forbade calculator use. Greenes and Rigol (1992) claimed that (as with computers) students *having* a calculator is not the biggest concern; the current equity issue is "a question of equal access to proper instruction with calculators rather than access to the devices themselves.... Students who have not been taught how and when to use a calculator face an unfair disadvantage compared to calculator-sophisticated students" (p. 187). They concluded that, as curricula and pedagogy change to accommodate greater availability and power of calculators, so too must standardized tests change in content and type of questions.

Because permitting calculators on tests affects the difficulty of items and the ability of different items to discriminate among ability levels (Bridgeman, Harvey, & Braswell, 1995; Dion et al., 2000), some authors have approached equity concerns through item design (Romberg, 1994). Kemp, Kissane, and Bradley (1996) developed an extensive "typology" identifying ten types of graphing calculator use in mathematics exams with sample questions and suggestions for examination design that could alleviate equity concerns brought about by differential access.

Student Attitudes

In the section Equity as Equal Treatment: Process Variables we examined student, teacher, and societal attitudes as factors affecting how and when technology is used. There we outlined the social and psychological issues underlying inequities related to access and experiences of using educational technology. In this section we consider student attitudes as outcomes of technology use. There is evidence that attitudes and computer achievement are linked (Liu & Johnson, 1998; Zhang & Espinoza, 1998), and that technology-based instruction is associated with reduced anxiety and better attitudes toward mathematics (Bitter & Hatfield, 1993; Ellington, 2003; Hennessy et al., 2001; Zand & Crowe, 1997) and technology (Ruthven, 1996); however, the direction of the causal relationship is not clear. In a recent study, Ma and Xu (2004) claimed that mathematics achievement has "causal predominance" (p. 286) over attitude toward mathematics. If technology use improves achievement, then attitude changes might be a secondary outcome of technology use. By contrast, the impact of technology on student attitudes toward using technology may be related to availability and time spent with the technology—factors that differ for specific populations.

As noted in the section titled Equity as Equal Treatment: Process Variables, use of technology at home and parental support are significant factors in building children's levels of competence and confidence with technology. Selwyn (1998) concluded that access to computers in the home improves students' attitudes toward technology, particularly levels of anxiety and perceived usefulness. Conversely, those children who use computers less often outside formal lesson time portray more anxiety when using them in school, thus amplifying the inequalities of home access (Facer & Furlong, 2000). Indeed, home use may have a stronger effect on students' attitudes toward technology than school use (Kirkman, 1993; Wenglinsky, 1998) and can influence affective and cognitive attitudes toward computers more than gender can (Comber et al., 1997; Levin & Gordon, 1989). (This is explored in subsequent discussion of gender differences in attitudes.) Facer and Furlong (2000) point out that the social pressure on young people—including by their teachers—to use technology confidently as members of the digital generation means that those with difficulties in accessing and using computers, or resistance to doing so, can be made to feel inadequate.

Differences in availability and frequency of technology use among groups (e.g., Becker, 2000a) can promote unequal outcomes in attitudes. While computer experience is clearly related to anxiety levels and student attitudes toward computers (e.g., Kirkman, 1993; Levin & Gordon, 1989; Loyd, Loyd, & Gressard, 1987), it is uncertain whether frequent use promotes a positive attitude, or vice versa. Robertson and others (1995) found a positive correlation at the beginning of their portable computing project between high frequency of use (by students and teachers) and low computer anxiety. Previous experience was also correlated with intention to use computers and with enjoyment, although not with confidence or with competence ratings. Accessibility of portables can help to improve motivation by overcoming the frustration of waiting for turns on desktop computers (Bowell et al., 1994). Ruthven (1996) concluded that, "ready availability is an important factor in generating the motivation to make a personal investment in learning to use a technology" (p. 437). Frequency of use was found to be associated with more positive attitudes toward the technology, but some researchers reported declines in confidence or attitudes toward calculators in short-term treatments (Merriweather & Tharp, 1999). Lagrange (1999) reported that a class with limited calculator experience felt more anxiety, had more trouble using the technology to do mathematics, and had mixed feelings toward mathematics and technology after using graphing calculators for a few weeks; however, members of another class with more experience were more comfortable and thought the calculators helped them understand the mathematics better.

Gender differences in attitudes. We saw earlier that boys enjoy greater physical and psychological access to technology. Their greater experience and confidence in turn results in their greater enthusiasm to use technology (Culley, 1988; Loyd et al., 1987; Underwood, 1994). The cycle is self-perpetuating since confident, enthusiastic users—mainly boys—tend to compete more strongly and more successfully for computer time. Colley and Comber (2003) found gender differences in attitudes have persisted despite a narrowing of gender differences in computer use in the last decade; they claimed that boys remain more self-confident about computer use, and they like computers more, but now boys sex-type computers less than girls do. Butler's (2000) review of research on computer equity also noted the role of cultural bias in computer attitudes. Society promotes technology as a male domain, and computers are often paired with mathematics, another domain perceived to be male. Butler concluded that, although boys and girls both believed computers will be important in their futures, boys were more positive, had more role models, more encouragement, and more opportunities to use computers. Negative and masculine images of "technophiles" have persisted for more than a decade (Culley, 1998; Durndell & Thomson, 1997); they particularly affect adolescent girls and clearly influence their voluntary participation in computing activities and courses (e.g., Howlett Sunley, in press). Attitudes formed at home are especially important in shaping students' attitudes toward computers, both generally and at school; in particular, parents' positive attitudes are crucial in motivating girls to use computers (Comber et al., 1997; Shashaani, 1994).

The gender differences noted above are widespread. Reinen and Plomp (1997) reported differences favoring males on the "enjoyment" scale for students at all Grade levels in 20 countries except for U.S. and Japanese elementary students and Indian secondary students. Makrakis and Sawada (1996) found that Japanese and Swedish secondary students showed significant gender differences in attitudes toward computers when the authors controlled for attitudes toward mathematics and science; boys reported more positive attitudes toward mathematics and science and gave higher ratings to computer usefulness, liking, and aptitude than girls. Australian high school students exhibited similar gender differences for computer interest and anxiety; interest was correlated with computer experience (Okebukola, 1993).

Worthington and Zhao (1999) have criticized studies of computer anxiety for being inconsistent, often poorly designed and lacking clear definitions of computer anxiety. They cite conflicting results that have consequently emerged with respect to gender differences (e.g., Rendulic & Terrell, 2000). Moreover, the research does not account for the changing nature of technology. Yet, when Todman (2000) investigated longitudinal patterns for gender differences in computer anxiety among university students, he found a significant reduction in reported computer anxiety between 1992 and 1998 for men only; women's anxiety levels remained stable despite improvements in computer technology and its pervasive presence in society, including in homes.

Differences in attitudes related to gender do seem to dissipate with technology use over time. Robertson and others (1995) found that initially girls were significantly less competent, less confident, and less positive about using technology. After eight months of Pocket Book and other computing in school, there was a striking effect: Gender differences had all disappeared, except on the confidence subscale. This resonates with the findings of Todman (2000), although in the case of the younger students here, the difference in confidence was at least reduced. These results also complement those of Sacks, Bellisimo, and Mergendoller's (1994) study of low-achieving secondary students. Findings showed no overall gender differences in computer use, but girls' attitudes toward computers improved over the four-month study while boys' attitudes did not. In sum, with experience over time, girls become more positive about using technology while their confidence in doing so increases only marginally and remains less than that of boys.

Studies show a possible interaction of age with gender with respect to attitudes; while for younger age groups, there are no gender differences endorsing sex-stereotyped views, older girls are significantly less likely to endorse sex-stereotyped views than are their male peers (Harrell, 1998). Girls—including Native American students (Grignon, 1993)—begin to lose interest in computers around Grade 7 (age 12), so middle school years are critical for intervention (Butler, 2000). Facer and others (2001) also reported a gendered approach to valuing publicly displayed computer expertise in 13- to 14-year-olds (downplayed among girls but a currency for constructing friendships between boys) while 9- to 10-year-olds emphasized computing experience as the central issue in determining enjoyment and competence; this confirms that computer expertise becomes a gendered issue as children enter adolescence. Comber and colleagues (1997), in a study examining the relationship of age and gender to computer attitudes for secondary students of ages 11 to 12 and ages 15 to 16, found similar interactions. Boys had more experience and more positive computer attitudes than girls, but younger students (both boys and girls) surpassed older students in experience with, positive attitudes toward, and enjoyment of computers. The authors suggested that either girls lose interest in computers as they grow older (consistent with studies cited above), or younger girls in the study represent a real change over time—"catching up" with boys and taking more interest in home computers as technology becomes more prevalent. A follow-up study confirmed that older girls had the least positive attitudes toward computers and were most likely to be influenced by cultural stereotypes (Colley & Comber, 2003).

In the late 1950s and early 1960s, women made up almost half of programmers and system analysts; yet, despite a booming computing industry, the percent of women among computer science entrants decreased to only 18% by 1998 (Halligan, 1999). The dropout of adolescent girls from participation in computing courses has been noted in several studies (Halligan, 1999; Looker & Thiessen, 2003; Shashaani, 1994) and it has negative implications for women in the workforce if this trend continues. To help students participate fully in the world of employment, schools and parents need to help the majority of girls who do not choose computing to abandon their stereotypic views by providing positive role models and building up their confidence with technology.

Portable technologies may reduce gender differences. Robertson and colleagues (1995) found that girls and boys displayed the same overall pattern of use of the Pocket Book for homework, for personal use, for different applications, and in different subjects. Similarly, the NCET survey found that girls were as positive as boys about the use of portables, so perhaps these personal machines are more appealing to girls than are desktop machines. The benefits of personal ownership of portable handheld computers, laptops (NCET, 1993), and calculators include improved attitudes (especially enjoyment), increased motivation and confidence, and feelings of empowerment (Bitter & Hatfield, 1993; Hennessy, 1999). Further evidence of portable computers promoting positive attitudes comes from the PLAIT project. Gardner, Morrison, Jarman, Reilly, and McNally (1994) reported that the girls in the experimental group enjoyed mathematics significantly more than their control counterparts while the boys showed an opposite trend.

Girls also have generally positive attitudes toward calculator use (e.g., Bitter & Hatfield, 1993). Work by Smart (1992) confirmed that calculators may benefit girls because they value the opportunity to use more personal forms of technology (concealing mistakes from their computer-literate male peers), and that the processes of investigation and discussion lead to unusually high levels of confidence about their work.

SES and ethnicity differences in attitude. Shashaani (1994), in a study of 1730 secondary students, reported that the strongest effect on students' attitudes toward technology came from parental encouragement, then parental sex-typed views, with SES having the weakest effect of the three in a stepwise regression model. The moderate correlations of SES with attitude were more significant for girls than boys, with girls from low-SES families less interested in computers than girls from high-SES homes. Several studies of minority, disadvantaged, or at-risk students linked improved performance in mathematics to increased confidence, motivation, and positive attitudes brought about by technology use (Diem & Katims, 2002; Page, 2002; Waxman & Huang, 1997).

Ability and attitude effects. Students with learning difficulties who used an intelligent tutoring system for solving mathematical word problems exhibited low anxiety, increased confidence in ability to solve word problems, and increased motivation to use the computer (Steele & Steele, 1999). The researchers attributed the program's success to its combination of individualization, immediate feedback, privacy, and lack of competition with verbal rehearsal, repetition, modeling, and review. These positive results contrast with findings from an investigation of ability effects on levels of adopting portable computing innovations within a class of learning-disabled students using laptops in an American secondary school (Anderson-Inman, Knox-Quinn, & Horney, 1996). The authors described skilled Power Users, who used the technology extensively, independently, and appropriately, as highly motivated and persistent in the face of obstacles. Reluctant Users, who had basic skills but depended on teacher supervision, failed to apply what they knew. Since higher levels of use were significantly related to higher intelligence and reading ability, the authors concluded that IQ may be a good predictor of (learning-disabled) students who will adopt and effectively use computer-based strategies.

Further investigation is needed to establish whether this relationship generalizes to the wider student population, but it is corroborated by Robertson and colleagues (1995) who found a correlation between nonverbal reasoning tests and attitudes toward computers. Two possible explanations were offered: (a) students with low scores may perceive computers as complex, incomprehensible machines; or (b) students with high scores may belong to a higher SES group with greater access to computers at home. In accordance with (a), which is quite plausible, the indication from the work previously reviewed that high ability students make more use of portable computers could be a reflection, not of greater previous experience, but of these students' realization that such a tool can—initially at least—provide an interesting challenge at their own level of ability and can help them achieve more.

Student Behavior

Outcomes relative to classroom behavior due to technology use—though not directly related to equity—have implications for groups that traditionally experience inequities in mathematics education. Several studies indicate that technology use can promote student behaviors that lead to better problem solving and mathematics learning. From an equity perspective, many of the same behaviors (discussion, collaboration, communication, knowledge construction based in experience) are those cited as important factors in the "friendly pedagogies" described in the section titled Equity as Equal Treatment: Process Variables. For example, Farrell

(1996) observed that when technology was in use in mathematics classrooms, students assumed a wider variety of roles; they became less passive "listeners" and became more active learners as they engaged in more investigation, conjecturing, problem solving, group work, and discussion. Smith and Shotsberger (1997) reported that both male and female students used a greater variety of problem-solving methods with calculators, blending both algebraic and graphic approaches.

The "Leveling Effect" of Technology

In the achievement section, we reported positive benefits for groups of students who traditionally do less well than the general population. In effect, technology "leveled the playing field" so that previously disadvantaged groups, who—because of different cognitive styles, learning disabilities, or special circumstances—had usually achieved less, performed as well or better than the main group on outcome measures when using computers or calculators. We have identified studies in which technology reduced differences in achievement for female students and ethnic minorities or economically disadvantaged students. If we extend our equity concerns beyond the traditional categories of gender, ethnicity, and SES, we find evidence that technology use can alleviate difficulty for non-visualizers or those with low spatial visualization (Shoaf-Grubbs, 1995; Travis & Lennon, 1997), low-ability and at-risk students (Harskamp et al., 2000; Hong et al., 2000; Page, 1998); adult students (Zand & Crowe, 1997), and students with learning disabilities (Chan, 1989; Steele & Steele, 1999; Woodward & Rieth, 1997).

We have reported that low-achieving and low-ability groups tend to be confined to drill-and-practice software (Becker, 2000a; Swain & Pearson, 2003), that nonroutine uses of computers and calculators in mathematics instruction promote conceptual development and higher achievement (Guerrero et al., 2003; Hickey et al., 2001), and that using technology primarily for drill or mathematics games is associated with lower achievement (Braswell et al., 2001). Researchers such as Heid and Blume (2008) describe how a carefully designed software environment can provide scaffolding that structures mathematical problem solving; by offloading some of the process tasks and simplifying the activity, conceptual leaps could become easier for low-ability students. Several studies within the last decade reported that lower ability students who were taught and tested with graphing calculators made greater gains in mathematics achievement than middle- or high-achieving students (Harskamp et al., 2000; Hong et al., 2000). The leveling effect, especially for low-ability students, is one of the strongest arguments for using technology to achieve equity for disadvantaged groups. Horton, Lovitt, and White (1992) have described the effect as removing the "computational onus," as seen in their study of a technology-enriched curriculum for general education students and students classified as educable mentally handicapped. Technology use also relieves inequities through a complicated mix of curricular and pedagogical outcomes. Exposure to appropriate technology can provide greater access to advanced mathematics for students in remedial courses by (a) introducing higher-level thinking skills in low-level courses, (b) allowing students to focus on concept development, and (c) permitting the use of relevant real-world examples (Oakes & Franke, 1999; Roy, 2000).

Because technology allows students to spend their time on problem solving instead of spending long periods of time in doing computations, it allows for different patterns of course taking and can play an integral role in detracking (Oakes & Franke, 1999). Course taking continues to be an important variable in observed differences in mathematical performance; gaps in performance are correlated with amount and level of mathematics taken with similar achievement gains for diverse populations taking courses at the same level. Tate (1997) found that "secondary students of every racial-ethnic and SES group benefited from additional mathematics coursework in high school" (p. 673). Naturally, course-taking patterns also influence frequency and type of technology use experienced by students.

Technology also enables changes in practice and classroom structure that create more equitable settings for learning mathematics, that is, so-called "friendly" environments (Butler, 2000; Damarin, 1998; Ladson-Billings, 1997). The relationships among appropriate pedagogy (Boaler, 2002), classroom environment, and meaningful learning are critical features determining the impact of computers in schools (Clements, 2000; Guerrero et al., 2004). Ladson-Billings (1997) notes that "culturally relevant pedagogy" designed to foster high mathematical achievement for African American students focuses on problem solving and offers instructional scaffolding, through more hands-on problem solving. Classroom organization can differentially affect outcomes too. Mathematics instruction with technology in small group or collaborative settings results in greater individual achievement than does traditional instruction (Lou, Abrami, & d'Appollonia, 2001), and this mode of working is continually observed to support more effective use of computers by girls (Littleton & Hoyles, 2002). Small groups (which can provide social and academic support for students from previously disadvantaged groups) seem to have been especially effective with low-SES and minority students (Oakes & Franke, 1999; Page, 2002; Springer et al., 1999; Waxman & Huang, 1997). Hickey, Moore, and Pellegrino's (2001) study of a technology-based mathematics and science curriculum featuring constructivist principles supports this view. Disadvantaged students in low-SES schools experienced greater gains in mathematics achievement than students in higher-SES schools; the authors concluded that disadvantaged students can benefit from challenging curricula that use technology in complex and non-routine ways.

Summary

In this section we examined equity from the perspective of research on outcomes associated with technology use: traditional mathematics achievement, student performance on technology-present assessment, student attitudes toward technology and mathematics, and student behavior. Research indicates that implementation of technology in mathematics education must provide students with continual, long-term exposure to computers and calculators. Students with long-term exposure have been able to perform more advanced computations on more realistic problems and attained mathematics achievement levels equal to or better than those exhibited by students using more traditional paper-and-pencil computations, whereas some short-term exposures have had an adverse effect on achievement. Because mathematics teachers use technology in ways that mirror their own beliefs, technology's potential for transforming instruction can be reduced by ineffective or routine use; moreover, students frequently misuse or underuse technology so that they do not receive its maximum benefits (Burrill et al., 2002). There is evidence of a positive correlation between achievement in mathematics and home access to technology, putting those who do not have adequate access to technology (usually low-SES students) at a grave disadvantage by denying them access to innovations that promote increased mathematical understanding. Technology's role in assessment is still emerging, but studies show that access to technology during assessments has an impact on the difficulty of the question or task presented, raising equity concerns about the type of calculator available on assessments, especially for high-stakes national tests. Students without access to more advanced calculators may be seriously disadvantaged, increasing the digital divide accordingly.

Research consistently demonstrates a relationship between the combination of computer experience (and competence) and attitudes toward technology (including anxiety) and a circular feedback effect of computer-related attitudes (especially enjoyment) upon performance. Home access and support are critical factors influencing attitudes. Experience with technology over time can counter negative attitudes, so that building up students' experience through offering more encouragement and opportunities for both home and school use may help. The gender effect is very pronounced with regard to attitudes toward computing technology, although not toward portable computers and calculators, which seem to suit girls very well. The culture of computer technology is more alien to girls (particularly adolescents) who show more dislike and disinclination than boys to participate in computer activities, as well as more anxiety than boys, and a greater lack of confidence in using the technology. The gender difference in attitudes is unsurprising since, as the discussion in the section titled Equity as Equal Treatment: Process Variables indicated, girls continue to lack the motivation, encouragement, and opportunities to use technology which boys enjoy.

Frequent use of computers and calculators in a technology-integrated program and access to technology for testing seems to alleviate differences in performance for some traditionally disadvantaged or low-performing groups; thus, the introduction of technology has pedagogical implications for eliminating pre-existing inequities. Reasons for improvement with technology include reduction of computational deficiencies, changes in student behavior and confidence, and incorporation of "friendly" pedagogies that promote more equitable instruction and learning. In particular, despite evidence of differences in attitudes about technology and mathematics for male and female students, gender-related gaps in mathematics achievement diminish when students use technology (especially calculators).

RECOMMENDATIONS AND CONCLUSION

We began this chapter with educational and economic reasons for the importance of teaching mathematics with technology and made a case for the necessity of equity in that endeavor. Defining equity as a fairness or justice issue, we offered three perspectives for organizing the research on equity in technology use in the sections that followed: equal access, equal treatment, and equal outcomes. In this section, we describe policies and initiatives to promote greater equity in technology use.

Achieving Equity: Policy Recommendations

Given that inequities in the use of computers and calculators exist, what strategies can bring about a more just situation in terms of access to and interactions with technology so that equitable outcomes result? Clearly one option is funding to ease the differences between haves and have-nots, but funding is by no means a panacea. Programs to provide equipment and resources to targeted groups have had some impact on outcomes but have not eliminated inequities for all. We have also seen that teachers' attitudes, practices, experience, and knowledge affect equity, so ongoing professional development is a necessary part of equity intervention, as is curricular development. Deeper societal issues must be addressed as well; to change attitudes about technology use, education efforts must include parents, the wider population, and the media as well as students. Damarin (2000) summarizes the current aims for educators in terms of "attend[ing] to principles for making digital content maximally accessible," not through emphasizing increasingly high-tech implementations but through "helping students to structure their in- and out-of school activities to make optimal use of the time and technological resources available at each location" (p. 21). Strategies for achieving this are considered the best means of addressing equity issues and increasing participation of all learners.

Equipment initiatives. Some national programs targeted to low-income, minority, and rural schools have been instrumental in reducing the "digital divide" among schools in the United States (Butler, 2000; Kleiner & Lewis, 2003). In the United States, the 1996 Telecommunications Act[27] funded high-speed connections to schools and libraries in low-income communities, and a substantial part of the $2 billion for educational technology appropriated by the No Child Left Behind Act of 2001[28] has been directed to at-risk schools. Similarly, a network of on-line learning centers in educational, business, and non-traditional settings has created 6000 public computer and Internet access points in Britain[29] and 7000 in France, where in 2000 the government promised 3 billion francs to close the digital divide. Many countries are extending access to school premises outside of school hours. The British government implemented an ambitious £10 million pilot program ("Wired Up Communities") which successfully introduced recycled or new computers and the Web into 100,000 homes within deprived communities across England (Devins, Darlow, Burden, & Petrie, 2003). Schools within those communities will also be wired up through technology such as laptops and electronic whiteboards via the e-Learning Foundation charity,[30] whose mission is to bridge the digital divide by ensuring that all children—irrespective of their background—have their own laptop computer. There is, however, some skepticism about overcoming educational, economic, and societal obstacles in implementing these expensive initiatives; critically, opportunities provided may not be seized, so inequities may persist. A notable exception is Sweden, where a progressive commitment to equity and major investment in administrative and pedagogic strategies to develop digital literacy as a basic competence have resulted in extensive and equitable availability of technology resources. (For example, every child with a severe physical disability is provided with a personal computer: OECD, 2000).

District and regional policies are critical, too, in supplying resources for technology and teacher training, but they also create inequities because local policies and priorities, and therefore levels of implementation and progress, vary enormously by area (e.g., Brush, 1999). This is particularly true in the United States where 14,000 districts combine local control with state and federal programs, resulting often in an isolation of city systems from more prosperous suburban districts (Wong, 1994). Even with state and federal aid, the gap between poor urban and rural districts and wealthy suburban districts gets wider and will continue to do so. To achieve more equitable resource allocation, Wong suggests that the current system must be restructured to provide policy coherence and program coordination through statewide coalitions that promote collective solutions to resource distribution. Page (1998) agreed that distributing resources, especially computers, equally throughout each region would be more equitable than district-by-district funding.

Lack of follow-through also hinders equity efforts (Sanders, 1989). Thus policymakers and agencies must move beyond one-time expenditures for equipment to consider ongoing technical support and professional development as integral parts of initiatives to combat inequities. National programs can set access in motion but do not solve the problem of keeping that access available and useful. Because infrastructures and equipment are quickly outmoded as technology changes,[31] schools must restructure their budgets; instead of one-time investments in equipment, they must consider ways to fund continuous upgrades in technology resources and ongoing staff development. The issue of ongoing support creates a difficult problem for poorer districts.

Teacher programs. Policies must recognize the critical role of teachers in establishing equitable technology use. Models for achieving equity must address professional development, staffing issues, and curriculum concerns, and they must build leadership to overcome the problem (Swain & Pearson, 2003). Discrepancies between public support for integrating technology into education and actual classroom practice—reflected in teachers' underuse of educational technology—result from many barriers (as discussed in the section Equity as Equal Treatment: Process Variables). Although expenditures for equipment and technical support can relieve some of the barriers, retraining through ongoing professional development is most important. Some teachers may not be convinced of the usefulness of computers because of inadequate training in educational uses of technology (Manoucherhri, 1999). Other teachers may experience a generational lag with respect to technology; older teachers who succeeded in school without technology may not see computers as essential to their jobs, but their students need to be technologically literate for future jobs and see computers as essential (Sanders, 1989). Professional development can help teachers understand the lag and overcome it. The nature of effective inservice training must be carefully considered, however. Lessons may be learned from the £230 million lottery-funded program undertaken by 79% of all British teachers between 1998-2003, whose lack of subject-specificity and daunting quantities of material rendered it "a cause of severe disappointment" to both teachers and evaluators (Ofsted, 2004a, p. 8). While most teachers are now much more competent and enthusiastic users of technology, in the vast majority of secondary mathematics departments there remains little evidence of an impact of technology on the quality of teaching or on pupil achievement, and technology use is neither consistent nor an established part of the curriculum (Ofsted, 2002). In-house training and peer support programs appear to be much more effective than external initiatives, as confirmed in a recent study of teachers' dissemination of innovative technology-integrated practice to colleagues by Hennessy and Deaney (2004). The British government's new "Hands-on Support" initiative[32] seeks to address the difficulties many teachers face in implementing new approaches within the complexities of their working environment by providing individual, face-to-face, on-site specialist support.

Inservice training should address more than content, technology skills, and pedagogy; it should raise teachers' awareness of equity issues and ensure that computing is taught in a way that enthuses and engages all students, not just boys. This involves some appreciation of the psychological issues that affect engagement with technology (Miller et al.,1999). Page (1998) suggested that teachers and administrators must be made aware of type-of-use inequities due to oversight, indifference, or unconscious stereotyping, and they should be strongly encouraged to involve minority and low-SES students in more advanced uses of computers instead of solely CAI and remedial tutorial software. Finally, teachers need to be aware of curriculum issues that promote bias and unequal use (Warren-Sams, 1997). They should also monitor use at school to ensure that more confident learners with home access do not continue to dominate available technology.[33]

Successful professional development programs take many forms. "Girls and Computers" is a project from the German Institute for Distance Learning to provide inservice training on gender awareness for teachers implementing computers in mathematics, computer studies, German, and social studies. The project used case studies and research on gender differences to make teachers aware that boys and girls are treated differently in classrooms and to reconsider their practices in light of what they learned (Niederdrenk-Felgner, 1995). The "European Computer Driving

License,"[34] originating in Finland and the world's largest computer-skills certification of its kind, with over four million participants in 137 countries, specifies what technology skills should take priority in enabling teachers to become "technologically functional" in the classroom (Fisher & Solliday-McRoy, 1999). Clouse and Alexander (1998) evaluated the Educational Improvement Act, an initiative to increase equitable access to information technology in Tennessee's 139 districts, by providing equipment, training, and classroom models for implementation of technology. They concluded that "[i]nservice training in the form of staff development courses should concentrate on the conceptual/pedagogical aspects of integrating educational technology instead of stopping at a brief hardware and software orientation" (p. 109).

Student programs. Earlier, we described general classroom practices and pedagogies that promote equity for female and minority students and features of supportive learning environments that incorporate technology (Damarin, 1998; Harrell, 1998; Ladson-Billings, 1997). Some successful intervention programs foster equitable outcomes with technology by building on the cultural experiences of minority students (e.g., Chisholm, 1995-1996; Kinard & Bitter, 1997). Harrell (1998) noted that teachers also need to give students opportunities and support in working cooperatively and equitably with fellow students whose native language, cultural or religious background, and abilities may be dissimilar to their own. Encouraging students to share their knowledge and expertise with less experienced peers additionally benefits more students when they do have computer access.

Other programs aim to alleviate gender differences (e.g., Jacobs & Becker, 1997). Butler (2000), summarizing results of several programs to improve girls' experiences with computers, concluded that adolescence (middle school age) is the best time for successful technology interventions for girls. Those interventions should include requiring students to take computer classes, monitoring computer use in labs to ensure equal access, establishing policies for software selection and use, training more women as computer teachers, and taking direct action to change perceptions about who uses computers. A related need, identified by Valentine and colleagues (2002), is addressing explicitly children's real-life concerns about social exclusion from peer group cultures (e.g., by encouraging children to use e-mail and the Internet—activities connected to their off-line lives and activities) so that information technology becomes more inclusive and less threatening. The "Playground" project reported by Littleton and Hoyles (2002) illustrated how a constructionist approach of placing children in the role of designers and builders rather than as players of games allows girls and boys to bring their own cultures to bear in devising activities, thus shaping the prevailing computer culture rather than being shaped by it.

Further strategies to ensure access to technology for both sexes include time sign-ups and girls-only free access sessions to avoid "first-come, first-served" inequities (Warren-Sams, 1997) and competition for instructors' time. The Science and Mathematics Equity (SAME) Project devised very successful girls-only Lego/LOGO programming workshops based on scaffolded instruction, learning through tinkering ("bricolage") and peer collaboration, and (as in Playground) self-determined goals (Edwards, 2002). However, segregated teaching sessions remain controversial, considered unlikely to shift attitudes, and useful only in the short term (Littleton & Hoyles, 2002). Embedding technology within the curriculum is believed to pre-empt emergence of "the male computer lab culture" and helps to develop understanding of when it is useful to use a spreadsheet or calculator, for instance (Littleton & Hoyles, 2002, p. 14).

Underwood (1998) reported that gender differences in attitudes toward computers disappear if girls perceive the relevance of using them; she also emphasizes the importance of first experiences of computers in developing girls' motivation. Stradling, Sims, and Jamison (1994) found that good induction programs were critical for school students using graphing calculators during the NCET portables scheme. Students with less developed IT skills needed more support and input from teachers to sustain initial motivation, and less able students were less resistant to the effects of computer illiteracy in teachers. Most positive impacts on student motivation and attitudes were evident where effective induction programs for staff had been established, including opportunities for them to experiment with the portables at home before the study began—and to discuss their uses with colleagues.

Home and community programs. Parents and the public need increased awareness of equity in technology use as much as students and teachers do. Fabry and Higgs (1997) recommend a needs assessment with input from teachers, staff, parents, community and business leaders, and students, and a final plan that involves collaboration with all concerned parties and includes information about equity issues. There is also an ongoing need to counter messages from print and electronic media, family, and friends (and teachers) that computers are for [White] male students (Sanders, 1989). For example, a report from the Northwest Educational Technology Consortium (NETC) listed assumptions by the general population (e.g., believing that low-SES, minority, or low-achieving students will not need computers as much as high-achieving, college-bound students) that contribute unconsciously to unequal access and patterns of inequitable use (Warren-Sams, 1997). The report also stressed the importance of increasing out-of-school access for families with limited means. Although some programs have provided home computers to disadvantaged students (e.g., DfES, 2003), that approach may not be sufficient. Because those without computers at home are least motivated and confident about using them, schemes to bring technology into disadvantaged communities may have a limited impact in the same way that a lack of access to books in homes was never completely solved by public libraries (Lord Stevenson, quoted by Johnston, 2000). Even where home access exists, technology may not be exploited for educational purposes, especially when parents are inexperienced users of technology themselves. However, schools can help parents who lack experience and confidence with educational technology by providing workshops for parents and advice in selecting software for home use.

Opportunities for access are only a starting point; they may mask physical or psychological restrictions on use (at home or at school) and may not translate into equitable use of technology in practice. Haddad, quoted in OECD (2000), asserts that

> putting a computer in every classroom, and wiring every building to the Internet does not automatically solve the problem. The most serious divide is in the *extent and quality of human knowledge and learning*. It is not digital, it is educational. (p. 52)

The conclusion is that we need to "empower people with appropriate educational, cognitive and behavioural skills and tools to access the information avenues efficiently, effectively and wisely" (p. 56) so that knowledge is acquired, internalized, applied, and continuously upgraded. This may support the notion that schooling should move away from knowledge transmission toward a culture of knowledge creation. In sum, it is naive to expect technology skills development or increased use to automatically break down traditional barriers of difference (Harrell, 1998). Downes (1998) points out that this is no excuse for failing to recognize and capitalize on the skills and understanding that children with home computers bring to school. Action to plug the gap, then, needs to purposefully avoid increasing inequity in the classroom between those students with and without home experience with technology. Specifically, teachers need to develop strategies aimed at developing the skills and understanding of students in both groups, using a wide range of resources (Downes, 1998); this is a significant challenge for teachers already having to differentiate work by subject ability.

Collaboratives. Some programs feature collaborative projects between advantaged and disadvantaged groups. The QUASAR project,[35] a partnership between university faculty and six urban middle schools with significant minority enrollments, provided professional development for mathematics faculty to develop relevant curriculum, teaching practices, and assessment consistent with their state standards (Silver & Stein, 1996). With a goal to reach all students regardless of ability, language skills, or behavioral problems, QUASAR emphasized access to computers, calculators, and manipulatives to present students with multiple representations of mathematical concepts and to allow them to solve multistep problems. It also promoted practices such as cooperative learning, discussion, problem solving, and exploration (Boaler, 2002). McKenna, McKenna, Stratton, and Vassel (1999), in a report of a partnership between U.S. and Jamaican educators to promote Internet opportunities in the developing nation, offered suggestions on how to establish partnerships, how to share technological expertise and facilitate "professional give-and-take," and how to find Internet resources that are pertinent to the needs of teachers in the developing nation.

Research Needs

We have presented evidence of inequities in technology access and use for various populations, we have shown ways in which technology use can aggravate or alleviate performance differences, and we have described some policies and programs that can reduce inequities. Now we turn to some implications for future research.

Sutton (1991) declared that equity issues are very complex and research must recognize and reflect this complexity; she recommended that research should focus more on between-school differences in access and outcomes and on computer practice among poor and minority children. Page (1998) called for more research on computer attitudes and knowledge with respect to minority students, together with better ways to communicate findings from research and effective ways to put research results into practice. Selwyn (2000), observing that recent changes in the role of information technology in education reform are influencing policymaking, has also argued that we need improved research on technology use to guide policymakers. Sutton (1991) questions the value of merely *describing* gender or ethnic differences in access to, use of, and competence with technology. She calls for more theoretically driven research (detailed descriptions of classroom interactions or quantitative multivariate research) to help us understand the *causes* of inequity. There is also a dearth of reliable information on which—and how—teachers integrate new technologies into their teaching as well as on the role of professional development in shaping practice (OECD, 2000).

To understand inequities in the emerging information age, we cannot focus on the provision of the technology alone; rather, we need to understand how and why it is understood, valued, embraced, or rejected differently by different groups (Valentine et al., 2002). Research may provide some of that understanding. Butler (2000), describing emerging themes in gender equity research, observed that newer studies have moved from the old research paradigms—focused on identifying "gaps" and stereotyping about gender and technology—to looking at girls' perspectives for their models. Researchers are asking how use of technology (including use of the Internet) common to girls differs from that more common to boys and are investigating how to create more female-friendly computer environments which take account of how girls think, solve problems, and interact within technology-rich settings (Edwards, 2002). Other studies are exploring language and stereotypes affecting perceptions about computer careers, and how dynamics of race and class influence interactions of gender with technology. These questions can be applied in research on technology inequities among students identified by other characteristics such as income, class, or ethnicity. Related equity issues concerned with home access, including the role of parental attitudes, are also becoming prevalent.

The body of research on equity issues suffers from some design and reporting flaws that should be remedied (e.g., failure to consider alternate hypotheses or to distinguish correlation from causation). As Burrill and colleagues (2002) noted in a review of 43 graphing calculator studies, equity issues were usually "included as an afterthought rather than a central issue for investigation" (p. 50), and interactions were reported but rarely explained or examined with follow-up studies. Research designs and findings reviewed in this chapter offer great variation in methodological rigor. Relying on self-reported survey data to quantify degrees of access to and use of technology in schools may be very misleading; independent validation and smaller-scale, more focused studies involving classroom observation are needed to address this. In addition, achievement-focused studies vary considerably in the degree of insight provided into *how* the technology being tested benefits members of certain groups, and results from these studies must be treated with caution. Many of the research studies reporting learning gains as a consequence of using technology rely on a highly impoverished pedagogical model, with no attempt at integration of computer-based tasks with other learning (e.g., Woodward & Rieth, 1997); others fail to measure the degree of technology-based activity undertaken by their subjects; most ignore the potentially confounding factor of learners' use of technology at home, and many inaccurately assume a direct relationship between levels of technology integration into learning tasks and performance in attainment measures (McFarlane, Harrison, Somekh, Scrimshaw, Harrison, & Lewin, 2000). These research studies rarely, if ever, offer a detailed cognitive model of likely cause-and-effect regarding performance improvements. However, there are exceptions, for example, Moseley, Higgins, Bramald, Hardman, Miller, and Mroz (1999). Correlation between technology use and attainment gains using national tests as standard measures is particularly weak; these large-scale, often content-knowledge oriented, measures cannot capture what and how students are learning with technology. By contrast, other outcome measures, which are directly or indirectly related to improved learning, have been regularly demonstrated, for example, enhancements in specific skills such as information handling, higher-level conceptualization and critical thinking, better problem solving, more complex small-group talk, improved motivation, and confidence (McFarlane et al., 2000). As PLAIT and other studies have indicated, we cannot assume that positive effects on student motivation and attitude will improve or even relate to actual performance consistently and significantly (Hennessy, 1999). There is some evidence that use of technology can improve problem solving and the other skills listed above at the expense of resulting in a negative impact on content knowledge. The ImpacT2 team asserted the following:

> Increasingly, simple causal models of the impact of ICT [*information and communications technology*] are being replaced by models which acknowledge a complex set of interactions between the learner, the task and new technology, a set of interactions which do not posit an inevitable causal linkage between ICT and attainment, but rather propose that useful learning occurs only when certain conditions are met (and that these are met comparatively rarely in most learners' school experience). (McFarlane et al., 2000, p. 18)

Until this becomes the norm, however, research studies purporting to measure attainment outcomes without considering the wider context and issues involved cannot offer us clear or compelling evidence of how technology use affects learning in mathematics and other subjects.

Conclusion

There is a danger that rapidly increasing access to information technology in homes and in schools will continue to exacerbate the basic inequities within and between most modern societies. However, careful implementation of appropriate strategies for effective and equitable use of technology could contribute significantly to alleviating previous inequities. Since the notion of the multi-faceted and shifting digital divide is far more complex than an equipment differential, any approach to narrowing the technology gap between the haves and the have-nots must be multi-pronged. Ensuring equitable distribution of school resources must be a priority; however, funding for hardware, software and networking alone does not provide the requisite curricular and teacher support that is crucial. Integrating technology into classroom practice may help to overcome the disadvantages of those without home access. Moreover, while children may have equal access to technology they will not all necessarily value it or take up the opportunities offered to them to develop digital literacy. It is not enough for governments merely to provide access within schools, rather there is also a need to explicitly address issues such as the ways in which information technology is introduced within the school context and children's real-life concerns about social exclusion. In the same vein, Furlong, Furlong, Facer, and Sutherland (2000), assert that offering students better and more open access to technology is essential as schools risk alienating young people if teachers continue to deny students time for exploration and fail to celebrate their expertise. Ongoing professional development for this new age must incorporate pedagogical issues, technology inequity awareness, the ever-emerging and important role of technology in economic development, and the importance of computers and calculators in building conceptual understanding. Teachers need help to improve their understanding of technology before they can use it effectively for mathematics instruction (Swain & Pearson, 2003).

There is a need for collaborative efforts between universities and school districts and between developed and underdeveloped nations. It is also clear that there must be a concerted effort to increase public awareness of the inequities experienced by the disadvantaged. In particular, parental opposition to the use of technology must be addressed. Just as teachers who lack computer experience do not believe in the power of technology in the classroom, parents who lack computer experience are also resistant to its incorporation. Schools can take a proactive role in increasing community awareness. District planning to establish technology policies must rely on the synergism of an informed community to ensure success.

Finally, researchers have a role to play in reducing technology inequities by helping the education community to better understand the source of inequities and to devise and affirm appropriate instructional strategies and public policies for addressing the gaps. Research on the role that technology plays in developing mathematical understanding and cognition, the relationship between access and achievement, the effect of the home technology environment, computer practice among different social and ethnic groups, and effective intervention strategies are all needed.

Waxman, Williams, and Bright's (1994) discussion of future directions for calculator research makes some pertinent observations:

> The good news is that technology seems likely to revitalize the process of curriculum more than any other change in the history of the school curriculum.... The bad news is that technology is changing so rapidly that once we think we understand important relationships between the use of technology and the quality of the teachers and teaching, the technology will have changed dramatically. (p. 135)

As technology changes and new technologies emerge, so do equity issues associated with technology use. It is up to researchers and educators to identify the changes and find solutions to guarantee a fair and just technology experience for all students.

SUMMARY POINTS

Our synthesis has revealed conclusions in the three areas of equity.

- **Equal opportunity to learn:** School and home access to technology have increased astronomically, but:
  - o Disparities in computer/Internet availability persist between richer and poorer nations and along racial, gender, geographic and socioeconomic lines, however, availability of calculators is more equitable across groups.
  - o Interactions between home and school access exacerbate the inequities.
- **Equal educational treatment:** Despite increased access, inequities can result from social, psychological, and instructional factors that affect amount, type, and quality of technology use.
  - o Students' interactions with technology are affected by gender, a complex mix of ethnicity, social class, ability, and teacher beliefs.
- **Equal educational outcomes:** Differences in technology use can lead to unequal outcomes for mathematics achievement and student attitudes.
  - o Mathematics achievement is associated with amount and type of technology use.
  - o Home access and achievement are positively correlated.
  - o Calculator functionality can affect assessment results.
  - o Frequent use of technology in cognitively challenging ways and in supportive learning environments can reduce outcome inequities for some traditionally disadvantaged groups.

o Computer experience and competence is related to attitudes toward technology creating a circular feedback effect of computer attitudes upon performance.

Educational technology has not reached its full potential for all groups, but policy and curricular changes, along with research, can promote more equitable outcomes by increasing technology opportunities for all groups. We recommend the following:

- Policies should provide for more equitable distribution of school resources, continued technical support, ongoing professional development for teachers, curricula that feature higher order technology use, and supportive environments and pedagogies that build on cultural experiences.
- Teachers and parents should monitor computer use to guarantee equal access and avoid stereotyped applications, and they should develop home-school collaborations.
- Research is needed to document technology use through direct classroom observation and to develop models that acknowledge complex interactions among technology, learners, family, peer group, teachers, and activities.

NOTES

1. Examples include the No Child Left Behind Act of 2001 in the United States and the e-Learning Foundation in Great Britain. See the Recommendations and Conclusions section for other initiatives.
2. Retrieved April 3, 2005 from http://www.algebra.org/index.html
3. We note that most data available are self-reported by institutions completing written surveys; access figures themselves are therefore unreliable to some extent, although trends in increases over time or comparisons between different groups within an institution are likely to be more accurate.
4. In Britain "special schools" serve students with special educational needs, for example, emotionally or behaviorally disturbed children or those with mental or physical disabilities.
5. For example, the 25th percentile for student-to-computer ratios in Portugal's secondary schools is 20:1 but the 75th percentile is 100:1 (OECD, 2003).
6. Becker (2001b) found that only 4% of secondary mathematics teachers in the United States used the Web for instruction.
7. Retrieved March 29, 2005 from www.ngfl.gov.uk
8. Retrieved March 29, 2005 from www.nicer.go.jp/english/

9. The study used percent of students qualifying for free or reduced-price lunch programs as a poverty indicator.

10. ICT is the British acronym for "information and communications technology."

11. Because the terminology referring to racial groups has changed over the years, we use different terms when referring to racial groups. Whenever possible, we have used the same terminology that was used in the studies that are cited.

12. On some reservations few homes have phone lines or cable access, restricting Internet availability (Wiburg, 2003).

13. "Portable" is used as a term to include laptops and palmtops.

14. In the 2000 NAEP results, 86% of Grade 8 teachers reported using calculators for instruction and 48% used computers.

15. The SAT I: Reasoning Test (SAT) measures verbal and mathematical reasoning abilities. It is typically taken by college-bound students in Grades 11 or 12. Until 2005 scores were reported for two scales, mathematics (SAT-M) and verbal (SAT-V). About 1.5 million students in the U.S. take the SAT each year.

16. This policy might be one source of a decline from 1996 to 2000 in the NAEP statistics for teachers' reported calculator use (Braswell et al., 2001).

17. The study operationally defined "frequent use" to mean a typical student in the class used a computer 20 or more times in a school year.

18. See Hedges et al. (2003) for a discussion of such discrepancies.

19. Clements (2000) argues for a continued presence of programming, especially Logo, in the mathematics curriculum.

20. These were not necessarily mathematics drills.

21. TIMSS data indicate that 75% of U.S. eighth-grade students attended schools with several mathematics tracks compared to dramatically lower rates for other countries: 10% to 20% of schools in Canada, England, and Germany had multiple tracks, and less than 1% of schools in Japan, Korea, and France did (Linn, 2000).

22. In 2000, Grade 8 students whose teachers used computers primarily for drill or math games had lower NAEP scores than those whose teachers never used computers (Braswell et al., 2001). Hedges and colleagues (2003) dispute Wenglinsky's conclusion, however, and caution against using correlational data like these to imply causality.

23. Sutton (1991) found more stereotyping by boys, but Colley and Comber (2003) reported that girls rather than boys had more biased views of computers, perhaps attributable to a reduction in boys' stereotyping.

24. Howlett Sunley (in press) reported that girls in one secondary school described how boys went so far as to forego their lunch in order to rush to claim the free-access machines.

25. NAEP survey data are not collected for Grade 12 teachers.

26. The SAT-M measures mathematical reasoning skills; it assumes a familiarity with algebra and geometry.

27. Retrieved April 2, 2005 from www.fcc.gov/telecom.html

28. Retrieved April 2, 2005 from www.ed.gov/nclb/

29. Retrieved April 2, 2005 from www.helpisathand.gov.uk
30. Retrieved April 2, 2005 from www.e-learningfoundation.com
31. Maintaining updated technology is a challenge because new software is often incompatible with old hardware.
32. Information can be found at www.dfes.gov.uk/ictinschools/ict_teaching/ (retrieved April 2, 2005).
33. In the words of one teacher interviewed by Hennessy, "if they're in control of it ... those who have, get more and those who don't have, get less."
34. Retrieved April 2, 2005 from www.ecdl.com
35. See program references at http://www.cptm.us/BI_FOCAL.html (retrieved April 2, 2005).

REFERENCES

Anderson-Inman, L., Knox-Quinn, C., & Horney, M. A. (1996). Computer-based study strategies for students with learning difficulties: Individual differences associated with adoption level. *Journal of Learning Disabilities, 29*, 461-484.

Ansell, E., & Doerr, H. M. (2000). NAEP findings regarding gender: Achievement, affect, and instructional experiences. In E. A. Silver & P. A. Kenney (Eds.), *Results from the Seventh Mathematics Assessment of the National Assessment of Educational Progress* (pp. 73-106). Reston, VA: National Council of Teachers of Mathematics.

Arnold, M., & Lassmann, M. E. (2003). Overrepresentation of minority students in special education. *Education, 124*, 230-236.

Becker, H. J. (2000a). Who's wired and who's not: Children's access to and use of computer technology. *The Future of Children: Children and Computer Technology, 10*, 44-75.

Becker, H. J. (2000b). Findings from the Teaching, Learning, and Computing survey: Is Larry Cuban right? *Education Policy Analysis Archives, 8*(51), 1-35. Retrieved October 25, 2004, from http://epaa.asu.edu/epaa/v8n51/

Becker, H. J., & Ravitz, J. L. (1998). The equity threat of promising innovations: Pioneering Internet-connected schools. *Journal of Educational Computing Research, 19*, 1-26.

Bitter, G. G., & Hatfield, M. M. (1992). Implementing calculators in middle school mathematics: Impact on teaching and learning. In J. T. Fey (Ed.), *Calculators in mathematics education: 1992 Yearbook of the National Council of Teachers of Mathematics* (pp. 200-207). Reston, VA: National Council of Teachers of Mathematics.

Bitter, G. G., & Hatfield, M. M. (1993). Integration of the Math Explorer calculator into mathematics curriculum: The Calculator Project report. *Journal of Computers in Mathematics and Science Teaching, 12*, 59-81.

Boaler, J. (2002). Learning from teaching: Exploring the relationship between reform curriculum and equity. *Journal for Research in Mathematics Education, 33*, 239-258.

Boers, M. A. M., & Jones, P. L. (1993). Exam performance and the graphics calculator in calculus. In B. Atweh, C. Kanes, M. Carss, & G. Booker (Eds.), *Proceed-

ings of the sixteenth annual conference of the Mathematics Education Research Groups of Australasia (pp. 123-128). Brisbane, Australia: Queensland University of Technology.

Bowell, B., France, S., & Redfern, S. (1994). *Portable computers in action.* Coventry, England: National Council for Educational Technology (NCET, now the British Educational Communications and Technology Agency [Becta]).

Braswell, J. S., Lutkus, A. D., Grigg, W. S., Santapau, S. S., Tay-Lim, B., & Johnson, M. (2001). *The nation's report card: Mathematics 2000* (NCES Publication 2001-517). Washington, DC: U.S. Department of Education. Retrieved February 20, 2005, from http://nces.ed.gov/pubsearch/pubsinfo.asp?pubid=2001517

Bridgeman, B., Harvey, A., & Braswell, J. (1995). Effects of calculator use on scores on a test of mathematical reasoning. *Journal of Educational Measurement, 32,* 323-340.

Bright, G. W., & Love, W. P. (1994). Introductory calculator inservice for middle school mathematics teachers. *Journal of Technology and Teacher Education 2,* 197-210.

British Education and Communications Technology Agency. (2001). *The 'digital divide': A discussion paper.* Coventry, England: Author.

British Educational Suppliers Association. (2003). *ICT in UK Schools Survey 2003.* London: Author.

Brush, T. A. (1999). Technology planning and implementation in public schools: A five-state comparison. *Computers in the Schools, 15,* 11-23.

Burrill, G., Allison, J., Breaux, G., Kastberg, S., Leatham, K., & Sanchez, W. (2002). *Handheld graphing technology in secondary mathematics: Research findings and implications for classroom practice.* Dallas, TX: Texas Instruments.

Burton, N. (1996). Have changes in the SAT affected women's mathematics performance? *Educational Measurement: Issues and Practices, 15*(4), 5-9.

Butler, D. (2000). Gender, girls, and computer technology: What's the status now? *The Clearing House, 73,* 225-229.

Byrnes, J. P. (2003). Factors predictive of mathematics achievement in White, Black, and Hispanic 12th graders. *Journal of Educational Psychology, 95,* 316-326.

Cakiroglu, E., Cagiltay, K., Cakiroglu, J. U., & Cagiltay, N. (2001, April). *Elementary and secondary teachers' perspectives about the computer use in education.* Paper presented at the annual meeting of the American Educational Research Association, Seattle, WA.

Campbell, J. R., Hombo, C. M., & Mazzeo, J. (2000). *NAEP 1999 trends in academic progress: Three decades of student performance* (NCES Publication 2000-469). Washington, DC: U.S. Department of Education.

Castor, B. (1994, February). Guest editorial. *T.H.E. Journal, 21,*10.

Chan, C. (1989). Computer use in the elementary classroom: An assessment of CAI software. *Computers & Education, 13,* 109-115.

Chisholm, I. M. (1995-1996). Computer use in a multicultural classroom. *Journal of Research on Computing in Education, 28,* 162-174.

Christmann, E. P., Lucking, R. A., & Badgett, J. L. (1997). The effectiveness of computer-assisted instruction on the academic achievement of secondary students: A meta-analytic comparison between urban, suburban, and rural educational settings. *Computers in the Schools, 13*, 31-40.

Clements, D. H. (2000). From exercises and tasks to problems and projects—Unique contributions of computers to innovative mathematics education. *The Journal of Mathematical Behavior, 19*, 9-47.

Clouse, R. W., & Alexander, E. (1998). Classrooms of the 21st century: Teacher competence, confidence, and collaboration. *Journal of Educational Technology Systems, 26*, 97-111.

Colley, A., & Comber, C. (2003). Age and gender differences in computer use and attitudes among secondary school students: What has changed? *Educational Research, 45*, 155-165.

Comber, C., Colley, A., Hargreaves, D. J., & Dorn, L. (1997). The effects of age, gender, and computer experience upon computer attitudes. *Educational Research, 39*, 123-133.

Copley, J. V., Williams, S. E., Huang, S. Y. L., & Waxman, H. C. (1994). Research on calculator use in middle school mathematics classrooms. In G. W. Bright, H. C. Waxman, & S. E. Williams (Eds.), *Impact of calculators on mathematics instruction* (pp. 67-78). Lanham, MD: University Press of America.

Council of Ministers of Education, Canada. (2000). *Education indicators in Canada: Report of the Pan-Canada Education Indicators Project 1999* (Government Report No. 81-582-XPE). Ottawa, Canada: Canada Education Statistics Council.

Cox, M., Webb, M., Abbott, C., Blakely, B., Beauchamp, T., & Rhodes, V. (2003). *ICT and pedagogy: A review of the research literature*. London, England: Department for Education and Skills & British Educational Communications Technology Agency.

Croom, L. (1997). Mathematics for all students: Access, excellence, and equity. In J. Trentacosta & M. J. Kenney (Eds.), *Multicultural and gender equity in the mathematics classroom: The gift of diversity, NCTM 1997 Yearbook* (pp. 1-9). Reston: National Council of Teachers of Mathematics.

Culley, L. (1988). Girls, boys and computers. *Educational Studies, 14*, 3-8.

Damarin, S. K. (1998). Technology and multicultural education: The question of convergence. *Theory into Practice, 37*, 11-19.

Damarin, S. K. (2000). The "digital divide" versus digital differences: Principles for equitable use of technology in education. *Educational Technology, 40*, 17-21.

DeBell, M., & Chapman, C. (2003). *Computer and internet use by children and adolescents in 2001* (NCES Publication 2004-014). Retrieved April 4, 2005 from the Department of Education Web site: http://nces.ed.gov/pubs2004/2004014.pdf

Department for Education and Skills. (2003). *Statistics of education: Survey of information and communications technology in schools*. London: Her Majesty's Stationery Office.

Devins, D., Darlow, A., Burden, T., & Petrie, A. (2003) *Connecting communities to the Internet: Evaluation of the Wired up Communities Programme (2000-2002)*. London: Department for Education and Skills.

Diem, R. A., & Katims, D. S. (2002). The introduction of computers in an at-risk learning environment: A seven-year retrospective view. *Computers in the Schools, 19*, 19-32.

Dion, G., Jackson, C. A., Klag, P. A., & Wright, C. L. (2000). The use of calculators on College Board mathematics tests: A look back and a look ahead. In G. Goodell (Ed.), *Proceedings of the eleventh International Conference on Technology in Collegiate Mathematics* (pp. 107-111). Reading, MA: Addison-Wesley Longman.

Dion, G., Harvey, A., Jackson, C. A., Klag, P. A., Liu, J., & Wright, C. L. (2001). A survey of calculator usage in high school. *School Science and Mathematics, 101*, 427-438.

Doerr, H.M., & Zangor, R. (2000). Creating meaning for and with the graphing calculator. *Educational Studies in Mathematics, 41*, 143-163.

Downes, T. (1998). Using the computer at home. In M. Monteith (Ed.), *IT for learning enhancement* (pp. 61-78). Exeter, England: Intellect.

Dugdale, S., DeKoven, E., & Ju, M. K. (1998). Computer course enrollment, home computer access, and gender: Relationships to high school students' success with computer spreadsheet use for problem solving in pre-algebra. *Journal of Educational Computing Research, 18*, 49-62.

Dunham, P. H. (2000). Hand-held calculators in mathematics education: A research perspective. In E. D. Laughbaum (Ed.), *Hand-held technology in mathematics and science education: A collection of papers* (pp. 39-47). Columbus, OH: The Ohio State University.

Dunham, P. H., & Dick, T. P. (1994). Research on graphing calculators. *Mathematics Teacher, 87*, 440-445.

Durndell, A., & Thomson, K. (1997). Gender and computing: A decade of change? *Computers & Education, 28*, 1-9.

Edwards, L. (2002). Learning by design: Environments that support girls' learning with technology. In N. Yelland, & A. Rubin (Eds.), *Ghosts in the machine: Women's voices in research with technology* (pp. 119-129). New York: Peter Lang.

Ellington, A. J. (2003). A meta-analysis of the effects of calculators on students' achievement and attitude levels in precollege mathematics classes. *Journal for Research in Mathematics Education, 34*, 433-463.

Eurydice. (2004). *Key data on information and communication technology in schools in Europe: 2004 Edition.* Retrieved March 31, 2005 from www.eurydice.org

Fabry, D. L., & Higgs, J. R. (1997). Barriers to the effective use of technology in education: Current status. *Journal of Educational Computing Research, 17*, 385-395.

Facer, K., & Furlong, R. (2000, May). *Beyond the myth of the 'cyberkid': Young people at the margins of the information revolution.* Paper presented at the Virtual Society Get Real Conference, Ashridge.

Facer, K., Furlong, J., Furlong, R., & Sutherland, R. (2003). *ScreenPlay: Children and computing in the home.* London: Routledge Falmer.

Facer, K., Sutherland, R., Furlong, R., & Furlong, J. (2001). What's the point of using computers? The development of young people's computer expertise in the home. *New Media and Society, 3*, 199-219.

Farrell, A. M. (1996). Roles and behaviors in technology-integrated precalculus classrooms. *Journal of Mathematical Behavior, 15*, 35-53.

Fennema, E. (1990). Justice, equity and math education. In E. Fennema & G. Leder (Eds.), *Mathematics and gender* (pp. 1-9). New York: Teachers College Press.

Fife-Schaw, C., Breakwell, G. M., Lee, T., & Spencer, J. (1986). Patterns of teenage computer usage. *Journal of Computer Assisted Learning, 2,* 152-161.

Fisher, M., & Solliday-McRoy, C. (1999). The European computer driving license: A model for teacher education. *Journal of Educational Technology Systems, 27,* 225-230.

Fleener, M. J. (1995). A survey of mathematics teachers' attitudes about calculators: The impact of philosophical orientation. *Journal of Computers in Mathematics and Science Teaching, 14,* 481-498.

Forster, P. A., & Mueller, U. (2002). What effect does the introduction of graphics calculators have on the performance of boys and girls in assessment in tertiary entrance calculus? *International Journal of Mathematical Education in Science and Technology, 33,* 801-818.

Furlong, J., Furlong, R., Facer, K., & Sutherland, R. (2000). The curriculum without walls. *Cambridge Journal of Education, 30,* 91-110.

Gardner, J., Morrison, H., & Jarman, R. (1993). The impact of high access to computers on learning. *Journal of Computer Assisted Learning, 9,* 2-16.

Gardner, J., Morrison, H., Jarman, R., Reilly, C., & McNally, H. (1994). Learning with portable computers. *Computers and Education, 22,* 161-171.

Goos, M., Galbraith, P., Renshaw, P., & Geiger, V. (2003). Perspectives on technology mediated learning in secondary school mathematics classrooms. *Journal of Mathematical Behavior, 22,* 73-89.

Greene, T. C. (2000, March). Disabled people represent the true digital divide. *The Register.* Retrieved February 22, 2004 from www.theregister.co.uk

Greenes, C. E., & Rigol, G. W. (1992). The use of calculators on College Board standardized tests. In J. T. Fey (Ed.), *Calculators in mathematics education: 1992 Yearbook of the National Council of Teachers of Mathematics* (pp. 186-194). Reston, VA: National Council of Teachers of Mathematics.

Grignon, J. (1993). Computer experience of Menominee Indian students: Gender differences in coursework and use of software. *Journal of American Indian Education, 32*(3), 1-15.

Guerrero, S., Walker, N., & Dugdale, S. (2004). Technology in support of middle grade mathematics: What have we learned? *Journal of Computers in Mathematics and Science Teaching, 23,* 5-20.

Haberman, M. (1991). The pedagogy of poverty versus good teaching. *Phi Delta Kappan, 73,* 290-294.

Halligan, J. (1999). *Gender issues and computing—Why girls are opting out: A literature review* (CITE Technical Report No. 250). Milton Keynes, United Kingdom: The Open University, Institute of Educational Technology.

Hammond, M. (1994). Measuring the impact of IT on learning. *Journal of Computer Assisted Learning, 10,* 251-260.

Harrell, W., Jr. (1998). Gender and equity issues affecting educational computer use. *Equity & Excellence in Education, 31*(3), 46-53.

Harris, S. (1999). Secondary school students' use of computers at home. *British Journal of Educational Technology, 30,* 331-339.

Harrison, C., Comber, C., Fisher, T., Haw, K., Lewin, C., Lunzer, E. (2002). *ImpaCT2: The impact of information and communication technologies on pupil learning and attainment. A report to the DfES (ICT in Schools Research and Evaluation*

Series No. 7). Coventry, England: British Education and Communications Technology Agency.

Harskamp, E. G., Suhre, C. J. M., & van Streun, A. (2000). The graphics calculator and students' solution strategies. *Mathematics Education Research Journal, 12,* 37-52.

Hativa, N., & Shorer, D. (2001). Socioeconomic status, aptitude, and gender differences in CAI gains of arithmetic. *Journal of Educational Research, 83,* 11-21.

Hedges, L. V., Konstantopoulos, S., & Thoreson, A. (2003). *NAEP validity studies: Computer use and its relation to academic achievement in mathematics, reading, and writing* (Working Paper No. 2003-15). Retrieved April 4, 2005 from the National Center for Education Statistics Web site: http://nces.ed.gov/pubsearch/pubsinfo.asp?pubid=200315

Heid, M. K. (1988). Resequencing skills and concepts in applied calculus using the computer as a tool. *Journal for Research in Mathematics Education, 19,* 3-25.

Heid, M. K. (1997). The technological revolution and the reform of school mathematics. *American Journal of Education, 106,* 5-61.

Heid, M. K., & Blume, G. W. (2008). Technology and the development of algebraic understanding. In M. K. Heid & G. W. Blume (Eds.), *Research on technology and the teaching and learning of mathematics: Vol. 1. Research syntheses* (pp. 55-108). Charlotte, NC: Information Age.

Heid, M. K., Blume, G. W., Hollebrands, K., & Piez, C. (2002). Computer algebra systems in mathematics instruction: Implications from research. *Mathematics Teacher, 95,* 586-591.

Hembree, R., & Dessart, D. J. (1986). Effects of hand-held calculators in precollege mathematics education: A meta-analysis. *Journal for Research in Mathematics Education, 17,* 83-99.

Hembree, R., & Dessart, D. J. (1992). Research on calculators in mathematics education. In J. T. Fey (Ed.), *Calculators in mathematics education: 1992 yearbook of the National Council of Teachers of Mathematics* (pp. 22-31). Reston, VA: National Council of Teachers of Mathematics.

Hennessy, S. (1999). The potential of portable technologies for supporting graphing investigations. *British Journal of Educational Technology, 30,* 57-60.

Hennessy, S., & Deaney, R. (2004). *Sustainability and evolution of ICT-supported classroom practice: Final Report.* Coventry, England: British Educational Communications Technology Agency.

Hennessy, S., Fung, P., & Scanlon. E. (2001). The role of the graphic calculator in mediating graphing activity. *International Journal of Mathematical Education in Science and Technology, 32,* 267-290.

Hennessy, S., Ruthven, K., & Brindley, S. (2005). Teacher perspectives on integrating ICT into subject teaching: Commitment, constraints, caution and change. *Journal of Curriculum Studies, 37,* 155-192.

Hickey, D. T., Moore, A. L., & Pellegrino, J. W. (2001). The motivational and academic consequences of elementary mathematics environments: Do constructivist innovations and reforms make a difference? *American Educational Research Journal, 38,* 611-652.

Hong, Y., Toham, M., & Kiernan, C. (2000). Supercalculators and university entrance calculus examinations. *Mathematics Education Research Journal*, *12*, 321-336.

Horton, S. V., Lovitt, T. C., & White, O. R. (1992). Teaching mathematics to adolescents classified as mentally handicapped: Using calculators to remove the computational onus. *Remedial and Special Education*, *13*(3), 36-60.

Howlett, T. A. (2006). *Gender and the "new age" of computers: Identity, attitudes and use of the internet in education* (CITE Report No. 241). Milton Keynes, United Kingdom: The Open University.

Howlett Sunley, T. (in press). *A conceptualisation of psychological access to the Internet: Adolescents, gender and attitudes*. Unpublished doctoral dissertation, The Open University, Milton Keynes.

Hoyles, C. (Ed.). (1988). *Girls and computers* (Bedford Way Paper 34). London: University of London, Institute of Education.

Huang, S. -Y. L., & Waxman, H. C. (1996). Classroom observations of middle school students' technology use in mathematics. *School Science and Mathematics*, *96*, 28-34.

Hughes, M., Brackenridge, A., Bibby, A., & Greenhaugh, P. (1988). Girls, boys and turtles: Gender effects in young students' learning with Logo. In C. Hoyles (Ed.), *Girls and computers* (Bedford Way Paper 34) (pp. 31-39). London: University of London, Institute of Education.

Huinker, D. (1996). Teaching mathematics and science in urban elementary schools. *School Science and Mathematics*, *96*, 28-43.

Institute for Social and Economic Research. (1998). *The British Household Panel Study (BHPS)*. Colchester, United Kingdom: University of Essex.

Jacobs, J., & Becker, J. R. (1997). Creating a gender-equitable multicultural classroom using feminist pedagogy. In J. Trentacosta & M. J. Kenney (Eds.), *Multicultural and gender equity in the mathematics classroom: The gift of diversity, 1997 Yearbook of the National Council of Teachers of Mathematics* (pp. 107-114). Reston, VA: National Council of Teachers of Mathematics.

Johnston, C. (2000, January 7). Beware the digital divide. *Times Educational Supplement*, p. 10.

Joiner, R., Messer, D., Littleton, K., & Light, P. (1996). Gender, computer experience and computer-based problem solving. *Computers in Education*, *26*, 179-187.

Keller, B., Russell, C., & Thompson, H. (1999). A large-scale study clarifying the roles of the TI-92 and instructional format on student success in calculus. *International Journal of Computer Algebra in Mathematics Education*, *6*, 191-207.

Kemp, M., Kissane, B., & Bradley, J. (1996). Graphics calculator use in examinations: Accident or design? *Australian Senior Mathematics Journal*, *10*, 36-50.

Kinard, B., & Bitter, G. G. (1997). Multicultural mathematics and technology: The Hispanic Math Project. *Computers in the Schools*, *13*, 77-88.

Kirkman, C. (1993). Computer experience and attitudes of 12-year-old students: Implications for the UK National Curriculum. *Journal of Computer Assisted Learning*, *9*, 51-62.

Klawwe, M. K., Inkpen, K., Phillips, E., Upitis, R., & Rubin, A. (2002). E-GEMS: A project on computer games, mathematics and gender. In N. Yelland &

A. Rubin (Eds.), *Ghosts in the machine: Women's voices in research with technology* (pp. 209-227). New York: Peter Lang.

Kleiner, A., & Lewis, L. (2003). *Internet access in U.S. public schools and classrooms: 1994-2002* (NCES Publication 2004-011). Washington, DC: U.S. Department of Education.

Kutnick, P. (1997). Computer-based problem-solving: The effects of group composition and social skills on a cognitive, joint action task. *Educational Research, 39*, 135-147.

Ladson-Billings, G. (1997). It doesn't add up: African American students' mathematics achievement. *Journal for Research in Mathematics Education, 28*, 697-708.

Lagrange, J. -B. (1999). Techniques and concepts in precalculus using CAS: A two-year classroom experiment with the TI-92. *The International Journal of Computer Algebra in Mathematics Education, 6*, 143-165.

Levin, T., & Gordon, C. (1989). Effect of gender and computing experience on attitudes toward computers. *Journal of Educational Computing Research, 5*, 69-88.

Licht, B., & Dweck, C. (1984). Sex differences in achievement orientations: Consequences for academic choices and attainments. In *The English curriculum: Gender, material for discussion* (pp. 129-136). London: Inner London Education Authority English Centre.

Littleton, K., & Hoyles, C. (2002). Gendering IT. In N. Yelland & A. Rubin (Eds.), *Ghosts in the machine: Women's voices in research with technology* (pp. 3-32). New York: Peter Lang.

Littleton, K., Light, P., Joiner, R., Messer, D., & Barnes, P. (1992). Pairing and gender effects in students' computer-based learning. *European Journal of Psychology of Education, 7*, 311-324.

Liu, L., & Johnson, D. L. (1998). A computer achievement model: Computer attitude and computer achievement. *Computers in the Schools, 14*, 33-54.

Livingstone, S., & Bober, M. (2004). *UK children go online.* Retrieved April 1, 2005, from http://www.children-go-online.net

Looker, E. D., & Thiessen, V. (2003). *The digital divide in Canadian schools: Factors affecting student access to and use of information technology* (Research Report 81-597-XIE). Ottawa, Canada: Research Data Centre, Statistics Canada.

Lou, Y., Abrami, P. C., & d'Apollonia, S. (2001). Small group and individual learning with technology: A meta-analysis. *Review of Educational Research, 71*, 449-521.

Loyd, B. H., Loyd, D. E., & Gressard, C. P. (1987). Gender and computer experience as factors in the computer attitudes of middle school students. *Journal of Early Adolescence, 7*, 13-19.

Ma, X., & Xu, J. (2004). Determining the causal ordering between attitude toward mathematics and achievement in mathematics. *American Journal of Education, 110*, 256-280.

Makrakis, V., & Sawada, T. (1996). Gender, computers, and other school subjects among Japanese and Swedish students. *Computers & Education, 26*, 225-231.

Manoucherhri, A. (1999). Computers and school mathematics reform: Implications for mathematics teacher education. *Journal of Computers in Mathematics and Science Teaching, 18*, 31-48.

Mathematical Association. (2002). *ICT and mathematics: A guide to learning and teaching mathematics [for ages] 11-19*. London: Teacher Training Agency.

McChesney, J. (1995). The difficult road ahead for the simple calculator. In J. Neyland (Ed.), *Mathematics education: A handbook for teachers,* (Vol. 2, pp. 2-12). New Zealand: Wellington College of Education.

McFarlane, A., Harrison, C., Somekh, B., Scrimshaw, P., Harrison, A., & Lewin, C. (2000). *ImpacT2 Project Preliminary Study 1: Establishing the relationship between networked technology and attainment*. Retrieved April 1, 2005, from www.becta.org.uk/research/reports/impact2

McKenna, M. C., McKenna, B. A., Stratton, B. D., & Vassel, M. (1999). Using the Internet to foster literacy growth in developing nations. *Computers in the Schools, 15*, 25-31.

Merriweather, M., & Tharp, M. L. (1999). The effect of instruction with graphing calculators on general mathematics students naturalistically solving algebraic problems. *Journal of Computers in Mathematics and Science Teaching, 18*, 7-22.

Millard, E. (1997a). *Differently literate: Boys, girls and the schooling of literacy*. London: Falmer.

Millard, E. (1997b, September). *New technologies, old inequalities: Variations found in the use of computers by pupils at home with implications for the school curriculum*. Paper presented at the annual meeting of the British Educational Research Association Conference, University of York, England.

Miller, L., Wood, T., Halligan, J., Keller, L., Hutchinson-Pyke, C., Kornbrot, D., et al. (1999). Saying 'welcome' is not enough: Women, information systems and equity in work. *Career Development International, 5*, 379-389.

Milou, E. (1999). The graphing calculator: A survey of classroom usage. *School Science and Mathematics, 99*, 133-139.

Moghaddam, F. M., & Lebedeva, N. M. (2004). Carriers, dual perceptions, and the information communication revolution. *Educational Technology Research and Development, 52*, 83-87.

Morgan, R., & Stevens, J. (1991). *Experimental study of the effects of calculator use on the advanced placement calculus exam* (Report No. ETS-RR-91-5). Princeton, NJ: Educational Testing Service. (ERIC Document Reproduction Service No. ED392816)

Moseley, D., Higgins, S., Bramald, R., Hardman, F., Miller, J., Mroz, M., et al. (1999). *Ways forward with ICT: Effective pedagogy using information and communications technology for literacy and numeracy in primary schools*. Newcastle, United Kingdom: University of Newcastle.

Moses, R. P., & Cobb, C. E. (2001). *Radical equations: Math literacy and civil rights*. Boston: Beacon Press.

Murphy, P. (1996). Defining pedagogy. In P. F. Murphy & C. V. Gipps (Eds.), *Equity in the classroom: Toward effective pedagogy for girls and boys* (pp. 9-22). Washington, DC: UNESCO.

National Council for Educational Technology. (1993). *Choosing and using portable computers*. Coventry, England: Author.

National Council of Teachers of Mathematics. (2000). *Principles and standards for school mathematics*. Reston, VA: Author.

Ndura, E., Robinson, M., & Ochs, G. (2003). Minority students in high school Advanced Placement courses: Opportunity and equity denied. *American Secondary Education, 32*(1), 21-38.

Nelson-Sofres, T. (2002*). Young people and ICT.* London: Her Majesty's Stationery Office. Retrieved March 29, 2005, from the Department for Education and Skills (DfES) Department Web site: www.becta.org.uk

Niederdrenk-Felgner, C. (1995). Girls and computers: Making teachers aware of the problems. In P. Rogers & G. Kaiser (Eds.), *Equity in mathematics education: Influences of feminism and culture* (pp. 72-76). London: Falmer Press.

Norris, C., Sullivan, T., Poirot, J., & Soloway, E. (2003). No access, no use, no impact: Snapshot surveys of educational technology in K-12. *Journal of Research on Technology in Education, 36*, 15-27.

Oakes, J., & Franke, M. (1999, April). *Detracking, mathematics, and the possibility of equitable reform.* Paper presented at the annual meeting of the American Educational Research Association, Montreal, Canada.

Office of Educational Research and Improvement. (2000). *Teacher use of computers and the Internet in public schools* (NCES Publication 2000-090). Washington, DC: U.S. Department of Education.

Office for Standards in Education. (2002). *ICT in schools: Effect of government initiatives—Secondary mathematics.* London: Author.

Office for Standards in Education. (2004a). *ICT in Schools: The impact of government initiatives five years on.* London: Author.

Office for Standards in Education. (2004b). *ICT in schools—The impact of government initiatives: Secondary mathematics.* London: Author.

Okebukola, P. (1993). The gender factor in computer anxiety and interest among some Australian high school children. *Educational Research, 35*, 81-188.

Oldknow, A. (1997, October). *International study on graphing calculators in secondary education.* Paper presented at the International Federation of Information Processors Conference, Working Group 3.1, Grenoble, France.

Oldknow, A. (2000). [T^3 Europe survey of hand-held technology]. Unpublished raw data.

Organisation for Economic Cooperation and Development. (2000). *Schooling for tomorrow: Learning to bridge the digital divide.* Paris: Author.

Organisation for Economic Cooperation and Development. (2003). *Education at a glance—OECD Indicators.* Paris: Author.

Ortiz-Franco, L. (1999). Latinos, income, and mathematics achievement: Beating the odds. In L. Ortiz-Franco, N. Z. Hernandez, & Y. De La Cruz (Eds.), *Changing the faces of mathematics: Perspectives on Latinos* (pp. 13-20). Reston, VA: National Council of Teachers of Mathematics.

Owens, E. W., & Waxman, H. C. (1998). Sex- and ethnic-related differences among high school students' technology use in science and mathematics. *International Journal of Instructional Media, 25*, 43-54.

Page, M. S. (1998). Conflicts of inequity: Educational technology in America. *Computers in the Schools, 14*, 134-153.

Page, M. S. (2002). Technology-enriched classrooms: Effects on students of low socioeconomic status. *Journal of Research on Technology in Education, 34*, 389-409.

Pea, R. D. (1987). Cognitive technologies for mathematics education. In A. H. Schoenfeld (Ed.), *Cognitive science and mathematics education* (pp. 89-122). Hillsdale, NJ: Erlbaum.

Penglase, M., & Arnold, S. (1996). The graphics calculator in mathematics education: A critical review of recent research. *Mathematics Education Research Journal, 8,* 58-90.

Pittard, V., Bannister, P., & Dunn, J. (2003). *The big* London: Department for Education and Skills.

Price, G. (1994). *The use of portable computers with dyslexic students* (Occasional Papers 26). Southampton, United Kingdom: Southampton University, Centre for Language Education.

Pryor, J. (1995). Gender issues in group work: A case study involving work with computers. *British Educational Research Journal, 21,* 277-288.

Ralston, A. (1999). Let's abolish pencil-and-paper arithmetic. *Journal of Computers in Mathematics and Science Teaching, 18,* 173-194.

Reinen, I. J., & Plomp, T. (1997). Information technology and gender equality: A contradiction in terminis? *Computers & Education, 28,* 65-78.

Rendulic, P., & Terrell, S. (2000). Anxiety toward statistics and the use of computers: A study of graduate level education majors. *Journal of Computing in Higher Education, 11*(2), 104-120.

Robertson, S. I., Calder, J., Fung, P., Jones, A., & O'Shea, T. (1995). *The use of Pocket Book computers in education: Report on the Pocket Book Project* (CITE Report No 217). Milton Keynes, United Kingdom: Open University.

Romberg, T. A. (1994). Assessment and technology. In G. W. Bright, H. C. Waxman, & S. E. Williams (Eds.), *Impact of calculators on mathematics instruction* (pp. 7-25). Lanham, MD: University Press of America.

Roy, F. M. (2000). Technology and equity: A consistent vision for school mathematics? In W. G. Secada (Ed.), *Changing the faces of mathematics: Perspectives on multiculturalism and gender equity* (pp. 37-45). Reston, VA: National Council of Teachers of Mathematics.

Ruthven, K. (1990). The influence of graphic calculator use on translation from graphic to symbolic forms. *Educational Studies in Mathematics, 21,* 431-450.

Ruthven, K. (1996). Calculators in the mathematics curriculum: The scope of personal computational technology. In A. Bishop, K. Clements, C. Keitel, J. Kilpatrick, & C. Laborde (Eds.), *International handbook of mathematics education* (pp. 435-468). Dordrecht, The Netherlands: Kluwer Academic.

Ruthven, K., & Hennessy, S. (2002). A practitioner model of the use of computer-based tools and resources to support mathematics teaching and learning. *Educational Studies in Mathematics, 49,* 47-88.

Ryan, A. W. (1991). Meta-analysis of achievement effects of microcomputer applications in elementary schools. *Educational Administration Quarterly, 27,* 161-184.

Sacks, C. H., Bellisimo, Y., & Mergendoller, J. (1994). Attitudes toward computers and computer use: The issue of gender. *Journal of Research on Computing in Education, 26,* 256-269.

Sanders, J. (1989). Equity and technology in education: An applied researcher talks to the theoreticians. In W. G. Secada (Ed.), *Equity in education* (pp. 158-179). London: Falmer Press.

Scales, J. (1999, January 22). Home PCs delete hope for the poorest. *Times Educational Supplement*, p. 30.

Schacter, J., & Fagnano, C. (1999). Does computer technology improve student learning and achievement? How, when, and under what conditions? *Journal of Educational Computing Research, 20*, 329-343.

Schmidt, M. E. (1999). Middle grades teachers' beliefs about calculator use: Pre-project and two years later. *Focus on Learning Problems in Mathematics, 21*, 18-34.

Selwyn, N. (1998). The effect of using a home computer on students' educational use of IT. *Computers & Education, 31*, 211-227.

Selwyn, N. (2000). Researching computers and education—glimpses of the wider picture. *Computers & Education, 34*, 93-101.

Shashaani, L. (1994). Socioeconomic status, parents' sex-role stereotypes, and the gender gap in computing. *Journal of Research on Computing in Education, 26*, 433-451.

Shoaf-Grubbs, M. M. (1995). Research results on the effect of the graphic calculator on female students' cognitive levels and visual thinking. In L. Burton & B. Jaworski (Eds.), *Technology in mathematics teaching: A bridge between teaching and learning* (pp. 213-230). Lund, Sweden: Chartwell-Bratt.

Siann, G., & Macleod, H. (1986). Computers and students of primary school age: Issues and questions. *British Journal of Educational Technology, 17*, 133-144.

Silver, E. A., & Stein, M. K. (1996). The QUASAR Project: The "revolution of the possible" in mathematics instructional reform in urban middle schools. *Urban Education, 30*, 476-521.

Siskind, T. G. (1995). The effect of calculator use on mathematics achievement for rural high school students. *Rural Educator, 16*(2), 1-4.

Smart, T. (1992). A graphic boost for girls. *Micromath, 8*(3), 41-42.

Smerdon, B., Cronen, S., Lanahan, L., Anderson, J., Iannotti, N., & Angeles, J. (2000). *Teachers' tools for the 21st century: A report on teachers' use of technology* (NCES Publication 2000-102). Retrieved April 4, 2005, from the U.S. Department of Education Web site: nces.ed.gov/pubsearch/pubsinfo.asp?pubid =2000102

Smith, K. B., & Shotsberger, P. G. (1997). Assessing the use of graphing calculators in college algebra: Reflecting on dimensions of teaching and learning. *School Science and Mathematics, 97*, 368-376.

Sparrow, L., & Swan, P. (2000, August). *Calculators and number sense: The way to go?* Paper presented at the Ninth International Congress on Mathematical Education, Working Group 11 (Technology), Makuhari, Japan.

Springer, L., Stanne, M. E., & Donovan, S. S. (1999). Effects of small-group learning in undergraduates in science, mathematics, engineering, and technology: A meta-analysis. *Review of Educational Research, 69*, 21-51.

Steele, M. M., & Steele, J. W. (1999). DISCOVER: An intelligent tutoring system for teaching students with learning difficulties to solve word problems. *Journal of Computers in Mathematics and Science Teaching, 18*, 351-359.

Stradling, R., Sims, D., & Jamison, J. (1994). *Portable computers pilot evaluation report*. Coventry, United Kingdom: National Council for Educational Technology.

Strutchens, M. E., & Silver, E. A. (2000). NAEP findings regarding race/ethnicity: Students' performance, school experiences, and attitudes and beliefs. In E. A. Silver & P. A. Kenney (Eds.), *Results from the seventh mathematics assessment of the National Assessment of Educational Progress* (pp. 45-72). Reston, VA: National Council of Teachers of Mathematics.

Sutherland, R., Facer, K., Furlong, R., & Furlong, J. (2000). A new environment of re-education? The computer in the home. *Computers & Education, 34*, 195-212.

Sutherland, R., & Hoyles, C. (1988). Gender perspectives on Logo programming in the mathematics curriculum. In C. Hoyles (Ed.), *Girls and computers* (Bedford Way Paper 34) (pp. 40-63). London: University of London, Institute of Education.

Sutton, R. E. (1991). Equity and computers in the schools: A decade of research. *Review of Educational Research, 61*, 475-503.

Swain, C., & Pearson, T. (2003). Educators and technology standards: Influencing the digital divide. *Journal of Research on Technology in Education, 34*, 326-335.

Tarr, J. E., Uekawa, K., Mittag, K. C., & Lennex, L. (2000). A comparison of calculator use in eighth-grade mathematics classrooms in the United States, Japan, and Portugal: Results for the Third International Mathematics and Science Study. *School Science and Mathematics, 100*, 139-150.

Tate, W. F. (1997). Race-ethnicity, SES, gender, and language proficiency trends in mathematics achievement: An update. *Journal for Research in Mathematics Education, 28*, 652-679.

Todman, J. (2000). Gender differences in computer anxiety among university entrants since 1992. *Computers & Education, 34*, 27-35.

Travis, B., & Lennon, E. (1997). Spatial skills and computer-enhanced instruction in calculus. *Journal of Computers in Mathematics and Science Teaching, 16*, 467-475.

Underwood, G. (1994). Collaboration and problem solving: Gender differences and the quality of discussion. In J. Underwood (Ed.), *Computer based learning: Potential into practice* (pp. 9-19). London: David Fulton.

Underwood, J. D. M. (1998). Introduction: Where are we now and where are we going? In J. Underwood (Ed.), *Computer based learning: Potential into practice* (pp. 1-8). London: David Fulton.

Usnick, V. E., Lamphere, P., & Bright, G. W. (1995). Calculators in elementary school mathematics instruction. *School Science and Mathematics, 95*, 11-19.

Valentine, G., Holloway, S., & Bingham, N. (2002). The digital generation?: Children, ICT and the everyday nature of social exclusion. *Antipode, 34*, 296-315.

Volman, M. & van Eck, E. (2001). Gender equity and information technology in education. *Review of Educational Research, 71*, 613-634.

Warren-Sams, B. (1997). *Closing the equity gap in technology access and use: A practical guide for K-12 educators*. Portland, OR: Northwest Regional Educational Laboratory.

Waxman, H. C., & Huang, S. L. (1997). Classroom instruction and learning environment differences between effective and ineffective urban elementary schools for African American students. *Urban Education, 32*, 7-44.

Waxman, H. C., Huang, S. L., & Padron, Y. N. (1994, July). The influence of calculator use on limited-English proficient Hispanic students' mathematics problem-solving achievement. In G. H. Marks (Ed.), *Mathematics/science education and technology, 1994: Proceedings of the international symposium on mathematics/science education and technology* (pp. 239-240). San Diego, CA. Association for the Advancement of Computing in Education. (ERIC Document Reproduction Service No. ED375801)

Waxman, H. C., & Padron, Y. N. (1994, July). Eliminating the pedagogy of poverty in mathematics and science classrooms through technology use. In G. H. Marks (Ed.), *Mathematics/science education and technology, 1994: Proceedings of the international symposium on mathematics/science education and technology* (pp. 194-198). San Diego, CA: Association for the Advancement of Computing in Education. (ERIC Document Reproduction Service No. ED375801)

Waxman, H. C., Williams, S. E., & Bright, G. W. (1994). Future directions for the study of calculators in mathematics classrooms. In G. W. Bright, H. C. Waxman, & S. E. Williams (Eds.), *Impact of calculators on mathematics instruction* (pp. 131-138). Lanham, MD: University Press of America.

Webb, N. M. (1985). The role of gender in computer programming learning processes. *Journal of Educational Computing Research, 1*, 441-458.

Wenglinsky, H. (1998). *Does it compute? The relationship between educational technology and student achievement in mathematics*. Princeton, NJ: Educational Testing Service Policy Information Center.

Wiburg, K. M. (2003). Technology and the new meaning of educational equity. *Computers in the Schools, 20*, 113-128.

Wong, K. K. (1994). Governance structure, resource allocation, and equity policy. *Review of Research in Education, 20*, 257-289.

Woodward, J., & Rieth, H. (1997). A historical review of technology research in special education. *Review of Educational Research, 67*, 503-536.

Worthington, V. L., & Zhao, Y. (1999). Existential computer anxiety and changes in computer technology: What past research on computer anxiety has missed. *Journal of Educational Computing Research, 20*, 299-315.

Zand, H., & Crowe, W. D. (1997). Novices entering mathematics 2: The graphic calculator and distance learners. *Computers in Education, 29*, 25-32.

Zhang, Y., & Espinoza, S. (1998). Relationships among computer self-efficacy, attitudes toward computers, and desirability of learning computing skills. *Journal of Research on Computing in Education, 30*, 420-431.

CHAPTER 9

TECHNOLOGY AND THE TEACHING AND LEARNING OF MATHEMATICS

Cross-Content Implications

M. Kathleen Heid and Glendon W. Blume

Although individual research studies on technology in the teaching and learning of mathematics tend to focus on learning in a single area of mathematics, a look across this research generates themes that characterize teaching and learning in mathematics as opposed to teaching and learning in a particular content area. These themes cluster in four categories: (a) the interaction of teachers and students with technology, (b) changes in curriculum in technological settings, (c) mathematical activity in technological settings, and (d) consequent changes in mathematical thinking as a result of that activity.

CROSS-CONTENT IMPLICATIONS

The clearest message from research is that technology alone is not what makes the difference in mathematics teaching and learning. As has been

Research on Technology and the Teaching and Learning of Mathematics:
Vol. 1. Research Syntheses, pp. 419–431
Copyright © 2008 by Information Age Publishing
All rights of reproduction in any form reserved.

reflected in a number of chapters throughout this volume, it is the confluence of technological environment, teachers, learners, curriculum, and mathematical activity that sets the stage for changes in the teaching and learning of mathematics in the context of technology. With examples drawn from the chapters on research on technology in rational number, algebra, geometry, mathematical modeling, and calculus, this chapter will review ways in which the interaction of technological environment, teachers, learners, curriculum, and mathematical activity affects learning.

The Interaction of Teachers With Technology

The ways in which technology is used in the mathematics classroom is determined by choices the teacher makes in engaging students in technology-supported mathematics. Choices teachers make include emphasizing procedures or concepts (Zbiek & Hollebrands, 2008) and electing to use one representation over another. This privileging of representation type affects what representations students choose to use, and privileging of subject matter affects what students learn (Zbiek & Hollebrands). Although a variety of external factors (e.g., time, support staff, support from fellow teachers, external assessments, logistics) impact the ways in which teachers use technology in their teaching (Zbiek & Hollebrands), the choices teachers make are also related to internal factors such as how the teacher and the students relate to the technology. Those relationships change as a function of the technology-related experiences of teachers and students. The development of this relationship has been called instrumental genesis (Guin & Trouche, 1999; Hollebrands, Laborde, & Sträßer, 2008). In the process of their individual instrumental geneses, the teacher and students shape the tool for their own purposes and the tool shapes the way the teacher and students think about the mathematics. Moreover, the development of instrumentation processes with one tool affects the instrumentation processes developed with subsequent tools (Hollebrands et al., 2008).

Zbiek and Hollebrands (2008) propose a four-stage process in which teachers experience growth in their use of technology in the mathematics classroom. Teachers first learn technology, then learn to do mathematics with technology, then use technology with students, and finally attend to student learning in the context of technology. These experiences mold teachers' understandings, conceptions, and perceptions—the key to what happens as technology enters their classrooms. As they use technology in their teaching, teachers may improve their own knowledge of mathematics (Hollebrands et al., 2008) and as they use technology with their students, their conception of school mathematics changes. A teacher's conception of school mathematics greatly influences his or her use of technology in teaching mathematics, in particular, it influences the mathematics that students encounter in their technology experiences and what students do with technology (Zbiek & Hollebrands, 2008). Rule-based teachers in studies surveyed by Zbiek and Hollebrands were likely to control the use of technology as a tool and relegate tool use solely to remediation and drill-and-practice. Teachers rely on their own experiences with technology to determine what students will need in their experiences with technology, with, for example, teachers who needed to know the technology step-by-step concluded that their students also needed this step-by-step approach (Zbiek & Hollebrands, 2008). Moreover, teachers' perceptions of student ability influence the ways they engage students in technology, with teachers unwilling to ask students to do things that they perceive to be beyond the students' abilities (Tall, Smith, & Piez, 2008; Zbiek & Hollebrands, 2008).

In their synthesis of research, Zbiek and Hollebrands (2008) highlight several studies that documented the roles and responsibilities that underwent significant changes as technology entered the mathematics classroom. The teachers and students shared roles as fellow investigators, technical assistants, and resources; teachers faced new challenges in allocation of time, management of technology, and construction of new ways to assess student understanding; and students were challenged to determine the level of their understanding in these new environments (Heid, Sheets, & Matras, 1990). Ironically, teaching mathematics using technology allowed teachers to engage students in exploratory tasks that made the use of technology exciting for them and their students, but these same activities generated significant management problems for teachers (Zbiek & Hollebrands). Thus, the promise of technology is accompanied by a corresponding challenge of implementation.

A major responsibility for teachers, regardless of the role of technology, is the orchestration of mathematical activities in the classroom. These activities vary in myriad ways, including the amount of assistance provided by the teacher and the amount of control allowed to the student. Whatever the balance of teacher and student control, interaction with a teacher is necessary for meaningful learning to take place (Olive & Lobato, 2008). In their synthesis of research on technology in elementary and middle grades geometry, Clements, Sarama, Yelland, and Glass (2008) identify as important features in teaching mathematics in technological environments the amount of control given to students, the amount of scaffolding provided by the teacher, and the amount of student reflection built into the mathematical activities. They point out that carefully planned sequences of activities with teacher scaffolding are important to the development of specific understandings. For example, Clements and colleagues (2008) point out the critical scaffolding role that teachers play by directing students' attention to salient aspects of the activity, and by designing activities that foster the development of metacognitive skills. They cite research results (see Yelland & Masters, 1997) that scaffolding to support technology-assisted exploration of spatial concepts can assist students in exploring powerful ideas at earlier ages.

Changes in Curriculum in Technological Situations

Technology can serve as a cognitive technology, a medium that helps "transcend the limitations of the mind ... in thinking, learning, and problem-solving activities" (Pea, 1987, p. 91). A cognitive technology can affect school mathematics curricula in two major ways: as an amplifier or as a reorganizer (Pea, 1985). As an amplifier, technology extends the existing mathematics curriculum by increasing the number and nature of examples that students encounter; as a reorganizer, technology changes the nature and arrangement of the curriculum (see Heid, 1997, for a synthesis of research based on this idea). The metaphor of technology as a reorganizer fits the body of research well since much of the research on the impact of technology on the teaching and learning of mathematics has been situated in curricular settings that are fashioned to be fundamentally different from traditional school mathematics curricula. For example, research has been conducted on the effects of computer algebra systems on the teaching and learning of algebra and calculus (Heid & Blume, 2008; Tall et al., 2008), on the effects of Logo and dynamical geometry systems on the teaching and learning of geometry (Clements et al., 2008; Hollebrands et al., 2008), and on the effects of a range of technological applications on the teaching and learning of rational number (Olive & Lobato, 2008). The incursion of technology into school mathematics classrooms brought with it the opportunity to develop curricula that focused on mathematical objects instead of primarily on the procedures to be performed on those objects. Algebra courses, for example, were afforded the opportunity to focus on the concept and uses of function instead of solely on solving equations and generating equivalent expressions (Heid & Blume, 2008) and geometry classes could focus on generating conjectures to prove instead of on proving statements whose logical necessity had long been established (Hollebrands et al., 2008). These approaches to school mathematics substantially change the usual foci of these courses.

Technology has the potential for affecting the content of school mathematics because of its capacity for changing the mathematical activities in which students engage. Olive and Lobato (2008) describe experiments conducted by Lobato that engaged students in reconceiving the static situation of a wheelchair ramp as a dynamic situation in which the dimensions of the ramp, and hence the slope, could be changed. This capacity for varying the parameters of an initially static situation allowed students to explore factors determining change in slope—and consequently changes in the values of rational numbers. In this case, technology afforded students the opportunity for a dynamic view of equivalence of fractions.

The Calculus Reform Movement in the United States was precipitated by, among other things, the advent of personal access to function graphers and computer algebra systems (Tall et al., 2008). These tools allowed researchers to craft curricula that focused student attention on the concepts of calculus instead of solely on its gamut of procedures, and it did so through the use of multiple, linked representations. The differences in conceptual understanding that arose in the calculus experiments occurred, not always when technology was integrated in the curriculum, but when, in addition, the technology-assisted curriculum allowed curricular emphasis to be placed on development of conceptual understanding (Tall et al., 2008). In a series of experiments by Dubinsky and colleagues (Asiala et al., 1996; Brown, DeVries, Dubinsky, & Thomas, 1998), students used ISETL programming to generate examples in the service of constructing mathematical concepts and engaged in activities designed to facilitate reflection on those examples. Students in the studies seemed to develop more sophisticated conceptual understanding than they would have without the programming activities.

Certain features that characterize much mathematics technology enable a reconceptualization of school mathematics curricula. Chief among those features is the treatment of mathematical representations, with multiple, linked, and dynamic capabilities. Movement between and among representations is essential in mathematical problem solving in which progress is made by moving from one representation with its tools and methods to another with tools and methods that offer more promising paths to solution (Hollebrands et al., 2008). Access to multiple representations has afforded the opportunity for the creation of algebra curricula driven by the concept of function and made robust through the varied lenses enabled by multiple representations. Technology-intensive algebra curricula have been developed that provide viable alternatives to algebra courses that focus almost exclusively on honing symbolic manipulation techniques (Chazan, 1999; Fey & Heid, 1995/1999; Heid & Blume, 2008; Yerushalmy, 1991).

The increased availability of dynamically controlled geometric sketches offered by technology fosters a more global understanding than the traditional analytic and sequential approach of nontechnological Euclidean geometry courses (Hollebrands et al., 2008). Sometimes, nevertheless, the availability of mathematics technologies inadvertently brings to the fore deficits in students' mathematical thinking. For example, spreadsheets can unintentionally focus students on additive strategies when multiplicative strategies would better lead students to strong rational number concepts. Also, it is debatable whether technology discourages the need for proof—with students in technological environments treating computer-generated evidence as proof or treating proof as merely one piece of evidence that needs to be corroborated by other evidence (Chazan, 1993; Hollebrands et al., 2008). Whether the technology generates the misconceptions or brings to light otherwise hidden misconceptions is an open question.

The Nature of Mathematical Activity in Technological Settings

Technology-assisted approaches to mathematics foster different mathematical activity from what is typical in nontechnological approaches. The availability of technology does not, however, guarantee enhanced learning. What matters is the action taken as well as the reflection on that action (Heid & Blume, 2008; Simon, Tzur, Heinz, & Kinzel, 2004). The nature of that action is important in addressing inequities in mathematical education since "Frequent use of technology in cognitively challenging ways and in supportive learning environments can reduce outcome inequities for some traditionally disadvantaged groups" (Dunham & Hennessy, 2008).

There is debate among researchers concerning the extent to which students generally need to pre-plan away from the computer (Clements et al., 2008), although Doerr and Pratt (2008) cite evidence that students need activity away from the computer before programming tools are used. Once the action is taken, however, there is generally agreement that reflection on the results of that action is needed. At times, technology affords students the opportunity for deeper reflection, resulting in students reflecting on the results of their action in different ways. For example (Schwarz & Hershkowitz, 1999), junior high school students in a class that was using technology (multirepresentational software and graphing calculators) to learn about function used prototypes in different ways from those of students in a comparable non-technology class. The researchers observed that offloading routine tasks such as symbol manipulation and function graphing to technology allowed students more time to think more reflectively about the problems on which they were working. Students in the technology class used prototypical functions to create functions with given attributes and as reference points, making the prototypes levers for their learning. Students in the nontechnology classes were more likely to overgeneralize from prototypes and extend self-attributes of prototypes to all examples, using prototypes as brakes that inhibited their understanding of function.

The nature of a mathematical activity depends not only on the mathematical demands of the task but also on the purpose of the task as constructed by the doer. Doerr and Pratt (2008) point out the importance of the task purpose in the role of validation in mathematical modeling: "We believe that validation as an activity is intrinsically linked to the need to reveal the potential and the limitations of a model, and if validation activity is to be spontaneous then students must have a reason for wanting to pursue such a direction. Any such reason will inevitably be wrapped up in their construction of the purpose for the activity as a whole" (p. 277). They warn that tasks should be designed to suggest a purpose likely to engage students in principal mathematical ideas. Even when mathematical activities are designed for a particular mathematical purpose, however, students can engage in those activities without appreciating the mathematical ideas intended by the designers of the activities (Hollebrands et al., 2008; Olive & Lobato, 2008). When this phenomenon occurs in the context of students playing in an exploratory environment, Hoyles and Noss (1992) refer to this as the "play paradox" and advise that this result can be circumvented if students are encouraged to reflect on their activity.

Different types of technology afford opportunities for engagement in a range of mathematical activities that are different from those generally available in environments that lack such technological support. Hoyles and Noss (1992) refer to strategies that are supported by technology but unavailable with paper and pencil alone as strategic apertures (Olive & Lobato, 2008). An essential mathematical activity is that of identifying mathematical invariances across objects and representations, and some mathematical technologies are particularly suited to actions that are formulated to reveal such invariances. Dynamical and interactive geometry tools such as Cabri, Geometer's Sketchpad, and Geo-Logo, provide platforms on which students can investigate the properties of various geometric objects (Clements et al., 2008; Hollebrands et al., 2008). Algebraic tools such as function graphers, computer algebra systems, Function Probe, and Function Explorer, foster student's development of a more global understanding of the properties of functions (Heid & Blume, 2008). The dynamic interactivity afforded by these tools allows users to treat graphs as a single object (Tall et al., 2008), making invariant properties more salient. Although some tools might suggest particular types of mathematical activity, Doerr and Pratt (2008) distinguish between expressive and exploratory mathematical modeling activities and suggest that the same tool might be used to generate these quite different mathematical activities. For example, students can be asked to engage in an expressive activity creating their own dynamical geometry sketches or to work on in an exploratory activity with a prepared dynamical geometry sketch.

Studies on the effects of different types of mathematical activity have included two recurring themes. First, researchers have found that uses of different technologies in geometric settings have resulted in development of an object understanding of the geometric phenomena being observed. Clements and colleagues (2008) have observed that manipulation of screen objects in a Logo environment encourages students' thinking of them as mathematical objects and that technology with the capacity for dynamically linked alternative representations can provide an environment amenable to the development of an object understanding of geometric transformation. The second recurring theme is that when a student constructs technology-based tools for the benefit of other students, it is the constructor of the tools who seems to benefit the most. When students engaged in building Logo tools for younger children to use in learning fraction, it was the creators of the tools who learned fractions (Harel, 1990; Olive & Lobato, 2008), and when students programmed StarLogo models so that others could investigate behavioral phenomena, it appeared that it was the creator of the model who gained the most (Doerr & Pratt, 2008). These results resonate with the global result that mathematical activity in the context of technology has the greatest effect when there is sufficient provision for reflection on the results of the activity. In these cases, students assumed the role of instructor, creating tools from which others could learn. It is probable that they reflected on the likely effects of the mathematical activity in which they intended to engage others.

Effects on Mathematical Thinking of Technology-Present Mathematical Activity

Three themes emerge as researchers have examined mathematical thinking in the context of mathematical activity that occurs in technological environments: (a) the extent to which students develop tools for mathematical thinking and learning in these environments, (b) the ways in which students engage in metacognitive activity as a result of mathematical activity in these environments, and (c) the level of generality of the mathematical thinking of students in these environments.

First, a number of studies have addressed the extent to which students develop tools for mathematical thinking and learning in technology-based environments. Among these tools are the capacity for symbolic reasoning and conceptual understanding. There has long been a concern among practitioners about the extent to which the use of technology inhibits mathematical thinking, and chief among those concerns has been the fear that symbolic manipulation skills would suffer in the context of technology-intensive mathematics instruction. Research results are mixed regarding whether symbolic manipulation skills are comparable in the context of technology-intensive mathematics instruction (Heid & Blume, 2008). Moreover, although symbolic manipulation skills do not appear to develop automatically in the context of student use of computer algebra systems, students do seem to learn how to use and interpret symbolic results (Yerushalmy, 1991). What seems to be consistently corroborated is that technology-intensive instruction that focuses on conceptual development while using technology for symbolic manipulation skills results in enhanced development of conceptual tools and understandings (Heid & Blume, 2008; Tall et al., 2008). One manifestation of the development of conceptual tools is the difference in use of prototypical functions, with technology group students using prototypes in a productive and generative manner and non-technology-using students' mathematical thinking being thwarted by the way they used prototypes.

The second theme about the nature of mathematical thinking in technological environments concerns the ways in which students engage in metacognitive activity as a result of mathematical activity in technological environments. Technological environments have two features that may enhance metacognitive activity: When used as tools they have the capacity to offload some of the routine work associated with mathematical activity leaving more time for reflection, and with their strict communication requirements they may help bring to consciousness mathematical ideas and procedures (Clements et al., 2008; Tall et al., 2008). Examples of this encouragement of metacognition occur at a range of grade levels: In a Calculus&Mathematica course students seemed to the researcher to have had greater opportunities to reexamine their thinking and to question whether their line of reasoning made sense (Meel, 1996); and Logo experience seemed to help middle school and elementary school students to become more aware of their mathematical intuitions, facilitating their growth from visual thinking to descriptive/analytical thinking (Clements et al., 2008).

The third theme about the nature of mathematical thinking in technological environments concerns the level of generality of mathematical thinking in these environments. Some studies reported a higher level of generality in the thinking of students in the technology-based group. Clements and Battista (1989) observed that the responses of Logo students in their study "indicated more generalized and mathematically oriented conceptualizations" (p. 456). In her study of eighth-grade students who were first learning about algebraic functions, Yerushalmy observed that multirepresentational technological environments seemed to facilitate students' movement from a local approach to a global approach to mathematical thinking. Other studies cautioned that students may not generalize beyond the situation in which they were learning. In the context of secondary geometry, Hollebrands and colleagues (2008) observed that within milieux such as microworlds, learners' generalizations were likely to be situated abstractions, not generalizing beyond the situation in which they were developed. Doerr and Pratt (2008) noted "the lack of evidence for any claim that the students reasoned better about real-world phenomena, even when they reasoned appropriately within the microworld" (p. 268) and that "there is however little evidence that students can abstract beyond the modeling context" (p. 272).

THE ROLE OF TECHNOLOGY IN
RESEARCH ON MATHEMATICAL THINKING

Not only has the context of research on technology in mathematics teaching and learning yielded conjectures and insights about mathematical activity and mathematics thinking and learning, but research on technology in mathematics teaching and learning has also provided tools for developing an understanding of students' mathematical thinking. Two landmark examples of this technology as research tool perspective arise in Olive and Lobato's synthesis of research on technology and rational number. University of Georgia work (Olive & Lobato, 2008) has operationalized the use of technology to help in the development of cognitive models of children's construction of the concept of fraction by providing students with technological aids for enacting psychological operations that are difficult to perform with nontechnological physical materials. Lobato and colleagues have used technology to help students view the static as dynamic allowing the researcher to identify cognitive markers in students' understanding of ratio-as-measure (Olive & Lobato, 2008). This perspective of technology as research tool does not confine itself to construction of understanding of rational number, with syntheses of research on both elementary and secondary geometry emphasizing that technology allows us to attend to or refine our thinking about students' mathematical thinking (Clements et al., 2008) and "the computer acts as a window on students' understandings and construction of meaning" (Hollebrands et al., 2008, p. 190).

CONCLUSION

A connected set of themes arises from the research syntheses reported in this volume. These cross-cutting themes characterize the ways in which technology can impact the teaching and learning of mathematics, be it algebra, geometry, rational number, calculus or mathematical modeling. As is echoed in many of these syntheses, technology does not act alone in producing an effect on teaching and learning. Such effects are the result of a range of configurations of technologies, teachers and learners, curriculum, mathematical activity, mathematical thinking, and other aspects of teaching-learning settings. Certain features of these configurations impact others; for example, teachers' experiences, perceptions, and backgrounds influence the mathematical activities they orchestrate for students, and those activities, when appropriately reflected on, affect the mathematical thinking in which students engage. Many of the uses of technology reported in these volumes have a positive effect on students' mathematical thinking and learning; nevertheless, there are particular uses of technology that may not enhance learning. It is the many affordances of technology in mathematics teaching and learning, however, that make further research in these areas a promising endeavor.

REFERENCES

Asiala, M., Brown, A., DeVries, D., Dubinsky, E., Mathews, D., & Thomas, K. (1996). A framework for research and curriculum development in undergraduate mathematics education. In J. Kaput, A. H. Schoenfeld, & E. Dubinsky (Eds.), *Research in collegiate mathematics education* (Vol. 2, pp. 1-32). Providence, RI: The American Mathematical Society.

Brown, A., DeVries, D., Dubinsky, E., & Thomas, K. (1998). Learning binary operations, groups, and subgroups. *Journal of Mathematical Behavior, 16,* 187-239.

Chazan, D. (1993). High school geometry students' justification for their views of empirical evidence and mathematical proof. *Educational Studies in Mathematics, 24,* 359-387.

Chazan, D. (1999). On teachers' mathematical knowledge and student exploration: A personal story about teaching a technologically supported approach to school algebra. *International Journal of Computers for Mathematical Learning, 4,* 121-149.

Clements, D. H., & Battista, M. T. (1989). Learning of geometric concepts in a Logo environment. *Journal for Research in Mathematics Education, 20,* 450-467.

Clements, D., Sarama, J., Yelland, N. J., & Glass, B. (2008). Learning and teaching geometry with computers in the elementary and middle school. In M. K. Heid & G. W. Blume (Eds.), *Research on technology and the teaching and learning of mathematics: Vol. 1. Research syntheses* (pp. 109–154). Charlotte, NC: Information Age.

Doerr, H. M., & Pratt, D. (2008). The learning of mathematics and mathematical modeling. In M. K. Heid & G. W. Blume (Eds.), *Research on technology and the teaching and learning of mathematics: Vol. 1. Research syntheses* (pp. 259-286). Charlotte, NC: Information Age.

Dunham, P., & Hennessy, S. (2008). Equity and use of educational technology in mathematics. In M. K. Heid & G. W. Blume (Eds.), *Research on technology and the teaching and learning of mathematics: Vol. 1. Research syntheses* (pp. 345–418). Charlotte, NC: Information Age.

Fey, J. T., & Heid, M. K. (with Good, R. A., Sheets, C., Blume, G., & Zbiek, R. M.). (1999). *Concepts in algebra: A technological approach.* Chicago: Everyday Learning Corporation. (Original work published 1995)

Guin, D., & Trouche, L. (1999). The complex process of converting tools into mathematical instruments: The case of calculators. *International Journal of Computers for Mathematical Learning, 3,* 195-227.

Harel, I. (1990). Children as software designers: A constructionist approach for learning mathematics. *Journal of Mathematical Behavior, 9,* 3-93.

Heid, M. K. (1997). The technological revolution and mathematics reform. *American Journal of Education, 106,* 5–61.

Heid, M. K., & Blume, G. W. (2008). Technology and the development of algebric understanding. In M. K. Heid & G. W. Blume (Eds.), *Research on technology and the teaching and learning of mathematics: Vol. 1. Research syntheses* (pp. 55–108). Charlotte, NC: Information Age.

Heid, M. K., Sheets, C., & Matras, M. A. (1990). Computer-enhanced algebra: New roles and challenges for teachers and students. In T. J. Cooney (Ed.), *Teaching and learning mathematics in the 1990s* (1990 NCTM yearbook) (pp. 194-204). Reston, VA: National Council of Teachers of Mathematics.

Hollebrands, K., Laborde, C., & Sträßer, R. (2008). Technology and the learning of geometry at the secondary level. In M. K. Heid & G. W. Blume (Eds.), *Research on technology and the teaching and learning of mathematics: Vol. 1. Research syntheses* (pp. 155-206). Charlotte, NC: Information Age.

Hoyles, C., & Noss, R. (1992). A pedagogy for mathematical microworlds. *Educational Studies in Mathematics, 23,* 31-57.

Meel, D. E. (1996). A comparative study of honor students' understandings of central calculus concepts as a result of completing a Calculus&Mathematica or a traditional calculus curriculum (Doctoral dissertation, University of Pittsburgh, 1995). *Dissertation Abstracts International, 57*(01), 142.

Olive, J., & Lobato, J. (2008). The learning of rational number concepts using technology. In M. K. Heid & G. W. Blume (Eds.), *Research on technology and the teaching and learning of mathematics: Vol. 1. Research syntheses* (pp. 1-53). Charlotte, NC: Information Age.

Pea, R. D. (1985). Beyond amplification: Using the computer to reorganize mental functioning. *Educational Psychologist, 20,* 167-182.

Pea, R. D. (1987). Cognitive technologies for mathematics education. In A. H. Schoenfeld (Ed.), *Cognitive science and mathematics education.* Hillsdale, NJ: Erlbaum.

Schwarz, B., & Hershkowitz, R. (1999). Prototypes: Brakes or levers in learning the function concept? The role of computer tools. *Journal for Research in Mathematics Education, 30*, 362–389.

Simon, M. A., Tzur, R., Heinz, K., & Kinzel, M. (2004). Explicating a mechanism for conceptual learning: Elaborating the construct of reflective abstraction. *Journal for Research in Mathematics Education, 35*, 305–329.

Tall, D., Smith, D., & Piez, C. (2008). Technology and calculus. In M. K. Heid & G. W. Blume (Eds.), *Research on technology and the teaching and learning of mathematics: Vol. 1. Research syntheses* (pp. 207–258). Charlotte, NC: Information Age.

Yelland, N. J., & Masters, J. E. (1997). Learning mathematics with technology: Young children's understanding of paths and measurement. *Mathematics Education Research Journal, 9*, 83–99.

Yerushalmy, M. (1991). Student perceptions of aspects of algebraic function using multiple representation software. *Journal of Computer Assisted Learning, 7*, 42-57.

Zbiek, R. M. & Hollebrands, K. (2008). A research-informed view of the process of incorporating mathematics technology into classroom practice by inservice and prospective teachers. In M. K. Heid & G. W. Blume (Eds.), *Research on technology and the teaching and learning of mathematics: Vol. 1. Research syntheses* (pp. 287–344). Charlotte, NC: Information Age.

LIST OF CONTRIBUTORS

Glendon W. Blume
Professor of Mathematics Education
The Pennsylvania State University
269 Chambers Building
University Park, PA 16802-3205
gblume@psu.edu

Douglas H. Clements
Professor
University at Buffalo
State University of New York
Department of Learning and Instruction Graduate School of Education
505 Baldy Hall,
Buffalo, NY 14260
clements@buffalo.edu

Helen M. Doerr
Professor
Syracuse University
Mathematics and Mathematics Education
215 Carnegie Hall
Syracuse, NY 13244-1150
hmdoerr@syr.edu

Penelope Dunham
Professor
Muhlenberg College
Department of Mathematical Sciences
2400 W. Chew Street
Allentown, PA 18104
pdunham@muhlenberg.edu

Brad Glass
Assistant Professor
University of Delaware
132 Pearson Hall
Newark, DE 19716
bjglass@udel.edu

M. Kathleen Heid
Distinguished Professor of
    Mathematics Education
The Pennsylvania State University
271 Chambers Building
University Park, PA, 16802-3205
mkh2@psu.edu

Sara Hennessy
Lecturer in Teacher Development and
    Pedagogical Innovation
University of Cambridge
Faculty of Education
184 Hills Road
Cambridge, CB2 2PQ, UK
SCH30@cam.ac.uk

Karen Hollebrands
Associate Professor
Department of Mathematics, Science,
    and Technology Education
North Carolina State University
326-K Poe Hall
Campus Box 7801
2310 Stinson Drive
Raleigh, NC 27695-7801
karen_hollebr

Colette Laborde
Professeure Emérite
Institut Universitaire de Formation
    des Maitres (IUFM)
Equipe IAM
Laboratoire d' Informatique de
    Grenoble - LIG
46 Avenue Félix Viallet
38 031 Grenoble Cedex, France
Colette.Laborde@imag.fr

Joanne Lobato
Associate Professor
San Diego State University
Department of Mathematics and
    Statistics
Center for Research in Mathematics
    and Science Education (CRMSE)
6475 Alvarado Road, Suite 238
San Diego, CA 92120
lobato@saturn.sdsu.edu

John Olive
Professor
The University of Georgia
Department of Mathematics and
    Science Education
105 Aderhold Hall
Athens, GA 30602-7124
jolive@uga.edu

Cynthia Piez
Senior Instructor
University of Idaho
Department of Mathematics
300 Brink Hall
Moscow, ID 83844-1103
cpiez@uidaho.edu

Dave Pratt
Professor of Mathematics Education
Faculty Director for Research,
    Consultancy and Knowledge
    Transfer (Culture and Pedagogy)
Institute of Education
University of London
dpratt@ioe.ac.uk

Julie Sarama
Associate Professor
University at Buffalo
State University of New York
Department of Learning and
    Instruction
Graduate School of Education
593 Baldy Hall, Buffalo, NY 14260
jsarama@buffalo.edu

David Smith
Associate Professor Emeritus
Duke University
1408 Shepherd Street
Durham, NC 27707
das@math.duke.edu

Rudolf Sträßer
Professor
Justus Liebig University
Karl-Gloeckner-Str. 21 C
D- 35394 Giessen
Germany
Rudolf.Straesser@math.uni-giessen.de

David Tall
Emeritus Professor in Mathematical
    Thinking
Institute of Education
University of Warwick
Coventry, CV4 7AL UK
david.tall@warwick.ac.uk

Nicola J. Yelland
Professor of Education
Victoria University
School of Education
Ballarat Road, Footscray 3011
Victoria, Australia
nicola.yelland@vu.edu.au

Rose Mary Zbiek
Associate Professor
The Pennsylvania State University
272 Chambers Building
University Park, PA 16802-3205
rmz101@psu.edu

Printed in the United States
144534LV00003B/3/P

9 781931 576185